D0880799

WITHDRAWN
FROM
UNIVERSITY OF PENNSYLVANIA
LIBRARIES

THE
Sherwood
Anderson
READER

Edited, with an Introduction,

by Paul Rosenfeld

HOUGHTON MIFFLIN COMPANY · BOSTON 1947

The Riverside Press Cambridge

WITHDRAWN
FROM
UNIVERSITY OF PENNSYLVANIA
LIBRARIES

PS
3501
N4
A6
1947

Grateful acknowledgment is made to Charles Scribner's Sons for the use of material from *Puzzled America* and *Kit Brandon*; to Harcourt, Brace and Company, Inc. for the use of material from *Sherwood Anderson's Memoirs*; to Liveright Publishing Corporation for the use of material from *Dark Laughter, Sherwood Anderson's Notebook, A New Testament, Hello Towns!, Perhaps Women, Beyond Desire,* and *Death in the Woods*; and to the Viking Press for the use of material from *A Story-Teller's Story* and *Winesburg, Ohio.*

Winesburg, Ohio, COPYRIGHT, 1919, BY B. W. HUEBSCH, INC.
REPRINTED BY PERMISSION OF THE VIKING PRESS, INC., NEW YORK

A Story-Teller's Story, COPYRIGHT, 1922, BY B. W. HUEBSCH, INC.
REPRINTED BY PERMISSION OF THE VIKING PRESS, INC., NEW YORK

COPYRIGHT, 1925, 1926, 1929, 1931, 1932, AND 1933, BY LIVERIGHT PUBLISHING
CORPORATION

COPYRIGHT, 1935, 1936, AND 1940, BY SHERWOOD ANDERSON

COPYRIGHT, 1916, 1918, 1921, 1923 1931, 1934, 1937, 1939, 1941, 1942, 1943, AND 1946
BY ELEANOR ANDERSON

COPYRIGHT, 1947, BY ELEANOR ANDERSON

ALL RIGHTS RESERVED INCLUDING THE RIGHT TO REPRODUCE
THIS BOOK OR PARTS THEREOF IN ANY FORM

The Riverside Press
CAMBRIDGE · MASSACHUSETTS
PRINTED IN THE U.S.A.

UNIVERSITY
OF
PENNSYLVANIA
LIBRARIES

In Memory of
A Muse-Like Woman
LAURA LOU COPENHAVER

VB. C30890 Dup Tu

A. 2. S.

Contents

Introduction

SHERWOOD ANDERSON's WORK resembles field-flowers. Flowing rhythmically as it does, made like them with zest, it has the freshness of clover, buttercups, black-eyed Susans. It has their modesty, their innocence. No personal interest, neither desire for display or prestige, money or applause, motivated these writings. They are the uninduced, naïve consequences of a simple need for understanding and the communication of that understanding, fulfilled by an extraordinary imagination.

Life to Anderson was chaos: a pellmell of bitter and sweet, loveliness and ugliness, comic but with more than touches of the terrible; the predestination of all creatures even under the rarely fortunate circumstance to incompleteness, solitude, twisting hunger. However life also was curiously wonderful to him, an ingenious constantly resourceful disorder the author of unexpected sometimes miraculous events and shapes. Struggling to adjust himself to it he sought to discover its spirit, laws of motion, the heaven in its depths; went about with eyes mainly directed on his own inwardness, but with fraternal feeling towards the world.

Human faces, semi-consciously noticed, and picked up by his mind, rose into it with mute significance during states of intense emotion and the intoxication of creation. Or human figures making mysterious gestures or performing inexplicable actions. During semi-waking hours certain of these figures and faces assembled about themselves settings as imaginary as they: vital circumstances, motives, dramas, experiences, to which they stood in clear and logical relationships. The tiny worlds or systems now before the dreamer showed forth the secrets he wished to learn. His understanding and the emotion to which it gave birth temporarily relieved the ache of separateness, by creating a participation of the fragment in the whole of life. The business of communicating prolonged the state. . . .

In a striking way Anderson's work also possesses the field-flowers' crudeness and delicacy. The style sometimes is careless, tends to loquacity, makes insufficient distinctions between the unimportant and the important. In instances it quite lacks concision and methodical disposition and structure. One also finds smiling indulgent palpations of banal or coarse situations, a simplicity almost bizarre, and ideas insufficiently pondered or incomplete. At the same time the writings please with their fineness. Often they make deeply significant points, sometimes with great irony, and subtly release tension. Their psychological intuitions are exquisite. Then, too, we come upon original, accurate metaphors, the play of rich moods, an uncanny sense of the interaction of individual and community, and on fresh air, tenderness, pathos, fullness and rarity of meaning, and a tense form, of Anderson's invention: an impressionistic form curiously akin to that in certain paintings by the young Renoir. Out of blobs of color, scatterings of color-dots and small eddies of events connected by invisible filaments, it composes shapes that grow solid to the distant eye. . . .

Probably a resemblance of Anderson's work to little living things also flows from the fact that as a whole and in representative cases it is so complex. (So is all life, be it called Earthly, Devilish, or Divine. 'Nothing living is a One / Ever 'tis a Many' sang Goethe.) One means not only that with simplest materials the man arrived at great contrasts in his novels and autobiographies, his tales and lyrical and general pieces; not only that these simultaneously say 'No!' and 'Yes!' to things. One means that the mass of his work is the result of the joint operation of several very different impulses of art and methods of experience hitherto infrequently co-operative, rarely in such equal proportions, almost never we are certain in prose fiction. Causing the old boundaries of the genres in which he worked to oscillate, to overlap one another, the joint operations of different impulses made these genres the masters of new effects and performances.

For a quarter-century, the length of Anderson's literary career, the freshness, innocence, fineness, steadily maintained themselves. So too did the complexity, in particular the uncommon manifold of methods and impulses. The latter fact, we think, requires emphasis.

I

Primarily we find naturalism. Anderson stands in the midst of the American sustainers of the movement of Zola. A critic, Francis Hackett, perceived it immediately after the appearance of Anderson's first novels and first *Winesburg, Ohio* stories. He tagged the new Chicago author with the phrase which remains accurate at this very moment, when Anderson's work, saving only that portion of it thwarted by the accident of death, lies entire before us. The phrase was 'a naturalist with a skirl of music.'

Possibly our fresh insistence on the Zolaesque aspect of his work might have startled Anderson. His first lights in fiction, to be sure, had been Bennett and Dreiser. His early novels, including *Poor White,* were cast in the scenic, occasionally pamphletary form he derived through them from Zola. But later he used to laugh when people even called his fictions realistic: despite the fact that he knew his stories introduced readers to a world in which they felt at home; made poetry with reference to the every-day, humble, or anonymous; presented characters who seem true to nature and almost universally have been taken for expressions of American peasants or small-townsmen. And naturalism is or is supposed to be the intensification of realism, the strenuous impulse towards the poetry of reality.

Possibly, too, our insistence on the naturalism of his narratives may startle many of his enthusiasts. We can see them wondering what the ground for it conceivably can be; asking where in all Anderson, for ex-ample, one finds scientifically observed detail worked up into reconstruc-tions of entire social *milieux,* of the sort usual in Zolaesque fictions from Zola's own to Dreiser's and Thomas Mann's? Or massive material pat-ently long-reserved by the mind and methodically disposed? Or cyclopean proportions and cyclic treatment of themes?

Their questions without a doubt are valid. The thought of Sherwood Anderson fortifying himself with physiological studies, or experimentally applying scientific theories to the sources of character and behavior, in the manner of the naturalists, is inconceivable! And everything in his work suggests improvisation, sudden ideas, caprice, and material accommodable to small designs. Anderson was distinctly a miniaturist, achieving unity of impression most frequently in the dramatic tale and short story or in the lyrical expression of mood. In his very novels he was happiest when in-crustating them with short-story-like episodes. Sometimes he achieved unity in his novels, certainly in *Poor White,* but even there with his loose, impressionistic method.

One can hear his enthusiasts also protesting that Anderson had a chuck-ling humor and child-terribleness. And what naturalist other than the

Irishman George Moore ever was humorous? No, we can hear them saying, possibly an association of the work of the great Gypsy of American
literature with the realistic movement may be necessary! There are reasons
why it might appear to be so — Anderson's superficial faithfulness to
aspects of ordinary American life, for example; his predilection for homely
color; or the fact that his laughter, when people called his work realistic,
was meant only to convey the truth that he never *copied* actuality, that if
he sought to imitate anything actual, it was merely the spirit creative in
things. But though the association is unavoidable, they will conclude, let
it be made not with the art of those late-nineteenth-century and twentieth-
century realists, the naturalists, but rather with that of their mid-nineteenth-
century predecessors, realists like Dickens, Gogol, and Gottfried Keller!
The spiritual mobility beneath Anderson's writings certainly resembles
Dickens's, Gogol's, Keller's. His fund of pathos similarly resembles theirs,
and the kindling quality of much of his detail; his tone, too, pitched as it
is in the middle register of the human voice — intimate, friendly, and
warm; and his amenity, and the breadth and leisureliness of his tempo,
andante-like for all the tension. Again, like the mid-nineteenth-century
realists, but unlike Zola and his wake, he had a feeling for character, and
loved his personages. (Humanitarian and socialistic though they were, the
naturalists never created their personages in any feeling warmer than pity.)
Anderson, however, embraced his people. No doubt the majority of them
are grotesques, at once dignified and insignificant, obstinate or without
volition, comic or unbalanced. The unprecedented and unrepeated actions
through which they reveal themselves are awkward, abrupt, paroxystic
often. None of these figures is quite equal to life. Yet not one is unsympathetic or devoid of dignity. Each is stoical and decent in his sense of his
defeat. Each is sweet; as their author himself said, 'like gnarled little
russets rejected by the apple-pickers in the fall in the American countryside, clinging late to the bare trees.'

In the face of this laughter and these protests we dare affirm the complete accuracy of Francis Hackett's phrase! What after all was naturalism;
the ideal and practice formulated by Zola? In a nutshell, it was 'the omis-
sion of everything not founded on and limited by actual experience, the
negation of fancy (i.e., fantasy), the exclusion of "the ideal."' Of
novelists, in other words, there was required the antithesis both of classical
and of romantic literature; of classical literature which exploits traditional
material in attitudes imposed by authority, and of romantic, which, if it

deals with experience, does so in a spirit uncontrolled by any sense of the events through which the novelist himself has lived. Sheer experience alone was wanted; only the writer's actual enjoyment and suffering, delivered in complete sincerity; only the veritable effects produced by direct and objective perception upon his feeling and his judgment, and a treatment of material strictly controlled by the spirit of events. And few American novelists, if indeed any, have been at greater pains than Anderson always was to set down in complete sincerity only their veritable enjoyment and suffering, only the effects really produced on their feeling and judgment by personal and direct perceptions. Visionary though he was, he steadily made the effort to 'treat material in utter truthfulness' — the phrase of W. D. Howells at the time he was naturalism's American herald. The adjuration, 'never sell out your characters,' often on his lips, was always in Anderson's heart. What though he did not permit himself to be limited by the actual; honored and cultivated his fantasy; made subject-matter and symbols to an exceptional degree of his own fantasying and that of his personages? He demarcated fantasy; was always definite in distinguishing what in his own mind and in theirs harmonized with 'the world of fact,' what with the world of 'fancy,' as he called dream. Never in the manner of the romanticists or the surrealists did he confound the two substances or attempt their confusion. Thus, to demarcate fantasy was to treat events in the spirit of those through which he himself had lived.

Naturalism in the second place demanded the dissipation of genteel, conventional ideas of human psychology, the presentation of psychological man in his totality. No experienced trait in its eyes was unworthy of literature. Anderson's fiction, again, not only provided a consciousness of an unexplored psychology, that of those demi-poets the advertising men, and contributed to understanding of the Artist's experiences during the creative process and the curious interaction of his life with his art and of his life with woman, as in *The Man's Story*. It extended his predecessors' audacious grasp of pushing vital forces and yearning, emotionally starved people. Beginning with *Winesburg* it penetrated the buried life, the unconscious psyche — that seat of touch, source of energies, desires, sentience, and the power of love and unity. The real scene of his dramas frequently is the subliminal; and in tale upon tale, mischievously sometimes but always sharply, he illuminated this hidden realm by relating normal-abnormal behavior, loud personal protests and over-determinations to their origins in erotic wounds and catastrophes. One thinks of *The Sad Horn-Blowers*. He also took as his themes subjects hitherto as obscure as the history of puberty — in *An Ohio Pagan,* for example — or the shocks of adolescence — in *The Man Who Became a Woman,* say; or the abrupt erotic impulses of solitaries who spasmodically transcend their isolation; and states of connection occurring as nervously and fitfully as sunlight in spring weather. Significantly the typical genteel persecution of the naturalist, which at various times sought out Flaubert, the Goncourts, Zola, Moore, Dreiser, also directed itself against Anderson. Librarians cast out some of his books. Boston banned *Winesburg.* Letters to him, mainly from ladies, mostly unsigned, reproached him for filthiness and the mentality of adolescence at its ugliest.

Naturalism, moreover, asked of the literary man that in combination with the true artist's full earnestness and sincerity, he possess first and foremost an irony, a skepticism equally remote from classic dogmatism and romantic Byronism, fanaticism, posturing. Already in introducing *Winesburg,* Anderson with characteristic playfulness wrote out the thought

> 'that in the beginning when the world was young there were a great many thoughts but no such thing as a truth. Man made the truths himself and each truth was a composite of a great many vague thoughts. All about in the world were the truths and they were beautiful. . . . And then the people came along. Each as he appeared snatched up one of the truths and some who were quite strong snatched up a dozen of them. . . . It was the truths that made the people grotesques. The moment one of them took one of the truths to himself, called it his truth and tried to live his life by it, he became a grotesque and the truth he embraced became a falsehood.'

And an unclassic and unromantic, almost Nietzschean, skepticism and irony tempers every bit of writing by the always earnest, never 'adolescent' or 'unsophisticated,' Anderson. It expressed itself in the continual gentle suspensions of judgment, the continual smiling self-questionings, the continual question of the coherent and consistent things which men consider themselves and their actions to be.

II

The very fact of his frequent exploitation of fantasy in itself might apprise us that Anderson's fiction is not regularly naturalistic; and inspection of his stories reveals that, naturalistic in point of symbol though all of them are, many indeed of them in their narrative method simultaneously do carry forward and illustrate another very dissimilar kind of fiction. It is the one usually called lyrical. Specimens of this kind on the one hand are extremely musical, filled as they are with effects of melody, rhythm and harmony; on the other, liquidly and immediately expressive of the feelings or 'subjects' of the personages, which often have a singing substance; at times of those of the very author. They really are lyrics with epic characteristics, lyrics narrative of events. A sort of forerunner of them may be thought to exist in the *Decameron,* in the shape of the Prologue to the stories of the Fourth Day. There, speaking in his own person, Boccaccio begins a lyrical address to all ladies which unexpectedly becomes narrative of a story. After concluding the narrative he reverts to oratorical lyricism in the manner of the start.

Entire little stories, to say nothing of passage of narrative, giving poem-like expression to the mood of author or personage in a style sometimes approaching music in point of undulance, mysterious suggestiveness, infinity, survive in the work of the German romanticists about 1800, notably in Jean Paul's. More realistic variants, pantheistic in feeling, occur in the work of Stifter, in stories by him such as *The Timber Woods;* and variants even more realistic, soberly colored, in that of Turgenev, in sketches like *An Excursion to the Forest Belt.* All of them contain the singing expression of the effects of the life of things upon the authors' dreaming selves. Where rhythm became insistent in the lyric story was in the variant form of it, produced shortly before Anderson began writing, by Gertrude Stein. Stories such as *Ada, Miss Furr and Miss Skeene,* and *A Family of Perhaps Three* — all studies for *The Making of Americans* — convey the drama and the author's meanings definitely and almost exclusively through the sheer sound and movement of language-masses. The constant reiteration of a deliberately limited vocabulary and the scarcely perceptible variation of monotonous, sonorous, rhythmic patterns convey the states of feminine fixation, of a practically immobile libido and its scarcely perceptible displacements. (The jerky final acceleration in *Miss Furr and Miss Skeene* projects the growing inner 'freedom,' the demoralization, of the cultivated Miss Skeene. The stately crescendo and pathos at the close of *A Family of Perhaps Three* points the ultimate sublimation of libido in the aging, maternal elder of the two entangled sisters.)

Anderson's inclusion among the authors of the lyric story for its part flows first of all from the fact that, using the language of actuality, he nonetheless invariably wrings sonority and cadence from it; unobtrusively indeed, without transcending the easy pitch of familiar prose, but with a definiteness greater than any requisite to the sheer formation of style. He sustains tones broadly with assonances and with repeated or echoing words and phrases. He creates accent-patterns and even stanza-like paragraphs with the periodic repetition or alternation of features such as syllables, sounds, words, phrases, entire periods; lengthily maintains levels of vibration. Open any of his volumes, any of his stories:

'For one thing the man was too big. There was about him an unnatural bigness. It was in his hands, his arms, his shoulders, his body, his head, a bigness like you might see in trees and bushes in a tropical country perhaps. I've never been in a tropical country but I've seen pictures. Only his eyes were small. In his big head they looked like the eyes of a bird.'

Or:

'The rain stopped and he went silently out of the barn, towards a small apple orchard that lay beside the farm house, but when he came to a fence and was about to climb over, he stopped. "If Jesus is there he will not want me to find him," he thought. As he turned again toward the barn, he could see, across a field, a low grass-covered hill. He decided that Jesus was not after all in the orchard. The long slanting rays of the evening sun fell on the crest of the hill and touched with light the grass stalks, heavy with drops of rain, and for a moment the hill was crowned as with a crown of jewels. A million tiny drops of water, reflecting the light, made the hilltop sparkle as though set with gems. "Jesus is there," muttered the boy. "He lies on his belly in the grass. He is looking at me over the edge of the hill."'

Again: because of sudden elevations of the pitch and tension, the creation of a definite expectancy of rhythm, the prose sometimes delivers impassioned ariosos:

'I sat watching, drunk with this as I have seldom been drunk. Long, long I had felt something of the soil in the Negro I wanted in myself too. I mean a sense of earth and skies and trees and rivers, not as a thing thought about but as a thing in me. I wanted earth in me and skies and fields and rivers and people. I wanted these things to come out of me, as song, as singing prose, as poetry even. What else have I ever cared for as I have cared to have this happen, what woman, what possessions, what promise of life after death, all that? I have wanted this unity of things, this song, this earth, this sky, this human brotherhood.'

Sometimes too Anderson's story-telling not only in his prose poems but in his straight prose strangely has the quality of the narratives formerly combined with song and instrumental effects, the folk-songs and ballads. One feels it in stories like *Tandy, Paper Pills, Brothers*. Noticeably they share the legendary tone, the repetitions of slow rhythms and the loose joints of these artless pieces. — Meanwhile the very characters in the stories themselves are vocal, clamorous: the most humble, anonymous ones. Here is the language of a fifteen-year-old vagrant:

> 'When the racing season comes and the horses go to the races and there is all the talk on the streets in the evenings about the new colts, and everyone says when they are going over to Lexington or to the spring meeting at Churchill Downs or to Latonia, and the horsemen that have been down to New Orleans or maybe at the winter meeting at Havana in Cuba come home to spend a week before they start out again, at such a time when everything talked about in Beckersville is just horses and nothing else and the outfits start out and horse racing is in every breath of air you breathe, Bildad shows up with a job as cook for some outfit. Often when I think about it, his always going all season to the races and working in the livery barn in the winter where horses are and where men like to come and talk about horses, I wish I was a nigger. It's a foolish thing to say, but that's the way I am about being around horses, just crazy.'

And how often he introduces not only the 'subjects' and feelings of his personages but the personal note, at least that of the self which said 'I' through him, and not only in the manner of the epic authors as the impersonal narrator of rhapsode — but in that of the lyric poet! How frequently do his sonorities convey his personal sentiment; the stir he heard, often during the creative process in listening to his dreaming 'subject'; the feeling that rose from the region between his conscious and unconscious minds. In fine, again and again through the whole, the vocal personages and all, one feels, nay, hears, a singing state of soul, an inwardness filled with the mysterious melody of things.

Incidentally, the sonorities and cadences deliberately and sapiently wrung by him from language constitute his prime and economical means of depiction; to the degree that the reader insensible of them cannot quite gather his meanings, cannot clearly see the objects, the symbols present to Anderson's mind, the featureless personages tagged by him with undistinguished names, and their mid-American circumstance. These objects, no less than the other meanings, are fully realized. The featureless personages are corporally present to the mind, and behind them, like a physical presence, there stretches the land of the long straight turnpikes, rolling fields of corn, dark-blue, well-nigh blue-black patches of woods; the land with the clusters of small farmhouses and big silos and barns; the shapeless little towns of bricky factories, Main Streets with parked autos, shading maples, and all sorts and conditions of dwellings. But these evocations are not principally the work of the descriptions and the other exploitations of the sign-power in the language. The descriptions and the signs in fact are sketchy, almost rudimentary. Similes occur infrequently. It is not even the result of the homely phraseology and charming colloquialisms . . . 'The farmer had planted his field to apple and pear,' for example, or 'There has been a new pattern being made.' No: the evocation is the result of the fact that the sound and rhythm are twin to the descriptions — collateral, emphatic reflections of the quality of the objects present to the writer's mind and indicated by him; sonorous equivalents of the sensations that these objects rouse, thus giving rise in us to sensations and feelings similar to those which these objects, were they present to us, independently would excite. Assisted by the sign-power of the language in this way they powerfully communicate the author's sense. — Casual illustrations must suffice. Here is the interior of an automobile factory:

'The "belt" — is a big steel conveyor, a kind of moving sidewalk, waist-high. It is a great river running down through the plant. Various tributary streams come into the main stream, the main belt. They bring tires, they bring headlights, horns, bumpers for cars. They flow into the main stream. The main stream has its source at the freight cars, where the parts are unloaded, and it flows out to the other end of the factory and into other freight cars.'

However if mid-America lies as densely as it does about these stories it is also because as a whole their prose is one of those happy media which not only with their peculiar accent but their flavor and entire quality mysteriously represent special regions and entire lands. Anderson's prose is as American as that of Mark Twain, from which indubitably it was descended; an embodiment of the Western earth like Whitman's verse, Sullivan's architecture, the painting of Homer Martin or of Marin.

It is impossible to believe that such a writer could not but have received a suggestion of his method from certain previous specimens of the lyric story-kind. The thought that Anderson knew the work of the German romantics is not of course to be entertained: the German romantics, whose remote blood-connection he may conceivably have been — for there is evidence that his mother's mother, Grandma Myers, who 'populated half the state of Indiana' was a native of Hesse-Darmstadt; the romantic whose tricks such as concentrating interest upon the very machinery of illusion and toying with that machinery, he unconsciously repeated in passages like the River-Scene in *Dark Laughter*. And it is probable he never observed the Prologue to the Fourth Day, in the *Decameron,* so like in scheme to his own *When We Care.* But it is plain that he knew his Turgenev and Gertrude Stein. *Memoirs of a Sportsman* was a steady favorite of his: 'The sweetest thing in all literature,' he called the revolutionary book in a letter to one friend; and in another found it 'like low fine music'; and in autobiographic fragment depicted himself sitting in a Chicago restaurant

> 'reading of the peasant proprietor, Ovsyanikov, far away out there on the Russian steppe. Who but Turgenev could make you feel the way sunlight comes down among trees in the forest, or a field after summer rain, or the strange sweet smell of a river going across a plain when evening comes? Or reading about Yermolai and the Miller's wife, Bieyuk the forester, Bieyuk the wolf. Turgenev thou sweet man, thou sweetest of all prosemen, gentlemen strong. Thou of the aristocracy — so alive to common men!'

From the year of the re-impression of *Three Lives* — it was 1915 — and the publication of *Tender Buttons,* those playful pieces in which communication is attempted exclusively through the sound and essential color of words selected from the common vocabulary, and their rhythmic array, he had begun reading Gertrude Stein; thought that *Three Lives* 'contained some of the best writing ever done by an American'; in 1922 introduced *Geography and Plays,* the volume of *Ada, Miss Furr and Miss Skeene,* and *A Family of Perhaps Three* with the words, 'Since Miss Stein's work was first brought to my attention I have been thinking of it as the most important pioneer work done in the field of letters in my time.'

However it is equally impossible to believe that, if he did take a hint of his method from Turgenev and Gertrude Stein, more than a slight one was necessary. He was prepared for the lyrical form by the fact that, quite as much as an observer he was an auditor; always a listener and one who achieved connection with the nature of things through his auditory imagination. He was — a singer. Emotion must continually have suffused his consciousness. As such he undoubtedly figures in the imaginations of the mass of his readers: a warbler, a celebrant persistently of his own sorrow and delight. — As for his own specimens of the lyric story-kind, they have 'inner form' like Gertrude Stein's, but their rhythms are livelier, longer, more self-completive than those of the somnolent lady-Buddha of the *rue de Fleurus.* While wanting the suavity of expression in Turgenev's lyric tales, Anderson's share the warmly singing tone of the Russian's, surpass them of course in point of tension, and have the Andersonian qualities of subtlety of attack and humorous and acute feeling, perceptions of the essential in the singular, glamour over the commonplace, boldness of image . . . Wonderfully they 'stay by us.'

III

The art of the naturalists and that of the lyrists however are not the only literary bodies beside which Anderson's work ranges itself. Impulses still other than lyricism, as foreign to naturalism as this is, interplayed with the naturalistic impulse in his work. Indeed we feel the joint operation of an entire group of antithetic reactions.

Look if you will at Anderson's heroes, in particular those of his novels: Sam McPherson, 'Beaut' McGregor, Hugh McVey, Kit Brandon, say. All are in battle with reality. They preserve an independence to their milieux. At some time in their careers we see them endeavoring to withdraw from the influences of the living as well as the dead environments and seeking new paths and exits. All of them, Hugh McVey conspicuously, are inventors and reformers. This struggle in itself gives them a stature supe-

rior to the average one, and another circumstance increases it to the point
of heroism. All represent society, American society. The scene of their
struggle in some way is the total American one, in some way is within
the American soul. In fact they are American Heroes, among the only
truly living ones, with Phelps Putnam's abortive 'Bill,' whom contemporary
American literature has produced. One lays the promptness with which
Waldo Frank perceived the heroism of Sam McPherson immensely to the
credit of that writer; the perspicacity with which he related and compared
that clumsily questing figure to its passive, indolent, half-animal prede-
cessor Huckleberry Finn. (Even certain of the grotesques in Anderson's
tragi-comic short stories possess supernormal stature, the saloon-keeper in
The Egg, for example. He is the American seeking to solve all life's
problems by means of gadgets.) This superhumanity is the achievement
of Heroic feeling. Plainly, within the naturalistic framework, we face
an impulse as foreign to naturalism, almost as contradictory to it as is the
old mythical, hero-making one; the impulse to feel out the destiny of a
people and affirm it in creating the ideal citizen.

In association with this, we find yet another; equally opposed to the
realistic impulse and apparently also to the Heroic one, though in the past
it frequently has been found in association with the latter. It is the bu-
colic, idyllic reaction: the impulse to escape imaginatively from time into
a world smaller, stiller, less hurtful than the actual historical one; into the
small-town, the rural or the mountain milieux and even farther; towards
the inevitable natural form of existence and the elemental being without
an historical consciousness, withdrawn as it were from the stream of time.
Anderson made this escape in tales of the American small town and
countryside bringing into play the rural attitudes, the very country spirit
itself — it speaks in stories such *I'm A Fool;* setting in motion types of
the timeless unhistorical human creature and the inevitable natural forms
of life, hunger for earth and home, Pan of the shepherds. The attainment
of this goal of course constitutes the idyl or the pastoral; not, as the dic-
tionaries pretend, the fact of pictures of shepherds and shepherdesses,
descriptions of rustic life, pastoral settings. (That at least was Goethe's
opinion.) Anderson attained this goal again and again: for the traits to
clothe these types outside the stream of time Anderson actually had to
search no farther than his Chicago lodging-house. There indeed he found
the traits of the timeless people of *Winesburg,* since the average American
is the unhistorical being *par excellence,* coming 'out of nowhere,' going

'into nothing.' Anderson's prevalently fatalistic feeling of life to be sure made certain of his idyls unorthodox not only in the sense of less than jocund, but in the sense of tragi-comical: *Daughters,* for example, that dramatization of gynarchy. But then, who can deny the truthfulness of such pictures to the elemental state?

Last, likewise at the octave from naturalism, we encounter symbolism and mysticism: because of Anderson's singularly intense conviction that experience is more important than action, that the great events of life are connected not with external circumstances but with the development of consciousness; because he eminently was a man to whom interior world ever was more real than the visible one. His great stories are enveloped by an atmosphere of ideality: filled with suggestions of the immaterial and intangible, the general truth, the nature common to all his personages but always outside them. The best naturalistic novels do of course possess something of the atmospheric envelope of ideality and have the power to give impressions of ideas with images. Zola's themselves possess symbolistic aspects even in their crassest passages: the final passage in *La Terre,* for example, the depiction of the peasant lad's rape of his grandmother. We grasp: the human creature's savage approach to his ancestress, the Earth. But in Anderson the symbolism, the suggestion of the general truth, is almost constant. His language for one thing continually possesses concentrative depth. That new species of awkward persons he presents resemble the featureless, widely applicable quasi-human outlines in cubist paintings; resemble voices even. Through the gestures, acts and backgrounds of these persons, the houses they inhabit, the streets through which they pass, there transpires an entirely inner and psychic world, composed not only of the roots of character, of bents of temperament, attitudes and motives oftentimes semi or entirely unconscious, but of states of energy, objects of the libido, the direction of its interest. We face and participate in conditions of apathy, disconnection, solitude; conditions spasmodically transformed into those of vitality and sentiency. We overhear dialogues eternal in the human substance, born of eternally conflicting human attitudes towards woman, love, marriage, and much besides. Almost, it seems, we touch an absolute existence, a curious semi-animal, semi-divine life. Its chronic state is banality, prostration, dismemberment, unconsciousness; tensity with indefinite yearning and infinitely stretching desire. Its manifestation: the non-community of cranky or otherwise asocial solitaries, dispersed, impotent and imprisoned amid interior walls arising from acute differences in feeling, culture, opinion; arising also from insentience, from mendacious attitudes, from socially-dangerous incommunicable wishes. Its wonders — the wonders of its chaos — are fugitive heroes and heroines mutilated like the dismembered Osiris, the dismembered Dionysus. Painfully the absolute comes to itself in consciousness of universal dispersion and helplessness. Barriers have fallen. It realizes itself as feeling, sincerity, understanding, as connection and unity; sometimes almost at the cost of the death of its creatures. It triumphs in any one aware of its existence even in its sullen state. The moment of realization is tragically brief. Feeling, understanding, unity pass. The divine life sinks back again, dismembered and unconscious.

IV

Inevitably the manifold of impulses at this work's roots and its fusions of lyricism and visionary fiction refers us to a charming passage in *The Birth of Tragedy* by Nietzsche, the one seeking to explain the source of lyric poetry. For this passage describes the origin of metaphysical pictures, drawn in a lyrical and musical style, with resemblances to those of the story-teller Sherwood Anderson; and thus might be thought to cast light on the origins of Anderson's characteristic work. The lyrist, says Nietzsche, as a Dionysiac artist at first is united with the primordial, the ground of things, with its pain and basic contradictions, and produces an image of this pain, these contradictions, as music and the expression of what erroneously he takes to be his personal 'I.' In the process of the Apollonian dream however his music grows *visible* to him in parabolic pictures. That, Nietzsche continues, is what the Greeks meant by their depictions of Archilochus the intoxicated enthusiast who represented lyric poetry to them. They show him sunk in sleep while Appollo touches him with his laurel-bough. The sleeper's dionysiac-musical intoxication now casts picture-sparks about him which in their most evolved forms are Tragedies and Dithyrambic Poems. — The applicability of Nietzsche's theory flows of course not only from the resemblance of these picture-sparks to Anderson's fictions, but from a curious resemblance between the self-observing Anderson, the author of countless fugitive and divided personages, and the Archilochus of the Greek cameos. This is a consequence of the fact that Anderson composed in states of rapture like the little figure's, which, indubitably helped on by a few drinks nonetheless essentially were natural, nervous intoxicants. We have his word for it in his *Memoirs* and in the piece *A Part of Earth*.

If finally we turn from this suggestive page, it is that Anderson was not a pure lyric poet in the sense of the Greeks and Nietzsche. We are obliged to call him a special realization of the Writer in several of his faculties. Meanwhile there exists a scientific hypothesis regarding the cause of this special realization. We think it worth a statement. It is that Anderson harmoniously combined within himself the two great basic temperaments, and that the combination was the source of the teamwork of reactions in his art.

Everybody nowadays is familiar with the theory of these fundamental human temperaments, respectively called tough-minded and tender-minded by William James, one of their students; extraverted and introverted by another, Carl Jung; cyclothemic and schizoid by Ernst Kretschmer; syntonic and schizoid by still others, Bleuler and A. A. Brill. More antithetical than masculinity and femininity, both temperaments are said also to some degree to be of the essence of every human being and in most beings to remain at loggerheads. One of them, by a combination of character and circumstances, often suffers ruinous suppression in the other's favor.

In the last decades some of these students have made extended inquiries into the creative reactions and methods of the two temperaments.[1] Kretschmer for example refers the reactions of realism and humor, and of naturalism to a degree, to the cyclothemic or syntonic temperament. To the schizoid he refers those of lyricism, the heroic, the idyllic, and mysticism. While Brill does not see eye to eye with Kretschmer, and leans to finding naturalists like Zola in the schizoid camp, lyrists like Whitman and Nietzsche in the syntonic, he has been sufficiently impressed by Kretschmer's schematization to draw it emphatically to the attention of his own study's readers.

Now Anderson, in whose work we find interplay of three of the reactions which we are bidden to refer to the cyclothemic or syntonic temperament and four of those we are bidden to refer to the schizoid: Anderson was a man who again and again stressed his consciousness of the presence of two, sometimes conflicting, sometimes harmonious, dispositions,

---

[1] Readers are referred to Kretschmer's epoch-making *Koerperbau und Charakter* and to Brill's study *Schizoid and Syntonic Factors in Neuroses and Psychoses* in the *American Journal of Psychiatry* for 1925.

almost separate *dramatis personae,* in his own psyche. The first was called by him 'the slick fellow,' the other, 'the Artist.' On the surface of Anderson's pair might appear to be the individuality and the personality — the latter being of course the fusion of the individuality and the vocation. The contest between them might appear the struggle between the interestedness of the former and the latter's disinterestedness. But on inspection 'the slick fellow' looks to us merely like someone whose soul thoroughly is in accord with his actual environment; who readily approaches objects; whose feelings, ever influenced by the outer world, in turn influence his thought and action; who possesses a rapid eye for opportunity, and sociability, realism, friendliness and an infinite adjustability. The 'Artist' for his part has the look of a person who hesitates before the object; follows out his own aims; forever seeks new paths and exits; adapts himself to reality through inventions which transform it for his own ends; possesses a distinct feeling for doing good. While frequently turning inwardly to himself, he has the power to analyze himself and others.

Now mark! To an astounding degree each of these *personae* of Anderson's resembles one of the two basic human temperaments as their scientific students describe them, in particular as they are described by Kretschmer, Bleuler and Brill. Listen, if but a moment, to the recital of a few of the traits attributed by Kretschmer to the cyclothemic temperament. They are the power to work, and spontaneity, audacity, amiability, adaptability and astuteness in the matter of handling other people; balanced by superficiality and tactlessness and inconstancy. What else are these than the business and journalistic traits lumped together as 'slickness' by Anderson? Listen again to a recital of a few of the hallmarks of the schizoid as seen by Brill. 'A true psychologist' who 'because he can strive against his own primitive feelings — acquires the ability to express them in literature and art'; 'refinement and differentiation in expression greater than the syntonic's'; 'aversion to reality — that produces a desire to change it or to turn inwardly to the self'; 'the refusal of facile discharges of feeling, effecting not only a gain in power but the opportunity and time for reflection and modification'; 'disharmony with the environment, contributing to making a reformer or inventor or prophet of the subject.' What traits are these but those of Anderson's 'Artist?'

It is also significant that Brill places in the ranks of the rare cases of the harmonious combination of the two temperaments the leader who was one of Anderson's lifelong heroes, Abraham Lincoln: Lincoln who more-

over provided Anderson with the model for the agonist of the heroic fragment we present among his posthumous pieces.

Thus, there presses itself upon us the hypothesis that Anderson's work
derived its form from the circumstance that, stubbornly, irreducibly, the
two great human temperaments and their reactions existed side by side in
his psyche. Through others who similarly were medleys there often
sounded the voices of one temperament. The voices of the other temperament were suppressed. Anderson on the contrary caused all of them to
move contrapuntally. This in turn may well have been the cause of his distinguishing ability to combine various points of view in his stories, and of
his liberal attitude toward the world. . . . Independently too a circumstance other than the peculiar complexity of his art-work and the psycho-
analytic theories also moves us to the conclusion that an incorporation and
harmonization of the two prime temperaments was Anderson's secret.
This, is the ultimate magic of his work: its radiation of the American
ethos, our social group's distinguishing tone. Anderson, the reflector of the
yearning of the American Middle West, whose finest younger son he was,
is nothing if not the reflector of the communal good-will of the American
Middle West; of the benevolence happily so largely, so savingly, the
habitual attitude of all our folk. Our ethos glints in his love of his fictive
characters. It glances in his revelation through them of life's inalienable
core of sweetness; in his many discoveries of the relationships between a
myriad of hitherto apparently unrelated human characteristics. One sees
it in his unwillingness to let any odd-fellow go, in his refusal to see him
perish, in his effort towards a sympathetic understanding of his secret; in
his very warm, bantering, winning way of writing. Our national 'fanaticism' even generates itself through him, fatalist though he was and a maker
of grotesques. If the man himself as has been said was like a bonfire, warming hearts and hands, his expression's total effect is the substitution for
'feeling less kind and less needful for the well-being of mankind' of those
that are 'kinder and more needful to that end.' Removing the sense of
individual guilt and responsibility for insufficiency and failure, that poisoned spring, he transmutes it to the source of a miracle — reconciliation
with the fellow-citizen, with existence, with oneself. The very continual
attitude of mysticism is a stimulus to democratic feeling, which takes nour-
ishment from, indeed cannot survive without, the sense of the existence
of an absolute life.)

So rich a radiation of this conciliatory tone, this sympathetic attitude,

characteristic of the American people, we think to have been possible only
to an individual who, biologically a complex alloy and synthesis, himself
was a microcosm of the American macrocosm; an inner harmony of temperaments; a tiny but complete, active, friendly Humanity. For we more
than suspect the sympathetic attitude of the American community to have
been born of its inclusion within itself of all sorts of humanity and all manner of temperaments — from the extremely syntonic one of the Negro to
the extremely schizoid of the Amerindian — and of its effort to bring these
into working relationship and order. — Feeling besides corroborates our
reasoning about Anderson. Critics have long been telling us that the
writers treasured by humanity as its very own are timeless for the reason
that they brought to the making of their art the unity and totality of Man.
And feeling tells us that Anderson will survive with these writers: artists
in many cases of a versatility and workmanship, a scope, power of evocation
and vision vastly transcending his. Feeling that is to say has an intuition
that he too brought to his art — so like a miniature universal art made of
music and picture, realism and lyricism, naturalism, the heroic, the idyllic,
the mystical — much of the force brought by them to theirs.

V

Through its very form, the classificatory arrangements of the selections,
this anthology seeks to represent the essential complexity of Anderson's
work. Oh, it seeks to symbolize other elements no less, the literary power,
say, which for twenty-five years maintained itself at a single high pitch
while assimilating fresh themes! (Thus the order not only is classificatory
but chronological, and a handful of his last stories have been given final
position, that they may indicate the projected quality of the new short-
story collection on which he was at work when he died.) Mainly nonetheless its object is the display of the complex basic impulses. This is not
easily feasible. These reactions as has been said regularly arose in pairs,
in groups; took form in a homogeneous body of work that bridges the
boundaries of the recognized categories and really created a number of
new categories calling for barbarous compound names and the ability to
bestow them. And we do not possess the singular talent of Polonius.
What alone seemed possible was the indication of dominant impulses,
directly in some cases and in others through emphasis of the type of
material peculiarly connected with them.

What also may require explanation is the inclusion, in an anthology made up from Anderson's shorter work, of a few excerpts from his novels and autobiographies. But these excerpts are episodic enough to be able to function independently. Anderson himself published *Mill-Girls* from *Beyond Desire* as a novelette; and we have used nothing that suffers from isolation from its context. — And our reason for including the story of 1916, *Blackfoot's Masterpiece,* in a volume intended as a collection of the best of Anderson's shorter work in the forms in which it manifested itself? The author had rejected the story. No doubt it is brutal. Our motive for the inclusion was this: since our anthology represents an evolution, some picture of the commencement of this process of development was necessary to it, and among Anderson's early short work this piece admirably provides just that picture. With the brutality one feels in it the force and conviction of the Chicago School; the qualities reborn to American literature by that School. — The School's regional consciousness, the region's sensuous self-imagery and expression of the basis for its self-consciousness, meanwhile is represented by *The New Englander,* which was read to the present writer as early as the Christmas of 1919, in a version afterwards only very slightly altered.

As to the origins of certain of the posthumous pieces. — *Father Abraham* came to light in 1943 when a box of Anderson's manuscripts stored by him in the print-shop of his Marion, Virginia, newspapers was turned over to his executrix by his friend, David Greear. The box and its contents had been in the shop at least since 1929 and possibly for an even longer period. There is a possibility that the manuscript was a castoff. Whether or not, certainly it was a first draft, probably that of the work on Lincoln which Anderson had adumbrated to Roger Sergel in a letter of 1925 from Reno. Partly in typescript but mainly in handwriting, the fragmentary but strangely integral piece fell into two not quite perfectly related portions and along with seven complete chapters included several unplaced episodes and a few unfinished passages. The probability would seem to be that it had merely been put aside for later continuation. What makes one think so, is the fact that in recent years Anderson often referred to his entertainment of a project to write a book about Lincoln. One had the impression that it was to provide a place for some of his numerous, often extremely refreshing, ideas about the Civil War and the leaders on both sides.

The business of meshing the two portions of the manuscript, placing

the floating episodes, connecting the inconclusive passages, was not difficult. While it has been considered obligatory here and there to edit bits
of the piece, the paraphrases have been few and are represented chiefly by
a slight extension of the meaning in one paragraph and the transference
of the tenses in one passage from the past into the pluperfect.

A Part of Earth is a variant treatment of the topic of Chapter Eleven of
The Robin's Egg Renaissance book of the *Memoirs,* but not to be considered a rejected variant. The probability is too great that it was intended
for inclusion in the unfinished omnibus volume which Anderson got under
way about 1929 under the title *A Book of Days,* and in a pocket-notebook
later on entitled *My Journal.* — *Daughters* was found in a typescript including the first chapter of one of Anderson's unfinished novels. The
Daughters portion of the script had been corrected in ink by its author
and there is reason for supposing that this internally taut piece of story-
telling was intended for inclusion in the projected short-story volume. —
The idyllic social study *The American Small Town* is the very lightly
edited original of the last continuous piece of work carried toward com-
pletion by Anderson, the text for the volume *Home Town* in the illustrated
series *The Face of America.* Only half of the original was accommodated
in the volume. The manuscript bore the title *The American Small Town.*

PAUL ROSENFELD

About Sherwood Anderson

Sherwood Anderson was born in the town of Camden, Ohio, in 1876, the third of a family of seven children. His father, a Southerner, who had fought in the Union armies and lived romantic adventures in a world of fantasy, was a house-painter and not always able to support his family. Anderson's mother, who had been a bound-girl in her youth, sometimes got the bread by washing clothes. Her mother was an immigrant; some say, from Italy, others, from Hesse-Darmstadt. Anderson spent his boyhood in a succession of small Ohio towns and continued to attend high school until his eighteenth year, working at hours in the fields of the farmers of his vicinity, at county fairs with race-horses, at harvest time with threshing crews, and for a while in a bicycle factory. He was a laborer in Chicago at the time of the outbreak of the Spanish-American War, and volunteering, was sent to Cuba. Afterward he attended Wittenberg College, drifted thence into advertising work in Chicago, entered into marriage and later went into manufacturing and set up a factory in Ellyria, Ohio. Before 1912, he was trying to write, and on a day of that year walked out of his shop never to return. Again in Chicago, Anderson supported himself by composing advertisements for Critchfield and Company and worked on novels, poems in prose, short stories. Mainly through the influence of Theodore Dreiser his novel *Windy McPherson's Son* was published in 1916, while *The Little Review, The Seven Arts, The Forum* and *The Masses* began the presentation of his shorter work. Others of his books rapidly followed: in 1918 *Marching Men,* one of the first American novels about the labor movement; and in 1920 *Winesburg, Ohio,* the volume of short stories that startled an America lately become self-conscious. In 1921, Anderson went to Europe for the first time. *The Dial,* in 1922, made him the recipient of its annual $2,000 award: the next recipients were T. S. Eliot and Van Wyck Brooks. During these years he had been managing, now and then, to escape from business entirely to give his energies to writing, frequently to Fairhope, Alabama, and New Orleans and in them and the years immediately following he produced *Poor White,* one of the best of his novels, a study of the coming of the machine age to the Middle-West, *Many Marriages,* his 'Song of Songs,' and the non-realistic account of his life *A Story-Teller's Story.* His shorter work appeared in collections such as *The Triumph of the Egg* and *Horses and Men.* Yet Anderson's first and only commercial success was *Dark Laughter* (1925). With the proceeds of *Dark Laughter* he bought two newspapers in Marion, a prosperous town of Southwest Virginia; also some land in the mountains above the town where he built himself a beautiful stone house and generously began harboring his friends. Despite the fact that he was receiving a regular fee from the publisher, Horace Liveright, he found himself obliged to go on lecture-tours, for it was impossible permanently to turn him into a popular writer. In the mounting economic catastrophe, Anderson's mind freshly began occupying itself with the machine-age and its effect on the common man and woman. This was the period of *Perhaps Women,* of *Beyond Desire* and of *Kit Brandon* — probably the most objective of his novels. In winter he wandered observantly about the country, often to the South and Mexico. He was becoming the frequent subject of pulmonary infections. In summer he was at his Ripshin Farm. By this time his work had come to be as widely translated as that of any contemporary American author. Versions had appeared in Swedish, Danish, Polish, French, Hungarian, German, Japanese, Italian, Dutch and in Spain and practically every Latin American country. It was at the beginning of a trip to South America in 1941 that he died. A bit of toothpick lodged in a tid-bit eaten by him at a farewell cockktail-party perforated his intestine and he was removed from the ship at Colon in a dying condition. In his last years he had almost completed his *Memoirs* and had worked on several new books. His grave lies above the town of Marion.

Nobody Laughed

I. A CONTRAST

Nobody Laughed
Blackfoot's Masterpiece

Nobody Laughed

IT WASN'T, more than others of its size, a dull town. Buzz McCleary got drunk regularly, once a month, and got arrested, and for two summers there was a minor league professional baseball team. Sol Grey managed about getting up the ball team. He went about town to the druggist, the banker, the local Standard Oil manager, and others, and got them to put up money. Some of the players were hired outright. They were college boys having a little fun during their vacation time, getting board and cigarette money, playing under assumed names, not to hurt their amateur standing. Then there were two fellows from the coal-mining country, a hundred miles to the north in a neighboring state. The handle factory gave these men jobs. Bugs Calloway was one of them. He was a home-run hitter and afterwards got into one of the big leagues. That made the town pretty proud. 'It puts us on the map,' Sol Grey said.

However, the baseball team couldn't carry on. It had been in a small league and the league went to pieces. Things got dull after that. In such an emergency the town had to give attention to Hallie and Pinhead Perry.

The Perrys had been in Greenhope, Tennessee, since the town was very small. Greenhope was a town of the upper South and there had always been Perrys there, ever since long before the Civil War. There were rich Perrys, well-to-do Perrys, a Perry who was a preacher, and one who had been a brigadier general in the Northern army in the Civil War. That didn't go so well with the other well-to-do Perrys. They liked to keep reminding people that the Perrys were of the Old South.

'The Perrys are one of the oldest and best families of the Old

South,' they said. They kept pretty quiet about Brigadier General Perry who went over to the 'damned Yanks.'

As for Pinhead Perry, he, to be sure, belonged to the no-account branch of the Perrys. The tree of even the best Southern family must have some such branches. Look at the Pinametters. But let's not drag in names.

Pinhead Perry was poor. He was born poor, and he was simple. He was undersized. A girl named Mag Hunter had got into trouble with a Perry named Robert, also of the no-account Perrys, and Mag's father went over to Robert's father's house one night with a shotgun. After Robert married Mag, he left Greenhope. No one knew where he went, but everyone said he went over into a neighboring state, into the coal-mining country. He was a big man with a big nose and hard fists. 'What the hell'd I want a wife for? Why keep a cow when milk's so cheap?' he said before he went away.

They called his son Pinhead, began calling him that when he was a little thing. His mother worked in the kitchens of several well-to-do families in Greenhope, but it was a little hard for her to get a job, what with Negro help so low and her having Pinhead. Pinhead was a little off in the head from the first, but not so much.

His father was a big man, but the only thing big about Pinhead was his nose. It was gigantic. It was a mountain of a nose. It was very red. It looked very strange, even grotesque, sticking on Pinhead. He was such a little scrawny thing, sitting often for a half-day at a time on the kitchen step, at the back of the house of some well-to-do citizen. He was a very quiet child, and his mother, in spite of the rather hard life she had, always dressed him neatly. Other kitchen help, the white kitchen help, what there was of it in Greenhope, wouldn't have much to do with Mag Perry, and all the other Perrys were indignant at the very idea of her calling herself a Perry. It was confusing, they said. The other white kitchen help whispered. 'She was only married to Bob Perry a month when the Pinhead was born,' they said. They avoided Mag.

There was a philosopher in the town, a sharp-tongued lawyer who hadn't much practice. He explained. 'The sex morals of America are upheld by the working classes,' he said. 'The financial morals are in the hands of the middle classes.

'That keeps them busy,' he said.

Pinhead Perry grew up and his mother Mag died and Pinhead got married. He married one of the Albright girls — her name was Hallie — from out by Albright's Creek. She was the youngest of eight children and was a cripple. She was a little pale thing and had a twisted foot. 'It oughten to be allowed,' people said. They said such bad blood ought not be allowed to breed. They said, 'Look at them Albrights.' The Albrights were always getting into jail. They were horse-traders and chicken-thieves. They were moon-liquor-makers.

But just the same the Albrights were a proud and defiant lot. Old Will Albright, the father, had land of his own and he had money. If it came to paying a fine to get one of his boys out of jail, he could do it. He was the kind of man who, although he had less than a hundred acres of land — most of it hillside land and not much good — and a big family, mostly boys, always getting drunk, always fighting, always getting into jail for chicken-stealing or liquor-making — in spite, as they said in Greenhope, of hell and high water — in spite of everything, as you see, he had money. He didn't put it in a bank. He carried it. 'Old Will's always got a roll,' people in town said. 'It's big enough to choke a cow.' The town people were impressed. It gave Will Albright a kind of distinction. That family also had big noses and old Will had a walrus mustache.

They were rather a dirty and a disorderly lot, and they were sometimes pretty defiant, but just the same, like the Perrys and other big families of that Tennessee country, they had their family pride. They stuck together. Suppose you had a few drinks in town, on a Saturday night, and you felt a little quarrelsome and not averse to a fight yourself, and you met one of the Albright boys, say down in the lower end of town, down by the Greek restaurant, and he got gay and gave you a little of his lip and you said to him, 'Come on, you big stiff, let's see what you've got.'

And you got ready to sock him —

Better not do that. God only knows how many other Albrights you'd have on your hands. They'd be like Stonewall Jackson at the battle of Chancellorsville. They'd come down on you suddenly, seemingly out of nowhere, out of the woods, as it were.

'Now you take one of that crew. You can't trust 'em. One of them'll stick a knife into you. That's what he'll do.'

And, think of it, little quiet Pinhead Perry marrying into that crew. He had grown up. But that's no way to put it. He was still small and rather sick-looking. Only God knows how he had lived since his mother died.

He had become a beggar. That was it. He'd stand before one of the grocery stores, when people were coming out with packages in their hands. 'Hello!' He called all the other Perrys 'cousin' and that was pretty bad. 'Hello, Cousin John,' or 'Cousin Mary,' or 'Kate,' or 'Harry.' He smiled in that rather nice little way he had. His mouth looked very tiny under his big nose and his teeth had got black. He was crazy about bananas. 'Hello, Cousin Kate, give me a dime, please. I got to get me some bananas.'

And there were men, you know, the smart-alecks of the town, taking up with him too, men who should have known better, encouraging him.

That lawyer . . . his father was a Yank, from Ohio . . . the philosophic one, always making wise-cracks about decent people . . . getting Pinhead to sweep out his office . . . he let him sleep up there . . . and Burt McHugh, the plumber, and Ed Cabe, who ran the poolroom down by the tracks . . .

'Pinhead, I think you'd better go up and see your Cousin Tom. He was asking for you. I think he'll give you a quarter.'

Cousin Tom Perry was the cashier of the biggest bank in town.

One of those fellows, damn smart-alecks, had seen Judge Buchanan. The Perrys and the Buchanans were the two big families of the county. They'd seen Judge Buchanan go into the bank. He was a director. There was going to be a directors' meeting. There were other men going in. You could depend on Pinhead's walking right into the directors' room where they had the big mahogany table and the mahogany chairs. The Buchanans sure liked to take down the Perrys.

'You go in there, Pinhead. Cousin Tom has been asking for you. He wants to give you a quarter.'

'Lordy,' said Burt McHugh, the plumber, 'Cousin Tom give him a quarter, eh? Why, he'd as soon give him an automobile.'

Pinhead took up with the Albrights. They liked him. He'd go out there and stay for weeks. The Albright place was three miles out of town. On a Saturday night, and sometimes all day on Sundays, there'd be a party out there.

There'd be moon-whiskey, plenty of that, and sometimes there'd be some of the men from town, even sometimes men who should have known better, men like Ed Cabe and that smarty lawyer, or even maybe Willy Buchanan, the Judge's youngest son, the one who drank so hard and who, they said, had a cancer.

And all kinds of rough people too.

There were two older Albright girls, unmarried, Sally and Katherine, and it was said they were 'putting out.'

Drinking, and sometimes dancing and singing and general hell-raising and maybe a fight or two.

'What the hell?' old Will Albright said . . . his wife was dead and Sally and Katherine did the housework . . . 'What the hell? It's my farm. It's my house. A man's king in his own house, ain't he?'

Pinhead grew fond of the little crippled Albright girl, little twisted-footed Hallie, and he'd sit out there in that house, with dancing and that kind of a jamboree going on. He'd sit in a corner of the big untidy bare room at the front of the house, two of the Albright boys playing guitars and singing rough songs at the top of their voices.

If the Albright boys were sullen and looking for a fight when they came to town, they weren't so much like that at home. They'd be singing some song like 'Hand Me Down My Bottle of Moon,' and that one about the warden and the prisoners in the jail, you know, on a Christmas morning, the warden trying to be Santa Claus to the boys, and what the hard-boiled prisoners said to him, and the two older Albright girls would be dancing, maybe with a couple of the men from town, and old Will Albright . . . he was sure boss in his own family . . . sitting over near the fireplace, chewing tobacco and keeping time with his feet. He'd spit clean and sharp right through his walrus mustache and never leave a trace. That lawyer said he could keep perfect time, with his feet and his jaws going together. 'Look at it,' he said. 'There ain't another man in Tennessee can spit like old Will.'

Pinhead sitting quiet, over in a corner, with his Hallie. They both smiling softly, Pinhead didn't drink. He wouldn't. 'You let him alone. He's good. Don't bother him. He's got a pure heart and I understand that,' Will Albright said to his boys. The couple got married one Saturday night and there was a big party, everyone howling drunk. Two of the guests wrecked a car trying to get back to town, and one of them, Henry Howard . . . a nice young fellow, a clerk in Williamson's drygoods store . . . you wouldn't think he would want to associate with such people . . . got his arm broken. Will Albright gave Pinhead and Hallie ten acres of land . . . good enough land . . . not so almighty good . . . down by the creek at the foot of the hill, and he and the boys built them a house. It wasn't much of a house, but you could live in it if you were hardy.

Neither Pinhead nor Hallie was so very hardy.

They lived. They had children. People said there had been 'ten of them children.' Pinhead and Hallie were getting pretty old. It was after the Albrights were all gone. Pinhead was seventy and Hallie was even older. Women in town said . . . 'How could she ever have had all of those children?'

'I'd like to know,' they said.

The children were nearly gone. Some had died. An officer had descended on the family and four of the children had been carried off to a state institution.

There were left only Pinhead and Hallie and one daughter. They had managed to cling to her, and to the little strip of land given them by Will Albright, but the house, a mere shed in the beginning, was now in ruins. Every day the three people set out for town where now, the philosophic lawyer being dead, a new one had taken his place. There will always be at least one such smarty in every town. This one was a tall slender young man who had inherited money and was fond of race-horses.

He was also passionately fond of practical jokes.

The plumber, Burt McHugh, was also gone, but there were new men, Ed Hollman, the sheriff, Frank Collins, another young lawyer, Joe Walker, who owned the hotel, and Bob Cairn, who ran the weekly newspaper of Greenhope.

These were the men who with Sol Grey and others had helped organize the baseball team. They went to every game. When the team disbanded they were heartbroken.

And there was Pinhead, coming into town followed by Hallie and the one daughter. Ruby was her name. Ruby was tall and gaunt and cross-eyed. She was habitually silent and had an odd habit. Let some man or woman stop on the sidewalk and look steadily at her for a moment and she would begin to cry. When she did it, Pinhead and Hallie both ran to her. She was so tall that they had to stand on tiptoes and reach up, but they both began patting her thin cheeks, her gaunt shoulders. 'There, there,' they said.

It didn't turn out so badly. When someone had made Ruby cry, it usually ended by Pinhead collecting a nickel or a dime. He'd go up to the guilty one and smile softly. 'Give her a little something and she'll quit,' he'd say. 'She wants a banana.'

He had kept to his plea for bananas. It amused people, was the best way to get money. He, Hallie, and Ruby always walked into town single file, Pinhead walking in front . . . although he was old now, he was still alive and alert . . . then came Hallie . . . her hair hanging down in strings about her little pinched face, and she had a goiter . . . and then Ruby, very tall, and in the summer, barelegged. Summer or winter Hallie wore the same dress.

It had been black. It had been given her by a widow. There was a little black hat that perched oddly on her head. The dress had been black but it had been patched with cloth of many colors. The colors blended. There was a good deal of discussion of the dress in town. No two people agreed on its color. Everything depended on the angle at which she approached you.

Pinhead and his family came into town every day to beg. They begged food at the back doors of houses. The town had grown and many new people had come in. Formerly the Perrys came into town along a dirt road, passing town people, who, when there had been a shower and the road was not too dusty, were out for a drive in buggies and phaetons, but now the road was paved and they passed automobiles. It was too bad for the Perrys. The family was still prosperous and had increased in numbers and standing. None of the other Perrys drove out of town by that road.

It was Sol Grey, the man who had managed about getting up the baseball team, who got up the plan that dull summer for having fun with Pinhead.

He told the others. He told the two young lawyers and Ed Hollman, the sheriff. He told Joe Walker, the hotel man, and Bob Cairn, who was editor of the newspaper.

He explained. 'I was in front of Herd's grocery,' he said. He had just been standing there when the three Perrys had come along. He thought that Pinhead had intended to ask him for a nickel or a dime. Anyway Pinhead had stopped before Sol, and then Hallie and Ruby had stopped. Sol said he must have been thinking of something else. Perhaps he was trying to think of some new way to break the monotony of life in Greenhope that summer. He found himself staring hard and long, not at Ruby but at Hallie Perry.

He did it unconsciously, like that, and didn't know how long he had kept it up, but suddenly there had come a queer change over Pinhead.

'Why, you all know Pinhead,' Sol Grey said. They were all gathered that day before Doc Thomson's drugstore. Sol kept bending over and slapping his knees with his hands as he told of what had happened. He had been staring at Hallie that way, not thinking of what he was doing, and Pinhead had got suddenly and furiously jealous.

Up to that moment, no one in town had ever seen Pinhead angry. 'Well, did he get sore!' Sol Grey cried. He shook with laughter. Pinhead had begun to berate him. 'You let my woman alone!

'What do you mean, staring at my woman?

'I won't have any man fooling with my woman.'

It was pretty rich. Pinhead had got the idea into his head that Sol ... he was a lumber and coal dealer ... a man who took pride in his clothes ... a married man ... the crazy loon had thought Sol was trying to make up to his Hallie. It was something gaudy. It was something to talk and to laugh about. It was something to work on. Sol said that Pinhead had offered to fight him. 'My God!' cried Joe Walker. Pinhead Perry was past seventy by that time and there was Hallie with her lame foot and with her goiter.

And all three of the Perrys so hopelessly dirty.

'My God! Oh my Lord! He thinks she's beautiful!' Joe Walker cried.

'Swell,' said Bob Cairn. The newspaper man, who was always looking for ideas, had one at once.

The plan had innumerable funny angles and all the men went to work. They began stopping Pinhead on the street. He would be coming along, followed by the two women, but the man who had stopped the little procession would draw Pinhead aside. 'It's like this,' he'd say. He'd declare he hated to bring the matter up, but he thought he should. 'A man's a man,' he'd say. 'He can't have other men fooling around with his woman.' It was so much fun to see the serious, baffled, hurt look in old Pinhead's eyes.

The man, who had taken Pinhead aside, spoke of an evening — a night, in fact, of the past. He said he had been out at night and had come into town past Pinhead's house. There was no road out that way and Pinhead and his two women, when they made their daily trip into town, had to follow a cowpath along Albright Creek to get into the main road, but the man did not bother to take that into account.

'I was going along the road past your house,' he'd say and would suggest that no doubt Pinhead was asleep. Certain very respectable men of the town were named as having been seen creeping away from Pinhead's house. There was Hal Pawsey. He kept the jewelry store in Greenhope and was a very shy modest man.

Pinhead rushed into Pawsey's store and began to shout. The wife of the Baptist minister was in the store at the time. She was seeing about getting her watch fixed. Hallie and Ruby were outside on the sidewalk and they were both crying. Pinhead began beating with his fists on the glass show case in the store. He broke the case. He used such language that he frightened the Baptist minister's wife so that she ran out of the store.

That was one incident of the summer but there were many others. The hotel man, the newspaper man, the lawyer, Sol Grey and several others kept busily at work.

They got Pinhead to tackle a stranger in town, a traveling man, coming out of a store with bags in his hand, and Pinhead got arrested and had to serve a term in jail. It was the first time he'd ever been in a fight or in jail.

Then, when he was let out, they began again. It was swell. It was so much fun. There was a story going around town that Pinhead had begun to beat his wife and that she took it stoically. Someone had seen him doing it on the road into town. They said she just stood and took it and didn't cry much.

The men kept it going.

One evening, when the moon was shining and the corn was getting knee-high, several of the men went in a car out to Pinhead's house. They left the car in the road and crept through bushes until they got quite near to the house.

One of them had given Pinhead some money and had advised him to spend it on a small bag of flour. The men in the bushes could see into the open door of the shack. 'My God,' said Joe Walker. 'Look!' he said. 'He's got her tied to a chair!'

'Ain't that rich!' he said.

Pinhead had Hallie sitting in the one chair of the one-room house ... the roof was almost gone and when it rained the water poured in ... and he was tying her to the chair with a piece of rope. Someone of the men had told Pinhead that another man of the town had planned to visit the house that night.

The men from town lay in the bushes and watched. The tall daughter, Ruby, was on the porch outside and she was crying. Pinhead, having got his wife tied to the chair, was scattering flour on the floor of the room and on the porch outside. He backed away from Hallie, scattering the flour. Hallie was crying. When he had got to the door and, as he was backing across the narrow rickety front porch, he scattered the flour thickly. The idea was that if any one of Hallie's lovers came, his footprints would stay in the flour.

Pinhead came out into a little yard at the front and got under a bush. He sat on the ground under the bush. In the moonlight the men from town could see him quite plainly. They said afterwards that he also began to cry. For some reason, even to the men of Greenhope, who were trying as best they could to get through a dull summer, the scene from the bushes before Pinhead's house that night had suddenly lost its fun.

They crept out from under the bushes and got back to their car and into town. Sol Grey went to the drugstore and began telling the story. There was quite a crowd of men standing about and Sol told the story with a flourish but nobody laughed. It was as though they had all suddenly begun disliking each other. They just looked at Sol. One by one they walked quietly away.

Blackfoot's Masterpiece

I CAME OUT of the Fifth Avenue Auction Room and it was snowing. I had just seen Blackfoot's canvas sold for twenty thousand dollars and Ramsey, the connoisseur and dealer, had come up to my friend Trycup, who stood fingering a stick beside me, and had made a little speech. Trycup, like Blackfoot before him, is a painter of promise. Blackfoot, you know, went insane, is tucked away in some asylum upstate. Ramsey touched Trycup on the shoulder and spoke benevolently. I couldn't stand it. The speech made me half ill. 'Keep your shoulders straight, my boy,' said Ramsey. 'Breathe deeply and keep your shoulders straight.'

I went over to Fifty-Eighth Street and asked a woman to dine with me. She is a sensitive, aristocratic-looking woman, came from somewhere out in the Middle West, and I wanted to hurt her. I thought I should tell her the story and watch her sensitive face quiver. There was something almost perverse in my desire to hurt so lovely a child and there is some of the same perversion in my wanting to see Blackfoot's story spread upon the printed page. I want to hurt many people, if I can.

As I went into the restaurant with my woman friend that evening after the picture was sold, the proprietor stepped forward to take my coat. He is gray and unctuous and looks like Ramsey. His hand fell on my shoulder and I heard his voice saying softly, 'You've become a bit round-shouldered, my boy. Better straighten up. Get into the habit of breathing deeply and throw your shoulders back.'

I didn't hit the restaurant man. Perhaps my hand trembled too much. Instead I snatched the coat from his hands and ran and the woman ran after me. 'You go to the devil!' I shouted to the man and when the perplexed, evil-looking people who let the great Blackfoot go insane in their midst, telling the tale I now tell to you. It hurt my woman friend as I knew it would. I hope it will hurt you also.

Blackfoot was a poor artist in New York City twenty years ago. That isn't anything special, but then you see he was a real artist and that is always something special. He was married to the daughter of a laundryman and lived over in that medley of streets in lower Manhattan, known as Greenwich Village.

I won't talk of his poverty. It was horrible, but that isn't the point. Comfort and an established place in the world are sometimes quite as horrible. Anyway, there he was in the dark, cheap, little flat, with children crawling about underfoot, and other children always coming, and disorder and dirt everywhere about him.

Blackfoot was a thin, pale man of thirty, and he was round-shouldered. He should have straightened his shoulders and breathed more deeply, there can be no doubt of that. It is a good rule for any man to adopt who marries a laundryman's daughter, given to the having of babies, and who lives with her in a flat in Greenwich Village in New York City.

One day Blackfoot painted this picture. He got to work at it one gloomy morning in February and something happened. Order sprang out of disorder. His brush fairly sang across the canvas. All day he worked and half the next day, and his soul was glad. He forgot all of the facts of his disorderly life and just worked. The picture had everything in it — balance, poise, movement, and that most damnably elusive of all things in a work of art, sheer lyrical beauty.

Of course Blackfoot felt like quite a man when the job was done. He put on a frayed overcoat and hunted out a cane he hadn't carried for five years, and then he went striding off to see Ramsey. He knew Ramsey would know what he had done and that Ramsey had money. It is a combination hard to find. There wasn't anyone to go to but Ramsey, you see.

As Blackfoot went along he came to a resolution. The most absurd notion came to his mind. He put a price on the picture he had painted. 'I'll have twelve hundred dollars for it, by God,' he told himself.

Blackfoot met Fred Morris on the street. Everyone in New York knows Fred. He is a good soul who makes money out of art, and paints pictures that sell. He was genuinely interested in what Blackfoot had done and congratulated him. 'Good work, old man,' he said, when the excited artist had told him the story, and then he touched Blackfoot on the shoulder with his stick. 'You want to straighten yourself up,' he said. 'You're getting a little too round-shouldered. I take a walk every afternoon and throw my shoulders back. It has been good for me. You had better do that.'

Ramsey came the next morning to see Blackfoot's picture. You get a sense of him, gray and quiet and sure, picking his way through Blackfoot's place among the kids and into the room where the picture was hung. He knew at once that a big job had been done and frankly said so. 'Of course,' he said, 'you have come through big. What do you want for the thing? I'll take it right now.'

Blackfoot was glad. He knew what he had done, but he wanted Ramsey to know also. 'Twelve hundred dollars,' he said quickly.

Ramsey shook his head. 'I'll give a thousand,' he answered, and when Blackfoot got angry and began to storm about the room, he was very gentlemanly and decent, 'Let's let it go,' he said. 'It doesn't matter. No good our getting into a row. I think you are going to be a big man and frankly I don't want to quarrel with you.' He started toward the door. 'By George, Blackfoot, you have some fine children,' he muttered. 'Take good care of yourself. You have responsibility here. I've noticed you're getting a little round-shouldered. I was in the army myself. That started me right. I got into the right physical habits, you see.'

Blackfoot waited a week before he went back to Ramsey. In a way he thought he had been too hasty. 'A man's got to take things as they come, and I can't expect to have others feel as I do about my work,' he said. Putting on the frayed overcoat he went over to Ramsey's place, forgetting this time to carry the cane.

Ramsey showed his hoofs. He offered Blackfoot seven hundred dollars for the canvas. He was soft-voiced and gentlemanly, just as before, but that's all he would give and Blackfoot just turned and went out through the door, too furious to speak. He wanted to kill someone. Artists are that way. When you apply what the world calls common-sense business methods to your dealings with them, they don't understand.

Ramsey finally got the canvas for four hundred dollars. Blackfoot made two more trips to his place and the last time he gave up. He had come out of Ramsey's house and was standing in the gray twilight looking up and down the street, not intending to give in at all, and then he just did. Rushing back, he accepted the four hundred dollars for the canvas that later sold for twenty thousand, and took the money in bills on the spot.

I haven't, I hope, overdone Blackfoot's poverty. I don't really remember how many children he had, not more than three or four, perhaps, but there was another coming. Of course, he was in debt at the grocery and to the landlord and had no credit.

The four hundred helped a lot. Things were brought in and a woman was employed to clean up and feed the children. Blackfoot himself built a roaring fire in the fireplace in his wife's room. He seemed happy enough, but he was tired. At ten o'clock he went to bed in a room with two of the children.

That's the last anyone ever saw of Blackfoot. The chattering thing up in the asylum who runs about telling people to breathe deeply and straighten up their shoulders has nothing to do with the man who painted the canvas I saw sold today.

Blackfoot went out with a swing. Bless his heart for that. It must have been two o'clock in the morning when his wife awoke on her cot in the corner of the little living room, and saw her husband sitting in a chair by the open fire. He had on a torn pair of pajamas and one of the legs was ripped so that his long thin leg showed through, and the poor fool had searched out the walking stick and had it hanging on his arm. When his wife screamed, he paid no attention at first, but presently he got up and came on tiptoe across the room to her. With the cane he touched her on the arm. 'Straighten your shoulders,' he said softly. 'You must breathe deeply and throw your shoulders back.'

That's all he said, and the wonder is that his wife did not go insane also. For when the woman awoke she saw something that must have made her heart stop beating. The thing she saw was as fine as the painting of the great picture. There in the firelight, in the little flat in Greenwich Village, with the cane hooked over his arm, Blackfoot had done a lovely thing. Alone in the silence, with his mind gone, and everyone asleep, he had fed the bills given him by Ramsey one by one into the fire.

a couple two more trips to his place and the last time he gave up. He had come out of Ramsey's house and was standing in the gray twilight looking up and down the street, not intending to give in at all, and then he just did. Rushing back, he accepted the four hundred dollars for the canvas that later sold for twenty thousand, and took the money in bills on the spot.

I haven't I hope overdone Blackfoot's poverty. I don't really remember how many children he had, nor more than three or four, perhaps, but there was another coming. Of course, he was in debt at the grocery and to the landlord and had no credit.

The four hundred helped a lot. Things were brought in and a woman was employed to clean up and feed the children. Blackfoot himself built a roaring fire in the fireplace in his wife's room. He seemed happy enough, but he was used, at ten o'clock he went to bed in a room with two of the children.

That's the last anyone ever saw of Blackfoot. The chattering thing up in the asylum who runs about telling people to breathe deeply and straighten up their shoulders has nothing to do with the man who painted the canvas I saw sold today.

Blackfoot went out with a saving. Bless his heart for that. It must have been two o'clock in the morning when his wife awoke on her cot in the corner of the little living room, and saw her husband sitting in a chair by the open fire. He had on a torn pair of pajamas and one of the legs was ripped so that his long thin leg showed through, and the poor fool had searched out the walking stick and had it hanging on his arm. When his wife screamed, he paid no attention at first, but presently he got up and came on tiptoe across the room to her. With the cane he touched her on the arm. 'Straighten your shoulders,' he said softly. 'You must breathe deeply and throw your shoulders back.'

That's all he said, and the wonder is that his wife did not go insane also. For when the woman awoke she saw something that must have made her heart stop beating. The thing she saw was as fine as the painting of the great picture. There in the firelight, in the little flat in Greenwich Village, with the cane hooked over his arm, Blackfoot had done a lovely thing. Alone in the silence, with his mind gone and everyone asleep, he had fed the bills given him by Ramsey one by one into the fire.

II. THE BURIED LIFE

Paper Pills
Hands
Tandy
The Untold Lie
Unlighted Lamps

Paper Pills

HE WAS AN OLD MAN with a white beard and huge nose and hands. Long before the time during which we will know him, he was a doctor and drove a jaded white horse from house to house through the streets of Winesburg. Later he married a girl who had money. She had been left a large fertile farm when her father died. The girl was quiet, tall, and dark, and to many people she seemed very beautiful. Everyone in Winesburg wondered why she married the doctor. Within a year after the marriage she died.

The knuckles of the doctor's hand were extraordinarily large. When the hands were closed they looked like clusters of unpainted wooden balls as large as walnuts fastened together by steel rods. He smoked a cob pipe and after his wife's death sat all day in his empty office close by a window that was covered with cobwebs. He never opened the window. Once on a hot day in August he tried but found it stuck fast and after that he forgot all about it.

Winesburg had forgotten the old man, but in Doctor Reefy there were the seeds of something very fine. Alone in his musty office in the Heffner Block above the Paris Dry Goods Company's Store, he worked ceaselessly, building up something that he himself destroyed. Little pyramids of truth he erected and after erecting knocked them down again that he might have the truths to erect other pyramids.

Docor Reefy was a tall man who had worn one suit of clothes for ten years. It was frayed at the sleeves and little holes had appeared at the knees and elbows. In the office he wore also a linen duster with huge pockets into which he continually stuffed scraps of paper. After some weeks the scraps of paper became little hard round balls, and when the pockets were filled he dumped them out upon the floor. For ten years he had but one friend, another old man named John

Spaniard who owned a tree nursery. Sometimes, in a playful mood, old Doctor Reefy took from his pockets a handful of the paper balls and threw them at the nursery man. 'That is to confound you, you blithering old sentimentalist,' he cried, shaking with laughter.

The story of Doctor Reefy and his courtship of the tall dark girl who became his wife and left her money to him is a very curious story. It is delicious, like the twisted little apples that grow in the orchards of Winesburg. In the fall one walks in the orchards and the ground is hard with frost underfoot. The apples have been taken from the trees by the pickers. They have been put in barrels and shipped to the cities where they will be eaten in apartments that are filled with books, magazines, furniture, and people. On the trees are only a few gnarled apples that the pickers have rejected. They look like the knuckles of Doctor Reefy's hands. One nibbles at them and they are delicious. Into a little round place at the side of the apple has been gathered all of its sweetness. One runs from tree to tree over the frosted ground picking the gnarled, twisted apples and filling his pockets with them. Only the few know the sweetness of the twisted apples.

The girl and Doctor Reefy began their courtship on a summer afternoon. He was forty-five then and already he had begun the practice of filling his pockets with the scraps of paper that became hard balls and were thrown away. The habit had been formed as he sat in his buggy behind the jaded gray horse and went slowly along country roads. On the papers were written thoughts, ends of thoughts, beginnings of thoughts.

One by one the mind of Doctor Reefy had made the thoughts. Out of many of them he formed a truth that arose gigantic in his mind. The truth clouded the world. It became terrible and then faded away and the little thoughts began again.

The tall dark girl came to see Doctor Reefy because she was in the family way and had become frightened. She was in that condition because of a series of circumstances also curious.

The death of her father and mother and the rich acres of land that had come down to her had set a train of suitors on her heels. For two years she saw suitors almost every evening. Except two they were all alike. They talked to her of passion and there was a strained eager quality in their voices and in their eyes when they looked at her. The two who were different were much unlike each other. One of them, a slender young man with white hands, the son of a jeweler in Winesburg, talked continually of virginity. When he was with her he was never off the subject. The other, a black-haired boy with large ears, said nothing at all, but always managed to get her into the darkness where he began to kiss her.

For a time the tall dark girl thought she would marry the jeweler's son. For hours she sat in silence listening as he talked to her and then she began to be afraid of something. Beneath his talk of virginity she began to think there was a lust greater than in all the others. At times it seemed to her that as he talked he was holding her body in his hands. She imagined him turning it slowly about in the white hands and staring at it. At night she dreamed that he had bitten into her body and that his jaws were dripping. She had the dream three times, then she became in the family way to the one who said nothing at all, but who in the moment of his passion actually did bite her shoulder so that for days the marks of his teeth showed.

After the tall dark girl came to know Doctor Reefy it seemed to her that she never wanted to leave him again. She went into his office one morning and without her saying anything he seemed to know what had happened to her.

In the office of the doctor there was a woman, the wife of the man who kept the bookstore in Winesburg. Like all old-fashioned country practitioners, Doctor Reefy pulled teeth, and the woman who waited held a handkerchief to her teeth and groaned. Her husband was with her and when the tooth was taken out they both screamed and blood ran down on the woman's white dress. The tall dark girl did not pay any attention. When the woman and the man had gone the doctor smiled. 'I will take you driving into the country with me,' he said.

For several weeks the tall dark girl and the doctor were together almost every day. The condition that had brought her to him passed in an illness, but she was like one who has discovered the sweetness of the twisted apples, she could not get her mind fixed again upon the round perfect fruit that is eaten in the city apartments. In the fall after the beginning of her acquaintanceship with him she married Doctor Reefy and in the following spring she died. During the winter he read to her all of the odds and ends of thoughts he had scribbled on the bits of paper. After he had read them he laughed and stuffed them away in his pockets to become round hard balls.

Hands

THE SHERWOOD ANDERSON READER

U<small>PON</small> the half-decayed veranda of a small frame house that stood near the edge of a ravine near the town of Winesburg, Ohio, a fat little old man walked nervously up and down. Across a long field that had been seeded for clover but that had produced only a dense crop of yellow mustard weeds, he could see the public highway along which went a wagon filled with berry-pickers returning from the fields. The berry-pickers, youths and maidens, laughed and shouted boisterously. A boy clad in a blue shirt leaped from the wagon and attempted to drag after him one of the maidens, who screamed and protested shrilly. The feet of the boy in the road kicked up a cloud of dust that floated across the face of the departing sun. Over the long field came a thin girlish voice. 'Oh, you Wing Biddlebaum, comb your hair, it's falling into your eyes,' commanded the voice to the man, who was bald and whose nervous little hands fiddled about the bare white forehead as though arranging a mass of tangled locks.

Wing Biddlebaum, forever frightened and beset by a ghostly band of doubts, did not think of himself as in any way a part of the life of the town where he had lived for twenty years. Among all the people of Winesburg but one had come close to him. With George Willard, son of Tom Willard, the proprietor of the new Willard House, he had formed something like a friendship. George Willard was the reporter on the *Winesburg Eagle* and sometimes in the evenings he walked out along the highway to Wing Biddlebaum's house. Now as the old man walked up and down on the veranda, his hands moving nervously about, he was hoping that George Willard would come and spend the evening with him. After the wagon containing the berry-pickers had passed, he went across the field through the tall mustard

21

weeds and climbing a rail fence peered anxiously along the road to the town. For a moment he stood thus, rubbing his hands together and looking up and down the road, and then, fear overcoming him, ran back to walk again upon the porch on his own house.

In the presence of George Willard, Wing Biddlebaum, who for twenty years had been the town mystery, lost something of his timidity, and his shadowy personality, submerged in a sea of doubts, came forth to look at the world. With the young reporter at his side, he ventured in the light of day into Main Street or strode up and down on the rickety front porch of his own house, talking excitedly. The voice that had been low and trembling became shrill and loud. The bent figure straightened. With a kind of wriggle, like a fish returned to the brook by the fisherman, Biddlebaum the silent began to talk, striving to put into words the ideas that had been accumulated by his mind during long years of silence.

Wing Biddlebaum talked much with his hands. The slender expressive fingers, forever active, forever striving to conceal themselves in his pockets or behind his back, came forth and became the piston rods of his machinery of expression.

The story of Wing Biddlebaum is a story of hands. Their restless activity, like unto the beating of the wings of an imprisoned bird, had given him his name. Some obscure poet of the town had thought of it. The hands alarmed their owner. He wanted to keep them hidden away and looked with amazement at the quiet inexpressive hands of other men who worked beside him in the fields, or passed, driving sleepy teams on country roads.

When he talked to George Willard, Wing Biddlebaum closed his fists and beat with them upon a table or on the walls of his house. The action made him more comfortable. If the desire to talk came to him when the two were walking in the fields, he sought out a stump or the top board of a fence and with his hands pounding busily talked with renewed ease.

The story of Wing Biddlebaum's hands is worth a book in itself. Sympathetically set forth it would tap many strange, beautiful qualities in obscure men. It is a job for a poet. In Winesburg the hands had attracted attention merely because of their activity. With them Wing Biddlebaum had picked as high as a hundred and forty quarts of strawberries in a day. They became his distinguishing feature, the source of his fame. Also they made more grotesque an already grotesque and elusive individuality. Winesburg was proud of the hands of Wing Biddlebaum in the same spirit in which it was proud of Banker White's new stone house and Wesley Moyer's bay stallion, Tony Tip, that had won the two-fifteen trot at the fall races in Cleveland.

As for George Willard, he had many times wanted to ask about the hands. At times an almost overwhelming curiosity had taken hold of him. He felt that there must be a reason for their strange activity and their inclination to keep hidden away, and only a growing respect for Wing Biddlebaum kept him from blurting out the questions that were often in his mind.

Once he had been on the point of asking. The two were walking in the fields on a summer afternoon and had stopped to sit upon a grassy bank. All afternoon Wing Biddlebaum had talked as one inspired. By a fence he had stopped and beating like a giant woodpecker upon the top board had shouted at George Willard, condemning his tendency to be too much influenced by the people about him. 'You are destroying yourself,' he cried. 'You have the inclination to be alone and to dream and you are afraid of dreams. You want to be like others in town here. You hear them talk and you try to imitate them.'

On the grassy bank Wing Biddlebaum had tried again to drive his point home. His voice became soft and reminiscent, and with a sigh of contentment he launched into a long rambling talk, speaking as one lost in a dream.

Out of the dream Wing Biddlebaum made a picture for George Willard. In the picture men lived again in a kind of pastoral golden age. Across a green open country came clean-limbed young men, some afoot, some mounted upon horses. In crowds the young men came to gather about the feet of an old man who sat beneath a tree in a tiny garden and who talked to them.

Wing Biddlebaum became wholly inspired. For once he forgot the hands. Slowly they stole forth and lay upon George Willard's shoulders. Something new and bold came into the voice that talked. 'You must try to forget all you have learned,' said the old man. 'You must begin to dream. From this time on you must shut your ears to the roaring of the voices.'

Pausing in his speech, Wing Biddlebaum looked long and earnestly at George Willard. His eyes glowed. Again he raised the hands to caress the boy and then a look of horror swept over his face.

With a convulsive movement of his body, Wing Biddlebaum sprang to his feet and thrust his hands deep into his trousers pockets. Tears came to his eyes. 'I must be getting along home. I can talk no more with you,' he said nervously.

Without looking back, the old man had hurried down the hillside and across a meadow, leaving George Willard perplexed and frightened upon the grassy slope. With a shiver of dread the boy arose and went along the road toward town. 'I'll not ask him about his hands,' he thought, touched by the memory of the terror he had seen in the man's eyes. 'There's something wrong, but I don't want to know what it is. His hands have something to do with his fear of me and of everyone.'

And George Willard was right. Let us look briefly into the story of the hands. Perhaps our talking of them will arouse the poet who will tell the hidden wonder story of the influence for which the hands were but fluttering pennants of promise.

In his youth Wing Biddlebaum had been a school teacher in a town in Pennsylvania. He was not then known as Wing Biddlebaum, but went by the less euphonic name of Adolph Myers. As Adolph Myers he was much loved by the boys of his school.

Adolph Myers was meant by nature to be a teacher of youth. He was one of those rare, little-understood men who rule by a power so gentle that it passes as a lovable weakness. In their feeling for the boys under their charge, such men are not unlike the finer sort of women in their love of men.

And yet that is but crudely stated. It needs the poet there. With the boys of his school, Adolph Myers had walked in the evening or had sat talking until dusk upon the schoolhouse steps lost in a kind of dream. Here and there went his hands, caressing the shoulders of the boys, playing about the tousled heads. As he talked, his voice became soft and musical. There was a caress in that also. In a way the voice and the hands, the stroking of the shoulders and the touching of the hair, were a part of the schoolmaster's effort to carry a dream into the young minds. By the caress that was in his fingers he expressed himself. He was one of those men in whom the force that creates life is diffused, not centralized. Under the caress of his hands doubt and disbelief went out of the minds of the boys and they began also to dream.

And then the tragedy. A half-witted boy of the school became enamored of the young master. In his bed at night he imagined unspeakable things and in the morning went forth to tell his dreams as facts. Strange, hideous accusations fell from his loose-hung lips. Through the Pennsylvania town went a shiver. Hidden, shadowy doubts that had been in men's minds concerning Adolph Myers were galvanized into beliefs.

The tragedy did not linger. Trembling lads were jerked out of bed and questioned. 'He put his arms about me,' said one. 'His fingers were always playing in my hair,' said another.

One afternoon a man of the town, Henry Bradford, who kept a saloon, came to the schoolhouse door. Calling Adolph Myers into the school yard he began to beat him with his fists. As his hard knuckles beat down into the frightened face of the schoolmaster, his wrath became more and more terrible. Screaming with dismay, the children ran here and there like disturbed insects. 'I'll teach you to put your hands on my boy, you beast,' roared the saloonkeeper, who, tired of beating the master, had begun to kick him about the yard.

Adolph Myers was driven from the Pennsylvania town in the night. With lanterns in their hands a dozen men came to the door of the house where he lived alone and commanded that he dress and come forth. It was raining and one of the men had a rope in his hands. They had intended to hang the schoolmaster, but something in his figure, so small, white, and pitiful, touched their hearts and they let him escape. As he ran away into the darkness they repented of their weakness and ran after him, swearing and throwing sticks and great balls of soft mud at the figure that screamed and ran faster and faster into the darkness.

For twenty years Adolph Myers had lived alone in Winesburg. He was but forty but looked sixty-five. The name of Biddlebaum he got from a box of goods seen at a freight station as he hurried through an eastern Ohio town. He had an aunt in Winesburg, a black-toothed old woman who raised chickens, and with her he lived until she died. He had been ill for a year after the experience in Pennsylvania, and after his recovery worked as a day laborer in the fields, going timidly about and striving to conceal his hands. Although he did not understand what had happened, he felt that the hands must be to blame. Again and again the fathers of the boys had talked of the hands. 'Keep your hands to yourself,' the saloonkeeper had roared, dancing with fury in the schoolhouse yard.

Upon the veranda of his house by the ravine, Wing Biddlebaum continued to walk up and down until the sun had disappeared and the road beyond the field was lost in the gray shadows. Going into his house he cut slices of bread and spread honey upon them. When the rumble of the evening train that took away the express cars loaded with the day's harvest of berries had passed and restored the silence of the summer night, he went again to walk upon the veranda. In the darkness he could not see the hands and they became quiet. Although he still hungered for the presence of the boy, who was the medium through which he expressed his love of man, the hunger became again a part of his loneliness and his waiting. Lighting a lamp, Wing Biddlebaum washed the few dishes soiled by his simple meal and, setting up a folding cot by the screen door that led to the porch, prepared to undress for the night. A few stray white bread crumbs lay on the cleanly washed floor by the table; putting the lamp upon a low stool he began to pick up the crumbs, carrying them to his mouth one by one with unbelievable rapidity. In the dense blotch of light beneath the table, the kneeling figure looked like a priest engaged in some service of his church. The nervous expressive fingers, flashing in and out of the light, might well have been mistaken for the fingers of the devotee going swiftly through decade after decade of his rosary.

Tandy

UNTIL she was seven years old she lived in an old unpainted house on an unused road that led off Trunion Pike. Her father gave her but little attention and her mother was dead. The father spent his time talking and thinking of religion. He proclaimed himself an agnostic and was so absorbed in destroying the ideas of God that had crept into the minds of his neighbors that he never saw God manifesting himself in the little child that, half-forgotten, lived here and there on the bounty of her dead mother's relatives.

A stranger came to Winesburg and saw in the child what the father did not see. He was a tall, red-haired young man who was almost always drunk. Sometimes he sat in a chair before the New Willard House with Tom Hard, the father. As Tom talked, declaring there could be no God, the stranger smiled and winked at the bystanders. He and Tom became friends and were much together.

The stranger was the son of a rich merchant of Cleveland and had come to Winesburg on a mission. He wanted to cure himself of the habit of drink, and thought that by escaping from his city associates and living in a rural community he would have a better chance in the struggle with the appetite that was destroying him.

His sojourn in Winesburg was not a success. The dullness of the passing hours led to his drinking harder than ever. But he did succeed in doing something. He gave a name rich with meaning to Tom Hard's daughter.

One evening when he was recovering from a long debauch the stranger came reeling along the main street of the town. Tom Hard sat in a chair before the New Willard House with his daughter, then

27

a child of five, on his knees. Beside him on the board sidewalk sat young George Willard. The stranger dropped into a chair beside them. His body shook and when he tried to talk his voice trembled.

It was late evening and darkness lay over the town and over the railroad that ran along the foot of a little incline before the hotel. Somewhere in the distance, off to the west, there was a prolonged blast from the whistle of a passenger engine. A dog that had been sleeping in the roadway arose and barked. The stranger began to babble and made a prophecy concerning the child that lay in the arms of the agnostic.

'I came here to quit drinking,' he said, and tears began to run down his cheeks. He did not look at Tom Hard, but leaned forward and stared into the darkness as though seeing a vision. 'I ran away to the country to be cured, but I am not cured. There is a reason.' He turned to look at the child, who sat up very straight on her father's knee and returned the look.

The stranger touched Tom Hard on the arm. 'Drink is not the only thing to which I am addicted,' he said. 'There is something else. I am a lover and have not found my thing to love. That is a big point if you know enough to realize what I mean. It makes my destruction inevitable, you see. There are few who understand that.'

The stranger became silent and seemed overcome with sadness, but another blast from the whistle of the passenger engine aroused him. 'I have not lost faith. I proclaim that. I have only been brought to the place where I know my faith will not be realized,' he declared hoarsely. He looked hard at the child and began to address her, paying no more attention to the father. 'There is a woman coming,' he said, and his voice was now sharp and earnest. 'I have missed her, you see. She did not come in my time. You may be the woman. It would be like Fate to let me stand in her presence once, on such an evening as this, when I have destroyed myself with drink and she is as yet only a child.'

The shoulders of the stranger shook violently, and when he tried to roll a cigarette the paper fell from his trembling fingers. He grew angry and scolded. 'They think it's easy to be a woman, to be loved, but I know better,' he declared. Again he turned to the child. 'I understand,' he cried. 'Perhaps of all men I alone understand.'

His glance again wandered away to the darkened street. 'I know about her, although she has never crossed my path,' he said softly. 'I know about her struggles and her defeats. It is because of her defeats that she is to me the lovely one. Out of her defeats has been born a new quality in woman. I have a name for it. I call it Tandy. I made up the name when I was a true dreamer and before my body became vile. It is the quality of being strong to be loved. It is something men need from women and that they do not get.'

The stranger arose and stood before Tom Hard. His body rocked back and forth and he seemed about to fall, but instead he dropped to his knees on the sidewalk and raised the hands of the little girl to his drunken lips. He kissed them ecstatically. 'Be Tandy, little one,' he pleaded. 'Dare to be strong and courageous. That is the road. Venture anything. Be brave enough to dare to be loved. Be something more than man or woman. Be Tandy.'

The Untold Lie

RAY PEARSON and Hal Winters were farmhands employed on a farm three miles north of Winesburg. On Saturday afternoons they came into town and wandered about through the streets with other fellows from the country.

Ray was a quiet, rather nervous man of perhaps fifty, with a brown beard and shoulders rounded by too much and too hard labor. In his nature he was as unlike Hal Winters as two men can be unlike.

Ray was an altogether serious man and had a little sharp-featured wife who had also a sharp voice. The two, with half a dozen thin-legged children, lived in a tumble-down frame house beside a creek at the back end of the Wills farm where Ray was employed.

Hal Winters, his fellow employee, was a young fellow. He was not of the Ned Winters family, who were very respectable people in Winesburg, but was one of the three sons of the old man called Windpeter Winters who had a sawmill near Unionville, six miles away, and who was looked upon by everyone in Winesburg as a confirmed old reprobate.

People from the part of Northern Ohio in which Winesburg lies will remember old Windpeter by his unusual and tragic death. He got drunk one evening in town and started to drive home to Unionville along the railroad tracks. Henry Brattenburg, the butcher, who lived out that way, stopped him at the edge of the town and told him he was sure to meet the down train, but Windpeter slashed at him with his whip and drove on. When the train struck and killed him and his two horses, a farmer and his wife who were driving home along a near-by road saw the accident. They said that old Windpeter stood up on the seat of his wagon, raving and swearing at the onrushing locomotive, and that he fairly screamed with delight when the team, maddened by his incessant slashing at them, rushed straight ahead to certain death. Boys like young George Willard and Seth Richmond will remember the incident quite vividly because, although everyone in our town said that the old man would go straight to hell and that the community was better off without him, they had a secret conviction that he knew what he was doing and admired his foolish courage. Most boys have seasons of wishing they could die gloriously instead of just being grocery clerks and going on with their humdrum lives.

But this is not the story of Windpeter Winters nor yet of his son Hal who worked on the Wills farm with Ray Pearson. It is Ray's story. It will, however, be necessary to talk a little of young Hal so that you will get into the spirit of it.

Hal was a bad one. Everyone said that. There were three of the Winters boys in that family, John, Hal, and Edward, all broad-shouldered big fellows like old Windpeter himself and all fighters and woman-chasers and generally all-around bad ones.

Hal was the worst of the lot and always up to some devilment. He once stole a load of boards from his father's mill and sold them in Winesburg. With the money he bought himself a suit of cheap, flashy clothes. Then he got drunk, and when his father came raving into town to find him, they met and fought with their fists on Main Street and were arrested and put into jail together.

Hal went to work on the Wills farm because there was a country school-teacher out that way who had taken his fancy. He was only twenty-two then, but had already been in two or three of what were spoken of in Winesburg as 'women scrapes.' Everyone who heard of his infatuation for the school-teacher was sure it would turn out badly. 'He'll only get her into trouble, you'll see,' was the word that went around.

And so these two men, Ray and Hal, were at work in a field on a day in the late October. They were husking corn and occasionally something was said and they laughed. Then came silence. Ray, who was the more sensitive and always minded things more, had chapped hands and they hurt. He put them into his coat pockets and looked away across the fields. He was in a sad distracted mood and was affected by the beauty of the country. If you knew the Winesburg country in the fall and how the low hills are all splashed with yellows and reds, you would understand his feeling. He began to think of the time, long ago when he was a young fellow living with his father, then a baker in Winesburg, and how on such days he had wandered away to the woods to gather nuts, hunt rabbits, or just to loaf about and smoke his pipe. His marriage had come about through one of his days of wandering. He had induced a girl who waited on trade in his father's shop to go with him and something had happened. He was thinking of that afternoon and how it had affected his whole life when a spirit of protest awoke in him. He had forgotten about Hal and muttered words. 'Tricked, by Gad, that's what I was, tricked by life and made a fool of,' he said in a low voice.

As though understanding his thoughts, Hal Winters spoke up. 'Well, has it been worth while? What about it, eh? What about marriage and all that?' he asked and then laughed. Hal tried to keep on laughing, but he too was in an earnest mood. He began to talk earnestly. 'Has a fellow got to do it?' he asked. 'Has he got to be harnessed up and driven through life like a horse?'

Hal didn't wait for an answer, but sprang to his feet and began to walk back and forth between the corn shocks. He was getting more and more excited. Bending down suddenly he picked up an ear of the yellow corn and threw it at the fence. 'I've got Nell Gunther in trouble,' he said. 'I'm telling you, but you keep your mouth shut.'

Ray Pearson arose and stood staring. He was almost a foot shorter than Hal, and when the younger man came and put his two hands on the older man's shoulders they made a picture. There they stood in the big empty field with the quiet corn shocks standing in rows behind them and the red and yellow hills in the distance, and from being just two indifferent workmen they had become all alive to each other. Hal sensed it and because that was his way he laughed. 'Well, old daddy,' he said awkwardly, 'come on, advise me. I've got Nell in trouble. Perhaps you've been in the same fix yourself. I know what everyone would say is the right thing to do, but what do you say? Shall I marry and settle down? Shall I put myself into the harness to be worn out like an old horse? You know me, Ray. There can't any one break me, but I can break myself. Shall I do it or shall I tell Nell to go to the devil? Come on, you tell me. Whatever you say, Ray, I'll do.'

Ray couldn't answer. He shook Hal's hands loose and turning walked straight away toward the barn. He was a sensitive man and there were tears in his eyes. He knew there was only one thing to say to Hal Winters, son of old Windpeter Winters, only one thing that all his own training and all the beliefs of the people he knew would approve, but for his life he couldn't say what he knew he should say.

At half-past four that afternoon Ray was puttering about the barn-yard when his wife came up the lane along the creek and called him. After the talk with Hal he hadn't returned to the corn field but worked about the barn. He had already done the evening chores and had seen Hal, dressed and ready for a roistering night in town, come out of the farmhouse and go into the road. Along the path to his own house he trudged behind his wife, looking at the ground and thinking. He couldn't make out what was wrong. Every time he raised his eyes and saw the beauty of the country in the failing light he wanted to do something he had never done before, shout or scream or hit his wife with his fists or something equally unexpected and ter-rifying. Along the path he went scratching his head and trying to make it out. He looked hard at his wife's back, but she seemed all right.

She only wanted him to go into town for groceries and as soon as she had told him what she wanted began to scold. 'You're always puttering,' she said. 'Now I want you to hustle. There isn't any-thing in the house for supper and you've got to get to town and back in a hurry.'

Ray went into his own house and took an overcoat from a hook back of the door. It was torn about the pockets and the collar was shiny. His wife went into the bedroom and presently came out with a soiled cloth in one hand and three silver dollars in the other. Some-where in the house a child wept bitterly and a dog that had been sleeping by the stove arose and yawned. Again the wife scolded. 'The children will cry and cry. Why are you always puttering?' she asked.

Ray went out of the house and climbed the fence into a field. It was just growing dark and the scene that lay before him was lovely. All the low hills were washed with color and even the little clusters of bushes in the corners by the fences were alive with beauty. The whole world seemed to Ray Pearson to have become alive with something just as he and Hal had suddenly become alive when they stood in the corn field staring into each other's eyes.

The beauty of the country about Winesburg was too much for Ray on that fall evening. That is all there was to it. He could not stand it. Of a sudden he forgot all about being a quiet old farmhand and throwing off the torn overcoat began to run across the field. As he ran he shouted a protest against his life, against all life, against everything that makes life ugly. 'There was no promise made,' he cried into the empty spaces that lay about him. 'I didn't promise my Minnie anything and Hal hasn't made any promise to Nell. I know he hasn't. She went into the woods with him because she wanted to go. What he wanted she wanted. Why should I pay? Why should Hal pay? Why should anyone pay? I don't want Hal to become old and worn out. I'll tell him. I won't let it go on. I'll catch Hal before he gets to town and I'll tell him.'

Ray ran clumsily and once he stumbled and fell down. 'I must catch Hal and tell him,' he kept thinking, and although his breath came in gasps he kept running harder and harder. As he ran he thought of things that hadn't come into his mind for years — how at the time he married he had planned to go West to his uncle in Portland, Oregon — how he hadn't wanted to be a farmhand, but had thought when he got out West he would go to sea and be a sailor or get a job on a ranch and ride a horse into Western towns, shouting and laughing and waking the people in the houses with his wild cries. Then as he ran he remembered his children and in fancy felt their hands clutching at him. All of his thoughts of himself were involved with the thoughts of Hal and he thought the children were clutching at the younger man also. 'They are the accidents of life, Hal,' he cried. 'They are not mine or yours. I had nothing to do with them.'

Darkness began to spread over the fields as Ray Pearson ran on and on. His breath came in little sobs. When he came to the fence at the edge of the road and confronted Hal Winters, all dressed up and smoking a pipe as he walked jauntily along, he could not have told what he thought or what he wanted.

Ray Pearson lost his nerve and this is really the end of the story of what happened to him. It was almost dark when he got to the fence and he put his hands on the top bar and stood staring. Hal Winters jumped a ditch and coming up close to Ray put his hands into his pockets and laughed. He seemed to have lost his own sense of what had happened in the corn field and when he put up a strong hand and took hold of the lapel of Ray's coat he shook the old man as he might have shaken a dog that had misbehaved.

'You came to tell me, eh?' he said. 'Well, never mind telling me anything. I'm not a coward and I've already made up my mind.' He laughed again and jumped back across the ditch. 'Nell ain't no fool,' he said. 'She didn't ask me to marry her. I want to marry her. I want to settle down and have kids.'

Ray Pearson also laughed. He felt like laughing at himself and all the world.

As the form of Hal Winters disappeared in the dusk that lay over the road that led to Winesburg, he turned and walked slowly back across the fields to where he had left his torn overcoat. As he went some memory of pleasant evenings spent with the thin-legged children in the tumble-down house by the creek must have come into his mind, for he muttered words. 'It's just as well. Whatever I told him would have been a lie,' he said softly, and then his form also disappeared into the darkness of the fields.

Unlighted Lamps

Mary Cochran went out of the rooms where she lived with her father, Doctor Lester Cochran, at seven o'clock on a Sunday evening. It was June of the year nineteen hundred and eight and Mary was eighteen years old. She walked along Tremont to Main Street and across the railroad tracks to Upper Main, lined with small shops and shoddy houses, a rather quiet cheerless place on Sundays when there were few people about. She had told her father she was going to church, but did not intend doing anything of the kind. She did not know what she wanted to do. 'I'll get off by myself and think,' she told herself as she walked slowly along. The night she thought promised to be too fine to be spent sitting in a stuffy church and hearing a man talk of things that had apparently nothing to do with her own problem. Her own affairs were approaching a crisis and it was time for her to begin thinking seriously of her future.

The thoughtful serious state of mind in which Mary found herself had been induced in her by a conversation had with her father on the evening before. Without any preliminary talk and quite suddenly and abruptly he had told her that he was a victim of heart disease and might die at any moment. He had made the announcement as they stood together in the doctor's office, back of which were the rooms in which the father and daughter lived.

It was growing dark outside when she came into the office and found him sitting alone. The office and living rooms were on the second floor of an old frame building in the town of Huntersburg, Illinois, and as the doctor talked he stood beside his daughter near one of the windows that looked down into Tremont Street. The

36

hushed murmur of the town's Saturday night life went on in Main
Street just around a corner, and the evening train, bound to Chicago
fifty miles to the east, had just passed. The hotel bus came rattling
out of Lincoln Street and went through Tremont toward the hotel
on Lower Main. A cloud of dust kicked up by the horse's hoofs
floated on the quiet air. A straggling group of people followed the
bus and the row of hitching posts on Tremont Street was already lined
with buggies in which farmers and their wives had driven into town
for the evening of shopping and gossip.

After the station bus had passed three or four more buggies were
driven into the street. From one of them a young man helped his
sweetheart to alight. He took hold of her arm with a certain air of
tenderness, and a hunger to be touched thus tenderly by a man's
hand, that had come to Mary many times before, returned at almost
the same moment her father made the announcement of his approaching death.

As the doctor began to speak, Barney Smithfield, who owned a
livery barn that opened into Tremont Street directly opposite the
building in which the Cochrans lived, came back to his place of business from his evening meal. He stopped to tell a story to a group of
men gathered before the barn door and a shout of laughter arose. One
of the loungers in the street, a strongly built young man in a checkered suit, stepped away from the others and stood before the liveryman. Having seen Mary he was trying to attract her attention. He
also began to tell a story and as he talked he gesticulated, waved his
arms and from time to time looked over his shoulder to see if the
girl still stood by the window and if she were watching.

Doctor Cochran had told his daughter of his approaching death in
a cold quiet voice. To the girl it had seemed that everything concerning her father must be cold and quiet. 'I have a disease of the heart,'
he said flatly, 'have long suspected there was something of the sort
the matter with me and on Thursday when I went into Chicago I
had myself examined. The truth is I may die at any moment. I would
not tell you but for one reason — I will leave little money and you
must be making plans for the future.'

The doctor stepped nearer the window where his daughter stood
with her hand on the frame. The announcement had made her a
little pale and her hand trembled. In spite of his apparent coldness

he was touched and wanted to reassure her. 'There now,' he said hesitatingly, 'it'll likely be all right after all. Don't worry. I haven't been a doctor for thirty years without knowing there's a great deal of nonsense about these pronouncements on the part of experts. In a matter like this, that is to say when a man has a disease of the heart, he may putter about for years.' He laughed uncomfortably. 'I've even heard it said that the best way to insure a long life is to contract a disease of the heart.'

With these words the doctor had turned and walked out of his office, going down a wooden stairway to the street. He had wanted to put his arm about his daughter's shoulder as he talked to her, but never having shown any feeling in his relations with her could not sufficiently release some tight thing in himself.

Mary had stood for a long time looking down into the street. The young man in the checkered suit, whose name was Duke Yetter, had finished telling his tale and a shout of laughter arose. She turned to look toward the door through which her father had passed and dread took possession of her. In all her life there had never been anything warm and close. She shivered although the night was warm and with a quick girlish gesture passed her hand over her eyes.

The gesture was but an expression of a desire to brush away the cloud of fear that had settled down upon her, but it was misinterpreted by Duke Yetter who now stood a little apart from the other men before the livery barn. When he saw Mary's hand go up he smiled and turning quickly to be sure he was unobserved began jerking his head and making motions with his hand as a sign that he wished her to come down into the street where he would have an opportunity to join her.

On the Sunday evening Mary, having walked through Upper Main, turned into Wilmott, a street of workmen's houses. During that year the first sign of the march of factories westward from Chicago into the prairie towns had come to Huntersburg. A Chicago manufacturer of furniture had built a plant in the sleepy little farming town, hoping thus to escape the labor organizations that had begun to give him trouble in the city. At the upper end of town, in Wilmott, Swift, Harrison and Chestnut Streets and in cheap, badly constructed frame houses, most of the factory workers lived. On the warm summer evening they were gathered on the porches at the front of the houses and a mob of children played in the dusty streets. Redfaced men in white shirts and without collars and coats slept in chairs or lay sprawled on strips of grass or on the hard earth before the doors of the houses.

The laborers' wives had gathered in groups and stood gossiping by the fences that separated the yards. Occasionally the voice of one of the women arose sharp and distinct above the steady flow of voices that ran like a murmuring river through the hot little streets.

In the roadway two children had got into a fight. A thick-shouldered red-haired boy struck another boy, who had a pale sharp-featured face, a blow on the shoulder. Other children came running. The mother of the red-haired boy brought the promised fight to an end. 'Stop it, Johnny, I tell you to stop it. I'll break your neck if you don't,' the woman screamed.

The pale boy turned and walked away from his antagonist. As he went slinking along the sidewalk past Mary Cochran, his sharp little eyes, burning with hatred, looked up at her.

Mary went quickly along. The strange new part of her native town with the hubbub of life always stirring and asserting itself had a strong fascination for her. There was something dark and resentful in her own nature that made her feel at home in the crowded place where life carried itself off darkly, with a blow and an oath. The habitual silence of her father and the mystery concerning the unhappy married life of her father and mother, that had affected the atttitude toward her of the people of the town, had made her own life a lonely one and had encouraged in her a rather dogged determination to in some way think her own way through the things of life she could not understand.

And back of Mary's thinking there was an intense curiosity and a courageous determination toward adventure. She was like a little animal of the forest that has been robbed of its mother by the gun of a sportsman and has been driven by hunger to go forth and seek food. Twenty times during the year she had walked alone at evening in the new and fast-growing factory district of her town. She was eighteen and had begun to look like a woman, and she felt that other girls of the town of her own age would not have dared to walk in such a place alone. The feeling made her somewhat proud and as she went along she looked boldly about.

Among the workers in Wilmott Street, men and women who had been brought to town by the furniture manufacturer, were many who spoke in foreign tongues. Mary walked among them and liked the sound of the strange voices. To be in the street made her feel that she had gone out of her town and on a voyage into a strange land. In Lower Main Street or in the residence streets in the eastern part of town where lived the young men and women she had always known and where lived also the merchants, the clerks, the lawyers and the more well-to-do American workmen of Huntersburg, she felt always a secret antagonism to herself. The antagonism was not due to anything in her own character. She was sure of that. She had kept so much to herself that she was in fact but little known. 'It is because I am the daughter of my mother,' she told herself and did not walk often in the part of town where other girls of her class lived.

Mary had been so often in Wilmott Street that many of the people had begun to feel acquainted with her. 'She is the daughter of some farmer and has got into the habit of walking into town,' they said. A red-haired, broad-lipped woman who came out at the front door of one of the houses nodded to her. On a narrow strip of grass beside another house sat a young man with his back against a tree. He was smoking a pipe, but when he looked up and saw her he took the pipe from his mouth. She decided he must be an Italian, his hair and eyes were so black. 'Ne bella! si fai un onore a passare di qua,' he called, waving his hand and smiling.

Mary went to the end of Wilmott Street and came out upon a country road. It seemed to her that a long time must have passed since she left her father's presence, although the walk had in fact occupied but a few minutes. By the side of the road and on top of a small hill there was a ruined barn, and before the barn a great hole filled with the charred timbers of what had once been a farmhouse. A pile of stones lay beside the hole and these were covered with creeping vines. Between the site of the house and the barn there was an old orchard in which grew a mass of tangled weeds.

Pushing her way in among the weeds, many of which were covered with blossoms, Mary found herself a seat on a rock that had been rolled against the trunk of an old apple tree. The weeds half concealed her and from the road only her head was visible. Buried away thus in the weeds she looked like a quail that runs in the tall grass and that on hearing some unusual sound, stops, throws up its head and looks sharply about.

The doctor's daughter had been to the decayed old orchard many times before. At the foot of the hill on which it stood the streets of the town began, and as she sat on the rock she could hear faint shouts and cries coming out of Wilmott Street. A hedge separated the orchard from the fields on the hillside. Mary intended to sit by the tree until darkness came creeping over the land and to try to think out some plan regarding her future. The notion that her father was soon to die seemed both true and untrue, but her mind was unable to take hold of the thought of him as physically dead. For the moment death in relation to her father did not take the form of a cold inanimate body that was to be buried in the ground; instead it seemed to her that her father was not to die but to go away somewhere on a journey. Long ago her mother had done that. There was a strange hesitating sense of relief in the thought. 'Well,' she told herself, 'when the time comes I also shall be setting out. I shall get out of here and into the world.' On several occasions Mary had gone to spend a day with her father in Chicago and she was fascinated by the thought that soon she might be going there to live. Before her mind's eye floated a vision of long streets filled with thousands of people, all strangers to herself. To go into such streets and to live her life among strangers would be like coming out of a waterless desert and into a cool forest carpeted with tender young grass.

In Huntersburg she had always lived under a cloud, and now she was becoming a woman and the close stuffy atmosphere she had always breathed was becoming constantly more and more oppressive. It was true no direct question had ever been raised touching her own standing in the community life, but she felt that a kind of prejudice against her existed. While she was still a baby there had been a scandal involving her father and mother. The town of Huntersburg had rocked with it and when she was a child people had sometimes looked at her with mocking sympathetic eyes. 'Poor child! It's too bad,' they said. Once, on a cloudy summer evening when her father had driven off to the country and she sat alone in the darkness by his office window, she heard a man and woman in the street mention her name. The couple stumbled along in the darkness on the sidewalk below the office window. 'That daughter of Doc Cochran's is a nice girl,' said the man. The woman laughed. 'She's growing up and attracting men's attention now. Better keep your eyes in your head. She'll turn out bad. Like mother, like daughter,' the woman replied.

For ten or fifteen minutes Mary sat on the stone beneath the tree in the orchard and thought of the attitude of the town toward herself and her father. 'It should have drawn us together,' she told herself, and wondered if the approach of death would do what the cloud that had for years hung over them had not done. It did not at the moment seem to her cruel that the figure of Death was soon to visit her father. In a way Death had become for her and for the time a lovely and gracious figure intent upon good. The hand of Death was to open the door out of her father's house and into life. With the cruelty of youth she thought first of the adventurous possibilities of the new life.

Mary sat very still. In the long weeds the insects that had been disturbed in their evening song began to sing again. A robin flew into the tree beneath which she sat and struck a clear sharp note of alarm. The voices of people in the town's new factory district came softly up the hillside. They were like bells of distant cathedrals calling people to worship. Something within the girl's breast seemed to break and putting her head into her hands she rocked slowly back and forth. Tears came unaccompanied by a warm tender impulse toward the living men and women of Huntersburg.

And then from the road came a call. 'Hello there, kid,' shouted a voice, and Mary sprang quickly to her feet. Her mellow mood passed like a puff of wind and in its place hot anger came.

In the road stood Duke Yetter who from his loafing place before the livery barn had seen her set out for the Sunday evening walk and had followed. When she went through Upper Main Street and into the new factory district, he was sure of his conquest. 'She doesn't want to be seen walking with me,' he had told himself; 'that's all right. She knows well enough I'll follow but doesn't want me to put in an appearance until she is well out of sight of her friends. She's a little stuck up and needs to be brought down a peg, but what do I care? She's gone out of her way to give me this chance and maybe she's only afraid of her dad.'

Duke climbed the little incline out of the road and came into the orchard, but when he reached the pile of stones covered by vines he stumbled and fell. He arose and laughed. Mary had not waited for him to reach her, but had started toward him, and when his laugh broke the silence that lay over the orchard she sprang forward and with her open hand struck him a sharp blow on the cheek. Then she turned and as he stood with his feet tangled in the vines ran out to the road. 'If you follow or speak to me I'll get someone to kill you,' she shouted.

Mary walked along the road and down the hill toward Wilmott Street. Broken bits of the story concerning her mother that had for years circulated in town had reached her ears. Her mother, it was said, had disappeared on a summer night long ago and a young town rough, who had been in the habit of loitering before Barney Smithfield's Livery Barn, had gone away with her. Now another young rough was trying to make up to her. The thought made her furious.

Her mind groped about striving to lay hold of some weapon with which she could strike a more telling blow at Duke Yetter. In desperation it lit upon the figure of her father, already broken in health and now about to die. 'My father just wants the chance to kill some such fellow as you,' she shouted, turning to face the young man, who having got clear of the mass of vines in the orchard, had followed her into the road. 'My father just wants to kill someone because of the lies that have been told in this town about mother.'

Having given way to the impulse to threaten Duke Yetter, Mary was instantly ashamed of her outburst and walked rapidly along, the tears running from her eyes. With hanging head Duke walked at her heels. 'I didn't mean no harm, Miss Cochran,' he pleaded. 'I didn't mean no harm. Don't tell your father. I was only funning with you. I tell you I didn't mean no harm.'

The light of the summer evening had begun to fall and the faces of the people made soft little ovals of light as they stood grouped under the dark porches or by the fences in Wilmott Street. The voices of the children had become subdued and they also stood in groups. They became silent as Mary passed and stood with upturned faces and staring eyes. 'The lady doesn't live very far. She must be almost a neighbor,' she heard a woman's voice saying in English. When she turned her head she saw only a crowd of dark-skinned men standing before a house. From within the house came the sound of a woman's voice singing a child to sleep.

The young Italian, who had called to her earlier in the evening and who was now apparently setting out on his own Sunday evening's adventures, came along the sidewalk and walked quickly away into the darkness. He had dressed himself in his Sunday clothes and had put on a black derby hat and a stiff white collar, set off by a red necktie. The shining whiteness of the collar made his brown skin look almost black. He smiled boyishly and raised his hat awkwardly, but did not speak.

Mary kept looking back along the street to be sure Duke Yetter had not followed, but in the dim light could see nothing of him. Her angry excited mood went away.

She did not want to go home and decided it was too late to go to church. From Upper Main Street there was a short street that ran eastward and fell rather sharply down a hillside to a creek and a bridge that marked the end of the town's growth in that direction. She went down along the street to the bridge and stood in the failing light watching two boys who were fishing in the creek.

A broad-shouldered man dressed in rough clothes came down along the street and stopping on the bridge spoke to her. It was the first time she had ever heard a citizen of her home town speak with feeling of her father. 'You are Doctor Cochran's daughter?' he asked hesitatingly. 'I guess you don't know who I am, but your father does.' He pointed towards the two boys who sat with fishpoles in their hands on the weed-grown bank of the creek. 'Those are my boys and I have four other children,' he explained. 'There is another boy and I have three girls. One of my daughters has a job in a store. She is as old as yourself.' The man explained his relations with Doctor Cochran. He had been a farm laborer, he said, and had but recently moved to town to work in the furniture factory. During the previous winter he had been ill for a long time and had no money. While he lay in bed one of his boys fell out of a barn loft and there was a terrible cut in his head.

'Your father came every day to see us and he sewed up my Tom's head.' The laborer turned away from Mary and stood with his cap in his hand looking toward the boys. 'I was down and out and your father not only took care of me and the boys, but he gave my old woman money to buy the things we had to have from the stores in town here, groceries and medicines.' The man spoke in such low tones that Mary had to lean forward to hear his words. Her face almost touched the laborer's shoulder. 'Your father is a good man and I don't think he is very happy,' he went on. 'The boy and I got well and I got work here in town, but he wouldn't take any money from me. "You know how to live with your children and with your wife. You know how to make them happy. Keep your money and spend it on them," that's what he said to me.'

The laborer went on across the bridge and along the creek bank toward the spot where his two sons sat fishing and Mary leaned on the railing of the bridge and looked at the slow-moving water. It was almost black in the shadows under the bridge and she thought that it was thus her father's life had been lived. 'It has been like a stream running always in shadows and never coming out into the sunlight,' she thought, and fear that her own life would run on in darkness gripped her. A great new love for her father swept over her and in fancy she felt his arms about her. As a child she had continually dreamed of caresses received at her father's hands and now the dream came back. For a long time she stood looking at the stream and she resolved that the night should not pass without an effort on her part to make the old dream come true. When she again looked up the laborer had built a little fire of sticks at the edge of the stream. 'We catch bullheads here,' he called. 'The light of the fire draws them close to the shore. If you want to come and try your hand at fishing the boys will lend you one of the poles.'

'O, I thank you, I won't do it tonight,' Mary said, and then fearing she might suddenly begin weeping and that if the man spoke to her again she would find herself unable to answer, she hurried away. 'Good-bye!' shouted the man and the two boys. The words came quite spontaneously out of the three throats and created a sharp trumpet-like effect that rang like a glad cry across the heaviness of her mood.

When his daughter Mary went out for her evening walk Doctor Cochran sat for an hour alone in his office. It began to grow dark and the men who all afternoon had been sitting on chairs and boxes before the livery barn across the street went home for the evening meal. The noise of voices grew faint and sometimes for five or ten minutes there was silence. Then from some distant street came a child's cry. Presently church bells began to ring.

The doctor was not a very neat man and sometimes for several days he forgot to shave. With a long lean hand he stroked his half-grown beard. His illness had struck deeper than he had admitted even to himself and his mind had an inclination to float out of his body. Often when he sat thus his hands lay in his lap and he looked at them with a child's absorption. It seemed to him they must belong to someone else. He grew philosophic. 'It's an odd thing about my body. Here I've lived in it all these years and how little use I have had of it. Now it's going to die and decay, never having been used. I wonder why it did not get another tenant.' He smiled sadly over this fancy but went on with it. 'Well, I've had thoughts enough concerning people and I've had the use of these lips and a tongue, but I've let them lie idle. When my Ellen was here living with me I let her think me cold and unfeeling while something within me was straining and straining trying to tear itself loose.'

He remembered how often, as a young man, he had sat in the evening in silence beside his wife in this same office and how his hands had ached to reach across the narrow space that separated them and touch her hands, her face, her hair.

Well, everyone in town had predicted his marriage would turn out badly! His wife had been an actress with a company that came to Huntersburg and got stranded there. At the same time the girl became ill and had no money to pay for her room at the hotel. The young doctor had attended to that and when the girl was convalescent took her to ride about the country in his buggy. Her life had been a hard one and the notion of leading a quiet existence in the little town appealed to her.

And then after the marriage and after the child was born she had suddenly found herself unable to go on living with the silent cold man. There had been a story of her having run away with a young sport, the son of a saloon keeper, who had disappeared from town at the same time, but the story was untrue. Lester Cochran had himself taken her to Chicago, where she got work with a company going into the far western states. Then he had taken her to the door of her hotel, had put money into her hands and in silence and without even a farewell kiss had turned and walked away.

The doctor sat in his office living over that moment and other intense moments when he had been deeply stirred and had been on the surface so cool and quiet. He wondered if the woman had known. How many times he had asked himself that question. After he left her that night at the hotel door she never wrote. 'Perhaps she is dead,' he thought for the thousandth time.

A thing happened that had been happening at odd moments for more than a year. In Doctor Cochran's mind the remembered figure of his wife became confused with the figure of his daughter. When at such moments he tried to separate the two figures, to make them stand out distinct from each other, he was unsuccessful. Turning his head slightly he imagined he saw a white girlish figure coming through a door out of the rooms in which he and his daughter lived. The door was painted white and swung slowly in a light breeze that came in at an open window. The wind ran softly and quietly through the room and played over some papers lying on a desk in a corner. There was a soft swishing sound as of a woman's skirts. The doctor arose and stood trembling. 'Which is it? Is it you, Mary, or is it Ellen?' he asked huskily.

On the stairway leading up from the street there was the sound of heavy feet and the outer door opened. The doctor's weak heart fluttered and he dropped heavily back into his chair.

A man came into the room. He was a farmer, one of the doctor's patients, and coming to the center of the room he struck a match, held it above his head and shouted. 'Hello!' he called. When the doctor arose from his chair and answered, he was so startled that the match fell from his hand and lay burning faintly at his feet.

The young farmer had sturdy legs that were like two pillars of stone supporting a heavy building, and the little flame of the match that burned and fluttered in the light breeze on the floor between his feet threw dancing shadows along the walls of the room. The doctor's confused mind refused to clear itself of his fancies that now began to feed upon this new situation.

He forgot the presence of the farmer and his mind raced back over his life as a married man. The flickering light on the wall recalled another dancing light. One afternoon in the summer during the first year after his marriage his wife Ellen had driven with him into the country. They were then furnishing their rooms and at a farmer's house Ellen had seen an old mirror, no longer in use, standing against a wall in a shed. Because of something quaint in the design the mirror had taken her fancy and the farmer's wife had given it to her. On the drive home the young wife had told her husband of her pregnancy and the doctor had been stirred as never before. He sat holding the mirror on his knees while his wife drove and when she announced the coming of the child she looked away across the fields.

How deeply etched, that scene in the sick man's mind! The sun was going down over young corn and oat fields beside the road. The prairie land was black and occasionally the road ran through short lanes of trees that also looked black in the waning light.

The mirror on his knees caught the rays of the departing sun and sent a great ball of golden light dancing across the fields and among the branches of trees. Now as he stood in the presence of the farmer and as the little light from the burning match on the floor recalled that other evening of dancing lights, he thought he understood the failure of his marriage and of his life. On that evening long ago when Ellen had told him of the coming of the great adventure of their marriage, he had remained silent because he had thought no words he could utter would express what he felt. There had been a defense for himself built up. 'I told myself she should have understood without words and I've all my life been telling myself the same thing about Mary. I've been a fool and a coward. I've always been silent because I've been afraid of expressing myself — like a blundering fool. I've been a proud man and a coward.

'Tonight I'll do it. If it kills me I'll make myself talk to the girl,' he said aloud, his mind coming back to the figure of his daughter.

'Hey! What's that?' asked the farmer, who stood with his hat in his hand waiting to tell of his mission.

The doctor got his horse from Barney Smithfield's livery and drove off to the country to attend the farmer's wife who was about to give birth to her first child. She was a slender narrow-hipped woman and the child was large, but the doctor was feverishly strong. He worked desperately and the woman, who was frightened, groaned and struggled. Her husband kept coming in and going out of the room and two neighbor women appeared and stood silently about waiting to be of service. It was past ten o'clock when everything was done and the doctor was ready to depart for town.

The farmer hitched his horse and brought it to the door and the doctor drove off feeling strangely weak and at the same time strong.

How simple now seemed the thing he had yet to do. Perhaps when he got home his daughter would have gone to bed but he would ask her to get up and come into the office. Then he would tell the whole story of his marriage and its failure, sparing himself no humiliation. 'There was something very dear and beautiful in my Ellen and I must make Mary understand that. It will help her to be a beautiful woman,' he thought, full of confidence in the strength of his resolution.

He got to the door of the livery barn at eleven o'clock and Barney Smithfield with young Duke Yetter and two other men sat talking there. The liveryman took his horse away into the darkness of the barn and the doctor stood for a moment leaning against the wall of the building. The town's night watchman stood with the group by the barn door and a quarrel broke out between him and Duke Yetter, but the doctor did not hear the hot words that flew back and forth or Duke's loud laughter at the night watchman's anger. A queer hesitating mood had taken possession of him. There was something he passionately desired to do but could not remember. Did it have to do with his wife Ellen or Mary his daughter? The figures of the two women were again confused in his mind and to add to the confusion there was a third figure, that of the woman he had just assisted through childbirth. Everything was confusion. He started across the street toward the entrance of the stairway leading to his office and then stopped in the road and stared about. Barney Smithfield, having returned from putting his horse in the stall, shut the door of the barn and a hanging lantern over the door swung back and forth. It threw grotesque dancing shadows down over the faces and forms of the men standing and quarreling beside the wall of the barn.

Mary sat by a window in the doctor's office awaiting his return. So absorbed was she in her own thoughts that she was unconscious of the voice of Duke Yetter talking with the men in the street.

When Duke had come into the street, the hot anger of the early part of the evening had returned and she again saw him advancing toward her in the orchard with the look of arrogant male confidence in his eyes, but presently she forgot him and thought only of her father. An incident of her childhood returned to haunt her. One afternoon in the month of May when she was fifteen her father had asked her to accompany him on an evening drive into the country.

The doctor went to visit a sick woman at a farmhouse five miles from town and as there had been a great deal of rain the roads were heavy. It was dark when they reached the farmer's house and they went into the kitchen and ate cold food off a kitchen table. For some reason her father had, on that evening, appeared boyish and almost gay. On the road he had talked a little. Even at that early age Mary had grown tall and her figure was becoming womanly. After the cold supper in the farm kitchen he walked with her around the house and she sat on a narrow porch. For a moment her father stood before her. He put his hands into his trouser pockets and throwing back his head laughed almost heartily. 'It seems strange to think you will soon be a woman,' he said. 'When you do become a woman what do you suppose is going to happen, eh? What kind of a life will you lead? What will happen to you?'

The doctor sat on the porch beside the child and for a moment she had thought he was about to put his arm around her. Then he jumped up and went into the house leaving her to sit alone in the darkness.

As she remembered the incident Mary remembered also that on that evening of her childhood she had met her father's advances in silence. It seemed to her that she, not her father, was to blame for the life they had led together. The farm laborer she had met on the bridge had not felt her father's coldness. That was because he had himself been warm and generous in his attitude toward the man who had cared for him in his hour of sickness and misfortune. Her father had said that the laborer knew how to be a father and Mary remembered with what warmth the two boys fishing by the creek had called to her as she went away into the darkness. 'Their father has known how to be a father because his children have known how to give themselves,' she thought guiltily. She also would give herself. Before the night had passed she would do that. On that evening long ago and as she rode home beside her father he had made another unsuccessful effort to break through the wall that separated them. The heavy rains had swollen the streams they had to cross and when they had almost reached town he had stopped the horse on a wooden bridge. The horse danced nervously about and her father held the reins firmly and occasionally spoke to him. Beneath the bridge the swollen stream made a great roaring sound and beside the road in a long flat field there was a lake of flood water. At that moment the moon had come out from behind clouds and the wind that blew across the water made little waves. The lake of flood water was covered with dancing lights. 'I'm going to tell you about your mother and myself,' her father said huskily, but at that moment the timbers of the bridge began to crack dangerously and the horse plunged forward. When her father had regained control of the frightened beast, they were in the streets of the town and his diffident silent nature had reasserted itself.

Mary sat in the darkness by the office window and saw her father drive into the street. When his horse had been put away he did not, as was his custom, come at once up the stairway to the office, but lingered in the darkness before the barn door. Once he started to cross the street and then returned into the darkness.

Among the men who for two hours had been sitting and talking quietly a quarrel broke out. Jack Fisher the town nightwatchman had been telling the others the story of a battle in which he had fought during the Civil War and Duke Yetter had begun bantering him. The nightwatchman grew angry. Grasping his nightstick he limped up and down. The loud voice of Duke Yetter cut across the shrill angry voice of the victim of his wit. 'You ought to a flanked the fellow, I tell you, Jack. Yes sir 'ee, you ought to a flanked that reb and then when you got him flanked you ought to a knocked the stuffings out of the cuss. That's what I would a done,' Duke shouted, laughing boisterously. 'You would a raised hell, you would,' the nightwatchman answered, filled with ineffectual wrath.

The old soldier went off along the street followed by the laughter of Duke and his companions, and Barney Smithfield, having put the doctor's horse away, came out and closed the barn door. A lantern hanging above the door swung back and forth. Doctor Cochran again started across the street and when he had reached the foot of the stairway turned and shouted to the men. 'Good night,' he called cheerfully. A strand of hair was blown by the light summer breeze across Mary's cheek and she jumped to her feet as though she had been touched by a hand reached out to her from the darkness. A hundred times she had seen her father return from drives in the evening, but never before had he said anything at all to the loiterers by the barn door. She became half convinced that not her father but some other man was now coming up the stairway.

The heavy dragging footsteps rang loudly on the wooden stairs and Mary heard her father set down the little square medicine case he always carried. The strange cheerful hearty mood of the man continued but his mind was in a confused riot. Mary imagined she could see his dark form in the doorway. 'The woman has had a baby,' said the hearty voice from the landing outside the door. 'Who did that happen to? Was it Ellen or that other woman or my little Mary?'

A stream of words, a protest came from the man's lips. 'Who's been having a baby? I want to know. Who's been having a baby? Life doesn't work out. Why are babies always being born?' he asked.

A laugh broke from the doctor's lips and his daughter leaned forward and gripped the arms of her chair. 'A babe has been born,' he said again. 'It's strange eh, that my hands should have helped a baby be born while all the time Death stood at my elbow?'

Doctor Cochran stamped upon the floor of the landing. 'My feet are cold and numb from waiting for life to come out of life,' he said heavily. 'The woman struggled and now I must struggle.'

Silence followed the stamping of feet and the tired heavy declaration from the sick man's lips. From the street below came another loud shout of laughter from Duke Yetter.

And then Doctor Cochran fell backward down the narrow stairs to the street. There was no cry from him, just the clatter of his shoes upon the stairs and the terrible subdued sound of the body falling.

Mary did not move from her chair. With closed eyes she waited. Her heart pounded. A weakness complete and overmastering had possession of her and from feet to head ran little waves of feeling as though tiny creatures with soft hair-like feet were playing upon her body.

It was Duke Yetter who carried the dead man up the stairs and laid him on a bed in one of the rooms back of the office. One of the men who had been sitting with him before the door of the barn followed lifting his hands and dropping them nervously. Between his fingers he held a forgotten cigarette the light from which danced up and down in the darkness.

III. REGIONAL

The New Englander

HER NAME was Elsie Leander and her girlhood was spent on her father's farm in Vermont. For several generations the Leanders had all lived on the same farm and had all married thin women, and so she was thin. The farm lay in the shadow of a mountain and the soil was not very rich. From the beginning and for several generations there had been a great many sons and few daughters in the family. The sons had gone West or to New York City and the daughters had stayed at home and thought such thoughts as come to New England women who see the sons of their fathers' neighbors slipping away, one by one, into the West.

Her father's house was a small white frame affair and when you went out at the back door, past a small barn and chicken house, you got into a path that ran up the side of a hill and into an orchard. The trees were all old and gnarled. At the back of the orchard the hill dropped away and bare rocks showed.

Inside the fence a large gray rock stuck high up out of the ground. As Elsie sat with her back to the rock, with a mangled hillside at her feet, she could see several large mountains, apparently but a short distance away, and between herself and the mountains lay many tiny fields surrounded by neatly built stone walls. Everywhere rocks appeared. Large ones, too heavy to be moved, stuck out of the ground in the center of the fields. The fields were like cups filled with a green liquid that turned gray in the fall and white in the winter. The mountains, far off but apparently near at hand, were like giants ready at any moment to reach out their hands and take the cups one by one and drink off the green liquid. The large rocks in the fields were like the thumbs of the giants.

54

Elsie had three brothers, born before her, but they had all gone away. Two of them had gone to live with her uncle in the West and her oldest brother had gone to New York City where he had married and prospered. All through his youth and manhood her father had worked hard and had lived a hard life, but his son in New York City had begun to send money home, and after that things went better. He still worked every day about the barn or in the fields, but he did not worry about the future. Elsie's mother did housework in the mornings and in the afternoons sat in a rocking chair in her tiny living room and thought of her sons while she crocheted table covers and tidies for the backs of chairs. She was a silent woman, very thin and with very thin bony hands. She did not ease herself into a rocking chair, but sat down and got up suddenly, and when she crocheted her back was as straight as the back of a drill sergeant.

The mother rarely spoke to the daughter. Sometimes in the afternoons, as the younger woman went up the hillside to her place by the rock at the back of the orchard, her father came out of the barn and stopped her. He put a hand on her shoulder and asked her where she was going. 'To the rock,' she said, and her father laughed. His laughter was like the creaking of a rusty barn-door hinge and the hand he had laid on her shoulders was thin like her own hands and like her mother's hands. The father went into the barn, shaking his head. 'She's like her mother. She is herself like a rock,' he thought. At the head of the path that led from the house to the orchard there was a great cluster of bayberry bushes. The New England farmer came out of his barn to watch his daughter go along the path, but she had disappeared behind the bushes. He looked away past his house to the fields and to the mountains in the distance. He also saw the green cup-like fields and the grim mountains. There was an almost imperceptible tightening of the muscles of his half worn-out old body. For a long time he stood in silence, and then, knowing from long experience the danger of having thoughts, he went back into the barn and busied himself with the mending of an agricultural tool that had been mended many times before.

The son of the Leanders who went to live in New York was the father of one son, a thin sensitive boy who looked like Elsie. The son died when he was twenty-three years old and some years later the father died and left his money to the old people on the New England farm. The two Leanders who had gone West had lived there with their father's brother, a farmer, until they grew into manhood. Then Will, the younger, got a job on a railroad. He was killed one winter morning. It was a cold snowy day and when the freight train he was in charge of as conductor left the city of Des Moines, he started to run over the tops of the cars. His feet slipped and he shot down into space. That was the end of him.

Of the new generation there was only Elsie and her brother Tom, whom she had never seen, left alive. Her father and mother talked of going West to Tom for two years before they came to a decision. Then it took another year to dispose of the farm and make preparations. During the whole time Elsie did not think much about the change about to take place in her life.

The trip West on the railroad train jolted Elsie out of herself. In spite of her detached attitude toward life, she became excited. Her mother sat up very straight and stiff in the seat in the sleeping car and her father walked up and down in the aisle. After a night when the younger of the two women did not sleep, but lay awake with red burning cheeks and with her thin fingers incessantly picking at the bedclothes in her berth while the train went through towns and cities, crawled up the sides of hills and fell down into forest-clad valleys, she got up and dressed to sit all day looking at a new kind of land. The train ran for a day and through another sleepless night in a flat land where every field was as large as a farm in her own country. Towns appeared and disappeared in a continual procession. The whole land was so unlike anything she had ever known that she began to feel unlike herself. In the valley where she had been born and where she had lived all her days, everything had an air of finality. Nothing could be changed. The tiny fields were chained to the earth. They were fixed in their places and surrounded by aged stone walls. The fields, like the mountains that looked down at them, were as unchangeable as the passing days. She had a feeling they had always been so, would always be so.

Elsie sat like her mother, upright in the car seat and with a back like the back of a drill sergeant. The train ran swiftly along through Ohio and Indiana. Her thin hands like her mother's hands were crossed and locked. One passing casually through the car might have thought both women prisoners handcuffed and bound to their seats.

Night came on and she again got into her berth. Again she lay awake and her thin cheeks became flushed, but she thought new thoughts. Her hands were no longer gripped together and she did not pick at the bedclothes. Twice during the night she stretched herself and yawned, a thing she had never in her life done before. The train stopped at a town on the prairies, and as there was something the matter with one of the wheels of the car in which she lay, the train-men came with flaming torches to tinker it. There was a great pound-ing and shouting. When the train went on its way, she wanted to get out of her berth and run up and down in the aisle of the car. The fancy had come to her that the men tinkering with the car wheel were new men out of the new land who with strong hammers had broken away the doors of her prison. They had destroyed forever the pro-gramme she had made for her life.

Elsie was filled with joy at the thought that the train was still going on into the West. She wanted to go on forever in a straight line into the unknown. She fancied herself no longer on a train and imagined she had become a winged thing flying through space. Her long years of sitting alone by the rock on the New England farm had got her into the habit of expressing her thoughts aloud. Her thin voice broke the silence that lay over the sleeping car and her father and mother, both also lying awake, sat up in their berth to listen.

Tom Leander, the only living male representative of the new gen-eration of Leanders, was a loosely built man of forty inclined to corpulency. At twenty he had married the daughter of a neighboring farmer, and when his wife inherited some money, she and Tom moved into the town of Apple Junction in Iowa where Tom opened a grocery. The venture prospered as did Tom's matrimonial venture. When his brother died in New York City and his father, mother, and sister decided to come West, Tom was already the father of a daugh-ter and four sons.

On the prairies north of town and in the midst of a vast level stretch of corn fields, there was a partly completed brick house that had be-longed to a rich farmer named Russell who had begun to build the house intending to make it the most magnificent place in the county, but when it was almost completed he had found himself without money and heavily in debt. The farm, consisting of several hundred acres of corn land, had been split into three farms and sold. No one had wanted the huge unfinished brick house. For years it had stood vacant, its windows staring out over the fields that had been planted almost up to the door.

In buying the Russell house Tom was moved by two motives. He had a notion that in New England the Leanders had been rather magnificent people. His memory of his father's place in the Vermont valley was shadowy, but in speaking of it to his wife he became very definite. 'We had good blood in us, we Leanders,' he said, straightening his shoulders. 'We lived in a big house. We were important people.'

Wanting his father and mother to feel at home in the new place, Tom had also another motive. He was not a very energetic man, and, although he had done well enough as keeper of a grocery, his success was largely due to the boundless energy of his wife. She did not pay much attention to her household, and her children, like little animals, had to take care of themselves, but in any matter concerning the store her word was law.

To have his father the owner of the Russell place Tom felt would establish him as a man of consequence in the eyes of his neighbors. 'I can tell you what, they're used to a big house,' he said to his wife. 'I tell you what, my people are used to living in style.'

The exaltation that had come over Elsie on the train wore away in the presence of the gray empty Iowa fields, but something of the effect of it remained with her for months. In the big brick house life went on much as it had in the tiny New England house where she had always lived. The Leanders installed themselves in three or four rooms on the ground floor. After a few weeks the furniture that had been shipped by freight arrived and was hauled out from town in one of Tom's grocery wagons. There were three or four acres of ground covered with great piles of boards the unsuccessful farmer had intended to use in the building of stables. Tom sent men to haul the boards away and Elsie's father prepared to plant a garden. They had come West in April and as soon as they were installed in the house plowing and planting began in the fields nearby. The habit of a lifetime returned to the daughter of the house. In the new place there was no gnarled orchard surrounded by a half-ruined stone fence.

All of the fences in all of the fields that stretched away out of sight to the north, south, east, and west were made of wire and looked like spider webs against the blackness of the ground when it had been freshly plowed.

There was, however, the house itself. It was like an island rising out of the sea. In an odd way the house, although it was less than ten years old, was very old. Its unnecessary bigness represented an old impulse in men. Elsie felt that. At the east side there was a door leading to a stairway that ran into the upper part of the house that was kept locked. Two or three stone steps led up to it. Elsie could sit on the top step with her back against the door and gaze into the distance without being disturbed. Almost at her feet began the fields that seemed to go on and on forever. The fields were like the waters of a sea. Men came to plow and plant. Giant horses moved in a procession across the prairies. A young man who drove six horses came directly toward her. She was fascinated. The breasts of the horses as they came forward with bowed heads seemed like the breasts of giants. The soft spring air that lay over the fields was also like a sea. The horses were giants walking on the floor of a sea. With their breasts they pushed the waters of the sea before them. They were pushing the waters out of the basin of the sea. The young man who drove them also was a giant.

Elsie pressed her body against the closed door at the top of the steps. In the garden back of the house she could hear her father at work. He was raking dry masses of weeds off the ground preparatory to spading it for a family garden. He had always worked in a tiny, confined place and would do the same thing here. In this vast open place he would work with small tools, doing little things with infinite care, raising little vegetables. In the house her mother would crochet little tidies. She herself would be small. She would press her body against the door of the house, try to get herself out of sight. Only the feeling that sometimes took possession of her, and that did not form itself into a thought, would be large.

The six horses turned at the fence and the outside horse got entangled in the traces. The driver swore vigorously. Then he turned and stared at the pale New Englander, and with another oath pulled the heads of the horses about and drove away into the distance. The field in which he was plowing contained two hundred acres. Elsie did not wait for him to return, but went into the house and sat with folded arms in a room. The house, she thought, was a ship floating in a sea on the floor of which giants went up and down.

May came and then June. In the great fields work was always going on, and Elsie became somewhat used to the sight of the young man in the field that came down to the steps. Sometimes when he drove his horses down to the wire fence, he smiled and nodded.

In the month of August, when it is very hot, the corn in Iowa fields grows until the corn stalks resemble young trees. The corn fields become forests. The time for the cultivating of the corn has passed and weeds grow thick between the corn rows. The men with their giant horses have gone away. Over the immense fields silence broods.

When the time of the laying-by of the crop came that first summer after Elsie's arrival in the West, her mind, partially awakened by the strangeness of the railroad trip, awakened again. She did not feel like a staid thin woman with a back like the back of a drill sergeant, but like something new and as strange as the new land into which she had come to live. For a time she did not know what was the matter. In the field the corn had grown so high that she could not see into the distance. The corn was like a wall, and the little bare spot of land on which her father's house stood was like a house built behind the walls of a prison. For a time she was depressed, thinking that she had come West into a wide-open country, only to find herself locked up more closely than ever.

An impulse came to her. She arose and going down three or four steps seated herself almost on a level with the ground.

Immediately she got a sense of release. She could not see over the corn, but she could see under it. The corn had long wide leaves that met over the rows. The rows became long tunnels running away into infinity. Out of the black ground grew weeds that made a soft carpet of green. From above light sifted down. The corn rows were mysteriously beautiful. They were warm passageways running out into life. She got up from the steps and, walking timidly to the wire fence that separated her from the field, put her hand between the wires and took hold of one of the corn stalks. For some reason after she had touched the strong young stalk and had held it for a moment firmly in her hand, she grew afraid. Running quickly back to the step, she sat down and covered her face with her hands. Her body trembled. She tried to imagine herself crawling through the fence and wandering along one of the passageways. The thought of trying the experiment fascinated but at the same time terrified. She got quickly up and went into the house.

One Saturday night in August, Elsie found herself unable to sleep. Thoughts, more definite than any she had ever known before, came into her mind. It was a quiet hot night and her bed stood near a window. Her room was the only one the Leanders occupied on the second floor of the house. At midnight a little breeze came up from the south, and when she sat up in bed the floor of corn tassels lying below her line of sight looked in the moonlight like the face of a sea just stirred by a gentle breeze.

A murmuring began in the corn and murmuring thoughts and memories awoke in her mind. The long wide succulent leaves had begun to dry in the intense heat of the August days and as the wind stirred the corn they rubbed against each other. A call, far away, as of a thousand voices arose. She imagined the voices were like the voices of children. They were not like her brother Tom's children, noisy boisterous little animals, but something quite different, tiny little things with large eyes and thin sensitive hands. One after another they crept into her arms. She became so excited over the fancy that she sat up in bed and taking a pillow into her arms held it against her breast. The figure of her cousin, the pale sensitive young Leander who had lived with his father in New York City and who had died at the age of twenty-three, came into her mind. It was as though the young man had come suddenly into the room. She dropped the pillow and sat waiting, intense, expectant.

Young Harry Leander had come to visit his cousin on the New England farm during the late summer of the year before he died. He had stayed there for a month, and almost every afternoon had gone with Elsie to sit by the rock at the back of the orchard. One afternoon, when they had both been for a long time silent, he began to talk. 'I want to go live in the West,' he said. 'I want to go live in the West. I want to grow strong and be a man,' he repeated. Tears came into his eyes.

They got up to return to the house, Elsie walking in silence beside the young man. The moment marked a high spot in her life. A strange trembling eagerness for something she had not realized in her experience of life had taken possession of her. They went in silence through the orchard, but when they came to the bayberry bush her cousin stopped in the path and turned to face her. 'I want you to kiss me,' he said eagerly, stepping toward her.

A fluttering uncertainty had taken possession of Elsie and had been transmitted to her cousin. After he had made the sudden and unexpected demand and had stepped so close to her that his breath could be felt on her cheek, his own cheeks became scarlet and his hand that had taken her hand trembled. 'Well, I wish I were strong. I only wish I were strong,' he said hesitatingly and turning walked away along the path toward the house.

And in the strange new house, set like an island in its sea of corn, Harry Leander's voice seemed to arise again above the fancied voices of the children that had been coming out of the fields. Elsie got out of bed and walked up and down in the dim light coming through the window. Her body trembled violently. 'I want you to kiss me,' the voice said again, and to quiet it and to quiet also the answering voice in herself, she went to kneel by the bed and taking the pillow again into her arms pressed it against her face.

Tom Leander came with his wife and family to visit his father and mother on Sundays. The family appeared at about ten o'clock in the morning. When the wagon turned out of the road that ran past the Russell place, Tom shouted. There was a field between the house and the road and the wagon could not be seen as it came along the narrow way through the corn. After Tom had shouted, his daughter Elizabeth, a tall girl of sixteen, jumped out of the wagon. All five children came tearing toward the house through the corn. A series of wild shouts arose on the still morning air.

The groceryman had brought food from the store. When the horse had been unhitched and put into a shed, he and his wife began to carry packages into the house. The four Leander boys, accompanied by their sister, disappeared into the near-by fields. Three dogs that had trotted out from town under the wagon accompanied the children. Two or three children and occasionally a young man from a neighboring farm had come to join in the fun. Elsie's sister-in-law dismissed them all with a wave of her hand. With a wave of her hand she also brushed Elsie aside. Fires were lighted and the house reeked with the smell of cooking. Elsie went to sit on the step at the side of the house. The corn fields that had been so quiet rang with shouts and with the barking of dogs.

Tom Leander's oldest child, Elizabeth, was like her mother, full of energy. She was thin and tall like the women of her father's house, but very strong and alive. In secret she wanted to be a lady, but when she tried, her brothers, led by her father and mother, made fun of her. 'Don't put on airs,' they said. When she got into the country with no one but her brothers and two or three neighboring farm boys, she herself became a boy. With the boys she went tearing through the fields, following the dogs in pursuit of rabbits. Sometimes a young man came with the children from a near-by farm. Then she did not know what to do with herself. She wanted to walk demurely along the rows through the corn, but was afraid her brothers would laugh, and in desperation outdid the boys in roughness and noisiness. She screamed and shouted and running wildly tore her dress on the wire fences as she scrambled over in pursuit of the dogs. When a rabbit was caught and killed, she rushed in and tore it out of the grasp of the dogs. The blood of the little dying animal dripped on her clothes. She swung it over her head and shouted.

The farmhand who had worked all summer in the field within sight of Elsie became enamoured of the young woman from town. When the groceryman's family appeared on Sunday mornings, he also appeared, but did not come to the house. When the boys and dogs came tearing through the fields, he joined them. He also was self-conscious and did not want the boys to know the purpose of his coming, and when he and Elizabeth found themselves alone together he became embarrassed. For a moment they walked together in silence. In a wide circle about them, in the forest of the corn, ran the boys and dogs. The young man had something he wanted to say, but when he tried to find words his tongue became thick and his lips felt hot and dry. 'Well,' he began, 'let's you and me —'

Words failed him and Elizabeth turned and ran after her brothers and for the rest of the day he could not manage to get her out of their sight. When he went to join them she became the noisiest member of the party. A frenzy of activity took possession of her. With hair hanging down her back, with clothes torn, and with cheeks and hands scratched and bleeding, she led her brothers in the endless wild pursuit of the rabbits.

The Sunday in August that followed Elsie Leander's sleepless night was hot and cloudy. In the morning she was half ill, and as soon as the visitors from town arrived, she crept away to sit on the step at the side of the house. The children ran away into the fields. An almost overpowering desire to run with them, shouting and playing along the corn rows, took possession of her. She arose and went to the back of the house. Her father was at work in the garden, pulling weeds from between rows of vegetables. Inside the house she could hear her sister-in-law moving about. On the front porch her brother Tom was asleep with his mother beside him. Elsie went back to the step and then arose and went to where the corn came down to the fence. She climbed awkwardly over and went a little way along one of the rows. Putting out her hand she touched the firm stalks, and then, becoming afraid, dropped to her knees on the carpet of weeds that covered the ground. For a long time she stayed thus listening to the voices of the children in the distance.

An hour slipped away. Presently it was time for dinner, and her sister-in-law came to the back door and shouted. There was an answering whoop from the distance and the children came running through the fields. They climbed over the fence and ran shouting across her father's garden. Elsie also arose. She was about to attempt to climb back over the fence unobserved when she heard a rustling in the corn. Young Elizabeth Leander appeared. Beside her walked the plowman who but a few months earlier had planted the corn in the field where Elsie now stood. She could see the two people coming slowly along the rows. An understanding had been established between them. The man reached through between the corn stalks and touched the hand of the girl, who laughed awkwardly, and running to the fence climbed quickly over. In her hand she held the limp body of a rabbit the dogs had killed.

The farmhand went away and when Elizabeth had gone into the house Elsie climbed over the fence. Her niece stood just within the kitchen door holding the dead rabbit by one leg. The other leg had been torn away by the dogs. At sight of the New England woman, who seemed to look at her with hard unsympathetic eyes, she was ashamed and went quickly into the house. She threw the rabbit upon a table in the parlor and then ran out of the room. Its blood ran out on the delicate flowers of a white crocheted table cover that had been made by Elsie's mother.

The Sunday dinner, with all the living Leanders gathered about the table, was gone through in a heavy lumbering silence. When the dinner was over and Tom and his wife had washed the dishes, they went to sit with the older people on the front porch. Presently they were both asleep. Elsie returned to the step at the side of the house, but when the desire to go again into the corn fields came sweeping over her, she got up and went indoors.

The woman of thirty-five tiptoed about the big house like a frightened child. The dead rabbit that lay on the table in the parlor had become cold and stiff. Its blood had dried on the white table cover. She went upstairs, but did not go to her own room. A spirit of adventure had hold of her. In the upper part of the house there were many rooms and in some of them no glass had been put into the windows. The windows had been boarded up and narrow streaks of light crept in through the cracks between the boards.

Elsie tiptoed up the flight of stairs past the room in which she slept and opening doors went into other rooms. Dust lay thick on the floors. In the silence she could hear her brother snoring as he slept in the chair on the front porch. From what seemed a far away place there came the shrill cries of the children. The cries became soft. They were like the cries of unborn children that had called to her out of the fields on the night before.

Into her mind came the intense silent figure of her mother sitting on the porch beside her son and waiting for the day to wear itself out into night. The thought brought a lump into her throat. She wanted something and did not know what it was. Her own mood frightened her. In a windowless room at the back of the house one of the boards over a window had been broken and a bird had flown in and become imprisoned.

The presence of the woman frightened the bird. It flew wildly about. Its beating wings stirred up dust that danced in the air. Elsie stood perfectly still, also frightened, not by the presence of the bird but by the presence of life. Like the bird she was a prisoner. The thought gripped her. She wanted to go outdoors where her niece Elizabeth walked with the young plowman through the corn, but was like the bird in the room — a prisoner. She moved restlessly about. The bird flew back and forth across the room. It alighted on the window sill near the place where the board was broken away. She stared into the frightened eyes of the bird that in turn stared into her eyes. Then the bird flew away, out through the window, and Elsie turned and ran nervously downstairs and out into the yard. She climbed over the wire fence and ran with stooped shoulders along one of the tunnels.

Elsie ran into the vastness of the corn fields, filled with but one desire. She wanted to get out of her life and into some new and sweeter life she felt must be hidden away somewhere in the fields. After she had run a long way, she came to a wire fence and crawled over. Her hair became unloosed and fell down over her shoulders. Her cheeks became flushed and for the moment she looked like a young girl. When she climbed over the fence, she tore a great hole in the front of her dress. For a moment her tiny breasts were exposed, and then her hand clutched and held nervously the sides of the tear. In the distance she could hear the voices of the boys and the barking of the dogs. A summer storm had been threatening for days, and now black clouds had begun to spread themselves over the sky. As she ran nervously forward, stopping to listen and then running on again, the dry corn blades brushed against her shoulders and a fine shower of yellow dust from the corn tassels fell on her hair. A continued crackling noise accompanied her progress. The dust made a golden crown about her head. From the sky overhead a low rumbling sound, like the growling of giant dogs, came to her ears.

The thought that having at last ventured into the corn she would never escape became fixed in the mind of the running woman. Sharp pains shot through her body. Presently she was compelled to stop and sit on the ground. For a long time she sat with closed eyes. Her dress became soiled. Little insects that live in the ground under the corn came out of their holes and crawled over her legs.

Following some obscure impulse, the tired woman threw herself on her back and lay still with closed eyes. Her fright passed. It was warm and close in the room-like tunnels. The pain in her side went away. She opened her eyes and between the wide green corn blades could see patches of a black threatening sky. She did not want to be alarmed and so closed her eyes again. Her thin hand no longer gripped the tear in her dress and her little breasts were exposed. They expanded and contracted in spasmodic jerks. She threw her hands back over her head and lay still.

It seemed to Elsie that hours passed as she lay thus, quiet and passive under the corn. Deep within here there was a feeling that something was about to happen, something that would lift her out of herself, that would tear her away from her past and the past of her people. Her thoughts were not definite. She lay still and waited as she had waited for days and months by the rock at the back of the orchard on the Vermont farm when she was a girl. A deep grumbling noise went on in the sky overhead, but the sky and everything she had ever known seemed very far away, no part of herself.

After a long silence, when it seemed to her that she had gone out of herself as in a dream, Elsie heard a man's voice calling. 'Aho, aho, aho,' shouted the voice, and after another period of silence there arose answering voices and then the sound of bodies crashing through the corn and the excited chatter of children. A dog came running along the row where she lay and stood beside her. His cold nose touched her face and she sat up. The dog ran away. The Leander boys passed. She could see their bare legs flashing in and out across one of the tunnels. Her brother had become alarmed by the rapid approach of the thunderstorm and wanted to get his family to town. His voice kept calling from the house and the voices of the children answered from the fields.

Elsie sat on the ground with her hands pressed together. An odd feeling of disappointment had possession of her. She arose and walked slowly along in the general direction taken by the children. She came to a fence and crawled over, tearing her dress in a new place. One of her stockings had become unloosed and had slipped down over her shoe top. The long sharp weeds had scratched her leg so that it was criss-crossed with red lines, but she was not conscious of any pain.

The distraught woman followed the children until she came within sight of her father's house and then stopped and again sat on the ground. There was another loud crash of thunder and Tom Leander's voice called again, this time half-angrily. The name of the girl Elizabeth was shouted in loud masculine tones that rolled and echoed like the thunder along the aisles under the corn.

And then Elizabeth came into sight accompanied by the young plowman. They stopped near Elsie and the man took the girl into his arms. At the sound of their approach, Elsie had thrown herself face downward on the ground and had twisted herself into a position where she could see without being seen. When their lips met, her tense hands grasped one of the corn stalks. Her lips pressed themselves into the dust. When they had gone on their way, she raised her head. A dusty powder covered her lips.

What seemed another long period of silence fell over the fields. The murmuring voices of unborn children, her imagination had created in the whispering fields, became a vast shout. The wind blew harder and harder. The corn stalks were twisted and bent. Elizabeth went thoughtfully out of the field and, climbing the fence, confronted her father. 'Where you been? What you been a-doing?' he asked. 'Don't you think we got to get out of here?'

When Elizabeth went toward the house, Elsie followed, creeping on her hands and knees like a little animal, and when she had come within sight of the fence surrounding the house, she sat on the ground and put her hands over her face. Something within herself was being twisted and whirled about as the tops of the corn stalks were now being twisted and whirled by the wind. She sat so that she did not look toward the house and when she opened her eyes she could again see along the long mysterious aisles.

Her brother with his wife and children went away. By turning her head Elsie could see them driving at a trot out of the yard back of her father's house. With the going of the younger woman the farmhouse in the midst of the corn field rocked by the winds seemed the most desolate place in the world.

Her mother came out at the back door of the house. She ran to the steps where she knew her daughter was in the habit of sitting and then in alarm began to call. It did not occur to Elsie to answer. The voice of the older woman did not seem to have anything to do with herself. It was a thin voice and was quickly lost in the wind and in the crashing sound that arose out of the fields. With her head turned toward the house, Elsie stared at her mother who ran wildly around the house and then went indoors. The back door of the house went shut with a bang.

The storm that had been threatening broke with a roar. Broad sheets of water swept over the corn fields. Sheets of water swept over the woman's body. The storm that had for years been gathering in her also broke. Sobs arose out of her throat. She abandoned herself to a storm of grief that was only partially grief. Tears ran out of her eyes and made little furrows through the dust on her face. In the lulls that occasionally came in the storm, she raised her head and heard, through the tangled mass of wet hair that covered her ears and above the sound of millions of raindrops that alighted on the earthen floor inside the house of the corn, the thin voices of her mother and father calling to her out of the Leander house.

Chicago

I AM MATURE, a man child, in America, in the West, in the great valley of the Mississippi. My head arises above the corn fields. I stand up among the new corn.

I am a child, a confused child in a confused world. There are no clothes made that fit me. The minds of men cannot clothe me. Great projects arise within me. I have a brain and it is cunning and shrewd.

I want leisure to become beautiful, but there is no leisure. Men should bathe me with prayers and with weeping, but there are no men.

Now — from now — from today I shall do deeds of fiery meaning. Songs shall arise in my throat and hurt me.

I am a little thing, a tiny little thing on the vast prairies. I know nothing. My mouth is dirty. I cannot tell what I want. My feet are sunk in the black swampy land, but I am a lover. I love life. In the end love shall save me.

The days are long — it rains — it snows. I am an old man. I am sweeping the ground where my grave shall be.

Look upon me, my beloved, my lover who does not come. I am raw and bleeding, a new thing in a new world. I run swiftly o'er bare fields. Listen — there is the sound of the tramping of many feet. Life is dying in me. I am old and palsied. I am just at the beginning of my life.

Do you not see that I am old, O my beloved? Do you not understand that I cannot sing, that my songs choke me? Do you not see that I am so young I cannot find the word in the confusion of words?

Song of the Soul of Chicago

ON THE BRIDGES, on the bridges — swooping and rising, whirling and circling — back to the bridges, always the bridges.

I'll talk forever — I'm damned if I'll sing. Don't you see that mine is not a singing people? We're just a lot of muddy things caught up by the stream. You can't fool us. Don't we know ourselves?

Here we are, out here in Chicago. You think we're not humble? You're a liar. We are like the sewerage of our town, swept up stream by a kind of mechanical triumph — that's what we are.

On the bridges, on the bridges — wagons and motors, horses and men — not flying, just tearing along and swearing.

By God, we'll love each other or die trying. We'll get to understanding too. In some grim way our own song shall work through.

We'll stay down in the muddy depths of our stream — we will. There can't any poet come out here and sit on the shaky rail of our ugly bridges and sing us into paradise.

We're finding out — that's what I want to say. We'll get at our own thing out here or die for it. We're going down, numberless thousands of us, into ugly oblivion. We know that.

But say, bards, you keep off our bridges. Keep out of our dreams, dreamers. We want to give this democracy thing they talk so big about a whirl. We want to see if we are any good out here, we Americans from all over hell. That's what we want.

Chicago Again

FEAR.

Something huge, not understandable. Streets thirty miles long, perfectly flat. Buildings and houses you dream about in distorted dreams. Boats crowded in the narrow river. Mills. Factories. Smoke, dirt, a low black swampy land, a wind-riven land, a climate so terrible in its extremes of heat and cold that only strong people can survive, really live.

Men, men, men. To the east, reaching up, Michigan. To the west, Wisconsin, Minnesota, the Northwest. Chicago lying where the long tongue of the Great Lakes reaches farthest down into the land. And to the south, smooth as a billiard table — fat land. No such corn land anywhere in the world. Innumerable droves of great sleepy hogs, eating the corn. Cattle off the dry Western lands, coming in lean and bony, getting fat and sleek, eating corn.

Railroads coming in, all the real railroads. Railroads everywhere.

I was a raw boy just out of my Ohio town when I first came to Chicago. What city man, come out of a small town, can forget his first hours in the city, the strangeness and terror of the tall buildings, the human jam?

I walked through the crowded streets with my brother. He was but a year or two older, but suddenly, what a gulf between us. This was not his first city. He had been away from our town for two or three years: in Cleveland, and in Chicago for at least a year. He seemed unimpressed. The bigness did not overwhelm him.

We were not in our family very demonstrative. 'Hello, kid,' 'Hello.' We walked through the flowing human stream, got aboard a streetcar. He was silent. He read a newspaper.

So he had me on his hands. Work had been hard to find in our little town. I had taken the great step, separated from my boyhood friends, from familiar streets, fields at the edge of town where I went with other boys to hunt rabbits or walk.

I was little more than a boy. It was too big for me, too terrible. Could people live in such streets, in such houses? Crowded together so?

You who have seen only the famous Michigan Boulevard, the North Side, Lincoln Park, Jackson Park, do not know Chicago. Why talk? There is the huge Northwest Side, the West Side, the South Side.

Millions of people of all nationalities packed in close, packed in among slaughter-houses, factories, warehouses, mills.

Long stretches of vacant lots. Five-, six-, and eight-storied apartment buildings, standing in the midst of acres of black weeds.

Brutal murders going on. Everything unfinished. Hope — hopelessness. Nothing to do but get drunk as often as possible.

I remember nights when I walked the streets of Chicago — half-drunk, hopeless — swimming in a sea of ugliness.

Then suddenly — a glimpse of the Chicago River — that great sewer. A sewer nothing. You wait. The Chicago River will some day become one of the lovely rivers of the world of cities. Sometimes it is unbelievably beautiful — from the bridges — the gulls soaring above, the strange, lovely chrysoprase river — the cries and oaths.

There is something inevitable about Chicago. So many people in one great flat place — where a real city had to be. A city not in the least like New York, Boston, Philadelphia, Baltimore.

Beside it Cleveland and Detroit are villages — grown suddenly to look like cities. From the first Chicago had to be, will always be while the land lasts, a real city, like New York, London, Paris.

A real city does not care too much what you, a mere man, think of it. 'Here I am. Go to hell.'

Los Angeles, Cleveland, Seattle, such places give themselves away too much. They are whistling in the dark.

A city to be a real one has to have something back of it. Land, a lot of it. Rich land — corn, wheat, iron, rivers, mountains, hogs, cattle. Chicago back of it has the Middle West — the empire called Mid-America. Corn, hogs, wheat, iron, coal, industrialism — a new age moving across a continent by railroads, moving unbelievable quantities of goods across a vast place, in the center of which Chicago stands.

Through Chicago. You'll be routed that way, going most anywhere.

It became the city of my own young manhood. Chicago is unformed, it is terrible. There is something terrible about the making of every great city. Who can tell what it will be? Leopold and Loeb? Carl Sandburg, Edgar Lee Masters, or Clarence Darrow?

And Chicago is still making. Yet when it is formed it will not be another New York, Paris, London. It will be Chicago. Here I am. Go to hell. In its very terribleness it is at moments beautiful in a way apparent only when you have lived there a long time. When you have been sick of it to the very marrow and accepted it, then at last, walking hopeless, endless streets — yourself hopeless — you begin to feel its beauty, its half-wild beauty. The beauty of the loose and undisciplined, unfinished and unlimited. Something half wild and very alive in yourself is there, too. The city you have dreaded and feared is like your own soul.

It remained my city after I had begun to comprehend the distinctiveness of the great city, almost as great as that of individuals, nations, trees, peoples, hills.

There I saw the first woman who rejected me — felt what men feel when they are rejected. There I first made ink flow, sang my first song. There after many efforts I wrote a sentence I could bear reading the next day.

There I first heard the sound of men's voices — related to streets, houses, cities — saw my first real actor walk upon a stage, heard music first, saw painting.

When I visit any other great city of the world, I am a guest. When I am in Chicago, I am at home. It is a little what I am. I am more than a little what Chicago is. No man can escape this city.

I am not proud of it. Chicago will not be proud. But it is a real city — my city.

Take it or leave it.

There it is.

And, God helping me, here am I —

IV. THE WONDERS OF CHAOS

The Egg

My FATHER was, I am sure, intended by nature to be a cheerful, kindly man. Until he was thirty-four years old he worked as a farmhand for a man named Thomas Butterworth whose place lay near the town of Bidwell, Ohio. He had then a horse of his own, and on Saturday evenings drove into town to spend a few hours in social intercourse with other farmhands. In town he drank several glasses of beer and stood about in Ben Head's saloon — crowded on Saturday evenings with visiting farmhands. Songs were sung and glasses thumped on the bar. At ten o'clock father drove home along a lonely country road, made his horse comfortable for the night, and himself went to bed, quite happy in his position in life. He had at that time no notion of trying to rise in the world.

It was in the spring of his thirty-fifth year that father married my mother, then a country school-teacher, and in the following spring I came wriggling and crying into the world. Something happened to the two people. They became ambitious. The American passion for getting up in the world took possession of them.

It may have been that mother was responsible. Being a school-teacher she had no doubt read books and magazines. She had, I presume, read of how Garfield, Lincoln, and other Americans rose from poverty to fame and greatness, and as I lay beside her — in the days of her lying-in — she may have dreamed that I would some day rule men and cities. At any rate she induced father to give up his place as a farmhand, sell his horse, and embark on an independent enterprise of his own. She was a tall silent woman with a long nose and troubled gray eyes. For herself she wanted nothing. For father and myself she was incurably ambitious.

76

The first venture into which the two people went turned out badly. They rented ten acres of poor stony land on Grigg's Road, eight miles from Bidwell, and launched into chicken-raising. I grew into boyhood on the place and got my first impressions of life there. From the beginning they were impressions of disaster, and if, in my turn, I am a gloomy man inclined to see the darker side of life, I attribute it to the fact that what should have been for me the happy joyous days of childhood were spent on a chicken farm.

One unversed in such matters can have no notion of the many and tragic things that can happen to a chicken. It is born out of an egg, lives for a few weeks as a tiny fluffy thing such as you will see pictured on Easter cards, then becomes hideously naked, eats quantities of corn and meal bought by the sweat of your father's brow, gets diseases called pip, cholera, and other names, stands looking with stupid eyes at the sun, becomes sick and dies. A few hens and now and then a rooster, intended to serve God's mysterious ends, struggle through to maturity. The hens lay eggs out of which come other chickens and the dreadful cycle is thus made complete. It is all unbelievably complex. Most philosophers must have been raised on chicken farms. One hopes for so much from a chicken and is so dreadfully disillusioned. Small chickens, just setting out on the journey of life, look so bright and alert and they are in fact so dreadfully stupid. They are so much like people they mix one up in one's judgments of life. If disease does not kill them, they wait until your expectations are thoroughly aroused and then walk under the wheels of a wagon — to go squashed and dead back to their maker. Vermin infest their youth, and fortunes must be spent for curative powders. In later life I have seen how a literature has been built up on the subject of fortunes to be made out of the raising of chickens. It is intended to be read by the gods who have just eaten of the tree of the knowledge of good and evil. It is a hopeful literature and declares that much may be done by simple ambitious people who own a few hens. Do not be led astray by it. It was not written for you. Go hunt for gold on the frozen hills of Alaska, put your faith in the honesty of a politician, believe if you will that the world is daily growing better and that good will triumph over evil, but do not read and believe the literature that is written concerning the hen. It was not written for you.

I, however, digress. My tale does not primarily concern itself with the hen. If correctly told it will center on the egg. For ten years my father and mother struggled to make our chicken farm pay and then they gave up that struggle and began another. They moved into the town of Bidwell, Ohio, and embarked in the restaurant business. After ten years of worry with incubators that did not hatch, and with tiny —and in their own way lovely—balls of fluff that passed on into semi-naked pullethood and from that into dead henhood, we threw all aside and, packing our belongings on a wagon, drove down Griggs's Road toward Bidwell, a tiny caravan of hope looking for a new place from which to start on our upward journey through life.

We must have been a sad-looking lot, not, I fancy, unlike refugees fleeing from a battlefield. Mother and I walked in the road. The wagon that contained our goods had been borrowed for the day from Mr. Albert Griggs, a neighbor. Out of its sides stuck the legs of cheap chairs, and at the back of the pile of beds, tables, and boxes filled with kitchen utensils was a crate of live chickens, and on top of that the baby carriage in which I had been wheeled about in my infancy. Why we stuck to the baby carriage I don't know. It was unlikely other children would be born and the wheels were broken. People who have few possessions cling tightly to those they have. That is one of the facts that make life so discouraging.

Father rode on top of the wagon. He was then a bald-headed man of forty-five, a little fat, and from long association with mother and the chickens he had become habitually silent and discouraged. All during our ten years on the chicken farm he had worked as a laborer on neighboring farms and most of the money he had earned had been spent for remedies to cure chicken diseases, on Wilmer's White Wonder Cholera Cure or Professor Bidlow's Egg Producer or some other preparations that mother found advertised in the poultry papers. There were two little patches of hair on father's head just above his ears. I remember that as a child I used to sit looking at him when he had gone to sleep in a chair before the stove on Sunday afternoons in the winter. I had at that time already begun to read books and have notions of my own, and the bald path that led over the top of his head was, I fancied, something like a broad road, such a road as Caesar might have made on which to lead his legions out of Rome and into the wonders of an unknown world. The tufts of hair that grew above father's ears were, I thought, like forests. I fell into a half-sleeping, half-waking state and dreamed I was a tiny thing going along the road into a far beautiful place where there were no chicken farms and where life was a happy eggless affair.

One might write a book concerning our flight from the chicken farm into town. Mother and I walked the entire eight miles — she to be sure that nothing fell from the wagon and I to see the wonders of the world. On the seat of the wagon beside father was his greatest treasure. I will tell you of that.

On a chicken farm, where hundreds and even thousands of chickens come out of eggs, surprising things sometimes happen. Grotesques are born out of eggs as out of people. The accident does not often occur — perhaps once in a thousand births. A chicken is, you see, born that has four legs, two pairs of wings, two heads, or what not. The things do not live. They go quickly back to the hand of their maker that has for a moment trembled. The fact that the poor little things could not live was one of the tragedies of life to father. He had some sort of notion that if he could but bring into henhood or roosterhood a five-legged hen or a two-headed rooster his fortune wuld be made. He dreamed of taking the wonder about to county fairs and of growing rich by exhibiting it to other farmhands.

At any rate, he saved all the little monstrous things that had been born on our chicken farm. They were preserved in alcohol and put each in its own glass bottle. These he had carefully put into a box, and on our journey into town it was carried on the wagon seat beside him. He drove the horses with one hand and with the other clung to the box. When we got to our destination, the box was taken down at once and the bottles removed. All during our days as keepers of a restaurant in the town of Bidwell, Ohio, the grotesques in their little glass bottles sat on a shelf back of the counter. Mother sometimes protested, but father was a rock on the subject of his treasure. The grotesques were, he declared, valuable. People, he said, liked to look at strange and wonderful things.

Did I say that we embarked in the restaurant business in the town of Bidwell, Ohio? I exaggerated a little. The town itself lay at the foot of a low hill and on the shore of a small river. The railroad did not run through the town and the station was a mile away to the north at a place called Pickleville. There had been a cider mill and

pickle factory at the station, but before the time of our coming they
had both gone out of business. In the morning and in the evening
busses came down to the station along a road called Turner's Pike
from the hotel on the main street of Bidwell. Our going to the out-
of-the-way place to embark in the restaurant business was mother's
idea. She talked of it for a year and then one day went off and rented
an empty store building opposite the railroad station. It was her idea
that the restaurant would be profitable. Traveling men, she said,
would be always waiting around to take trains out of town and town
people would come to the station to await incoming trains. They
would come to the restaurant to buy pieces of pie and drink coffee.
Now that I am older I know that she had another motive in going.
She was ambitious for me. She wanted me to rise in the world, to get
into a town school and become a man of the towns.

At Pickleville father and mother worked hard, as they always had
done. At first there was the necessity of putting our place into shape
to be a restaurant. That took a month. Father built a shelf on which
he put tins of vegetables. He painted a sign on which he put his name
in large red letters. Below his name was the sharp command — 'EAT
HERE' — that was so seldom obeyed. A showcase was bought and
filled with cigars and tobacco. Mother scrubbed the floor and the walls
of the room. I went to school in the town and was glad to be away
from the farm and from the presence of the discouraged, sad-looking
chickens. Still I was not very joyous. In the evening I walked home
from school along Turner's Pike and remembered the children I had
seen playing in the town school yard. A troop of little girls had gone
hopping about and singing. I tried that. Down along the frozen road
I went hopping solemnly on one leg. 'Hippity Hop To The Barber
Shop,' I sang shrilly. Then I stopped and looked doubtfully about. I
was afraid of being seen in my gay mood. It must have seemed to
me that I was doing a thing that should not be done by one who, like
myself, had been raised on a chicken farm where death was a daily
visitor.

Mother decided that our restaurant should remain open at night.
At ten in the evening a passenger train went north past our door followed by a local freight. The freight crew had switching to do in
Pickleville, and when the work was done they came to our restaurant
for hot coffee and food. Sometimes one of them ordered a fried egg.

In the morning at four they returned north-bound and again visited us. A little trade began to grow up. Mother slept at night and during the day tended the restaurant and fed our boarders while father slept. He slept in the same bed mother had occupied during the night and I went off to the town of Bidwell and to school. During the long nights, while mother and I slept, father cooked meats that were to go into sandwiches for the lunch baskets of our boarders. Then an idea in regard to getting up in the world came into his head. The American spirit took hold of him. He also became ambitious.

In the long nights when there was little to do, father had time to think. That was his undoing. He decided that he had in the past been an unsuccessful man because he had not been cheerful enough and that in the future he would adopt a cheerful outlook on life. In the early morning he came upstairs and got into bed with mother. She woke and the two talked. From my bed in the corner I listened.

It was father's idea that both he and mother should try to entertain the people who came to eat at our restaurant. I cannot now remember his words, but he gave the impression of one about to become in some obscure way a kind of public entertainer. When people, particularly young people from the town of Bidwell, came into our place, as on very rare occasions they did, bright entertaining conversation was to be made. From father's words I gathered that something of the jolly innkeeper effect was to be sought. Mother must have been doubtful from the first, but she said nothing discouraging. It was father's notion that a passion for the company of himself and mother would spring up in the breasts of the younger people of the town of Bidwell. In the evening bright happy groups would come singing down Turner's Pike. They would troop shouting with joy and laughter into our place. There would be song and festivity. I do not mean to give the impression that father spoke so elaborately of the matter. He was, as I have said, an uncommunicative man. 'They want some place to go. I tell you they want some place to go,' he said over and over. That was as far as he got. My own imagination has filled in the blanks.

For two or three weeks this notion of father's invaded our house. We did not talk much, but in our daily lives tried earnestly to make smiles take the place of glum looks. Mother smiled at the boarders and I, catching the infection, smiled at our cat. Father became a little

feverish in his anxiety to please. There was, no doubt, lurking somewhere in him, a touch of the spirit of the showman. He did not
waste much of his ammunition on the railroad men he served at
night, but seemed to be waiting for a young man or woman from
Bidwell to come in to show what he could do. On the counter in the
restaurant there was a wire basket kept always filled with eggs, and it
must have been before his eyes when the idea of being entertaining
was born in his brain. There was something pre-natal about the way
eggs kept themselves connected with the development of his idea. At
any rate, an egg ruined his new impulse in life. Late one night I was
awakened by a roar of anger coming from father's throat. Both
mother and I sat upright in our beds. With trembling hands she
lighted a lamp that stood on a table by her head. Downstairs the
front door of our restaurant went shut with a bang and in a few
minutes father tramped up the stairs. He held an egg in his hand
and his hand trembled as though he were having a chill. There was a
half-insane light in his eyes. As he stood glaring at us I was sure he
intended throwing the egg at either mother or me. Then he laid it
gently on the table beside the lamp and dropped on his knees beside
mother's bed. He began to cry like a boy, and I, carried away by his
grief, cried with him. The two of us filled the little upstairs room with
our wailing voices. It is ridiculous, but of the picture we made I can
remember only the fact that mother's hand continually stroked the
bald path that ran across the top of his head. I have forgotten what
mother said to him and how she induced him to tell her of what had
happened downstairs. His explanation also has gone out of my mind.
I remember only my own grief and fright and the shiny path over
father's head glowing in the lamplight as he knelt by the bed.

As to what happened downstairs. For some unexplainable reason
I know the story as well as though I had been a witness to my father's
discomfiture. One in time gets to know many unexplainable things.
On that evening young Joe Kane, son of a merchant of Bidwell, came
to Pickleville to meet his father, who was expected on the ten-o'clock
evening train from the South. The train was three hours late and Joe
came into our place to loaf about and to wait for its arrival. The local
freight train came in and the freight crew were fed. Joe was left alone
in the restaurant with father.

From the moment he came into our place the Bidwell young man must have been puzzled by my father's actions. It was his notion that father was angry at him for hanging around. He noticed that the restaurant-keeper was apparently disturbed by his presence and he thought of going out. However, it began to rain and he did not fancy the long walk to town and back. He bought a five-cent cigar and ordered a cup of coffee. He had a newspaper in his pocket and took it out and began to read. 'I'm waiting for the evening train. It's late,' he said apologetically.

For a long time father, whom Joe Kane had never seen before, remained silently gazing at his visitor. He was no doubt suffering from an attack of stage fright. As so often happens in life he had thought so much and so often of the situation that now confronted him that he was somewhat nervous in its presence.

For one thing, he did not know what to do with his hands. He thrust one of them nervously over the counter and shook hands with Joe Kane. 'How-de-do,' he said. Joe Kane put his newspaper down and stared at him. Father's eyes lighted on the basket of eggs that sat on the counter and he began to talk. 'Well,' he began hesitatingly, 'well, you have heard of Christopher Columbus, eh?' He seemed to be angry. 'That Christopher Columbus was a cheat,' he declared emphatically. 'He talked of making an egg stand on its end. He talked, he did, and then he went and broke the end of the egg.'

My father seemed to his visitor to be beside himself at the duplicity of Christopher Columbus. He muttered and swore. He declared it was wrong to teach children that Christopher Columbus was a great man when, after all, he cheated at the critical moment. He had declared he would make an egg stand on end and then, when his bluff had been called, he had done a trick. Still grumbling at Columbus, father took an egg from the basket on the counter and began to walk up and down. He rolled the egg between the palms of his hands. He smiled genially. He began to mumble words regarding the effect to be produced on an egg by the electricity that comes out of the human body. He declared that, without breaking its shell and by virtue of rolling it back and forth in his hands, he could stand the egg on its end. He explained that the warmth of his hands and the gentle rolling movement he gave the egg created a new center of gravity, and Joe Kane was mildly interested. 'I have handled thousands of eggs,' father said. 'No one knows more about eggs than I do.'

He stood the egg on the counter and it fell on its side. He tried the trick again and again, each time rolling the egg between the palms of his hands and saying the words regarding the wonders of electricity and the laws of gravity. When after a half-hour's effort he did succeed in making the egg stand for a moment, he looked up to find that his visitor was no longer watching. By the time he had succeeded in calling Joe Kane's attention to the success of his effort, the egg had again rolled over and lay on its side.

Afire with the showman's passion and at the same time a good deal disconcerted by the failure of his first effort, father now took the bottles containing the poultry monstrosities down from their place on the shelf and began to show them to his visitor. 'How would you like to have seven legs and two heads like this fellow?' he asked, exhibiting the most remarkable of his treasures. A cheerful smile played over his face. He reached over the counter and tried to slap Joe Kane on the shoulder as he had seen men do in Ben Head's saloon when he was a young farmhand and drove to town on Saturday evenings. His visitor was made a little ill by the sight of the body of the terribly deformed bird floating in the alcohol in the bottle and got up to go. Coming from behind the counter, father took hold of the young man's arm and led him back to his seat. He grew a little angry and for a moment had to turn his face away and force himself to smile. Then he put the bottles back on the shelf. In an outburst of generosity he fairly compelled Joe Kane to have a fresh cup of coffee and another cigar at his expense. Then he took a pan and filling it with vinegar, taken from a jug that sat beneath the counter, he declared himself about to do a new trick. 'I will heat this egg in this pan of vinegar,' he said. 'Then I will put it through the neck of a bottle without breaking the shell. When the egg is inside the bottle it will resume its normal shape and the shell will become hard again. Then I will give the bottle with the egg in it to you. You can take it about with you wherever you go. People will want to know how you got the egg in the bottle. Don't tell them. Keep them guessing. That is the way to have fun with this trick.'

Father grinned and winked at his visitor. Joe Kane decided that the man who confronted him was mildly insane but harmless. He drank the cup of coffee that had been given him and began to read his paper again. When the egg had been heated in vinegar, father carried it on a spoon to the counter and going into a back room got an empty bottle. He was angry because his visitor did not watch him as he began to do his trick, but nevertheless went cheerfully to work. For a long time he struggled, trying to get the egg to go through the neck of the bottle. He put the pan of vinegar back on the stove, intending to reheat the egg, then picked it up and burned his fingers. After a second bath in the hot vinegar, the shell of the egg had been softened a little, but not enough for his purpose. He worked and worked and a spirit of desperate determination took possession of him. When he thought that at last the trick was about to be consummated, the delayed train came in at the station and Joe Kane started to go nonchalantly out at the door. Father made a last desperate effort to conquer the egg and make it do the thing that would establish his repuation as one who knew how to entertain guests who came into his restaurant. He worried the egg. He attempted to be somewhat rough with it. He swore and the sweat stood out on his forehead. The egg broke under his hand. When the contents spurted over his clothes, Joe Kane, who had stopped at the door, turned and laughed.

A roar of anger rose from my father's throat. He danced and shouted a string of inarticulate words. Grabbing another egg from the basket on the counter, he threw it, just missing the head of the young man as he dodged through the door and escaped.

Father came upstairs to mother and me with an egg in his hand. I do not know what he intended to do. I imagine he had some idea of destroying it, of destroying all eggs, and that he intended to let mother and me see him begin. When, however, he got into the presence of mother, something happened to him. He laid the egg gently on the table and dropped on his knees by the bed as I have already explained. He later decided to close the restaurant for the night and to come upstairs and get into bed. When he did so, he blew out the light and after much muttered conversation both he and mother went to sleep. I suppose I went to sleep also, but my sleep was troubled. I awoke at dawn and for a long time looked at the egg that lay on the table. I wondered why eggs had to be and why from the egg came the hen who again laid the egg. The question got into my blood. It has stayed there, I imagine, because I am the son of my father. At any rate, the problem remains unsolved in my mind. And that, I conclude, is but another evidence of the complete and final triumph of the egg —at least as far as my family is concerned.

I Want to Know Why

W<small>E GOT UP</small> at four in the morning, that first day in the East. On the evening before we had climbed off a freight train at the edge of town, and with the true instinct of Kentucky boys had found our way across town and to the race-track and the stables at once. Then we knew we were all right. Hanley Turner right away found a nigger we knew. It was Bildad Johnson, who in the winter works at Ed Becker's livery barn in our home town, Beckersville. Bildad is a good cook as almost all our niggers are, and of course he, like everyone in our part of Kentucky who is anyone at all, likes the horses. In the spring Bildad begins to scratch around. A nigger from our country can flatter and wheedle anyone into letting him do most anything he wants. Bildad wheedles the stablemen and the trainers from the horse farms in our country around Lexington. The trainers come into town in the evening to stand around and talk and maybe get into a poker game. Bildad gets in with them. He is always doing little favors and telling about things to eat, chicken browned in a pan, and how is the best way to cook sweet potatoes and corn bread. It makes your mouth water to hear him.

When the racing season comes on and the horses go to the races and there is all the talk on the streets in the evenings about the new colts, and everyone says when they are going over to Lexington or to the spring meeting at Churchill Downs or to Latonia, and the horse-men that have been down to New Orleans or maybe at the winter meeting at Havana in Cuba come home to spend a week before they start out again, at such a time when everything talked about in Beck-ersville is just horses and nothing else and the outfits start out and

horse-racing is in every breath of air you breathe, Bildad shows up
with a job as cook for some outfit. Often, when I think about it, his
always going all season to the races and working in the livery barn in
the winter where horses are and where men like to come and talk
about horses, I wish I was a nigger. It's a foolish thing to say, but
that's the way I am about being around horses, just crazy. I can't
help it.

Well, I must tell you about what we did and let you in on what
I'm talking about. Four of us boys from Beckersville, all whites and
sons of men who live in Beckersville regular, made up our minds we
were going to the races, not just to Lexington or Louisville, I don't
mean, but to the big Eastern track we were always hearing our Beckersville men talk about, to Saratoga. We were all pretty young then.
I was just turned fifteen and I was the oldest of the four. It was my
scheme. I admit that and I talked the others into trying it. There
was Hanley Turner and Henry Rieback and Tom Tumberton and
myself. I had thirty-seven dollars I had earned during the winter
working nights and Saturdays in Enoch Myer's grocery. Henry Rieback had eleven dollars, and the others, Hanley and Tom, had only a
dollar or two each. We fixed it all up and laid low until the Kentucky spring meetings were over and some of our men, the sportiest
ones, the ones we envied the most, had cut out — then we cut out too.

I won't tell you the trouble we had beating our way on freights
and all. We went through Cleveland and Buffalo and other cities and
saw Niagara Falls. We bought things there, souvenirs and spoons
and cards and shells with pictures of the falls on them for our sisters
and mothers, but thought we had better not send any of the things
home. We didn't want to put the folks on our trail and maybe be
nabbed.

We got into Saratoga, as I said, at night and went to the track. Bildad fed us up. He showed us a place to sleep in hay over a shed and
promised to keep still. Niggers are all right about things like that.
They won't squeal on you. Often a white man you might meet, when
you had run away from home like that, might appear to be all right
and give you a quarter or a half dollar or something, and then go
right and give you away. White men will do that, but not a nigger.
You can trust them. They are squarer with kids. I don't know why.

At the Saratoga meeting that year there were a lot of men from home. Dave Williams and Arthur Mulford and Jerry Myers and others. Then there was a lot from Louisville and Lexington Henry Rieback knew, but I didn't. They were professional gamblers and Henry Rieback's father is one too. He is what is called a sheet writer and goes away most of the year to tracks. In the winter when he is home in Beckersville he don't stay there much, but goes away to cities and deals faro. He is a nice man and generous, is always sending Henry presents, a bicycle and a gold watch and a boy scout suit of clothes and things like that.

My own father is a lawyer. He's all right, but don't make much money and can't buy me things, and anyway I'm getting so old now I don't expect it. He never said nothing to me against Henry, but Hanley Turner and Tom Tumberton's fathers did. They said to their boys that money so come by is no good and they didn't want their boys brought up to hear gamblers' talk and be thinking about such things and maybe embrace them.

That's all right and I guess the men know what they are talking about, but I don't see what it's got to do with Henry or with horses either. That's what I'm writing this story about. I'm puzzled. I'm getting to be a man and want to think straight and be O.K., and there's something I saw at the race meeting at the Eastern track I can't figure out.

I can't help it, I'm crazy about thoroughbred horses. I've always been that way. When I was ten years old and saw I was growing to be big and couldn't be a rider, I was so sorry I nearly died. Harry Hellinfinger in Beckersville, whose father is postmaster, is grown up and too lazy to work, but likes to stand around in the street and get up jokes on boys like sending them to a hardware store for a gimlet to bore square holes and other jokes like that. He played one on me. He told me that if I would eat a half a cigar I would be stunted and not grow any more and maybe could be a rider. I did it. When father wasn't looking, I took a cigar out of his pocket and gagged it down some way. It made me awful sick and the doctor had to be sent for, and then it did no good. I kept right on growing. It was a joke. When I told what I had done and why, most fathers would have whipped me, but mine didn't.

Well, I didn't get stunted and didn't die. It serves Harry Hellinfinger right. Then I made up my mind I would like to be a stable boy, but had to give that up too. Mostly niggers do that work and I knew father wouldn't let me go into it. No use to ask him.

If you've never been crazy about thoroughbreds, it's because you've never been around where they are much and don't know any better. They're beautiful. There isn't anything so lovely and clean and full of spunk and honest and everything as some race-horses. On the big horse farms that are all around our town, Beckersville, there are tracks and the horses run in the early morning. More than a thousand times I've got out of bed before daylight and walked two or three miles to the tracks. Mother wouldn't of let me go, but father always says, 'Let him alone.' So I got some bread out of the bread box and some butter and jam, gobbled it and lit out.

At the tracks you sit on the fence with men, whites and niggers, and they chew tobacco and talk, and then the colts are brought out. It's early and the grass is covered with shiny dew and in another field a man is plowing and they are frying things in a shed where the track niggers sleep, and you know how a nigger can giggle and laugh and say things that make you laugh. A white man can't do it and some niggers can't, but a track nigger can every time.

And so the colts are brought out and some are just galloped by stable boys, but almost every morning on a big track owned by a rich man who lives maybe in New York, there are always, nearly every morning, a few colts and some of the old race-horses and geldings and mares that are cut loose.

It brings a lump up into my throat when a horse runs. I don't mean all horses but some. I can pick them nearly every time. It's in my blood like in the blood of race-track niggers and trainers. Even when they just go slop-jogging along with a little nigger on their backs, I can tell a winner. If my throat hurts and it's hard for me to swallow, that's him. He'll run like Sam Hill when you let him out. If he don't win every time it'll be a wonder and because they've got him in a pocket behind another or he was pulled or got off bad at the post or something. If I wanted to be a gambler like Henry Rieback's father, I could get rich. I know I could and Henry says so too. All I would have to do is to wait till that hurt comes when I see a horse and then bet every cent. That's what I would do if I wanted to be a gambler, but I don't.

When you're at the tracks in the morning — not the race-tracks but the training tracks around Beckersville — you don't see a horse, the kind I've been talking about, very often, but it's nice anyway. Any thoroughbred, that is sired right and out of a good mare and trained by a man that knows how, can run. If he couldn't, what would he be there for and not pulling a plow?

Well, out of the stables they come and the boys are on their backs and it's lovely to be there. You hunch down on top of the fence and itch inside you. Over in the sheds the niggers giggle and sing. Bacon is being fried and coffee made. Everything smells lovely. Nothing smells better than coffee and manure and horses and niggers and bacon frying and pipes being smoked out-of-doors on a morning like that. It just gets you, that's what it does.

But about Saratoga. We was there six days and not a soul from home seen us and everything came off just as we wanted it to, fine weather and horses and races and all. We beat our way home and Bildad gave us a basket with fried chicken and bread and other eatables in, and I had eighteen dollars when we got back to Beckersville. Mother jawed and cried, but Pop didn't say much. I told everything we done except one thing. I did and saw that alone. That's what I'm writing about. It got me upset. I think about it at night. Here it is.

At Saratoga we laid up nights in the hay in the shed Bildad had showed us and ate with the niggers early and at night when the race people had all gone away. The men from home stayed mostly in the grandstand and betting field, and didn't come out around the places where the horses are kept except to the paddocks just before a race when the horses are saddled. At Saratoga they don't have paddocks under an open shed as at Lexington and Churchill Downs and other tracks down in our country, but saddle the horses right out in an open place under trees on a lawn as smooth and nice as Banker Bohon's front yard here in Beckersville. It's lovely. The horses are sweaty and nervous and shine and the men come out and smoke cigars and look at them and the trainers are there and the owners, and your heart thumps so you can hardly breathe.

Then the bugle blows for post and the boys that ride come running out with their silk clothes on and you run to get a place by the fence with the niggers.

I always am wanting to be a trainer or owner, and at the risk of being seen and caught and sent home I went to the paddocks before every race. The other boys didn't, but I did.

We got to Saratoga on a Friday and on Wednesday the next week the big Mullford Handicap was to be run. Middlestride was in it and Sunstreak. The weather was fine and the track fast. I couldn't sleep the night before.

What had happened was that both these horses are the kind it makes my throat hurt to see. Middlestride is long and looks awkward and is a gelding. He belongs to Joe Thompson, a little owner from home who only has a half-dozen horses. The Mullford Handicap is for a mile and Middlestride can't untrack fast. He goes away slow and is always way back at the half, then he begins to run and if the race is a mile and a quarter, he'll just eat up everything and get there.

Sunstreak is different. He is a stallion and nervous and belongs on the biggest farm we've got in our country, the Van Riddle place that belongs to Mr. Van Riddle of New York. Sunstreak is like a girl you think about sometimes but never see. He is hard all over and lovely too. When you look at his head you want to kiss him. He is trained by Jerry Tillford who knows me and has been good to me lots of times, lets me walk into a horse's stall to look at him close and other things. There isn't anything as sweet as that horse. He stands at the post quiet and not letting on, but he is just burning up inside. Then when the barrier goes up he is off like his name, Sunstreak. It makes you ache to see him. It hurts you. He just lays down and runs like a bird dog. There can't anything I ever see run like him except Middlestride when he gets untracked and stretches himself.

Gee! I ached to see that race and those two horses run, ached and dreaded it too. I didn't want to see either of our horses beaten. We had never sent a pair like that to the races before. Old men in Beckersville said so and the niggers said so. It was a fact.

Before the race I went over to the paddocks to see. I looked a last look at Middlestride, who isn't such a much standing in a paddock that way, then I went to see Sunstreak.

It was his day. I knew when I see him. I forgot all about being seen myself and walked right up. All the men from Beckersville were there and no one noticed me except Jerry Tillford. He saw me and something happened. I'll tell you about that.

I was standing looking at that horse and aching. In some way, I can't tell how, I knew just how Sunstreak felt inside. He was quiet and letting the niggers rub his legs and Mr. Van Riddle himself put the saddle on, but he was just a raging torrent inside. He was like the water in the river at Niagara Falls just before it goes plunk down. That horse wasn't thinking about running. He don't have to think about that. He was just thinking about holding himself back till the time for the running came. I knew that. I could just in a way see right inside him. He was going to do some awful running and I knew it. He wasn't bragging or letting on much or prancing or making a fuss, but just waiting. I knew it and Jerry Tillford his trainer knew. I looked up and then that man and I looked into each other's eyes. Something happened to me. I guess I loved the man as much as I did the horse because he knew what I knew. Seemed to me there wasn't anything in the world but that man and the horse and me. I cried and Jerry Tillford had a shine in his eyes. Then I came away to the fence to wait for the race. The horse was better than me, more steadier, and now I know better than Jerry. He was the quietest and he had to do the running.

Sunstreak ran first, of course, and he busted the world's record for a mile. I've seen that if I never see anything more. Everything came out just as I expected. Middlestride got left at the post and was way back and closed up to be second, just as I knew he would. He'll get a world's record too some day. They can't skin the Beckerville country on horses.

I watched the race calm because I knew what would happen. I was sure. Hanley Turner and Henry Rieback and Tom Tumberton were all more excited than me.

A funny thing had happened to me. I was thinking about Jerry Tillford the trainer and how happy he was all through the race. I liked him that afternoon even more than I ever liked my own father. I almost forgot the horses thinking that way about him. It was because of what I had seen in his eyes as he stood in the paddocks beside Sunstreak before the race started. I knew he had been watching and working with Sunstreak since the horse was a baby colt, had taught him to run and be patient and when to let himself out and not to quit, never. I knew that for him it was like a mother seeing her child do something brave or wonderful. It was the first time I ever felt for a man like that.

After the race that night I cut out from Tom and Hanley and Henry. I wanted to be by myself and I wanted to be near Jerry Tillford if I could work it. Here is what happened.

The track in Saratoga is near the edge of town. It is all polished up and trees around, the evergreen kind, and grass and everything painted and nice. If you go past the track you get to a hard road made of asphalt for automobiles, and if you go along this for a few miles there is a road turns off to a little rummy-looking farmhouse set in a yard.

That night after the race I went along that road because I had seen Jerry and some other men go that way in an automobile. I didn't expect to find them. I walked for a ways and then sat down by a fence to think. It was the direction they went in. I wanted to be as near Jerry as I could. I felt close to him. Pretty soon I went up the side road — I don't know why — and came to the rummy farmhouse. I was just lonesome to see Jerry, like wanting to see your father at night when you are a young kid. Just then an automobile came along and turned in. Jerry was in it and Henry Rieback's father, and Arthur Bedford from home, and Dave Williams and two other men I didn't know. They got out of the car and went into the house, all but Henry Rieback's father who quarreled with them and said he wouldn't go. It was only about nine o'clock, but they were all drunk, and the rummy looking farmhouse was a place for bad women to stay in. That's what it was. I crept up along a fence and looked through a window and saw.

It's what give me the fantods. I can't make it out. The women in the house were all ugly mean-looking women, not nice to look at or be near. They were homely too, except one who was tall and looked a little like the gelding Middlestride, but not clean like him, but with a hard ugly mouth. She had red hair. I saw everything plain. I got up by an old rosebush by an open window and looked. The women had on loose dresses and sat around in chairs. The men came in and some sat on the women's laps. The place smelled rotten and there was rotten talk, the kind a kid hears around a livery stable in a town like Beckerville in the winter, but don't ever expect to hear talked when there are women around. It was rotten. A nigger wouldn't go into such a place.

I looked at Jerry Tillford. I've told you how I had been feeling about him on account of his knowing what was going on inside of Sunstreak in the minute before he went to the post for the race in which he made a world's record.

Jerry bragged in that bad woman house as I know Sunstreak

wouldn't never have bragged. He said that he made that horse, that it was him that won the race and made the record. He lied and bragged like a fool. I never heard such silly talk.

And then, what do you suppose he did! He looked at the woman in there, the one that was lean and hard-mouthed and looked a little like the gelding Middlestride, but not clean like him, and his eyes began to shine just as they did when he looked at me and at Sunstreak in the paddocks at the track in the afternoon. I stood there by the window — gee! — but I wished I hadn't gone away from the tracks, but had stayed with the boys and the niggers and the horses. The tall rotten-looking woman was between us just as Sunstreak was in the paddocks in the afternoon.

Then, all of a sudden, I began to hate that man. I wanted to scream and rush in the room and kill him. I never had such a feeling before. I was so mad clean through that I cried and my fists were doubled up so my fingernails cut my hands.

And Jerry's eyes kept shining and he waved back and forth, and then he went and kissed that woman, and I crept away and went back to the tracks and to bed and didn't sleep hardly any, and then next day I got the other kids to start home with me and never told them anything I seen.

I been thinking about it ever since. I can't make it out. Spring has come again and I'm nearly sixteen and go to the tracks mornings same as always, and I see Sunstreak and Middlestride and a new colt named Strident I'll bet will lay them all out, but no one thinks so but me and two or three niggers.

But things are different. At the tracks the air don't taste as good or smell as good. It's because a man like Jerry Tillford, who knows what he does, could see a horse like Sunstreak run, and kiss a woman like that the same day. I can't make it out. Darn him, what did he want to do like that for? I keep thinking about it and it spoils looking at horses and smelling things and hearing niggers laugh and everything. Sometimes I'm so mad about it I want to fight someone. It gives me the fantods. What did he do it for? I want to know why.

The Contract

ONE EVENING HE KISSED HER, and she got abruptly up from the bench in the garden back of her father's house and went to stand by a tree. How soft and still and lovely the night seemed to him! He felt absurdly set up, a little, perhaps, he thought, smiling indulgently at himself, as a warrior might feel after securing a position of advantage for a coming great battle. For the moment he had forgotten her and continued to sit alone on the bench smiling at himself. Had the still-ness of the garden been broken by the blast of a trumpet and himself proclaimed some kind of a conquering male hero, he would not have been too surprised. The notion of being a conqueror clung to him, and although he laughed at himself, he went on playing with the idea. There was Napoleon following his star of destiny and Alex-ander sighing for more worlds to conquer! Had he not suddenly kissed her without asking permission? Had he not stormed the for-tress? It was the way things were done among the bolder males. He laughed softly.

In a way she had been expecting the kiss, although she had been telling herself she did not want it. Still she was prepared for it as he was not. It was the third time they had been together.

For her the first time she had seen him had been the most stirring of all. He had come into town unheralded and then word had gone around that he was a figure of consequence in the intellectual world. He was invited to speak before an organization called the Thursday Club and she went with her father, the editor of the town's one news-paper.

His figure had swept like a flame across the field of her fancy that first evening. In what a daring way he had talked! His subject was the effect of Christianity on civilization and he spoke of Jesus, the man of Nazareth, in a way that disturbed and irritated the Thursday Club. With what fire and eloquence he talked. There was the sacred young man, a carpenter in an obscure village. He had thought his own thoughts, ignored the teachings of older men. When he was not at work at his trade, he went alone to talk in the hills. His own intense nature and the long hours and days of silent contemplation of life had made him a profound mystic. Had anyone thought, had anyone dared think, of the man Jesus as just an ordinary human being who had, in the face of the commonplace standards of life, had the courage to use his life as an adventurous experiment for the benefit of society!

The speaker before the Thursday Club, organized by her father and several other men for the purpose of studying literature, had quite startled his audience. After the meeting several of the members protested, saying the club had been organized for another purpose and that it was too bad to start a religious discussion.

They had, she felt, missed the whole point of his talk. It was not a religious discussion. As she sat beside her father and looked about at the other club members and their wives and at the few unmarried men scattered among them, a great gladness that such a man had come to live in her town swept over her. As he continued talking of the man of Galilee and how he walked up and down through many towns in a faraway country casting out devils by the power of his bold and lovely presence, she was so overcome with emotion that tears came to her eyes. The speaker was himself a man of thirty, and Jesus, the Christ of whom he talked so eloquently, had been a man of thirty when he set out on his mission to civilization. After the meeting and as the speaker walked home with herself and her father, she remained silent while the two men talked. Even then he was a little too conscious of her. She had wanted to worship from afar. She had wanted to repeat aloud the words of the officers of the Pharisees, sent to seize Jesus in the temple, the men who had returned from their mission empty-handed. 'Never man spake like this man,' they had said, filled with wonder.

As the three people walked under the trees, he continued to speak on the subject that had been the foundation of his talk before the club.

'They evidently misunderstood,' he said, laughing. 'I did not intend my talk to be concerned with religion. I was thinking only of the barbaric background of the life of Jesus Christ and its dramatic possibilities. You understand what I mean, the soft smiling land of Galilee, the lake with the white cities on the shore, ruled over by the cruel Herod Antipas, the fishermen leaving their nets to follow the man who taught the strange new doctrine of peace, forgiveness and love. And then the strange crowds in the streets of the towns and in the city of Jerusalem, the paralytic at Bethesda, the pool by the Sheep-gate, the prostitute who wiped his feet with her hair as he sat at the feast, the scene in the garden on the night before the crucifixion, the crucifixion itself — why should all this not be taken as profound and beautiful literature? That is how, I am sure, it has had its greatest effect upon mankind.'

As he had talked to her father during the walk homeward on that first evening, the speaker had occasionally turned to her and once he had made a feeble apology for the seriousness of the talk. 'Does all this bore you?' he asked, and a chill ran over her body. She made a gesture with her hand and looked away, and as soon as they had arrived at her father's house, she excused herself and went upstairs.

The two men continued talking for a long time and she undressed and lay in bed with her door open so she could hear the voices. What an evening that had been for her! Her father, usually a rather prosaic man, was excited and talked well, and she thought the newcomer the most wonderful being that had ever come into her consciousness. His strong boyish voice ran up the stairs and through the halls of the house and she sat up in bed and listened, her whole being strangely alive. The voice had carried her out of herself and into the land of Galilee he had described so vividly, and she stood in a vast crowd of people listening to another stranger of thirty who had suddenly come out of another place and was talking. A phrase remembered from her Bible-reading ran through her mind and she repeated it aloud. She became, not herself, but a strange woman in a strange land. 'Blessed be the womb that bare Thee and the breasts that Thou hast sucked,' she imagined herself shouting, quite carried away.

She saw him for the second time two weeks after that first meeting, and it was strange and also sad to think that during that second meeting he came off his pedestal with a thump.

He wrote her a note and asked her to go with him to a concert and she was stirred at the thought of sitting close beside him all evening and hearing music. Before the evening came, she went about her father's house, attending to the household affairs, with her mind floating away out of her body into a land of spiritual adventure. When her father spoke to her at the table, she was confused and her cheeks grew red. 'What's the matter with you?' he asked, laughing. 'You've begun acting like a schoolgirl. What's happened to you?'

After all, she was not very young and the new man was not the first who had been attracted to her. Already two men of the town had asked her to marry them — but she had never before got into such a strange exalted state. 'Between him and myself it will be different. We will go along a new road into a strange beautiful place,' she whispered to herself. She had no plan. It was enough, she thought, that the new man had come to town, that she could occasionally sit in silence beside him, that she could hear his voice, that she could come into the presence of his mind at work making beautiful images.

'It is quite true. There is a religion of the beautiful,' she thought. Her mother, who had died when she was fifteen, had been a devout church member, and as a young girl she had also given herself, for a time, to religious enthusiasm. Later she had given up churchgoing and had thought of herself as an intellectual woman.

Now she laughed at herself. 'I am a child beside him,' she thought, remembering how glowingly he had talked before the Thursday Club. Contentment settled down upon her. 'In every life there should be a deeply spiritual love,' she told herself. 'I am like that woman in the Bible who on a scorching day came down alone, out of a village, to the well in the dusty plain and found lying there on a stone bench the sacred man, he who knew the true way of life.'

At the concert he did several things to disturb her.

In the first place he was not at all absorbed or carried away by the music and all evening he kept looking at her with hungry eyes. As they walked homeward he did not talk, giving himself with abandon to ideas, but was silent and self-conscious.

And then he kissed her and her exalted mood went quickly away and something shrewd and determined took entire possession of her.

It was ten o'clock when they got to the house and her father was at the newspaper office. The moon shone and they went into the garden and sat together on a bench. After he had kissed her, she went to stand by the tree because it was necessary for her to make a new adjustment. She had been allowing herself to be a child and her child's hands had been building a temple. Now all the bricks and stone of the temple had fallen down and there was a great dust and racket.

To relieve the tenseness of the situation she led him out of the garden into the street. After all, she had not finished with him. There was something she wanted. They walked down a silent street under trees and a group of young men went past them singing some foolish love-song.

Presently they came to the end of the street and into a field, and it was then she understood the depth of his stupidity. Some elders grew in a little gully beside the field and he wanted her to go in among them. When she drew back, a little startled, he was angry. 'The kiss you let me take back there was a lie, then?' he asked sharply. 'It didn't mean anything? You are like all the other women who give kisses having no meaning?'

It was during the third time they were together that everything between them was settled. A war had broken out between the forces sleeping in each of them, but after that third meeting peace came. One Saturday afternoon they went together to spend a day in the country. She wore a heavy sweater and stout boots and on his shoulder he carried a small bag filled with the luncheon she had prepared. She was in a smiling, confident mood and he was disturbed and unhappy. When he looked at her he felt like one condemned to beat with bare hands against a cold stone wall. The wall was as hard as adamant, but was surfaced with some warm soft growth.

For a time after they set out, things went well and then the final struggle between them began. Several times during the afternoon, as they walked in a little strip of woodland among dry leaves and under the fragrant trees just in the fullness of the new spring life, she seemed about to yield to the hunger gnawing at him, but, as evening came on and when they had eaten the luncheon and sat on the grassy bank of a small stream, she became very business-like and determined. 'We must get back toward town before darkness comes,' she said, leading the way across a field and into a dusty road.

The battle came to a crisis quickly. When they had got almost to town, her energetic mood left her and they got out of the road and into an orchard. He built a little fire of twigs beside a rail fence and they leaned against the fence and watched it burn in silence. The thin column of smoke went up through the branches of the trees. 'It's like incense,' she said, creeping close to him. Their bodies pressed against each other. As the moon was full, darkness did not come and the day passed imperceptibly into night.

Two boys from a near-by farmhouse, who had been driving cows homeward along a lane, saw them standing thus, their arms about each other. They crawled over a fence and crept along in the shadows to wait and watch.

Overcome by a sudden fear she pushed herself out of his arms and moved slowly away along the fence. He followed, pressing her close. A wavering uncertainty had taken possession of her and the battle seemed lost. She wanted to escape and at the same time did not want to escape. She was tired.

With an effort she turned and walked in a very determined way across the orchard and he stood by the fence and let her go. One of the farm boys called to the other. 'Nothing's going to happen. She's going away,' he called. The boys climbed a fence and ran off along a lane toward a distant barn and again silence settled over the orchard. She returned to him, her eyes shining and her hands trembling.

'You see what you have brought me to, what has happened?' she asked sharply. For a moment she felt mean, beaten, and then quickly she became quite sure of herself. The whole fact of organized life stood back of her trembling figure.

He did not understand. 'There will be a scandal,' she said. 'I don't blame you. I blame myself. Why did I let myself make a show of myself with you?'

She tried to explain. 'Of course those boys know me,' she said, turning her face away. 'They have seen us, in this place, holding each other in that way and kissing. It's light enough to see everything. It's horrible. You are a man, but I'm a woman. There'll be a scandal and my name will be dragged in the mud.'

He watched her, perplexed and puzzled. The fact that they had been seen at the love-making had rather amused him and he had been on the point of breaking into laughter. Now he felt ashamed and penitent.

She went and put her face down on the top rail of the fence and her body shook with sobs. He stood awkwardly watching.

A thought came to him. 'Well,' he said hesitatingly, 'we could marry, we could get married.'

He looked away over her head and out into an open country washed with moonlight. A wind came up and clouds raced across the sky making fugitive shadows that played madly over the face of the fields. Some shadowy, lovely thing seemed fleeing out of him and out of her. He felt like a beast who in playing about at night in a forest has suddenly put his foot into a trap. A madness to run away from her, to flit half-crazily away over the fields like one of the cloud shadows and then to disappear forever into an unknown, mysterious distance, had possession of him, but his feet had become heavy. He was held fast, bound down to the earth, not by desire now, but by a strange hesitating sympathy with the thing that bound her to earth.

When she looked up, he took her into his arms and held her tightly while he continued looking over her head and into the distance. Her body that had been quivering with excitement became quiet. 'We had better be married at once,' he said. 'There are things I have never understood before. Let's go back to town and be married at once, tonight. That will solve all our difficulties, you see.'

The Sad Horn-Blowers

I

T HAD BEEN a disastrous year in Will's family. The Appletons lived on one of the outlying streets of Bidwell and Will's father was a house painter. In early February, when there was deep snow on the ground, and a cold bitter wind blew about the houses, Will's mother suddenly died. He was seventeen years old then, and rather a big fellow for his age.

The mother's death happened abruptly, without warning, as a sleepy man kills a fly with the hand in a warm room on a summer day. On one February day there she was coming in at the kitchen door of the Appletons' house, from hanging the wash out on the line in the back yard, and warming her long hands, covered with blue veins, by holding them over the kitchen stove — and then, looking about at the children with that half-hidden, shy smile of hers — there she was like that, as the three children had always known her, and then, but a week later, she was cold in death and lying in her coffin in the place vaguely spoken of in the family as 'the other room.'

After that, and when summer came and the family was trying hard to adjust itself to the new conditions, there came another disaster. Up to the very moment when it happened, it looked as though Tom Appleton, the house painter, was in for a prosperous season. The two boys, Fred and Will, were to be his assistants that year.

To be sure, Fred was only fifteen, but he was one to lend a quick alert hand at almost any undertaking. For example, when there was a job of paper-hanging to be done, he was the fellow to spread on the paste, helped by an occasional sharp word from his father.

Down off his stepladder Tom Appleton hopped and ran to the

long board where the paper was spread out. He liked this business of having two assistants about. Well, you see, one had the feeling of being at the head of something, of managing affairs. He grabbed the pastebrush out of Fred's hand. 'Don't spare the paste,' he shouted. 'Slap her on like this. Spread her out — so. Do be sure to catch all the edges.'

It was all very warm, and comfortable, and nice, working at paper-hanging jobs in the houses on the March and April days. When it was cold or rainy outside, stoves were set up in the new houses being built, and in houses already inhabited the folks moved out of the rooms to be papered, spread newspapers on the floors over the carpets and put sheets over the furniture left in the rooms. Outside it rained or snowed, but inside it was warm and cozy.

To the Appletons it seemed, at the time, as though the death of the mother had drawn them closer together. Both Will and Fred felt it, perhaps Will the more consciously. The family was rather in the hole financially — the mother's funeral had cost a good deal of money, and Fred was being allowed to stay out of school. That pleased him. When they worked in a house where there were other children, they came home from school in the late afternoon and looked in through the door to where Fred was spreading paste over the sheets of wall-paper. He made a slapping sound with the brush, but did not look at them. 'Ah, go on, you kids,' he thought. This was a man's business he was up to. Will and his father were on the stepladders, putting the sheets carefully into place on the ceilings and walls. 'Does she match down there?' the father asked sharply. 'O-kay, go ahead,' Will replied. When the sheet was in place, Fred ran and rolled out the laps with a little wooden roller. How jealous the kids of the house were! It would be a long time before any of them could stay out of school and do a man's work, as Fred was doing.

And then in the evening, walking homeward, it was nice, too. Will and Fred had been provided with suits of white overalls that were now covered with dried paste and spots of paint and looked really professional. They kept them on and drew their overcoats on over them. Their hands were stiff with paste, too. On Main Street the lights were lighted, and other men passing called to Tom Appleton. He was called Tony in the town. 'Hello, Tony!' some storekeeper shouted. It was rather too bad, Will thought, that his father hadn't more dignity. He was too boyish. Young boys growing up and merging into manhood do not fancy fathers being too boyish. Tom Appleton played a cornet in the Bidwell Silver Cornet Band and didn't do the job very well — rather made a mess of it, when there was a bit of solo work to be done — but was so well liked by the other members of the band that no one said anything. And then he talked so grandly about music, and about the lip of a cornet player, that everyone thought he must be all right. 'He has an education. I tell you what, Tony Appleton knows a lot. He's a smart one,' the other members of the band were always saying to each other.

'Well, the devil! A man should grow up after a time, perhaps. When a man's wife had died but a short time before, it was just as well to walk through Main Street with more dignity — for the time being, anyway.'

Tom Appleton had a way of winking at men he passed in the street, as though to say, 'Well, now I've got my kids with me, and we won't say anything, but didn't you and I have the very hell of a time last Wednesday night, eh? Mum's the word, old pal. Keep everything quiet. There are gay times ahead for you and me. We'll cut loose, you bet, when you and me are out together next time.'

Will grew a little angry about something he couldn't exactly understand. His father stopped in front of Jake Mann's meat market. 'You kids go along home. Tell Kate I am bringing a steak. I'll be right on your heels,' he said.

He would get the steak and then he would go into Alf Geiger's saloon and get a good, stiff drink of whiskey. There would be no one now to bother about smelling it on his breath when he got home later. Not that his wife had ever said anything when he wanted a drink — but you know how a man feels when there's a woman in the house. 'Why, hello, Bildad Smith — how's the old game leg? Come on, have a little nip with me. Were you on Main Street last band meeting night and did you hear us do that new gallop? It's a humdinger. Turkey White did that trombone solo simply grand.'

Will and Fred had got beyond Main Street now, and Will took a small pipe with a curved stem out of his overcoat pocket and lighted it. 'I'll bet I could hang a ceiling without father there at all, if only someone would give me a chance,' he said. Now that his father was no longer present to embarrass him with his lack of dignity, he felt comfortable and happy. Also, it was something to be able to smoke a pipe without discomfiture. When mother was alive, she was always kissing a fellow when he came home at night, and then one had to be mighty careful about smoking. Now it was different. One had become a man and one accepted manhood with its responsibilities. 'Don't it make you sick at all?' Fred asked. 'Huh, naw!' Will answered contemptuously.

The new disaster to the family came late in August, just when the fall work was all ahead, and the prospects good too. A. P. Wrigley, the jeweler, had just built a big, new house and barn on a farm he had bought the year before. It was a mile out of town on the Turner Pike.

That would be a job to set the Appletons up for the winter. The house was to have three coats outside, with all the work inside, and the barn was to have two coats — and the two boys were to work with their father and were to have regular wages.

And just to think of the work to be done inside that house made Tom Appleton's mouth water. He talked of it all the time, and in the evenings liked to sit in a chair in the Appletons' front yard, get some neighbor over, and then go on about it. How he slung house painter's lingo about! The doors and cupboards were to be grained in imitation of weathered oak, the front door was to be curly maple, and there was to be black walnut, too. Well, there wasn't another painter in the town could imitate all the various kinds of wood as Tom could. Just show him the wood, or tell him — you didn't have to show him anything. Name what you wanted — that was enough. To be sure, a man had to have the right tools, but give him the tools and then just go off and leave everything to him. What the devil! When A. P. Wrigley gave him this new house to do, he showed he was a man who knew what he was doing.

As for the practical side of the matter, everyone in the family knew that the Wrigley job meant a safe winter. There wasn't any speculation, as when taking work on the contract plan. All work was to be paid for by the day, and the boys were to have their wages, too. It meant new suits for the boys, a new dress and maybe a hat for Kate, the house rent paid all winter, potatoes in the cellar. It meant safety — that was the truth.

In the evenings, sometimes, Tom got out his tools and looked at them. Brushes and graining tools were spread out on the kitchen table, and Kate and the boys gathered about. It was Fred's job to see that all brushes were kept clean and, one by one, Tom ran his fingers over them, and then worked them back and forth over the palm of his hand. 'This is a camel's-hair,' he said, picking a soft fine-haired brush up and handing it to Will. 'I paid four dollars and eighty cents for that.' Will also worked it back and forth over the palm of his hand, just as his father had done, and then Kate picked it up and did the same thing. 'It's as soft as the cat's back,' she said. Will thought that rather silly. He looked forward to the day when he would have brushes, ladders, and pots of his own, and could show them off before people, and through his mind went words he had picked up from his father's talk. One spoke of the 'heel' and 'toe' of a brush. The way to put on varnish was to 'flow' it on. Will knew all the words of his trade now and didn't have to talk like one of the kind of muts who just does, now and then, a jack job of house-painting.

On the fatal evening a surprise party was held for Mr. and Mrs. Bardshare, who lived just across the road from the Appletons on Piety Hill. That was a chance for Tom Appleton. In any such affair he liked to have a hand in the arrangements. 'Come on now, we'll make her go with a bang. They'll be setting in the house after supper, and Bill Bardshare will be in his stocking feet, and Ma Bardshare washing the dishes. They won't be expecting nothing, and we'll slip up, all dressed in our Sunday clothes, and let out a whoop. I'll bring my cornet and let out a blast on that too. "What in Sam Hill is that?" Say, I can just see Bill Bardshare jumping up and beginning to swear, thinking we're a gang of kids come to bother him, like Hallowe'en, or something like that. You just get the grub, and I'll make the coffee over to my house and bring it over hot. I'll get ahold of two big pots and make a whooping lot of it.'

In the Appleton house all was in a flurry. Tom, Will, and Fred were painting a barn, three miles out of town, but they knocked off work at four and Tom got the farmer's son to drive them to town. He himself had to wash up, take a bath in a tub in the woodshed, shave and everything — just like Sunday. He looked more like a boy than a man when he got all dogged up.

And then the family had to have supper, over and done with, a little after six, and Tom didn't dare go outside the house until dark.

It wouldn't do to have the Bardshares see him so fixed up. It was their wedding anniversary, and they might suspect something. He kept trotting about the house, and occasionally looked out of the front window toward the Bardshare house. 'You kid, you,' Kate said, laughing. Sometimes she talked up to him like that, and after she said it he went upstairs and getting out his cornet blew on it so softly you could hardly hear him downstairs. When he did that, you couldn't tell how badly he played, as when the band was going it on Main Street and he had to carry a passage right through alone. He sat in the room upstairs thinking. When Kate laughed at him, it was like having his wife back, alive. There was the same shy sarcastic gleam in her eyes.

Well, it was the first time he had been out anywhere since his wife had died, and there might be some people think it would be better if he stayed at home now — look better, that is. When he had shaved, he had cut his chin, and the blood had come. After a time he went downstairs and stood before the looking glass, hung above the kitchen sink, and dabbed at the spot with the wet end of a towel.

Will and Fred stood about.

Will's mind was working — perhaps Kate's, too. 'Was there — could it be? — well, at such a party — only older people invited — there were always two or three widow women thrown in for good measure, as it were.'

Kate didn't want any woman fooling around her kitchen. She was twenty years old.

'And it was just as well not to have any monkey-shine talk about motherless children,' such as Tom might indulge in. Even Fred thought that. There was a little wave of resentment against Tom in the house. It was a wave that didn't make much noise, just crept, as it were softly, up a low sandy beach.

'Widow women went to such places, and then, of course, people were always going home in couples.' Both Kate and Will had the same picture in mind. It was late at night and in fancy they were both peeking out at front upper windows of the Appleton house. There were all the people coming out at the front door of the Bardshare house, and Bill Bardshare was standing there and holding the door open. He had managed to sneak away during the evening, and got his Sunday clothes on all right.

And the couples were coming out. 'There was that woman now, that widow, Mrs. Childers.' She had been married twice, both husbands dead now, and she lived away over Maumee Pike way. 'What makes a woman of her age want to act silly like that? It is the very devil how a woman can keep looking young and handsome after she has buried two men. There are some who say that, even when her last husband was alive——'

'But whether that's true or not, what makes her want to act and talk silly that way?' Now her face is turned to the light and she is saying to old Bill Bardshare, 'Sleep light, sleep tight, sweet dreams to you tonight.'

'It's only what one may expect when one's father lacks a sense of dignity. There is that old fool Tom now, hopping out of the Bardshare house like a kid, and running right up to Mrs. Childers. "May I see you home?" he is saying, while all the others are laughing and smiling knowingly. It makes one's blood run cold to see such a thing.'

'Well, fill up the pots. Let's get the old coffee pots started, Kate. The gang'll be creeping along up the street pretty soon now,' Tom shouted self-consciously, skipping busily about and breaking the little circle of thoughts in the house.

What happened was that — just as darkness came and when all the people were in the front yard before the Appleton house — Tom went and got it into his head to try to carry his cornet and two big coffee pots at the same time. Why didn't he leave the coffee until later? There the people were in the dusk outside the house, and there was that kind of low whispering and tittering that always goes on at such a time — and then Tom stuck his head out at the door and shouted, 'Let her go!'

And then he must have gone quite crazy, for he ran back into the kitchen and grabbed both of the big coffee pots, hanging on to his cornet at the same time. Of course he stumbled in the darkness in the road outside and fell, and of course all of that boiling hot coffee had to spill right over him.

It was terrible. The flood of boiling hot coffee made steam under his thick clothes, and there he lay screaming with the pain of it. What a confusion! He just writhed and screamed, and the people ran round and round in the half darkness like crazy things. Was it some kind of joke the crazy fellow was up to at the last minute? Tom always was such a devil to think up things. 'You should see him down at Alf Geigers, sometimes on Saturday nights, imitating the way Joe Douglas got out on a limb, and then sawed it off between himself and the tree, and the look on Joe's face when the limb began to crack. It would make you laugh until you screamed to see him imitate that.'

'But what now? My God!' There was Kate Appleton trying to tear her father's clothes off, and crying and whimpering, and young Will Appleton knocking people aside. 'Say, the man's hurt! What's happened? My God! Run for the doctor, someone. He's burnt, something awful!'

Early in October Will Appleton sat in the smoking car of a day train that runs between Cleveland and Buffalo. His destination was Erie, Pennsylvania, and he had got on the passenger train at Ashtabula, Ohio. Just why his destination was Erie he couldn't very easily have explained. He was going there anyway, going to get a job in a factory or on the docks there. Perhaps it was just a quirk of the mind that had made him decide upon Erie. It wasn't as big as Cleveland or Buffalo or Toledo or Chicago, or any one of a lot of other cities to which he might have gone, looking for work.

At Ashtabula he came into the car and slid into a seat beside a little old man. His own clothes were wet and wrinkled, and his hair, eyebrows, and ears were black with coal dust.

At the moment, there was in him a kind of bitter dislike of his native town, Bidwell. 'Sakes alive, a man couldn't get any work there — not in the winter.' After the accident to his father, and the spoiling of all the family plans, he had managed to find employment during September on the farms. He worked for a time with a threshing crew, and then got work cutting corn. It was all right. 'A man made a dollar a day and board, and as he wore overalls all the time, he didn't wear out no clothes. Still and all, the time when a fellow could make any money in Bidwell was past now, and the burns on his father's body had gone pretty deep, and he might be laid up for months.'

Will had just made up his mind one day, after he had tramped about all morning from farm to farm without finding work, and then he had gone home and told Kate. 'Dang it all,' he hadn't intended lighting out right away — had thought he would stay about for a week or two, maybe. Well, he would go uptown in the evening, dressed up in his best clothes, and stand around. 'Hello, Harry, what you going to do this winter? I thought I would run over to Erie, Pennsylvania. I got an offer in a factory over there. Well, so long — if I don't see you again.'

Kate hadn't seemed to understand, had seemed in an almighty hurry about getting him off. It was a shame she couldn't have a little more heart. Still, Kate was all right — worried a good deal, no doubt. After their talk she had just said, 'Yes, I think that's best, you had better go,' and had gone to change the bandages on Tom's legs and back. The father was sitting among pillows in a rocking chair in the front room.

Will went upstairs and put his things, overalls and a few shirts, into a bundle. Then he went downstairs and took a walk — went out along a road that led into the country, and stopped on a bridge. It was near a place where he and other kids used to come swimming on summer afternoons. A thought had come into his head. There was a young fellow worked in Pawsey's jewelry store came to see Kate sometimes on Sunday evenings and they went off to walk together. 'Did Kate want to get married?' If she did, his going away now might be for good. He hadn't thought about that before. On that afternoon, and quite suddenly, all the world outside of Bidwell seemed huge and terrible to him and a few secret tears came into his eyes, but he managed to choke them back. For just a moment his mouth opened and closed queerly, like the mouth of a fish, when you take it out of the water and hold it in your hand.

When he returned to the house at suppertime, things were better. He had left his bundle on a chair in the kitchen and Kate had wrapped it more carefully, and had put in a number of things he had forgotten. His father called him into the front room. 'It's all right, Will. Every young fellow ought to take a whirl out in the world. I did it myself, at about your age,' Tom had said, a little pompously.

Then supper was served, and there was apple pie. That was a luxury the Appletons had perhaps better not have indulged in at that time, but Will knew Kate had baked it during the afternoon — it might be as a way of showing him how she felt. Eating two large slices had rather set him up.

And then, before he realized how the time was slipping away, ten o'clock had come, and it was time for him to go. He was going to beat his way out of town on a freight train, and there was a local going toward Cleveland at ten o'clock. Fred had gone off to bed, and his father was asleep in the rocking chair in the front room. He had picked up his bundle, and Kate had put on her hat. 'I'm going to see you off,' she had said.

Will and Kate had walked in silence along the streets to where he was to wait, in the shadow of Whaley's warehouse, until the freight came along. Later, when he thought back over that evening, he was glad, that although she was three years older, he was taller than Kate.

How vividly everything that happened later stayed in his mind. After the train came, and he had crawled into an empty coal car, he sat hunched up in a corner. Overhead he could see the sky, and when the train stopped at towns, there was always the chance the car in which he was concealed would be shoved into a siding, and left. The brakemen walked along the tracks beside the car shouting to each other and their lanterns made little splashes of light in the darkness.

'How black the sky!' After a time it began to rain. 'His suit would be in a pretty mess. After all, a fellow couldn't come right out and ask his sister if she intended to marry. If Kate married, then his father would also marry again. It was all right for a young woman like Kate, but for a man of forty to think of marriage — the devil! Why didn't Tom Appleton have more dignity? After all, Fred was only a kid and a new woman coming in, to be his mother — that might be all right for a kid.'

All during that night on the freight train Will had thought a good deal about marriage — rather vague thoughts — coming and going like birds flying in and out of a bush. It was all a matter — this business of man and woman — that did not touch him very closely — not yet. The matter of having a home — that was something else. A home was something at a fellow's back. When one went off to work all week at some farm, and at night maybe went into a strange room to sleep, there was always the Appleton house — floating, as it were, like a picture at the back of the mind — the Appleton house, and Kate moving about. She had been uptown, and now had come home and was going up the stairs. Tom Appleton was fussing about in the kitchen. He liked a bite before he went off to bed for the night, but presently he would go upstairs and into his own room. He liked to smoke his pipe before he slept and sometimes he got out his cornet and blew two or three soft sad notes.

At Cleveland Will had crawled off the freight train and had gone across the city in a streetcar. Workingmen were just going to the factories and he passed among them unnoticed. If his clothes were crumpled and soiled, their clothes weren't so fine. The workingmen were all silent, looking at the car floor, or out at the car windows. Long rows of factories stood along the streets through which the car moved.

He had been lucky, and had caught another freight out of a place called Collinswood at eight, but at Ashtabula had made up his mind it would be better to drop off the freight and take a passenger train. If he was to live in Erie, it would be just as well to arrive, looking more like a gentleman and having paid his fare.

As he sat in the smoking car of the train, he did not feel much like a gentleman. The coal dust had got into his hair and the rain had washed it in long dirty streaks down over his face. His clothes were badly soiled and wanted cleaning and brushing and the paper package, in which his overalls and shirts were tied, had become torn and dirty.

Outside the train window the sky was gray, and no doubt the night was going to turn cold. Perhaps there would be a cold rain.

It was an odd thing about the towns through which the train kept passing — all of the houses in all the towns looked cold and forbidding. 'Dang it all!' In Bidwell — before the night when his father got so badly burned being such a fool about old Bill Bardshare's party — all the houses had always seemed warm cozy places. When one was alone, one walked along the streets whistling. At night warm lights shone through the windows of the houses. 'John Wyatt, the drayman, lives in that house. His wife has a wen on her neck. In that barn over there old Doctor Musgrave keeps his bony old white horse. The horse looks like the devil, but you bet he can go.'

Will squirmed about on the car seat. The old man who sat beside him was small, almost as small as Fred, and he wore a queer-looking suit. The pants were brown, and the coat checked, gray and black. There was a small leather case on the floor at his feet.

Long before the man spoke, Will knew what would happen. It was bound to turn out that such a fellow played a cornet. He was a man, old in years, but there was no dignity in him. Will remembered his father's marchings through the main street of Bidwell with the band. It was some great day, Fourth of July, perhaps, and all the people were assembled, and there was Tony Appleton, making a show of blowing his cornet at a great rate. Did all the people along the street know how badly he played and was there a kind of conspiracy that kept grown men from laughing at each other? In spite of the seriousness of his own situation, a smile crept over Will's face.

The little man at his side smiled in return.

'Well,' he began, not stopping for anything but plunging headlong into a tale concerning some dissatisfaction he felt with life, 'well, you see before you a man who is up against it, young fellow.' The old man tried to laugh at his own words, but did not make much of a success of it. His lip trembled. 'I got to go home like a dog, with my tail 'twixt my legs,' he declared abruptly.

The old man balanced back and forth between two impulses. He had met a young man on a train, and hungered for companionship, and one got oneself in with others by being jolly, a little gay, perhaps. When one met a stranger on a train, one told a story—'By the way, Mister, I heard a new one the other day—perhaps you haven't heard it? It's about the miner up in Alaska who hadn't seen a woman for years.' One began in that way, and then later, perhaps, spoke of oneself, and one's affairs.

But the old man wanted to plunge at once into his own story. He talked, saying sad discouraged words, while his eyes kept smiling with a peculiar appealing little smile. 'If the words uttered by my lips annoy or bore you, do not pay any attention to them. I am really a jolly fellow, although I am an old man, and not of much use any more,' the eyes were saying. The eyes were pale blue and watery. How strange to see them set in the head of an old man! They belonged in the head of a lost dog. The smile was not really a smile. 'Don't kick me, young fellow. If you can't give me anything to eat, scratch my head. At least show you are a fellow of good intentions. I've been kicked about quite enough.' It was so very evident the eyes were speaking a language of their own.

Will found himself smiling sympathetically. It was true there was something dog-like in the little old man and Will was pleased with himself for having so quickly caught the sense of him. 'One who can see things with his eyes will perhaps get along all right in the world, after all,' he thought. His thoughts wandered away from the old man. In Bidwell there was an old woman lived alone and owned a shepherd dog. Every summer she decided to cut away the dog's coat, and then — at the last moment and after she had in fact started the job — she changed her mind. Well, she grasped a long pair of scissors firmly in her hand and started on the dog's flanks. Her hand trembled a little. 'Shall I go ahead, or shall I stop?' After two minutes she gave up the job. 'It makes him look too ugly,' she thought, justifying her timidity.

Later the hot days came, the dog went about with his tongue hanging out, and again the old woman took the scissors in her hand. The dog stood patiently waiting, but, when she had cut a long wide furrow through the thick hair of his back, she stopped again. In a sense, and to her way of looking at the matter, cutting away his splendid coat was like cutting away a part of himself. She couldn't go on. 'Now there — that made him look worse than ever,' she declared to herself. With a determined air she put the scissors away, and all summer the dog went about looking a little puzzled and ashamed.

Will kept smiling and thinking of the old woman's dog and then looked again at his companion of the train. The variegated suit the old man wore gave him something of the air of the half-sheared shepherd dog. Both had the same puzzled, ashamed air.

Now Will had begun using the old man for his own ends. There was something inside himself that wanted facing, he didn't want to face — not yet. Ever since he had left home, in fact ever since that day when he had come home from the country and had told Kate of his intention to set out into the world, he had been dodging something. If one thought of the little old man, and of the half-sheared dog, one did not have to think of oneself.

One thought of Bidwell on a summer afternoon. There was the old woman, who owned the dog, standing on the porch of her house, and the dog had run down to the gate. In the winter, when his coat had again fully grown, the dog would bark and make a great fuss about a boy passing in the street, but now he started to bark and growl, and then stopped. 'I look like the devil, and I'm attracting unnecessary attention to myself,' the dog seemed to have decided suddenly. He ran furiously down to the gate, opened his mouth to bark, and then, quite abruptly, changed his mind and trotted back to the house with his tail between his legs.

Will kept smiling at his own thoughts. For the first time since he had left Bidwell, he felt quite cheerful.

And now the old man was telling a story of himself and his life, but Will wasn't listening. Within the young man a cross-current of impulses had been set up and he was like one standing silently in the hallway of a house, and listening to two voices, talking at a distance. The voices came from two widely separated rooms of the house and one couldn't make up one's mind to which voice to listen.

To be sure, the old man was another cornet player like his father — he was a horn blower. That was his horn in the little worn leather case on the car floor.

And after he had reached middle age, and after his first wife had died, he had married again. He had a little property then and, in a foolish moment, went and made it all over to his second wife, who was fifteen years younger than himself. She took the money and bought a large house in the factory district of Erie, and then began taking in boarders.

There was the old man, feeling lost, of no account in his own house. It just came about. One had to think of the boarders — their wants had to be satisfied. His wife had two sons, almost fully grown now, both of whom worked in a factory.

Well, it was all right — everything on the square — the sons paid board all right. Their wants had to be thought of, too. He liked blowing his cornet awhile in the evenings, before he went to bed, but it might disturb the others in the house. One got rather desperate going about saying nothing, keeping out of the way, and he had tried getting work in a factory himself, but they wouldn't have him. His gray hairs stood in his way, and so one night he had just got out, had gone to Cleveland, where he had hoped to get a job in a band, in a movie theater, perhaps. Anyway, it hadn't turned out and now he was going back to Erie and to his wife. He had written and she had told him to come on home.

'They didn't turn me down back there in Cleveland because I'm old. It's because my lip is no good any more,' he explained. His shrunken old lip trembled a little.

Will kept thinking of the old woman's dog. In spite of himself, and when the old man's lip trembled, his lip also trembled.

What was the matter with him?

He stood in the hallway of a house hearing two voices. Was he trying to close his ears to one of them? Did the second voice, the one he had been trying all day, and all the night before, not to hear, did that have something to do with the end of his life in the Appleton house at Bidwell? Was the voice trying to taunt him, trying to tell him that now he was a thing swinging in air, that there was no place to put down his feet? Was he afraid? Of what was he afraid? He had wanted so much to be a man, to stand on his own feet, and now what was the matter with him? Was he afraid of manhood?

He was fighting desperately now. There were tears in the old man's eyes, and Will also began crying silently and that was the one thing he felt he must not do.

The old man talked on and on, telling the tale of his troubles, but Will could not hear his words. The struggle within was becoming more and more definite. His mind clung to the life of his boyhood, to the life in the Appleton house in Bidwell.

There was Fred, standing in the field of his fancy now, with just the triumphant look in his eyes that came when other boys saw him doing a man's work. A whole series of pictures floated up before Will's mind. He and his father and Fred were painting a barn and two farmer boys had come along a road and stood looking at Fred, who was on a ladder, putting on paint. They shouted, but Fred wouldn't answer. There was a certain air Fred had — he slapped on the paint, and then, turning his head, spat on the ground. Tom Appleton's eyes looked into Will's and there was a smile playing about the corners of the father's eyes and the son's eyes too. The father and his oldest son were like two men, two workmen, having a delicious little secret between them. They were both looking lovingly at Fred. 'Bless him! He's thinks he's a man already.'

And now Tom Appleton was standing in the kitchen of his house, and his brushes were laid out on the kitchen table. Kate was rubbing a brush back and forth over the palm of her hand. 'It's as soft as the cat's back,' she was saying.

Something gripped at Will's throat. As in a dream, he saw his sister Kate walking off along the street on Sunday evening with that young fellow who clerked in the jewelry store. They were going to church. Her being with him meant — well, it perhaps meant the beginning of a new home — it meant the end of the Appleton home.

Will started to climb out of the seat beside the old man in the smoking car of the train. It had grown almost dark in the car. The old man was still talking, telling his tale over and over. 'I might as well not have any home at all,' he was saying. Was Will about to begin crying aloud on a train, in a strange place, before many strange men? He tried to speak, to make some commonplace remark, but his mouth only opened and closed like the mouth of a fish taken out of the water.

And now the train had run into a train shed, and it was quite dark. Will's hand clutched convulsively into the darkness and alighted upon the old man's shoulder.

Then suddenly, the train had stopped, and the two stood half-embracing each other. The tears were quite evident in Will's eyes, when a brakeman lighted the overhead lamps in the car, but the luckiest thing in the world had happened. The old man, who had seen Will's tears, thought they were tears of sympathy for his own unfortunate position in life and a look of gratitude came into his blue watery eyes. Well, this was something new in life for him, too. In one of the pauses, when he had first begun telling his tale, Will had said he was going to Erie to try to get work in some factory, and now, as they got off the train, the old man clung to Will's arm. 'You might as well come live at our house,' he said. A look of hope flared up in the old man's eyes. If he could bring home with him, to his young wife, a new boarder, the gloom of his own home-coming would be somewhat lightened. 'You come on. That's the best thing to do. You just come on with me to our house,' he pleaded, clinging to Will.

Two weeks had passed and Will had, outwardly, and to the eyes of the people about him, settled into his new life as a factory hand at Erie, Pennsylvania.

Then suddenly, on a Saturday evening, the thing happened that he had unconsciously been expecting and dreading ever since the moment when he climbed aboard the freight train in the shadow of Whaley's warehouse at Bidwell. A letter, containing great news, had come from Kate.

At the moment of their parting, and before he settled himself down out of sight in a corner of the empty coal car, on that night of his leaving, he had leaned out for a last look at his sister. She had been standing silently in the shadows of the warehouse, but just as the train was about to start, stepped toward him and a light from a distant street lamp fell on her face.

Well, the face did not jump toward Will, but remained dimly outlined in the uncertain light.

Did her lips open and close, as though in an effort to say something to him, or was that an effect produced by the distant, uncertain, and wavering light? In the families of working people the dramatic and vital moments of life are passed over in silence. Even in the moments of death and birth, little is said. A child is born to a laborer's wife and he goes into the room. She is in bed with the little red bundle of new life beside her and her husband stands a moment, fumblingly, beside the bed. Neither he nor his wife can look directly into each other's eyes. 'Take care of yourself, Ma. Have a good rest,' he says, and hurries out of the room.

In the darkness by the warehouse at Bidwell, Kate had taken two or three steps toward Will, and then had stopped. There was a little strip of grass between the warehouse and the tracks, and she stood upon it. Was there a more final farewell trembling on her lips at the moment? A kind of dread had swept over Will, and no doubt Kate had felt the same thing. At the moment she had become altogether the mother, in the presence of her child, and the thing within that wanted utterance became submerged. There was a word to be said that she could not say. Her form seemed to sway a little in the darkness and, to Will's eyes, she became a slender indistinct thing. 'Goodbye,' he had whispered into the darkness, and perhaps her lips had formed the same words. Outwardly there had been only the silence, and in the silence she had stood as the train rumbled away.

And now, on the Saturday evening, Will had come home from the factory and had found Kate saying in the letter what she had been unable to say on the night of his departure. The factory closed at five on Saturday and he came home in his overalls and went to his room. He had found the letter on a little broken table under a spluttering oil lamp, by the front door, and had climbed the stairs carrying it in his hand. He read the letter anxiously, waiting as for a hand to come out of the blank wall of the room and strike.

His father was getting better. The deep burns that had taken such a long time to heal were really healing now and the doctor had said the danger of infection had passed. Kate had found a new and soothing remedy. One took slippery elm and let it lie in milk until it became soft. This applied to the burns enabled Tom to sleep better at night.

As for Fred, Kate and her father had decided he might as well go back to school. It was really too bad for a young boy to miss the chance to get an education, and anyway there was no work to be had. Perhaps he could get a job, helping in some store on Saturday afternoons.

A woman from the Woman's Relief Corps had had the nerve to come to the Appleton house and ask Kate if the family needed help. Well, Kate had managed to hold herself back, and had been polite, but, had the woman known what was in her mind, her ears would have been itching for a month. The idea!

It had been fine of Will to send a postcard, as soon as he had got to Erie and got a job. As for his sending money home — of course the family would be glad to have anything he could spare — but he wasn't to go depriving himself. 'We've got good credit at the stores. We'll get along all right,' Kate had said stoutly.

And then it was she had added the line, had said the thing she could not say that night when he was leaving. It concerned herself and her future plans. 'That night when you were going away I wanted to tell you something, but I thought it was silly, talking too soon.' After all, though, Will might as well know she was planning to be married in the spring. What she wanted was for Fred to come and live with her and her husband. He could keep on going to school, and perhaps they could manage so that he could go to college. Someone in the family ought to have a decent education. Now that Will had made his start in life, there was no point in waiting longer before making her own.

Will sat, in his tiny room at the top of the huge frame house, owned now by the wife of the old cornet-player of the train, and held the letter in his hand. The room was on the third floor, under the roof, in a wing of the house, and beside it was another small room, occupied by the old man himself. Will had taken the room because it was to be had at a low price and he could manage the room and his meals, get his washing done, send three dollars a week to Kate, and still have left a dollar a week to spend. One could get a little tobacco, and now and then see a movie.

'Ugh!' Will's lips made a little grunting noise as he read Kate's words. He was sitting in a chair, in his oily overalls, and where his fingers gripped the white sheets of the letter there was a little oily smudge. Also his hand trembled a little. He got up, poured water out of a pitcher into a white bowl, and began washing his face and hands.

When he had partly dressed, a visitor came. There was the shuffling sound of weary feet along a hallway, and the cornet-player put his head timidly in at the door. The dog-like appealing look Will had noted on the train was still in his eyes. Now he was planning something, a kind of gentle revolt against his wife's power in the house, and he wanted Will's moral support.

For a week he had been coming for talk to Will's room almost every evening. There were two things he wanted. In the evening sometimes, as he sat in his room, he wanted to blow upon his cornet, and he wanted a little money to jingle in his pockets.

And there was a sense in which Will, the newcomer in the house, was his property, did not belong to his wife. Often in the evenings he had talked to the weary and sleepy young workman, until Will's eyes had closed and he snored gently. The old man sat on the one chair in the room, and Will sat on the edge of the bed, while old lips told the tale of a lost youth, boasted a little. When Will's body had slumped down upon the bed, the old man got to his feet and moved with cat-like steps about the room. One mustn't raise the voice too loudly, after all. Had Will gone to sleep? The cornet-player threw his shoulders back and bold words came, in a half-whisper, from his lips. To tell the truth, he had been a fool about the money he had made over to his wife, and, if his wife had taken advantage of him, it wasn't her fault. For his present position in life he had no one to blame but himself. What from the very beginning he had most lacked was boldness. It was a man's duty to be a man and, for a long time, he had been thinking — well, the boarding house no doubt made a profit and he should have his share. His wife was a good girl all right, but when one came right down to it, all women seemed to lack a sense of a man's position in life.

'I'll have to speak to her — yes-siree, I'm going to speak right up to her. I may have to be a little harsh, but it's my money runs this house, and I want my share of the profits. No foolishness now. Shell out, I tell you,' the old man whispered, peering out of the corners of his blue, watery eyes at the sleeping form of the young man on the bed.

And now again the old man stood at the door of the room, looking anxiously in. A bell called insistently, announcing that the evening meal was ready to be served, and they went below, Will leading the way. At a long table in the dining room several men had already gathered, and there was the sound of more footsteps on the stairs.

Two long rows of young workmen eating silently. Saturday night and two long rows of young workmen eating in silence.

After the eating, and on this particular night, there would be a swift flight of all these young men down into the town, down into the lighted parts of the town.

Will sat at his place gripping the sides of his chair.

There were things men did on Saturday nights. Work was at an end for the week and money jingled in pockets. Young workmen ate in silence and hurried away, one by one, down into the town.

Will's sister Kate was going to be married in the spring. Her walking about with the young clerk from the jewelry store, in the streets of Bidwell, had come to something.

Young workmen employed in factories in Erie, Pennsylvania, dressed themselves in their best clothes and walked about in the lighted streets of Erie on Saturday evenings. They went into parks. Some stood talking to girls while others walked with girls through the streets. And there were still others who went into saloons and had drinks. Men stood talking together at a bar. 'Dang that foreman of mine! I'll bust him in the jaw if he gives me any of his lip.'

There was a young man from Bidwell, sitting at a table in a boarding house at Erie, Pennsylvania, and before him on a plate was a great pile of meat and potatoes. The room was not very well lighted. It was dark and gloomy, and there were black streaks on the gray wallpaper. Shadows played on the walls. On all sides of the young man sat other young men — eating silently, hurriedly.

Will got abruptly up from the table and started for the door that led into the street, but the others paid no attention to him. If he did not want to eat his meat and potatoes, it made no difference to them. The mistress of the house, the wife of the old cornet-player, waited on table when the men ate, but now she had gone away to the kitchen. She was a silent grim-looking woman, dressed always in a black dress.

To the others in the room — except only the old cornet-player — Will's going or staying meant nothing at all. He was a young workman, and at such places young workmen were always going and coming.

A man with broad shoulders and a black mustache, a little older than most of the others, did glance up from his business of eating. He nudged his neighbor, and then made a jerky movement with his thumb over his shoulder. 'The new guy has hooked up quickly, eh?' he said, smiling. 'He can't even wait to eat. Lordy, he's got an early date — some skirt waiting for him.'

At his place, opposite where Will had been seated, the cornet-player saw Will go, and his eyes followed, filled with alarm. He had counted on an evening of talk, of speaking to Will about his youth, boasting a little in his gentle hesitating way. Now Will had reached the door that led to the street, and in the old man's eyes tears began to gather. Again his lip trembled. Tears were always gathering in the man's eyes, and his lips trembled at the slightest provocation. It was no wonder he could no longer blow a cornet in a band.

And now Will was outside the house in the darkness and, for the cornet-player, the evening was spoiled, the house a deserted empty place. He had intended being very plain in his evening's talk with Will, and wanted particularly to speak of a new attitude he hoped to assume toward his wife in the matter of money. Talking the whole matter out with Will would give him new courage, make him bolder. Well, if his money had bought the house, that was now a boarding house, he should have some share in its profits. There must be profits. Why run a boarding house without profits? The woman he had married was no fool.

Even though a man were old, he needed a little money in his pockets. Well, an old man, like himself, has a friend, a young fellow, and now and then he wanted to be able to say to his friend, 'Come on, friend, let's have a glass of beer. I know a good place. Let's have a glass of beer and go to the movies. This is on me.'

The cornet-player could not eat his meat and potatoes. For a time he stared over the heads of the others, and then got up to go to his room. His wife followed into the little hallway at the foot of the stairs. 'What's the matter, dearie—are you sick?' she asked.

'No,' he answered, 'I just didn't want any supper.' He did not look at her, but tramped slowly and heavily up the stairs.

Will was walking hurriedly through the streets, but did not go down into the brightly lighted sections of town. The boarding house stood on a factory street, and, turning northward, he crossed several railroad tracks and went toward the docks, along the shore of Lake Erie. There was something to be settled with himself, something to be faced. Could he manage the matter?

He walked along, hurriedly at first, and then more slowly. It was getting into late October now and there was a sharpness like frost in the air. The spaces between street lamps were long, and he plunged in and out of areas of darkness. Why was it that everything about him seemed suddenly strange and unreal? He had forgotten to bring his overcoat from Bidwell and would have to write Kate to send it.

Now he had almost reached the docks. Not only the night, but his own body, the pavements under his feet, and the stars far away in the sky—even the solid factory buildings he was now passing—seemed strange and unreal. It was almost as though one could thrust out an arm and push a hand through the walls, as one might push his hand into a fog or a cloud of smoke. All the people Will passed seemed strange, and acted in a strange way. Dark figures surged toward him out of the darkness. By a factory wall there was a man standing—perfectly still, motionless. There was something almost unbelievable about the actions of such men and the strangeness of such hours as the one through which he was now passing. He walked within a few inches of the motionless man. Was it a man or a shadow on the wall? The life Will was now to lead alone had become a strange, a vast terrifying thing. Perhaps all life was like that, a vastness and emptiness.

He came out into a place where ships were made fast to a dock, and stood for a time, facing the high wall-like side of a vessel. It looked dark and deserted. When he turned his head, he became aware of a man and a woman passing along a roadway. Their feet made no sound in the thick dust of the roadway, and he could not see or hear them, but knew they were there. Some part of a woman's dress — something white — flashed faintly into view and the man's figure was a dark mass against the dark mass of the night. 'Oh, come on, don't be afraid,' the man whispered, hoarsely. 'There won't anything happen to you.'

'Do shut up,' a woman's voice answered, and there was a quick outburst of laughter. The figures fluttered away. 'You don't know what you are talking about,' the woman's voice said again.

Now that he had got Kate's letter, Will was no longer a boy. A boy is, quite naturally, and without his having anything to do with the matter, connected with something — and now that connection had been cut. He had been pushed out of the nest, and that fact, the pushing of himself off the nest's rim, was something accomplished. The difficulty was that, while he was no longer a boy, he had not yet become a man. He was a thing swinging in space. There was no place to put down his feet.

He stood in the darkness under the shadow of the ship, making queer little wriggling motions with his shoulders that had become now almost the shoulders of a man. No need now to think of evenings at the Appleton house with Kate and Fred standing about, and his father, Tom Appleton, spreading his paint brushes on the kitchen table, no need of thinking of the sound of Kate's feet going up a stairway of the Appleton house, late at night, when she had been out walking with her clerk. What was the good of trying to amuse oneself by thinking of a shepherd dog in an Ohio town, a dog made ridiculous by the trembling hand of a timid old woman?

One stood face to face with manhood now — one stood alone. If only one could get one's feet down upon something, could get over this feeling of falling through space, through a vast emptiness.

'Manhood' — the word had a queer sound in the head. What did it mean?

Will tried to think of himself as a man, doing a man's work in a factory. There was nothing in the factory, where he was now employed, upon which he could put down his feet. All day he stood at a machine and bored holes in pieces of iron. A boy brought to him the little, short, meaningless pieces of iron in a box-like truck and, one by one, he picked them up and placed them under the point of a drill. He pulled a lever and the drill came down and bit into the piece of iron. A little, smoke-like vapor arose, and then he squirted oil on the spot where the drill was working. Then the lever was thrown up again. The hole was drilled and now the meaningless piece of iron was thrown into another box-like truck. It had nothing to do with him. He had nothing to do with it.

At the noon hour, at the factory, one moved about a bit, stepped outside the factory door to stand for a moment in the sun. Inside, men were sitting along benches eating lunches out of dinner pails, and some had washed their hands while others had not bothered about such a trivial matter. They were eating in silence. A tall man spat on the floor and then drew his foot across the spot. Nights came and one went home from the factory to eat, sitting with other silent men, and later a boastful old man came into one's room to talk. One lay on a bed and tried to listen, but presently fell asleep. Men were like the pieces of iron in which holes had been bored — one pitched them aside into a box-like truck. One had nothing really to do with them. They had nothing to do with oneself. Life became a procession of days and perhaps all life was just like that — just a procession of days.

'Manhood.'

Did one go out of one place and into another? Were youth and manhood two houses, in which one lived during different periods in life? It was evident something of importance must be about to happen to his sister Kate. First, she had been a young woman, having two brothers and a father, living with them in a house at Bidwell, Ohio.

And then a day was to come when she became something else. She married and went to live in another house and had a husband. Perhaps children would be born to her. It was evident Kate had got hold of something, that her hands had reached out and had grasped something definite. Kate had swung herself off the rim of the home nest and, right away, her feet had landed on another limb of the tree of life — womanhood.

As he stood in the darkness, something caught at Will's throat. He was fighting again, but what was he fighting? A fellow like himself did not move out of one house and into another. There was a house in which one lived, and then suddenly and unexpectedly, it fell apart. One stood on the rim of the nest and looked about, and a hand reached out from the warmth of the nest and pushed one off into space. There was no place for a fellow to put down his feet. He was one swinging in space.

What — a great fellow, nearly six feet tall now, and crying in the darkness, in the shadow of a ship, like a child! He walked, filled with determination, out of the darkness, along many streets of factories and came into a street of houses. He passed a store where groceries were sold and looking in saw, by a clock on the wall, that it was already ten o'clock. Two drunken men came out at the door of a house and stood on a little porch. One of them clung to a railing about the porch, and the other pulled at his arm. 'Let me alone. It's settled. I want you to let me alone,' grumbled the man clinging to the railing.

Will went to his boarding house and climbed the stairs wearily. The devil — one might face anything if one but knew what was to be faced!

He turned on a light and sat down in his room on the edge of the bed, and the old cornet-player pounced upon him, pounced like a little animal, lying under a bush along a path in a forest, and waiting for food. He came into Will's room carrying his cornet, and there was an almost bold look in his eyes. Standing firmly on his old legs in the center of the room, he made a declaration. 'I'm going to play it. I don't care what she says, I'm going to play it,' he said.

He put the cornet to his lips and blew two or three notes — so softly that even Will, sitting so closely, could barely hear. Then his eyes wavered. 'My lip's no good,' he said. He thrust the cornet at Will. 'You blow it,' he said.

Will sat on the edge of the bed and smiled. There was a notion floating in his mind now. Was there something, a thought in which one could find comfort? There was now, before him, standing before him in the room, a man who was, after all, not a man. He was a child as Will was too really, had always been such a child, would always be such a child. One need not be too afraid. Children were all about, everywhere. If one were a child and lost in a vast, empty space, one could at least talk to some other child. One could have

conversations, understand perhaps something of the eternal childish-
ness of oneself and others.

Will's thoughts were not very definite. He only felt suddenly warm
and comfortable in the little room at the top of the boarding house.

And now the man was again explaining himself. He wanted to
assert his manhood. 'I stay up here,' he explained, 'and don't go down
there, to sleep in the room with my wife because I don't want to.
That's the only reason. I could if I wanted to. She has the bronchitis
— but don't tell anyone. Women hate to have anyone told. She isn't
so bad. I can do what I please.'

He kept urging Will to put the cornet to his lips and blow. There
was in him an intense eagerness. 'You can't really make any music —
you don't know how — but that don't make any difference,' he said.
'The thing to do is to make a noise, make a deuce of a racket, blow
like the devil.'

Again Will felt like crying, but the sense of vastness and loneliness,
that had been in him since he got aboard the train that night at Bidwell, had gone. 'Well, I can't go on forever being a baby. Kate has
a right to get married,' he thought, putting the cornet to his lips. He
blew two or three notes, softly.

'No, I tell you, no! That isn't the way! Blow on it! Don't be afraid!
I tell you I want you to do it. Make a deuce of a racket! I tell you
what, I own this house. We don't need to be afraid. We can do what
we please. Go ahead! Make a deuce of a racket!' the old man kept
pleading.

The Man Who Became a Woman

MY FATHER was a retail druggist in our town, out in Nebraska, which was so much like a thousand other towns I've been in since that there's no use fooling around and taking up your time and mine trying to describe it.

Anyway, I became a drug clerk, and after father's death the store was sold and mother took the money and went West, to her sister in California, giving me four hundred dollars with which to make my start in the world. I was only nineteen years old then.

I came to Chicago, where I worked as a drug clerk for a time, and then, as my health suddenly went back on me, perhaps because I was so sick of my lonely life in the city and of the sight and smell of the drugstore, I decided to set out on what seemed to me then the great adventure and became for a time a tramp, working now and then, when I had no money, but spending all the time I could loafing around out-of-doors or riding up and down the land on freight trains and trying to see the world. I even did some stealing in lonely towns at night — once a pretty good suit of clothes that someone had left hanging out on a clothesline, and once some shoes out of a box in a freight car — but I was in constant terror of being caught and put into jail, so realized that success as a thief was not for me.

The most delightful experience of that period of my life was when I once worked as a groom, or swipe, with race-horses and it was during that time I met a young fellow of about my own age who has since become a writer of some prominence.

The young man of whom I now speak had gone into race-track work as a groom, to bring a kind of flourish, a high spot, he used to say, into his life.

He was then unmarried and had not been successful as a writer. What I mean is he was free, and I guess, with him as with me, there was something he liked about the people who hang about a race-track, the touts, swipes, drivers, niggers, and gamblers. You know what a gaudy and undependable lot they are — if you've ever been around the tracks much — about the best liars I've ever seen, and not saving money or thinking about morals, like most druggists, drygoods merchants, and the others who used to be my father's friends in our Nebraska town — and not bending the knee much either, or kowtowing to people, they thought must be grander or richer or more powerful than themselves.

What I mean is, they were an independent, go-to-the-devil, come-have-a-drink-of-whiskey, kind of a crew, and when one of them won a bet, 'knocked 'em off,' we called it, his money was just dirt to him while it lasted. No king or president or soap manufacturer — gone on a trip with his family to Europe — could throw on more dog than one of them, with his big diamond rings and the diamond horseshoe stuck in his necktie and all.

I liked the whole blamed lot pretty well and he did too.

He was groom temporarily for a pacing gelding named Lumpy Joe, owned by a tall black-mustached man named Alfred Kreymborg, and trying the best he could to make the bluff to himself he was a real one. It happened that we were on the same circuit, doing the West Pennsylvania county fairs all that fall, and on fine evenings we spent a good deal of time walking and talking together.

Let us suppose it to be a Monday or Tuesday evening and our horses had been put away for the night. The racing didn't start until later in the week, maybe Wednesday, usually. There was always a little place called a dining hall, run mostly by the Woman's Christian Temperance Associations of the towns, and we would go there to eat where we could get a pretty good meal for twenty-five cents. At least then we thought it pretty good.

I would manage it so that I sat beside this fellow, whose name was Tom Means, and when we had got through eating we would go look at our two horses again, and when we got there Lumpy Joe would be eating his hay in his box stall and Alfred Kreymborg would be standing there, pulling his mustache and looking as sad as a sick crane.

But he wasn't really sad. 'You two boys want to go downtown to see the girls. I'm an old duffer and way past that myself. You go on along. I'll be setting here, anyway, and I'll keep an eye on both the horses for you,' he would say.

So we would set off, going, not into the town to try to get in with some of the town girls, who might have taken up with us because we were strangers and race-track fellows, but out into the country. Sometimes we got into a hilly country and there was a moon. The leaves were falling off the trees and lay in the road so that we kicked them up with the dust as we went along.

To tell the truth, I suppose I got to love Tom Means, who was five years older than me, although I wouldn't have dared say so then. Americans are shy and timid about saying things like that, and a man here don't dare own up he loves another man, I've found out, and they are afraid to admit such feelings to themselves even. I guess they're afraid it may be taken to mean something it don't need to at all.

Anyway, we walked along and some of the trees were already bare and looked like people standing solemnly beside the road and listening to what we had to say. Only I didn't say much. Tom Means did most of the talking.

Sometimes we came back to the race-track and it was late and the moon had gone down and it was dark. Then we often walked round and round the track, sometimes a dozen times, before we crawled into the hay to go to bed.

Tom talked always on two subjects, writing and race horses, but mostly about race-horses. The quiet sounds about the race-tracks and the smells of horses, and the things that go with horses, seemed to get him all excited. 'Oh, hell, Herman Dudley,' he would burst out suddenly, 'don't go talking to me. I know what I think. I've been around more than you have and I've seen a world of people. There isn't any man or woman, not even a fellow's own mother, as fine as a horse, that is to say a thoroughbred horse.'

Sometimes he would go on like that a long time, speaking of people he had seen and their characteristics. He wanted to be a writer later, and what he said was that when he came to be one he wanted to write the way a well-bred horse runs or trots or paces. Whether he ever did it or not I can't say. He has written a lot, but I'm not too good a judge of such things. Anyway, I don't think he has.

But when he got on the subject of horses he certainly was a darby. I would never have felt the way I finally got to feel about horses or enjoyed my stay among them half so much if it hadn't been for him. Often he would go on talking for an hour maybe, speaking of horses' bodies and of their minds and wills as though they were human beings. 'Lord help us, Herman,' he would say, grabbing hold of my arm, 'don't it get you up in the throat? I say now, when a good one, like that Lumpy Joe I'm swiping, flattens himself at the head of the stretch and he's coming, and you know he's coming, and you know his heart's sound, and he's game, and you know he isn't going to let himself get licked—don't it get you, Herman, don't it get you like the old Harry?'

That's the way he would talk, and then later, sometimes, he'd talk about writing and get himself all het up about that too. He had some notions about writing I've never got myself around to thinking much about, but just the same maybe his talk, working in me, has led me to want to begin to write this story myself.

There was one experience of that time on the tracks that I am forced, by some feeling inside myself, to tell.

Well, I don't know why, but I've just got to. It will be kind of like confession is, I suppose, to a good Catholic, or maybe, better yet, like cleaning up the room you live in, if you are a bachelor, like I was for so long. The room gets pretty mussy and the bed not made some days and clothes and things thrown on the closet floor and maybe under the bed. And then you clean all up and put on new sheets, and then you take off all your clothes and get down on your hands and knees, and scrub the floor so clean you could eat bread off it, and then take a walk and come home after a while and your room smells sweet and you feel sweetened-up and better inside yourself too.

What I mean is, this story has been on my chest, and I've often dreamed about the happenings in it, even after I married Jessie and was happy. Sometimes I even screamed out at night, and so I said to myself, 'I'll write the dang story,' and here goes.

Fall had come on and in the mornings now when we crept out of our blankets, spread out on the hay in the tiny lofts above the horse stalls, and put our heads out to look around, there was a white rime of frost on the ground. When we woke the horses woke too. You know how it is at the tracks — the little barn-like stalls with the tiny lofts above are all set along in a row and there are two doors to each stall, one coming up to a horse's breast and then a top one, that is only closed at night and in bad weather.

In the mornings the upper door is swung open and fastened back and the horses put their heads out. There is the white rime on the grass over inside the gray oval the track makes. Usually there is some outfit that has six, ten, or even twelve horses, and perhaps they have a Negro cook who does his cooking at an open fire in the clear space before the row of stalls, and he is at work now and the horses with their big fine eyes are looking about and whinnying, and a stallion looks out at the door of one of the stalls and sees a sweet-eyed mare looking at him and sends up his trumpet call, and a man's voice laughs, and there are no women anywhere in sight or no sign of one anywhere, and everyone feels like laughing and usually does.

It's pretty fine, but I didn't know how fine it was until I got to know Tom Means and heard him talk about it all.

At the time the thing happened of which I am trying to tell now, Tom was no longer with me. A week before his owner, Alfred Kreymborg, had taken his horse Lumpy Joe over into the Ohio Fair Circuit and I saw no more of Tom at the tracks.

There was a story going about the stalls that Lumpy Joe, a big rangy brown gelding, wasn't really named Lumpy Joe at all, that he was a ringer who had made a fast record out in Iowa and up through the Northwest country the year before, and that Kreymborg had picked him up and had kept him under wraps all winter and had brought him over into the Pennsylvania country under this new name and made a clean-up in the books.

I know nothing about that and never talked to Tom about it, but anyway he, Lumpy Joe, and Kreymborg were all gone now.

I suppose I'll always remember those days, and Tom's talk at night, and before that in the early September evenings how we sat around in front of the stalls, and Kreymborg sitting on an upturned feed box and pulling at his long black mustache and sometimes humming a little ditty one couldn't catch the words of. It was something about a deep well and a little gray squirrel crawling up the sides of it, and he never laughed or smiled much, but there was something in his solemn gray eyes, not quite a twinkle, something more delicate than that.

The others talked in low tones and Tom and I sat in silence. He never did his best talking except when he and I were alone.

For his sake — if he ever sees my story — I should mention that at the only big track we ever visited, at Readville, Pennsylvania, we saw old Pop Geers, the great racing driver, himself. His horses were at a place far away across the tracks from where we were stabled. I suppose a man like him was likely to get the choice of all the good places for his horses.

We went over there one evening and stood about and there was Geers himself, sitting before one of the stalls on a box tapping the ground with a riding whip. They called him, around the tracks, 'The silent man from Tennessee,' and he was silent — that night anyway. All we did was to stand and look at him for maybe a half-hour and then we went away, and that night Tom talked better than I had ever heard him. He said that the ambition of his life was to wait until Pop Geers died and then write a book about him, and to show in the book that there was at least one American who never went nutty about getting rich or owning a big factory or being any other kind of a hell of a fellow. 'He's satisfied, I think, to sit around like that and wait until the big moments of his life come, when he heads a fast one into the stretch, and then, darn his soul, he can give all of himself to the thing right in front of him,' Tom said, and then he was so worked up he began to blubber. We were walking along the fence on the inside of the tracks and it was dusk and, in some trees near-by, some birds, just sparrows maybe, were making a chirping sound, and you could hear insects singing, and, where there was a little light, off to the west between some trees, motes were dancing in the air. Tom said that about Pop Geers, although I think he was thinking most about something he wanted to be himself and wasn't, and then he went and stood by the fence and sort of blubbered, and I began to blubber too, although I didn't know what about.

But perhaps I did know, after all. I suppose Tom wanted to feel, when he became a writer, like he thought old Pop must feel when his horse swung around the upper turn, and there lay the stretch before him, and if he was going to get his horse home in front, he had to do it right then. What Tom said was that any man had something in him that understands about a thing like that, but that no woman ever did except up in her brain. He often got off things like that about women, but I notice he later married one of them just the same.

But to get back to my knitting. After Tom had left, the stable I was with kept drifting along through nice little Pennsylvania county-seat towns. My owner, a strange excitable kind of a man from over in Ohio, who had lost a lot of money on horses, but was always thinking he would maybe get it all back in some big killing, had been playing in pretty good luck that year. The horse I had, a tough little gelding, a five-year-old, had been getting home in front pretty regular and so he took some of his winnings and bought a three-year-old black pacing stallion named 'O My Man.' My gelding was called 'Pick-It-Boy,' because, when he was in a race and had got into the stretch, my owner always got half wild with excitement and shouted so you could hear him a mile and a half. 'Go, pick it boy, pick it boy, pick it boy,' he kept shouting, and so when he had got hold of this good little gelding he had named him that.

The gelding was a fast one, all right. As the boys at the tracks used to say, he 'picked 'em up sharp and set 'em down clean,' and he was what we called a natural race horse, right up to all the speed he had, and didn't require much training. 'All you got to do is to drop him down on the track and he'll go,' was what my owner was always saying to other men, when he was bragging about his horse.

And so you see, after Tom left, I hadn't much to do evenings and then the new stallion, the three-year-old, came on with a Negro swipe named Burt.

I liked him fine and he liked me, but not the same as Tom and me. We got to be friends all right, and I suppose Burt would have done things for me, and maybe me for him, that Tom and me wouldn't have done for each other.

But with a Negro you couldn't be close friends like you can with another white man. There's some reason you can't understand but it's true. There's been too much talk about the difference between whites and blacks and you're both shy, and anyway no use trying, and I suppose Burt and I both knew it and so I was pretty lonesome.

Something happened to me that happened several times, when I was a young fellow, that I have never exactly understood. Sometimes now I think it was all because I had got to be almost a man and had never been with a woman. I don't know what's the matter with me. I can't ask a woman. I've tried it a good many times in my life, but every time I've tried the same thing happened.

Of course, with Jessie now, it's different, but at the time of which I'm speaking Jessie was a long ways off and a good many things were to happen to me before I got to her.

Around a race-track, as you may suppose, the fellows who are swipes and drivers and strangers in the towns do not go without women. They don't have to. In any town there are always some fly girls will come around a place like that. I suppose they think they are fooling with men who lead romantic lives. Such girls will come along by the front of the stalls where the race-horses are and, if you look all right to them, they will stop and make a fuss over your horse. They rub their little hands over the horse's nose and then is the time for you — if you aren't a fellow like me who can't get up the nerve — then is the time for you to smile and say, 'Hello, kid,' and make a date with one of them for that evening uptown after supper. I couldn't do that, although the Lord knows I tried hard enough, often enough. A girl would come along alone, and she would be a little thing and give me the eye, and I would try and try, but couldn't say anything. Both Tom and Burt afterward, used to laugh at me about it sometimes, but what I think is that, had I been able to speak up to one of them and had managed to make a date with her, nothing would have come of it. We would probably have walked around the town and got off together in the dark somewhere, where the town came to an end, and then she would have to knock me over with a club before it got any further.

And so there I was, having got used to Tom and our talks together, and Burt, of course, had his own friends among the black men. I got lazy and mopy and had a hard time doing my work.

It was like this. Sometimes I would be sitting, perhaps under a tree in the late afternoon when the races were over for the day and the crowds had gone away. There were always a lot of other men and boys who hadn't any horses in the races that day and they would be standing or sitting about in front of the stalls and talking.

I would listen for a time to their talk and then their voices would seem to go far away. The things I was looking at would go far away too. Perhaps there would be a tree, not more than a hundred yards away, and it would just come out of the ground and float away like a thistle. It would get smaller and smaller, away off there in the sky, and then suddenly — bang, it would be back where it belonged, in the ground, and I would begin hearing the voices of the men talking again.

When Tom was with me that summer, the nights were splendid. We usually walked about and talked until pretty late and then I crawled up into my hole and went to sleep. Always out of Tom's talk I got something that stayed in my mind, after I was off by myself, curled up in my blanket. I suppose he had a way of making pictures as he talked and the pictures stayed by me as Burt was always saying pork chops did by him. 'Give me the old pork chops, they stick to the ribs,' Burt was always saying and with the imagination it was always that way about Tom's talks. He started something inside you that went on and on, and your mind played with it like walking about in a strange town and seeing the sights, and you slipped off to sleep and had splendid dreams and woke up in the morning feeling fine.

And then he was gone and it wasn't that way any more and I got into the fix I have described. At night I kept seeing women's bodies and women's lips and things in my dreams, and woke up in the morning feeling like the old Harry.

Burt was pretty good to me. He always helped me cool Pick-It-Boy out after a race and he did the things himself that take the most skill and quickness, like getting the bandages on a horse's leg smooth, and seeing that every strap is setting just right, and every buckle drawn up to just the right hole, before your horse goes out on the track for a heat.

Burt knew there was something wrong with me and put himself out not to let the boss know. When the boss was around, he was always bragging about me. 'The brightest kid I've ever worked with around the tracks,' he would say and grin, and that at a time when I wasn't worth my salt.

When you go out with the horses there is one job that always takes a lot of time. In the late afternoon, after your horse has been in a race and after you have washed him and rubbed him out, he has to be walked slowly, sometimes for hours and hours, so he'll cool out slowly and won't get muscle-bound. I got so I did that job for both our horses and Burt did the more important things. It left him free to go talk or shoot dice with the other niggers and I didn't mind. I rather liked it and after a hard race even the stallion, O My Man, was tame enough, even when there were mares about.

You walk and walk and walk, around a little circle, and your horse's head is right by your shoulder, and all around you the life of the place you are in is going on, and in a queer way you get so you aren't really a part of it at all. Perhaps no one ever gets as I was then, except boys that aren't quite men yet and who like me have never been with girls or women — to really be with them, up to the hilt, I mean. I used to wonder if young girls got that way too before they married or did what we used to call 'go on the town.'

If I remember it right, though, I didn't do much thinking then. Often I would have forgotten supper if Burt hadn't shouted at me and reminded me, and sometimes he forgot and went off to town with one of the other niggers and I did forget.

There I was with the horse, going slow-slow-slow, around a circle that way. The people were leaving the fair grounds now, some afoot, some driving away to the farms in wagons and fords. Clouds of dust floated in the air, and over to the west, where the town was, maybe the sun was going down, a red ball of fire through the dust. Only a few hours before the crowd had been all filled with excitement and everyone shouting. Let us suppose my horse had been in a race that afternoon and I had stood in front of the grandstand with my horse blanket over my shoulder, alongside of Burt, perhaps, and when they came into the stretch my owner began to call, in that queer high voice of his that seemed to float over the top of all the shouting up in the grandstand. And his voice was saying over and over, 'Go, pick it boy, pick it boy, pick it boy,' the way he always did, and my heart was thumping so I could hardly breathe, and Burt was leaning over and snapping his fingers and muttering, 'Come, little sweet. Come on home. Your Mama wants you. Come get your 'lasses and bread, little Pick-It-Boy.'

Well, all that was over now and the voices of the people left around were all low. And Pick-It-Boy — I was leading him slowly around the little ring, to cool him out slowly, as I've said — he was different too. Maybe he had pretty nearly broken his heart trying to get down to the wire in front, or getting down there in front, and now everything inside him was quiet and tired, as it was nearly all the time those days in me, except in me tired but not quiet.

You remember I've told you we always walked in a circle, round and round and round. I guess something inside me got to going round and round and round too. The sun did sometimes and the trees and the clouds of dust. I had to think sometimes about putting down my feet so they went down in the right place and I didn't go to staggering like a drunken man.

And a funny feeling came that it is going to be hard to describe. It had something to do with the life in the horse and in me. Sometimes, these late years, I've thought maybe Negroes would understand what I'm trying to talk about now better than any white man ever will. I mean something about men and animals, something between them, something that can perhaps only happen to a white man when he has slipped off his base a little, as I suppose I had then. I think maybe a lot of horsey people feel it sometimes, though. It's something like this, maybe — do you suppose it could be that something we whites have got, and think such a lot of, and are so proud about, isn't much of any good after all?

It's something in us that wants to be big and grand and important, maybe, and won't let us just be, like a horse or a dog or a bird can. Let's say Pick-It-Boy had won his race that day. He did that pretty often that summer. Well, he was neither proud, like I would have been in his place, nor mean in one part of the inside of him either. He was just himself, doing something with a kind of simplicity. That's what Pick-It-Boy was like and I got to feeling it in him as I walked with him slowly in the gathering darkness. I got inside him in some way I can't explain and he got inside me. Often we would stop walking for no cause and he would put his nose up against my face.

I wished he was a girl sometimes or that I was a girl and he was a man. It's an odd thing to say, but it's a fact. Being with him that way, so long, and in such a quiet way, cured something in me a little. Often after an evening like that I slept all right and did not have the kind of dreams I've spoken about.

But I wasn't cured for very long and couldn't get cured. My body seemed all right and just as good as ever, but there wasn't no pep in me.

Then the fall got later and later and we came to the last town we were going to make before my owner laid his horses up for the winter in his home town over across the State line in Ohio, and the track was up on a hill, or rather in a kind of high plain above the town.

It wasn't much of a place and the sheds were rather rickety and the track bad, especially at the turns. As soon as we got to the place and got stabled, it began to rain and kept it up all week so the fair had to be put off.

As the purses weren't very large, a lot of the owners shipped right out, but our owner stayed. The fair owners guaranteed expenses, whether the races were held the next week or not.

And all week there wasn't much of anything for Burt and me to do but clean manure out of the stalls in the morning, watch for a chance when the rain let up a little to jog the horses around the track in the mud and then clean them off, blanket them and stick them back in their stalls.

It was the hardest time of all for me. Burt wasn't so bad off, as there were a dozen or two blacks around and in the evening they went off to town, got liquored up a little and came home late, singing and talking, even in the cold rain.

And then one night I got mixed up in the thing I'm trying to tell you about.

It was a Saturday evening and when I look back at it now it seems to me everyone had left the tracks but just me. In the early evening swipe after swipe came over to my stall and asked me if I was going to stick around. When I said I was, he would ask me to keep an eye out for him, that nothing happened to his horse. 'Just take a stroll down that way now and then, eh, kid,' one of them would say. 'I just want to run up to town for an hour or two.'

I would say 'yes,' to be sure, and so pretty soon it was dark as dark as pitch up there in that little ruined fairground and nothing living anywhere around but the horses and me.

I stood it as long as I could, walking here and there in the mud and rain, and thinking all the time I wished I was someone else and not myself. 'If I were someone else,' I thought, 'I wouldn't be here, but down there in town with the others.' I saw myself going into saloons and having drinks and later going off to a house maybe and getting myself a woman.

I got to thinking so much that, as I went stumbling around up there in the darkness, it was as though what was in my mind was actually happening.

Only I wasn't with some cheap woman, such as I would have found had I had the nerve to do what I wanted, but with such a woman as I thought then I should never find in this world. She was slender and like a flower and with something in her like a race horse too, something in her like Pick-It-Boy in the stretch, I guess.

And I thought about her and thought about her until I couldn't stand thinking any more. 'I'll do something anyway,' I said to myself.

So, although I had told all the swipes I would stay and watch their horses, I went out of the fairgrounds and down the hill a ways. I went down until I came to a little low saloon, not in the main part of the town itself, but halfway up the hillside. The saloon had once been a residence, a farmhouse, perhaps, but if it was ever a farmhouse I'm sure the farmer who lived there and worked the land on that hillside hadn't made out very well. The country didn't look like a farming country, such as one sees all about the other county-seat towns we had been visiting all through the late summer and fall. Everywhere you looked there were stones sticking out of the ground and the trees mostly of the stubby, stunted kind. It looked wild and untidy and ragged, that's what I mean. On the flat plain, up above, where the fairground was, there were a few fields and pastures, and there were some sheep raised, and in the field right next to the tracks, on the furtherest side from town, on the back-stretch side, there had once been a slaughter-house, the ruins of which were still standing. It hadn't been used for quite some time, but there were bones of animals lying all about in the field, and there was a smell coming out of the old building that would curl your hair.

The horses hated the place, just as we swipes did, and in the morning when we were jogging them around the track in the mud, to keep them in racing condition, Pick-It-Boy and O My Man both raised old Ned every time we headed them up the back stretch and got near to where the old slaughter-house stood. They would rear and fight at the bit, and go off their stride and run until they got clear of the rotten smells, and neither Burt nor I could make them stop it. 'It's a hell of a town down there and this is a hell of a track for racing,' Burt kept saying. 'If they ever have their danged old fair someone's going to get spilled and maybe killed back here.' Whether they did or not I don't know, as I didn't stay for the fair, for reasons I'll tell you pretty soon, but Burt was speaking sense all right. A race horse isn't like a human being. He won't stand for it to have to do his work in any rotten ugly kind of a dump the way a man will, and he won't stand for the smells a man will either.

But to get back to my story again. There I was, going down the hillside in the darkness and the cold soaking rain and breaking my word to all the others about staying up above and watching the horses. When I got to the little saloon, I decided to stop and have a drink or two. I'd found out long before that about two drinks upset me so I was two-thirds piped and couldn't walk straight, but on that night I didn't care a tinker's dam.

So I went up a kind of path, out of the road, toward the front door of the saloon. It was in what must have been the parlor of the place when it was a farmhouse and there was a little front porch.

I stopped before I opened the door and looked about a little. From where I stood I could look right down into the main street of the town, like being in a big city, like New York or Chicago, and looking down out of the fifteenth floor of an office building into the street.

The hillside was mighty steep and the road up had to wind and wind or no one could ever have come up out of the town to their plagued old fair at all.

It wasn't much of a town I saw — a main street with a lot of saloons and a few stores, one or two dinky moving-picture places, a few Fords, hardly any women or girls in sight, and a raft of men. I tried to think of the girl I had been dreaming about, as I walked around in the mud and darkness up at the fairgrounds, living in the place, but I couldn't make it. It was like trying to think of Pick-It-Boy getting himself worked up to the state I was in then, and going into the ugly dump I was going into. It couldn't be done.

All the same I knew the town wasn't all right there in sight. There must have been a good many of the kinds of houses Pennsylvania miners live in back in the hills, or around a turn in the valley in which the main street stood.

What I suppose is that, it being Saturday night and raining, the women and kids had all stayed at home and only the men were out, intending to get themselves liquored up. I've been in some other mining towns since, and if I was a miner and had to live in one of them, or in one of the houses they live in with their women and kids, I'd get out and liquor myself up too.

So there I stood looking, and as sick as a dog inside myself, and as wet and cold as a rat in a sewer pipe. I could see the mass of dark figures moving about down below, and beyond the main street there was a river that made a sound you could hear distinctly, even up where I was, and over beyond the river were some railroad tracks with switch engines going up and down. I suppose they had something to do with the mines in which the men of the town worked. Anyway, as I stood watching and listening, there was, now and then, a sound like thunder rolling down the sky, and I suppose that was a lot of coal, maybe a whole carload, being let down plunk into a coal car.

And then besides there was, on the side of a hill far away, a long row of coke ovens. They had little doors, through which the light from the fire within leaked out, and as they were set closely, side by side, they looked like the teeth of some big man-eating giant lying and waiting over there in the hills.

The sight of it all, even the sight of the kind of hell-holes men are satisfied to go on living in, gave me the fantods and the shivers right down in my liver, and on that night I guess I had in me a kind of contempt for all men, including myself, that I've never had so thoroughly since. Come right down to it, I suppose women aren't so much to blame as men. They aren't running the show.

Then I pushed open the door and went into the saloon. There were about a dozen men, miners, I suppose, playing cards at tables in a little long dirty room, with a bar at one side of it, and with a big red-faced man with a mustache standing back of the bar.

The place smelled, as such places do where men hang around who have worked and sweated in their clothes and perhaps slept in them too, and have never had them washed but have just kept on wearing them. I guess you know what I mean if you've ever been in a city. You smell that smell in a city, in streetcars on rainy nights when a lot of factory hands get on. I got pretty used to that smell when I was a tramp and pretty sick of it too.

And so I was in the place now, with a glass of whiskey in my hand, and I thought all the miners were staring at me, which they weren't at all, but I thought they were and so I felt just the same as though they had been. And then I looked up and saw my own face in the old cracked looking-glass back of the bar. If the miners had been staring, or laughing at me, I wouldn't have wondered when I saw what I looked like.

It — I mean my own face — was white and pasty-looking, and for some reason, I can't tell exactly why, it wasn't my own face at all. It's a funny business I'm trying to tell you about and I know what you may be thinking of me as well as you do, so you needn't suppose I'm innocent or ashamed. I'm only wondering. I've thought about it a lot since and I can't make it out. I know I was never that way before that night and I know I've never been that way since. Maybe it was lonesomeness, just lonesomeness, gone on in me too long. I've often wondered if women generally are lonesomer than men.

The point is that the face I saw in the looking-glass back of that bar, when I looked up from my glass of whiskey that evening, wasn't my own face at all, but the face of a woman. It was a girl's face, that's what I mean. That's what it was. It was a girl's face, and a lonesome and scared girl too. She was just a kid at that.

When I saw that, the glass of whiskey came pretty near falling out of my hand, but I gulped it down, put a dollar on the bar, and called for another. 'I've got to be careful here — I'm up against something new,' I said to myself. 'If any of these men in here get on to me there's going to be trouble.' When I had got the second drink in me, I called for a third, and I thought, 'When I get this third drink down, I'll get out of here and back up the hill to the fairgrounds before I make a fool of myself and begin to get drunk.'

And then, while I was thinking and drinking my third glass of whiskey, the men in the room began to laugh and of course I thought they were laughing at me. But they weren't. No one in the place had really paid any attention to me.

What they were laughing at was a man who had just come in at the door. I'd never seen such a fellow. He was a huge big man, with red hair, that stuck straight up like bristles out of his head, and he had a red-haired kid in his arms. The kid was just like himself, big, I mean, for his age, and with the same kind of stiff red hair.

He came and set the kid up on the bar, close beside me, and called for a glass of whiskey for himself and all the men in the room began to shout and laugh at him and his kid. Only they didn't shout and laugh when he was looking, so he could tell which ones did it, but did all their shouting and laughing when his head was turned the other way. They kept calling him 'cracked.' 'The crack is getting wider in the old tin pan,' someone sang, and then they all laughed.

I'm puzzled, you see, just how to make you feel as I felt that night. I suppose, having undertaken to write this story, that's what I'm up against, trying to do that. I'm not claiming to be able to inform you or to do you any good. I'm just trying to make you understand some things about me, as I would like to understand some things about you, or anyone, if I had the chance. Anyway, the whole blamed thing, the thing that went on, I mean, in that little saloon on that rainy Saturday night, wasn't like anything quite real. I've already told you how I had looked into the glass back of the bar and had seen there, not my own face, but the face of a scared young girl. Well, the men, the miners, sitting at the tables in the half-dark room, the red-faced bartender, the unholy-looking big man who had come in and his queer-looking kid, now sitting on the bar — all of them were like characters in some play, not like real people at all.

There was myself, that wasn't myself — and I'm not any fairy. Anyone who has ever known me knows better than that.

And then there was the man who had come in. There was a feeling came out of him that wasn't like the feeling you get from a man at all. It was more like the feeling you get maybe from a horse, only his eyes weren't like a horse's eyes. Horses' eyes have a kind of calm something in them and his hadn't. If you've ever carried a lantern through a wood at night, going along a path, and then suddenly you felt something funny in the air and stopped, and there ahead of you somewhere were the eyes of some little animal, gleaming out at you from a dead wall of darkness — the eyes shine big and quiet, but there is a point right in the center of each, where there is something dancing and wavering. You aren't afraid the little animal will jump at you, you are afraid the little eyes will jump at you — that's what's the matter with you.

Only, of course, a horse, when you go into his stall at night, or a little animal you had disturbed in a wood that way, wouldn't be talking and the big man who had come in there with his kid was talking. He kept talking all the time, saying something under his breath, as they say, and I could only understand now and then a few words. It was his talking made him kind of terrible. His eyes said one thing and his lips another. They didn't seem to get together, as though they belonged to the same person.

For one thing the man was too big. There was about him an unnatural bigness. It was in his hands, his arms, his shoulders, his body, his head, a bigness like you might see in trees and bushes in a tropical country, perhaps. I've never been in a tropical country, but I've seen pictures. Only his eyes were small. In his big head they looked like the eyes of a bird. And I remember that his lips were thick, like Negroes' lips.

He paid no attention to me or to the others in the room, but kept on muttering to himself, or to the kid sitting on the bar — I couldn't tell to which.

First he had one drink and then, quick, another. I stood staring at him and thinking — a jumble of thoughts, I suppose.

What I must have been thinking was something like this. 'Well, he's one of the kind you are always seeing about towns,' I thought. I meant he was one of the cracked kind. In almost any small town you go to, you will find one, and sometimes two or three cracked people, walking around. They go through the street, muttering to themselves, and people generally are cruel to them. Their own folks make a bluff at being kind, but they aren't really, and the others in the town, men and boys, like to tease them. They send such a fellow, the mild silly kind, on some fool errand after a round square or a dozen post-holes or tie cards on his back saying 'Kick me,' or something like that, and then carry on and laugh as though they had done something funny.

And so there was this cracked one in that saloon and I could see the men in there wanted to have some fun putting up some kind of horseplay on him, but they didn't quite dare. He wasn't one of the mild kind, that was a cinch. I kept looking at the man and at his kid, and then up at that strange unreal reflection of myself in the cracked looking-glass back of the bar. 'Rats, rats, digging in the ground — miners are rats, little jack-rabbit,' I heard him say to his solemn-faced kid. I guess, after all, maybe he wasn't so cracked.

The kid sitting on the bar kept blinking at his father, like an owl caught out in the daylight, and now the father was having another glass of whiskey. He drank six glasses, one right after the other, and it was cheap ten-cent stuff. He must have had cast-iron insides all right.

Of the men in the room there were two or three (maybe they were really more scared than the others so had to put up a bluff of bravery by showing off) who kept laughing and making funny cracks about the big man and his kid, and there was one fellow was the worst of the bunch. I'll never forget that fellow because of his looks and what happened to him afterward.

He was one of the showing-off kind all right, and he was the one that had started the song about the crack getting bigger in the old tin pan. He sang it two or three times, and then he grew bolder and got up and began walking up and down the room singing it over and over. He was a showy kind of man with a fancy vest, on which there were brown tobacco spots, and he wore glasses. Every time he made some crack he thought was funny, he winked at the others, as though to say, 'You see me. I'm not afraid of this big fellow,' and then the others laughed.

The proprietor of the place must have known what was going on, and the danger in it, because he kept leaning over the bar and saying, 'Shush, now quit it,' to the showy-off man, but it didn't do any good. The fellow kept prancing like a turkey-cock and he put his hat on one side of his head and stopped right back of the big man and sang that song about the crack in the old tin pan. He was one of the kind you can't shush until they get their blocks knocked off, and it didn't take him long to come to it that time anyhow.

Because the big fellow just kept on muttering to his kid and drinking his whiskey, as though he hadn't heard anything, and then suddenly he turned and his big hand flashed out and he grabbed, not the fellow who had been showing off, but me. With just a sweep of his arm he brought me up against his big body. Then he shoved me over with my breast jammed against the bar and looking right into his kid's face and he said, 'Now you watch him, and if you let him fall I'll kill you,' in just quiet ordinary tones as though he was saying 'good-morning' to some neighbor.

Then the kid leaned over and threw his arms around my head, and in spite of that I did manage to screw my head around enough to see what happened.

It was a sight I'll never forget. The big fellow had whirled around, and he had the showy-off man by the shoulder now, and the fellow's face was a sight. The big man must have had some reputation as a bad man in the town, even though he was cracked, for the man with the fancy vest had his mouth open now, and his hat had fallen off his head, and he was silent and scared. Once, when I was a tramp, I saw a kid killed by a train. The kid was walking on the rail and showing off before some other kids, by letting them see how close he could let an engine come to him before he got out of the way. And the engine was whistling and a woman, over on the porch of a house near-by, was jumping up and down and screaming, and the kid let the engine get nearer and nearer, wanting more and more to show off, and then he stumbled and fell. God, I'll never forget the look on his face, in just the second before he got hit and killed, and now, there in that saloon, was the same terrible look on another face.

I closed my eyes for a moment and was sick all through me, and then, when I opened my eyes, the big man's fist was just coming down in the other man's face. The one blow knocked him cold and he fell down like a beast hit with an axe.

And then the most terrible thing of all happened. The big man had on heavy boots, and he raised one of them and brought it down on the other man's shoulder, as he lay white and groaning on the floor. I could hear the bones crunch, and it made me so sick I could hardly stand up, but I had to stand up and hold on to that kid or I knew it would be my turn next.

Because the big fellow didn't seem excited or anything, but kept on muttering to himself as he had been doing when he was standing peacefully by the bar drinking his whiskey, and now he had raised his foot again, and maybe this time he would bring it down in the other man's face and 'just eliminate his map for keeps,' as sports and prize-fighters sometimes say. I trembled, like I was having a chill, but thank God at that moment the kid, who had his arms around me and one hand clinging to my nose, so that there were the marks of his finger-nails on it the next morning, at that moment the kid, thank God, began to howl, and his father didn't bother any more with the man on the floor, but turned around, knocked me aside, and taking the kid in his arms tramped out of that place, muttering to himself as he had been doing ever since he came in.

I went out, too, but I didn't prance out with any dignity, I'll tell you that. I slunk out like a thief or a coward, which perhaps I am, partly, anyhow.

And so there I was, outside there in the darkness, and it was as cold and wet and black and God-forsaken a night as any man ever saw. I was so sick at the thought of human beings that night I could have vomited to think of them at all. For a while I just stumbled along in the mud of the road, going up the hill, back to the fairgrounds, and then, almost before I knew where I was, I found myself in the stall with Pick-It-Boy.

That was one of the best and sweetest feelings I've ever had in my whole life, being in that warm stall alone with that horse that night. I had told the other swipes that I would go up and down the row of stalls now and then and have an eye on the other horses, but I had altogether forgotten my promise now. I went and stood with my back against the side of the stall, thinking how mean and low and all balled-up and twisted-up human beings can become, and how the best of them are likely to get that way any time, just because they are human beings and not simple and clear in their minds, and inside themselves, as animals are, maybe.

Perhaps you know how a person feels at such a moment. There are things you think of, odd little things you had thought you had forgotten. Once, when you were a kid, you were with your father, and he was all dressed up, as for a funeral or Fourth of July, and was walking along a street holding your hand. And you were going past a railroad station, and there was a woman standing. She was a stranger in your town and was dressed as you had never seen a woman dressed before, and never thought you would see one, looking so nice. Long afterward you knew that was because she had lovely taste in clothes, such as so few women have really, but then you thought she must be a queen. You had read about queens in fairy stories and the thoughts of them thrilled you. What lovely eyes the strange lady had and what beautiful rings she wore on her fingers!

Then your father came out, from being in the railroad station, maybe to set his watch by the station clock, and took you by the hand and he and the woman smiled at each other, in an embarrassed kind of way, and you kept looking longingly back at her, and when you were out of her hearing you asked your father if she really were a queen. And it may be that your father was one who wasn't so very hot on democracy and a free country and talked-up bunk about a free citizenry, and he said he hoped she was a queen, and maybe, for all he knew, she was.

Or maybe, when you get jammed up as I was that night, and can't get things clear about yourself or other people and why you are alive, or for that matter why anyone you can think about is alive, you think, not of people at all, but of other things you have seen and felt — like walking along a road in the snow in the winter, perhaps out in Iowa, and hearing soft warm sounds in a barn close to the road, or of another time when you were on a hill and the sun was going down and the sky suddenly became a great soft-colored bowl, all glowing like a jewel-handled bowl a great queen in some faraway mighty kingdom might have put on a vast table out under the tree, once a year, when she invited all her loyal and loving subjects to come and dine with her.

I can't, of course, figure out what you try to think about when you are as desolate as I was that night. Maybe you are like me and inclined to think of women, and maybe you are like a man I met once, on the road, who told me that when he was up against it he never thought of anything but grub and a big nice clean warm bed to sleep in. 'I don't care about anything else and I don't ever let myself think of anything else,' he said. 'If I was like you and went to thinking about women, sometime I'd find myself hooked up to some skirt, and she'd have the old double cross on me, and the rest of my life maybe I'd be working in some factory for her and her kids.'

As I say, there I was, anyway, up there alone with that horse in that warm stall in that dark lonesome fairground and I had that feeling about being sick at the thought of human beings and what they could be like.

Well, suddenly I got again the queer feeling I'd had about him once or twice before, I mean the feeling about our understanding each other in some way I can't explain.

So having it again I went over to where he stood and began running my hands all over his body, just because I loved the feel of him and as sometimes, to tell the plain truth, I've felt about touching with my hands the body of a woman I've seen and who I thought was lovely too. I ran my hands over his head and neck and then down over his hard firm round body and then over his flanks and down his legs. His flanks quivered a little, I remember, and once he turned his head and stuck his cold nose down along my neck and nipped my shoulder a little, in a soft playful way. It hurt a little, but I didn't care.

So then I crawled up through a hole into the loft above, thinking that night was over anyway and glad of it, but it wasn't, not by a long sight.

As my clothes were all soaking wet and as we race-track swipes didn't own any such things as nightgowns or pajamas, I had to go to bed naked, of course.

But we had plenty of horse blankets and so I tucked myself in between a pile of them and tried not to think any more that night. The being with Pick-It-Boy and having him close right under me that way made me feel a little better.

Then I was sound asleep and dreaming and — bang! like being hit with a club by someone who has sneaked up behind you — I got another wallop.

What I suppose is that, being upset the way I was, I had forgotten to bolt the door to Pick-It-Boy's stall down below and two Negro men had come in there, thinking they were in their own place, and had climbed up through the hole where I was. They were half-lit-up, but not what you might call dead drunk, and I suppose they were up against something a couple of white swipes, who had some money in their pockets, wouldn't have been up against.

What I mean is that a couple of white swipes, having liquored themselves up and being down there in the town on a bat, if they wanted a woman or a couple of women would have been able to find them. There is always a few women of that kind can be found around any town I've ever seen or heard of, and of course a bartender would have given them the tip where to go.

But a Negro, up there in that country, where there aren't any, or anyway mighty few Negro women, wouldn't know what to do when he felt that way and would be up against it.

It's so always. Burt and several other Negroes I've known pretty well have talked to me about it, lots of times. You take now a young Negro man — not a race-track swipe or a tramp or any other low-down kind of a fellow — but, let us say, one who has been to college, and has behaved himself and tried to be a good man, the best he could, and be clean, as they say. He isn't any better off, is he? If he has made himself some money and wants to go sit in a swell restaurant, or go to hear some good music, or see a good play at the theater, he gets what we used to call on the tracks 'the messy end of the dung fork,' doesn't he?

And even in such a low-down place as what people call a 'bad house,' it's the same way. The white swipes and others can go into a place where they have Negro women fast enough, and they do it, too, but you let a Negro swipe try it the other way around and see how he comes out.

You see, I can think this whole thing out fairly now, sitting here in my own house and writing, and with my wife Jessie in the kitchen making a pie or something, and I can show just how the two Negro men who came into that loft, where I was asleep, were justified in what they did, and I can preach about how the Negroes are up against it in this country like a daisy, but I tell you what, I didn't think things out that way that night.

For, you understand, what they thought, they being half-liquored up, and when one of them had jerked the blankets off me, was that I was a woman. One of them carried a lantern, but it was smoky and dirty and didn't give out much light. So they must have figured it out — my body being pretty white and slender then, like a young girl's body, I suppose — that some white swipe had brought me up there. The kind of girls around a town that will come with a swipe to a race-track on a rainy night aren't very fancy females, but you'll find that kind in the towns all right. I've seen many a one in my day.

And so, I figure, these two big buck niggers, being piped that way, just made up their minds they would snatch me away from the white swipe who had brought me out there, and who had left me lying carelessly around.

'Jes' you lie still, honey. We ain't gwine hurt you none,' one of them said, with a little chuckling laugh that had something in it besides a laugh, too. It was the kind of laugh that gives you the shivers.

The devil of it was I couldn't say anything, not even a word. Why I couldn't yell out and say 'What the hell!' and just kid them a little and shoo them out of there I don't know, but I couldn't. I tried and tried so that my throat hurt, but I didn't say a word. I just lay there staring at them.

It was a mixed-up night. I've never gone through another night like it.

Was I scared? Lord Almighty, I'll tell you what, I was scared.

Because the two big black faces were leaning right over me now, and I could feel their liquored-up breaths on my cheeks, and their eyes were shining in the dim light from that smoky lantern, and right in the center of their eyes was that dancing flickering light I've told you about your seeing in the eyes of wild animals when you were carrying a lantern through the woods at night.

It was a puzzler! All my life, you see — me never having had any sisters, and at that time never having had a sweetheart either — I had been dreaming and thinking about women, and I suppose I'd always been dreaming about a pure innocent one, for myself, made for me by God, maybe. Men are that way. No matter how big they talk about 'let the women go hang,' they've always got that notion tucked away inside themselves, somewhere. It's a kind of chesty man's notion, I suppose, but they've got it and the kind of up-and-coming women we have nowadays who are always saying, 'I'm as good as a man and will do what the men do,' are on the wrong trail if they really ever want to, what you might say 'hog-tie' a fellow of their own.

So I had invented a kind of princess, with black hair and a slender willowy body, to dream about. And I thought of her as being shy and afraid to ever tell anything she really felt to anyone but just me. I suppose I fancied that if I ever found such a woman in the flesh I would be the strong sure one and she the timid shrinking one.

And now I was that woman, or something like her, myself.

I gave a kind of wriggle, like a fish you have just taken off the hook. What I did next wasn't a thought-out thing. I was caught and I squirmed, that's all.

The two niggers both jumped at me, but somehow — the lantern having been kicked over and having gone out the first move they made — well, in some way, when they both lunged at me they missed.

As good luck would have it my feet found the hole, where you put hay down to the horse in the stall below, and through which we crawled up when it was time to go to bed in our blankets up in the hay, and down I slid, not bothering to try to find the ladder with my feet but just letting myself go.

In less than a second I was out-of-doors in the dark and the rain and the two blacks were down the hole and out the door of the stall after me.

How long or how far they really followed me I suppose I'll never know. It was black dark and raining hard now and a roaring wind had begun to blow. Of course, my body being white, it must have made some kind of a faint streak in the darkness as I ran, and anyway I thought they could see me and I knew I couldn't see them and that made my terror ten times worse. Every minute I thought they would grab me.

You know how it is when a person is all upset and full of terror as I was. I suppose maybe the two niggers followed me for a while, running across the muddy race-track and into the grove of trees that grew in the oval inside the track, but likely enough, after just a few minutes, they gave up the chase and went back, found their own place and went to sleep. They were liquored-up, as I've said, and maybe partly funning too.

But I didn't know that, if they were. As I ran I kept hearing sounds, sounds made by the rain coming down through the dead old leaves left on the trees and by the wind blowing, and it may be that the sound that scared me most of all was my own bare feet stepping on a dead branch and breaking it or something like that.

There was something strange and scary, a steady sound, like a heavy man running and breathing hard, right at my shoulder. It may have been my own breath, coming quick and fast. And I thought I heard that chuckling laugh I'd heard up in the loft, the laugh that sent the shivers right down through me. Of course every tree I came close to looked like a man standing there, ready to grab me, and I kept dodging and going — bang — into other trees. My shoulders kept knocking against trees in that way and the skin was all knocked off, and every time it happened I thought a big black hand had come down and clutched at me and was tearing my flesh.

How long it went on I don't know, maybe an hour, maybe five minutes. But anyway the darkness didn't let up, and the terror didn't let up, and I couldn't, to save my life, scream or make any sound.

Just why I couldn't I don't know. Could it be because at the time I was a woman, while at the same time I wasn't a woman? It may be that I was too ashamed of having turned into a girl and being afraid of a man to make any sound. I don't know about that. It's over my head.

But anyway I couldn't make a sound. I tried and tried and my throat hurt from trying and no sound came.

And then, after a long time, or what seemed like a long time, I got out from among the trees inside the track and was on the track itself again. I thought the two black men were still after me, you understand, and I ran like a madman.

Of course, running along the track that way, it must have been up the back stretch, I came after a time to where the old slaughter-house stood, in that field, beside the track. I knew it by its ungodly smell, scared as I was. Then, in some way, I managed to get over the high old fairground fence and was in the field, where the slaughter-house was.

All the time I was trying to yell or scream, or be sensible and tell those two black men that I was a man and not a woman, but I couldn't make it. And then I heard a sound like a board cracking or breaking in the fence and thought they were still after me.

So I kept on running like a crazy man, in the field, and just then I stumbled and fell over something. I've told you how the old slaughter-house field was filled with bones, that had been lying there a long time and had all been washed white. There were heads of sheep and cows and all kinds of things.

And when I fell and pitched forward, I fell right into the midst of something, still and cold and white.

It was probably the skeleton of a horse lying there. In small towns like that, they take an old worn-out horse that has died, and haul him off to some field outside of town and skin him for the hide, that they can sell for a dollar or two. It doesn't make any difference what the horse has been, that's the way he usually ends up. Maybe even Pick-It-Boy, or O My Man, or a lot of other good fast ones I've seen and known, have ended that way by this time.

And so I think it was the bones of a horse lying there and he must have been lying on his back. The birds and wild animals had picked all his flesh away and the rain had washed his bones clean.

Anyway, I fell and pitched forward and my side got cut pretty deep and my hands clutched at something. I had fallen right in between the ribs of the horse and they seemed to wrap themselves around me close. And my hands, clutching upward, had got hold of the cheeks of that dead horse and the bones of his cheeks were cold as ice with the rain washing over them. White bones wrapped around me and white bones in my hands.

There was a new terror now that seemed to go down to the very bottom of me, to the bottom of the inside of me, I mean. It shook me like I have seen a rat in a barn shaken by a dog. It was a terror like a big wave that hits you when you are walking on a seashore maybe.

You see it coming and you try to run and get away, but when you start to run inshore there is a stone cliff you can't climb. So the wave comes high as a mountain, and there it is, right in front of you and nothing in all this world can stop it. And now it has knocked you down and rolled and tumbled you over and over and washed you clean, clean, but dead maybe.

And that's the way I felt — I seemed to myself dead with blind terror. It was a feeling like the finger of God running down your back and burning you clean, I mean.

It burned all that silly nonsense about being a girl right out of me.

I screamed at last and the spell that was on me was broken. I'll bet the scream I let out of me could have been heard a mile and a half.

Right away I felt better and crawled out from among the pile of bones, and then I stood on my own feet again, and I wasn't a woman, or a young girl any more, but a man and my own self, and as far as I know I've been that way ever since. Even the black night seemed warm and alive now, like a mother might be to a kid in the dark.

Only I couldn't go back to the race-track because I was blubbering and crying and was ashamed of myself and of what a fool I had made of myself. Someone might see me and I couldn't stand that, not at that moment.

So I went across the field, walking now, not running like a crazy man, and pretty soon I came to a fence and crawled over and got into another field, in which there was a straw stack I just happened to find in the pitch darkness.

The straw stack had been there a long time and some sheep had nibbled away at it until they had made a pretty deep hole, like a cave, in the side of it. I found the hole and crawled in and there were some sheep in there, about a dozen of them.

When I came in, creeping on my hands and knees, they didn't make much fuss, just stirred around a little and then settled down.

So I settled down amongst them too. They were warm and gentle and kind, like Pick-It-Boy, and being in there with them made me feel better than I would have felt being with any human person I knew at that time.

So I settled down and slept after a while, and when I woke up it was daylight and not very cold and the rain was over. The clouds were breaking away from the sky now and maybe there would be a fair the next week, but if there was I knew I wouldn't be there to see it.

Because what I expected to happen did happen. I had to go back across the fields and the fairground to the place where my clothes were, right in the broad daylight, and me stark naked, and of course I knew someone would be up and would raise a shout, and every swipe and every driver would stick his head out and would whoop with laughter.

And there would be a thousand questions asked, and I would be too mad and too ashamed to answer, and would perhaps begin to blubber, and that would make me more ashamed than ever.

It all turned out just as I expected, except that when the noise and the shouts of laughter were going the loudest, Burt came out of the stall where O My Man was kept, and when he saw me he didn't know what was the matter, but he knew something was up that wasn't on the square and for which I wasn't to blame.

So he got so all-fired mad he couldn't speak for a minute, and then he grabbed a pitchfork and began prancing up and down before the other stalls, giving that gang of swipes and drivers such a royal old dressing-down as you never heard. You should have heard him sling language. It was grand to hear.

And while he was doing it, I sneaked up into the loft, blubbering because I was so pleased and happy to hear him swear that way, and I got my wet clothes on quick and got down, and gave Pick-It-Boy a good-bye kiss on the cheek and lit out.

The last I saw of all that part of my life was Burt, still going it, and yelling out for the man who had put up a trick on me to come out and get what was coming to him. He had the pitchfork in his hand and was swinging it around, and every now and then he would make a kind of lunge at a tree or something, he was so mad through, and there was no one else in sight at all. And Burt didn't even see me cutting out along the fence through a gate and down the hill and out of the race-horse and the tramp life for the rest of my days.

Out of Nowhere into Nothing

ROSALIND WESTCOTT, a tall strong-looking woman of twenty-seven, was walking on the railroad track near the town of Willow Springs, Iowa. It was about four in the afternoon of a day in August, and the third day since she had come home to her native town from Chicago, where she was employed.

At that time Willow Springs was a town of about three thousand people. It has grown since. There was a public square with the town hall in the center and about the four sides of the square, and facing it, were the merchandising establishments. The public square was bare and grassless, and out of it ran streets of frame houses, long straight streets that finally became country roads running away into the flat prairie country.

Although she had told everyone that she had merely come home for a short visit because she was a little homesick, and although she wanted in particular to have a talk with her mother in regard to a certain matter, Rosalind had been unable to talk with anyone. Indeed she had found it difficult to stay in the house with her mother and father and all the time, day and night, she was haunted by a desire to get out of town. As she went along the railroad tracks in the hot afternoon sunshine, she kept scolding herself. 'I've grown moody and no good. If I want to do it, why don't I just go ahead and not make a fuss,' she thought.

For two miles the railroad tracks, eastward out of Willow Springs, went through corn fields on a flat plain. Then there was a little dip in the land and a bridge over Willow Creek. The creek was altogether dry now, but trees grew along the edge of the gray streak of

157

cracked mud that in the fall, winter, and spring would be the bed of the stream. Rosalind left the tracks and went to sit under one of the trees. Her cheeks were flushed and her forehead wet. When she took off her hat, her hair fell down in disorder and strands of it clung to her hot wet face. She sat in what seemed a kind of great bowl on the sides of which the corn grew rank. Before her and following the bed of the stream there was a dusty path along which cows came at evening from distant pastures. A great pancake formed of cow dung lay near-by. It was covered with gray dust and over it crawled shiny black beetles. They were rolling the dung into balls in preparation for the germination of a new generation of beetles.

Rosalind had come on the visit to her home town at a time of the year when everyone wished to escape from the hot dusty place. No one had expected her and she had not written to announce her coming. One hot morning in Chicago she had got out of bed and had suddenly begun packing her bag, and on that same evening there she was in Willow Springs, in the house where she had lived until her twenty-first year, among her own people. She had come up from the station in the hotel bus and had walked into the Wescott house unannounced. Her father was at the pump by the kitchen door and her mother came into the living room to greet her wearing a soiled kitchen apron. Everything in the house was just as it always had been. 'I just thought I would come home for a few days,' she said, putting down her bag and kissing her mother.

Ma and Pa Wescott had been glad to see their daughter. On the evening of her arrival they were excited and a special supper was prepared. After supper Pa Wescott went uptown as usual, but he stayed only a few minutes. 'I just want to run to the postoffice and get the evening paper,' he said apologetically. Rosalind's mother put on a clean dress and they all sat in the darkness on the front porch. There was talk, of a kind. 'Is it hot in Chicago now? I'm going to do a good deal of canning this fall. I thought later I would send you a box of canned fruit. Do you live in the same place on the North Side? It must be nice in the evening to be able to walk down to the park by the lake.'

Rosalind sat under the tree near the railroad bridge two miles from Willow Springs and watched the tumblebugs at work. Her whole body was hot from the walk in the sun and the thin dress she wore clung to her legs. It was being soiled by the dust on the grass under the tree.

She had run away from town and from her mother's house. All during the three days of her visit she had been doing that. She did not go from house to house to visit her old schoolgirl friends, the girls who unlike herself had stayed in Willow Springs, had got married and settled down there. When she saw one of these women on the street in the morning, pushing a baby carriage and perhaps followed by a small child, she stopped. There was a few minutes of talk. 'It's hot. Do you live in the same place in Chicago? My husband and I hope to take the children and go away for a week or two. It must be nice in Chicago where you are so near the lake.' Rosalind hurried away.

All the hours of her visit to her mother and to her home town had been spent in an effort to hurry away.

From what? Rosalind defended herself. There was something she had come from Chicago hoping to be able to say to her mother. Did she really want to talk with her about things? Had she thought, by again breathing the air of her home town, to get strength to face life and its difficulties?

There was no point in her taking the hot uncomfortable trip from Chicago only to spend her days walking in dusty country roads or between rows of corn fields in the stifling heat along the railroad tracks.

'I must have hoped. There is a hope that cannot be fulfilled,' she thought vaguely.

Willow Springs was a rather meaningless, dreary town, one of thousands of such towns in Indiana, Illinois, Wisconsin, Kansas, Iowa, but her mind made it more dreary.

She sat under the tree by the dry bed of Willow Creek thinking of the street in town where her mother and father lived, where she had lived until she had become a woman. It was only because of a series of circumstances she did not live there now. Her one brother, ten years older than herself, had married and moved to Chicago. He had asked her to come for a visit and after she got to the city she stayed. Her brother was a traveling salesman and spent a good deal of time away from home. 'Why don't you stay here with Bess and learn stenography?' he asked. 'If you don't want to use it you don't have to.

Dad can look out for you all right. I just thought you might like to learn.'

'That was six years ago,' Rosalind thought wearily. 'I've been a city woman for six years.' Her mind hopped about. Thoughts came and went. In the city, after she became a stenographer, something for a time awakened her. She wanted to be an actress and went in the evening to a dramatic school. In an office where she worked there was a young man, a clerk. They went out together, to the theater or to walk in the park in the evening. They kissed.

Her thoughts came sharply back to her mother and father, to her home in Willow Springs, to the street in which she had lived until her twenty-first year.

It was but an end of a street. From the windows at the front of her mother's house six other houses could be seen. How well she knew the street and the people in the houses! Did she know them? From her eighteenth and until her twenty-first year she had stayed at home, helping her mother with the housework, waiting for something. Other young women in town waited just as she did. They like herself had graduated from the town high school and their parents had no intention of sending them away to college. There was nothing to do but wait. Some of the young women — their mothers and their mothers' friends still spoke of them as girls — had young men friends who came to see them on Sunday and perhaps also on Wednesday or Thursday evenings. Others joined the church, went to prayer meetings, became active members of some church organization. They fussed about.

Rosalind had done none of these things. All through those three trying years in Willow Springs she had just waited. In the morning there was the work to do in the house and then, in some way, the day wore itself away. In the evening her father went uptown and she sat with her mother. Nothing much was said. After she had gone to bed, she lay awake, strangely nervous, eager for something to happen that never would happen. The noises of the Wescott house cut across her thoughts. What things went through her mind!

There was a procession of people always going away from her. Sometimes she lay on her belly at the edge of a ravine. Well, it was not a ravine. It had two walls of marble and on the marble face of the walls strange figures were carved. Broad steps led down — always down and away. People walked along the steps, between the marble walls, going down and away from her.

What people! Who were they? Where did they come from? Where were they going? She was not asleep but wide awake. Her bedroom was dark. The walls and ceiling of the room receded. She seemed to hang suspended in space, above the ravine — the ravine with walls of white marble over which strange beautiful lights played.

The people who went down the broad steps and away into infinite distance — they were men and women. Sometimes a young girl like herself, but in some way sweeter and purer than herself, passed alone. The young girl walked with a swinging stride, going swiftly and freely like a beautiful young animal. Her legs and arms were like the slender top branches of trees swaying in a gentle wind. She also went down and away.

Others followed along the marble steps. Young boys walked alone. A dignified old man followed by a sweet-faced woman passed. What a remarkable man! One felt infinite power in his old frame. There were deep wrinkles in his face and his eyes were sad. One felt he knew everything about life, but had kept something very precious alive in himself. It was that precious thing that made the eyes of the woman who followed him burn with a strange fire. They also went down along the steps and away.

Down and away along the steps went others — how many others, men and women, boys and girls, single old men, old women who leaned on sticks and hobbled along.

In the bed in her father's house as she lay awake, Rosalind's head grew light. She tried to clutch at something, understand something.

She couldn't. The noises of the house cut across her waking dream. Her father was at the pump by the kitchen door. He was pumping a pail of water. In a moment he would bring it into the house and put it on a box by the kitchen sink. A little of the water would slop over on the floor. There would be a sound like a child's bare foot striking the floor. Then her father would go to wind the clock. The day was done. Presently there would be the sound of his heavy feet on the floor of the bedroom above and he would get into bed to lie beside Rosalind's mother.

The night noises of her father's house had been in some way terrible to the girl in the years when she was becoming a woman. After chance had taken her to the city, she never wanted to think of them again. Even in Chicago, where the silence of nights was cut and slashed by a thousand noises, by automobiles whirling through the streets, by the belated footsteps of men homeward bound along the cement sidewalks after midnight, by the shouts of quarreling men drunk on summer nights, even in the great hubbub of noises there was comparative quiet. The insistent clanging noises of the city nights were not like the homely insistent noises of her father's house. Certain terrible truths about life did not abide in them, they did not cling so closely to life and did not frighten as did the noises in the one house on the quiet street in the town of Willow Springs. How often, there in the city, in the midst of the great noises she had fought to escape the little noises! Her father's feet were on the steps leading into the kitchen. Now he was putting the pail of water on the box by the kitchen sink. Upstairs her mother's body fell heavily into bed. The visions of the great marble-lined ravine down along which went the beautiful people flew away. There was the little slap of water on the kitchen floor. It was like a child's bare foot striking the floor. Rosalind wanted to cry out. Her father closed the kitchen door. Now he was winding the clock. In a moment his feet would be on the stairs—

There were six houses to be seen from the windows of the Wescott house. In the winter smoke from six brick chimneys went up into the sky. There was one house, the next one to the Wescotts' place, a small frame affair, in which lived a man who was thirty-five years old when Rosalind became a woman of twenty-one and went away to the city. The man was unmarried and his mother, who had been his housekeeper, had died during the year in which Rosalind graduated from the high school. After that the man lived alone. He took his dinner and supper at the hotel, downtown on the square, but he got his own breakfast, made his own bed and swept out his own house. Sometimes he walked slowly along the street past the Wescott house when Rosalind sat alone on the front porch. He raised his hat and spoke to her. Their eyes met. He had a long, hawk-like nose and his hair was long and uncombed.

Rosalind thought about him sometimes. It bothered her a little that he sometimes went stealing softly, as though not to disturb her, across her daytime fancies.

As she sat that day by the dry creek bed, Rosalind thought about the bachelor, who had now passed the age of forty and who lived on the street where she had lived during her girlhood. His house was separated from the Wescott house by a picket fence. Sometimes in the morning he forgot to pull his blinds and Rosalind, busy with the housework in her father's house, had seen him walking about in his underwear. It was — uh, one could not think of it.

The man's name was Melville Stoner. He had a small income and did not have to work. On some days he did not leave his house and go to the hotel for his meals, but sat all day in a chair with his nose buried in a book.

There was a house on the street occupied by a widow who raised chickens. Two or three of her hens were what the people who lived on the street called 'high flyers.' They flew over the fence of the chicken yard and escaped and almost always they came at once into the yard of the bachelor. The neighbors laughed about it. It was significant, they felt. When the hens had come into the yard of the bachelor Stoner, the widow with a stick in her hand ran after them. Melville Stoner came out of his house and stood on a little porch in front. The widow ran through the front gate waving her arms wildly and the hens made a great racket and flew over the fence. They ran down the street toward the widow's house. For a moment she stood by the Stoner gate. In the summer time when the windows of the Wescott house were open, Rosalind could hear what the man and woman said to each other. In Willow Springs it was not thought proper for an unmarried woman to stand talking to an unmarried man near the door of his bachelor establishment. The widow wanted to observe the conventions. Still she did linger a moment, her bare arm resting on the gatepost. What bright eager little eyes she had! 'If those hens of mine bother you I wish you would catch them and kill them,' she said fiercely. 'I am always glad to see them coming along the road,' Melville Stoner replied, bowing. Rosalind thought he was making fun of the widow. She liked him for that. 'I'd never see you if you did not have to come here after your hens. Don't let anything happen to them,' he said, bowing again.

For a moment the man and woman lingered, looking into each other's eyes. From one of the windows of the Wescott house Rosalind watched the woman. Nothing more was said. There was something about the woman she had not understood — well, the widow's senses were being fed. The developing woman in the house next door had hated her.

Rosalind jumped up from under the tree and climbed up the railroad embankment. She thanked the gods she had been lifted out of the life of the town of Willow Springs and that chance had set her down to live in a city. 'Chicago is far from beautiful. People say it is just a big noisy dirty village and perhaps that's what it is, but there is something alive there,' she thought. In Chicago, or at least during the last two or three years of her life there, Rosalind felt she had learned a little something of life. She had read books for one thing, such books as did not come to Willow Springs, books that Willow Springs knew nothing about, she had gone to hear the Symphony Orchestra, she had begun to understand something of the possibility of line and color, had heard intelligent, understanding men speak of these things. In Chicago, in the midst of the twisting squirming millions of men and women, there were voices. One occasionally saw men, or at least heard of the existence of men, who, like the beautiful old man who had walked away down the marble stairs in the vision of her girlhood nights, had kept some precious thing alive in themselves.

And there was something else — it was the most important thing of all. For the last two years of her life in Chicago she had spent hours, days in the presence of a man to whom she could talk. The talks had awakened her. She felt they had made her a woman, had matured her.

'I know what these people here in Willow Springs are like and what I would have been like had I stayed here,' she thought. She felt relieved and almost happy. She had come home at a crisis of her own life hoping to be able to talk a little with her mother, or if talk proved impossible hoping to get some sense of sisterhood by being in her presence. She had thought there was something buried away, deep within every woman, that at a certain call would run out to other women. Now she felt that the hope, the dream, the desire she had cherished, was altogether futile. Sitting in the great flat bowl in the midst of the corn lands two miles from her home town where no breath of air stirred and seeing the beetles at their work of preparing to propagate a new generation of beetles, while she thought of the town and its people, had settled something for her. Her visit to Willow Springs had come to something after all.

Rosalind's figure had still much of the spring and swing of youth in it. Her legs were strong and her shoulders broad. She went swinging along the railroad track toward town, going westward. The sun had begun to fall rapidly down the sky. Away over the tops of the corn in one of the great fields she could see in the distance to where a man was driving a motor along a dusty road. The wheels of the car kicked up dust through which the sunlight played. The floating cloud of dust became a shower of gold that settled down over the fields. 'When a woman most wants what is best and truest in another woman, even in her own mother, she isn't likely to find it,' she thought grimly. 'There are certain things every woman has to find out for herself, there is a road she must travel alone. It may only lead to some more ugly and terrible place, but if she doesn't want death to overtake her and live within her while her body is still alive, she must set out on that road.'

Rosalind walked for a mile along the railroad track and then stopped. A freight train had gone eastward as she sat under the tree by the creek bed, and now, there beside the tracks, in the grass was the body of a man. It lay still, the face buried in the deep burned grass. At once she concluded the man had been struck and killed by the train. The body had been thrown thus aside. All her thoughts went away and she turned and started to tiptoe away, stepping carefully along the railroad ties, making no noise. Then she stopped again. The man in the grass might not be dead, only hurt, terribly hurt. It would not do to leave him there. She imagined him mutilated but still struggling for life and herself trying to help him. She crept back along the ties. The man's legs were not twisted, and beside him lay his hat. It was as though he had put it there before lying down to sleep, but a man did not sleep with his face buried in the grass in such a hot uncomfortable place. She drew nearer. 'O, you Mister,' she called, 'O, you — are you hurt?'

The man in the grass sat up and looked at her. He laughed. It was Melville Stoner, the man of whom she had just been thinking and in thinking of whom she had come to certain settled conclusions regarding the futility of her visit to Willow Springs. He got to his feet and picked up his hat. 'Well, hello, Miss Rosalind Wescott,' he said heartily. He climbed a small embankment and stood beside her. 'I knew you were at home on a visit, but what are you doing out here?' he asked, and then added, 'What luck this is! Now I shall have the privilege of walking home with you. You can hardly refuse to let me walk with you after shouting at me like that.'

They walked together along the tracks, he with his hat in his hand. Rosalind thought he looked like a gigantic bird, an aged wise old bird, 'perhaps a vulture,' she thought. For a time he was silent and then he began to talk, explaining his lying with his face buried in the grass. There was a twinkle in his eyes and Rosalind wondered if he was laughing at her as she had seen him laugh at the widow who owned the hens.

He did not come directly to the point and Rosalind thought it strange that they should walk and talk together. At once his words interested her. He was so much older than herself and no doubt wiser. How vain she had been to think herself so much more knowing than all the people of Willow Springs! Here was this man and he was talking and his talk did not sound like anything she had ever expected to hear from the lips of a native of her home town.

'I want to explain myself, but we'll wait a little. For years I've been wanting to get at you, to talk with you, and this is my chance. You've been away now five or six years and have grown into womanhood.

'You understand it's nothing specially personal, my wanting to get at you and understand you a little,' he added quickly. 'I'm that way about everyone. Perhaps that's the reason I live alone, why I've never married or had personal friends. I'm too eager. It isn't comfortable to others to have me about.'

Rosalind was caught up by this new viewpoint of the man. She wondered. In the distance along the tracks the houses of the town came into sight. Melville Stoner tried to walk on one of the iron rails, but after a few steps lost his balance and fell off. His long arms whirled about. A strange intensity of mood and feeling had come over Rosalind. In one moment Melville Stoner was like an old man and then he was like a boy. Being with him made her mind, that had been racing all afternoon, race faster than ever.

When he began to talk again, he seemed to have forgotten the explanation he had intended making. 'We've lived side by side, but we've hardly spoken to each other,' he said. 'When I was a young man and you were a girl, I used to sit in the house thinking of you. We've really been friends. What I mean is we've had the same thoughts.'

He began to speak of life in the city where she had been living, condemning it. 'It's dull and stupid here, but in the city you have your own kind of stupidity, too,' he declared. 'I'm glad I do not live there.'

In Chicago, when she had first gone there to live, a thing had sometimes happened that had startled Rosalind. She knew no one but her brother and his wife and was sometimes very lonely. When she could no longer bear the eternal sameness of the talk in her brother's house, she went out to a concert or to the theater. Once or twice, when she had no money to buy a theater ticket, she grew bold and walked alone in the streets, going rapidly along without looking to the right or left. As she sat in the theater or walked in the street, an odd thing sometimes happened. Someone spoke her name, a call came to her. The thing happened at a concert and she looked quickly about. All the faces in sight had that peculiar, half-bored, half-expectant expression one grows accustomed to seeing on the faces of people listening to music. In the entire theater no one seemed aware of her. On the street or in the park the call had come when she was utterly alone. It seemed to come out of the air, from behind a tree in the park.

And now, as she walked on the railroad tracks with Melville Stoner, the call seemed to come from him. He walked along apparently absorbed with his own thoughts, the thoughts he was trying to find words to express. His legs were long and he walked with a queer loping gait. The idea of some great bird, perhaps a sea-bird stranded far inland, stayed in Rosalind's mind, but the call did not come from the bird part of him. There was something else, another personality hidden away. Rosalind fancied the call came this time from a young boy, from such another clear-eyed boy as she had once seen in her waking dreams at night in her father's house, from one of the boys who walked on the marble stairway, walked down and away. A thought came that startled her. 'The boy is hidden away in the body of this strange birdlike man,' she told herself. The thought awoke fancies within her. It explained much in the lives of men and women. An expression, a phrase, remembered from her childhood when she had gone to Sunday School in Willow Springs, came back to her mind. 'And God spoke to me out of a burning bush.' She almost said the words aloud.

Melville Stoner loped along, walking on the railroad ties and talking. He seemed to have forgotten the incident of his lying with his nose buried in the grass and was explaining his life lived alone in the house in town. Rosalind tried to put her own thoughts aside and to listen to his words, but did not succeed very well. 'I came home here hoping to get a little closer to life, to get, for a few days, out of the company of a man so I could think about him. I fancied I could get what I wanted by being near mother, but that hasn't worked. It would be strange if I got what I am looking for by this chance meeting with another man,' she thought. Her mind went on recording thoughts. She heard the spoken words of the man beside her, but her own mind went on, also making words. Something within herself felt suddenly relaxed and free. Ever since she had got off the train at Willow Springs three days before, there had been a great tenseness. Now it was all gone. She looked at Melville Stoner, who occasionally looked at her. There was something in his eyes, a kind of laughter — a mocking kind of laughter. His eyes were gray, of a cold grayness, like the eyes of a bird.

'It has come into my mind — I have been thinking — well, you see you have not married in the six years since you went to live in the city. It would be strange and a little amusing if you are like myself, if you cannot marry or come close to any other person,' he was saying.

Again he spoke of the life he led in his house. 'I sometimes sit in my house all day, even when the weather is fine outside,' he said. 'You have no doubt seen me sitting there. Sometimes I forget to eat. I read books all day, striving to forget myself, and then night comes and I cannot sleep.

'If I could write or paint or make music, if I cared at all about expressing what goes on in my mind, it would be different. However, I would not write as others do. I would have but little to say about what people do. What do they do? In what way does it matter? Well, you see they build cities such as you live in and towns like Willow Springs, they have built this railroad track on which we are walking, they marry and raise children, commit murders, steal, do kindly acts. What does it matter? You see we are walking here in the hot sun. In five minutes more we will be in town and you will go to your house and

I to mine. You will eat supper with your father and mother. Then your father will go uptown and you and your mother will sit together on the front porch. There will be little said. Your mother will speak of her intention to can fruit. Then your father will come home and you will all go to bed. Your father will pump a pail of water at the pump by the kitchen door. He will carry it indoors and put it on a box by the kitchen sink. A little of the water will be spilled. It will make a soft little slap on the kitchen floor — '

'Ha!'

Melville Stoner turned and looked sharply at Rosalind, who had grown a little pale. Her mind raced madly, like an engine out of control. There was a kind of power in Melville Stoner that frightened her. By the recital of a few commonplace facts he had suddenly invaded her secret places. It was almost as though he had come into the bedroom in her father's house where she lay thinking. He had in fact got into her bed. He laughed again, an unmirthful laugh. 'I'll tell you what, we know little enough here in America, either in the towns or in the cities,' he said rapidly. 'We are all on the rush. We are all for action. I sit still and think. If I wanted to write I'd do something. I'd tell what everyone thought. It would startle people, frighten them a little, eh? I would tell you what you have been thinking this afternoon while you walked here on this railroad track with me. I would tell you what your mother has been thinking at the same time and what she would like to say to you.'

Rosalind's face had grown chalky white and her hands trembled. They got off the railroad tracks and into the streets of Willow Springs. A change came over Melville Stoner. Of a sudden he seemed just a man of forty, a little embarrassed by the presence of the younger woman, a little hesitant. 'I'm going to the hotel now and I must leave you here,' he said. His feet made a shuffling sound on the sidewalk. 'I intended to tell you why you found me lying out there with my face buried in the grass,' he said. A new quality had come into his voice. It was the voice of the boy who had called to Rosalind out of the body of the man as they walked and talked on the tracks. 'Sometimes I can't stand my life here,' he said, almost fiercely, and waved his long arms about. 'I'm alone too much. I grow to hate myself. I have to run out of town.'

The man did not look at Rosalind but at the ground. His big feet continued shuffling nervously about. 'Once in the wintertime I thought I was going insane,' he said. 'I happened to remember an orchard, five miles from town, where I had walked one day in the late fall when the pears were ripe. A notion came into my head. It was bitter cold, but I walked the five miles and went into the orchard. The ground was frozen and covered with snow, but I brushed the snow aside. I pushed my face into the grass. In the fall when I had walked there the ground was covered with ripe pears. A fragrance arose from them. They were covered with bees that crawled over them, drunk, filled with a kind of ecstasy. I had remembered the fragrance. That's why I went there and put my face into the frozen grass. The bees were in an ecstasy of life and I had missed life. I have always missed life. It always goes away from me. I always imagined people walking away. In the spring this year I walked on the railroad track out to the bridge over Willow Creek. Violets grew in the grass. At that time I hardly noticed them, but today I remembered. The violets were like the people who walk away from me. A mad desire to run after them had taken possession of me. I felt like a bird flying through space. A conviction that something had escaped me and that I must pursue it had taken possession of me.'

Melville Stoner stopped talking. His face also had grown white and his hands also trembled. Rosalind had an almost irresistible desire to put out her hand and touch his hand. She wanted to shout, crying — 'I am here. I am not dead. I am alive.' Instead she stood in silence, staring at him, as the widow who owned the high-flying hens had stared. Melville Stoner struggled to recover from the ecstasy into which he had been thrown by his own words. He bowed and smiled. 'I hope you are in the habit of walking on railroad tracks,' he said. 'I shall in the future know what to do with my time. When you come to town, I shall camp on the railroad tracks. No doubt, like the violets, you have left your fragrance out there.' Rosalind looked at him. He was laughing at her as he had laughed when he talked to the widow standing at his gate. She did not mind. When he had left her, she went slowly through the streets. The phrase that had come into her mind as they walked on the tracks came back and she said it over and over. 'And God spoke to me out of a burning bush.' She kept repeating the phrase until she got back into the Wescott house.

Rosalind sat on the front porch of the house where her girlhood had been spent. Her father had not come home for the evening meal. He was a dealer in coal and lumber and owned a number of unpainted sheds facing a railroad siding west of town. There was a tiny office with a stove and a desk in a corner by a window. The desk was piled high with unanswered letters and with circulars from mining and lumber companies. Over them had settled a thick layer of coal dust. All day he sat in his office looking like an animal in a cage, but unlike a caged animal he was apparently not discontented and did not grow restless. He was the one coal and lumber dealer in Willow Springs. When people wanted one of these commodities, they had to come to him. There was no other place to go. He was content. In the morning as soon as he got to his office he read the Des Moines paper and then if no one came to disturb him he sat all day, by the stove in winter and by an open window through the long hot summer days, apparently unaffected by the marching change of seasons pictured in the fields, without thought, without hope, without regret that life was becoming an old worn-out thing for him.

In the Wescott house Rosalind's mother had already begun the canning of which she had several times spoken. She was making gooseberry jam. Rosalind could hear the pots boiling in the kitchen. Her mother walked heavily. With the coming of age she was beginning to grow fat.

The daughter was weary from much thinking. It had been a day of many emotions. She took off her hat and laid it on the porch beside her. Melville Stoner's house next door had windows that were like eyes staring at her, accusing her. 'Well, now, you see, you have gone too fast,' the house declared. It sneered at her. 'You thought you knew about people. After all, you knew nothing.' Rosalind held her head in her hands. It was true she had misunderstood. The man who lived in the house was no doubt like other people in Willow Springs. He was not, as she had smartly supposed, a dull citizen of a dreary town, one who knew nothing of life. Had he not said words that had startled her, torn her out of herself?

Rosalind had an experience not uncommon to tired nervous people. Her mind, weary of thinking, did not stop thinking, but went on faster than ever. A new plane of thought was reached. Her mind was like a flying machine that leaves the ground and leaps into the air.

It took hold upon an idea expressed or implied in something Melville Stoner had said. 'In every human being there are two voices, each striving to make itself heard.'

A new world of thought had opened itself before her. After all, human beings might be understood. It might be possible to understand her mother and her mother's life, her father, the man she loved, herself. There was the voice that said words. Words came forth from lips. They conformed, fell into a certain mold. For the most part the words had no life of their own. They had come down out of old times, and many of them were no doubt once strong living words, coming out of the depth of people, out of the bellies of people. The words had escaped out of a shut-in place. They had once expressed living truth. Then they had gone on being said, over and over, by the lips of many people, endlessly, wearily.

She thought of men and women she had seen together, that she had heard talking together as they sat in the streetcars or in apartments or walked in a Chicago park. Her brother, the traveling salesman, and his wife had talked half-wearily through the long evenings she had spent with them in their apartment. It was with them as with the other people. A thing happened. The lips said certain words, but the eyes of the people said other words. Sometimes the lips expressed affection while hatred shone out of the eyes. Sometimes it was the other way about. What a confusion!

It was clear there was something hidden away within people that could not get itself expressed except accidentally. One was startled or alarmed and then the words that fell from the lips became pregnant words, words that lived.

The vision that had sometimes visited her in her girlhood as she lay in bed at night came back. Again she saw the people on the marble stairway, going down and away, into infinity. Her own mind began to make words that struggled to get themselves expressed through her lips. She hungered for someone to whom to say the words and half-arose to go to her mother, to where her mother was making gooseberry jam in the kitchen, and then sat down again. 'They were going down into the hall of the hidden voices,' she whispered to herself. The words excited and intoxicated her as had the words from the lips of Melville Stoner. She thought of herself as having quite suddenly grown amazingly, spiritually, even physically. She felt relaxed, young, wonderfully strong. She imagined herself as walking, as had the young girl she had seen in the vision, with swinging arms and shoulders, going down a marble stairway — down into the hidden places in people, into the hall of the little voices. 'I shall understand after this; what shall I not understand?' she asked herself.

Doubt came and she trembled a little. As she walked with him on the railroad track, Melville Stoner had gone down within herself. Her body was a house, through the door of which he had walked. He had known about the night noises in her father's house — her father at the well by the kitchen door, the slap of the spilled water on the floor. Even when she was a young girl and had thought herself alone in the bed in the darkness in the room upstairs in the house before which she now sat, she had not been alone. The strange bird-like man who lived in the house next door had been with her, in her room, in her bed. Years later he had remembered the terrible little noises of the house and had known how they had terrified her. There was something terrible in his knowledge too. He had spoken, given forth his knowledge, but as he did so there was laughter in his eyes, perhaps a sneer.

In the Wescott house the sounds of housekeeping went on. A man who had been at work in a distant field, who had already begun his fall plowing, was unhitching his horses from the plow. He was far away, beyond the street's end, in a field that swelled a little out of the plain. Rosalind stared. The man was hitching the horses to a wagon. She saw him as through the large end of a telescope. He would drive the horses away to a distant farmhouse and put them into a barn. Then he would go into a house where there was a woman at work. Perhaps the woman like her mother would be making gooseberry jam. He would grunt as her father did when at evening he came home from the little hot office by the railroad siding. 'Hello,' he would say, flatly, indifferently, stupidly. Life was like that.

Rosalind became weary of thinking. The man in the distant field had got into his wagon and was driving away. In a moment there would be nothing left of him but a thin cloud of dust that floated in the air. In the house the gooseberry jam had boiled long enough. Her mother was preparing to put it into glass jars. The operation produced a new little side current of sounds. She thought again of Melville Stoner. For years he had been sitting, listening to sounds. There was a kind of madness in it.

She had got herself into a half-frenzied condition. 'I must stop it,' she told herself. 'I am like a stringed instrument on which the strings have been tightened too much.' She put her face into her hands, wearily.

And then a thrill ran through her body. There was a reason for Melville Stoner's being what he had become. There was a locked gateway leading to the marble stairway that led down and away, into infinity, into the hall of the little voices and the key to the gateway was love. Warmth came back into Rosalind's body. 'Understanding need not lead to weariness,' she thought. Life might after all be a rich, a triumphant thing. She would make her visit to Willow Springs count for something significant in her life. For one thing she would really approach her mother, she would walk into her mother's life. 'It will be my first trip down the marble stairway,' she thought, and tears came to her eyes. In a moment her father would be coming home for the evening meal, but after supper he would go away. The two women would be alone together. Together they would explore a little into the mystery of life, they would find sisterhood. The thing she had wanted to talk about with another understanding woman could be talked about then. There might yet be a beautiful outcome to her visit to Willow Springs and to her mother.

II

The story of Rosalind's six years in Chicago is the story of thousands of unmarried women who work in offices in the city. Necessity had not driven her to work nor kept her at her task, and she did not think of herself as a worker, one who would always be a worker. For a time after she came out of the stenographic school she drifted from office to office, acquiring always more skill, but with no particular interest in what she was doing. It was a way to put in the long days. Her father, who in addition to the coal and lumber yards owned three farms, sent her a hundred dollars a month. The money her work brought was spent for clothes, so that she dressed better than the women she worked with.

Of one thing she was quite sure. She did not want to return to Willow Springs to live with her father and mother, and after a time she knew she could not continue living with her brother and his wife.

For the first time she began seeing the city that spread itself out before her eyes. When she walked at the noon hour along Michigan Boulevard or went into a restaurant or in the evening went home in the streetcar, she saw men and women together. It was the same when on Sunday afternoons in the summer she walked in the park or by the lake. On a streetcar she saw a small round-faced woman put her hand into the hand of her male companion. Before she did it she looked cautiously about. She wanted to assure herself of something. To the other women in the car, to Rosalind and the others, the act said something. It was as though the woman's voice had said aloud, 'He is mine. Do not draw too close to him.'

There was no doubt that Rosalind was awakening out of the Willow Springs torpor in which she had lived out her young womanhood. The city had at least done that for her. The city was wide. It flung itself out. One had but to let his feet go thump, thump upon the pavements to get into strange streets, see always new faces.

On Saturday afternoon and all day Sunday one did not work. In the summer it was a time to go to places — to the park, to walk among the strange colorful crowds in Halsted Street, with a half-dozen young people from the office, to spend a day on the sand dunes at the foot of Lake Michigan. One got excited and was hungry, hungry, always hungry — for companionship. That was it. One wanted to possess something — a man — to take him along on jaunts, be sure of him, yes — own him.

She read books — always written by men or by man-like women. There was an essential mistake in the viewpoint of life set forth in the books. The mistake was always being made. In Rosalind's time it grew more pronounced. Someone had got hold of a key with which the door to the secret chamber of life could be unlocked. Others took the key and rushed in. The secret chamber of life was filled with a noisy vulgar crowd. All the books that dealt with life at all dealt with it through the lips of the crowd that had newly come into the sacred place. The writer had hold of the key. It was his time to be heard. 'Sex,' he cried. 'It is by understanding sex I will untangle the mystery.'

It was all very well and sometimes interesting, but one grew tired of the subject.

She lay abed in her room at her brother's house on a Sunday night in the summer. During the afternoon she had gone for a walk and on a street on the Northwest Side had come upon a religious procession. The Virgin was being carried through the streets. The houses were decorated and women leaned out at the windows of houses. Old priests dressed in white gowns waddled along. Strong young men carried the platform on which the Virgin rested. The procession stopped. Someone started a chant in a loud clear voice. Other voices took it up. Children ran about gathering in money. All the time there was a loud hum of ordinary conversation going on. Women shouted across the street to other women. Young girls walked on the sidewalks and laughed softly as the young men in white, clustered about the Virgin, turned to stare at them. On every street corner merchants sold candies, nuts, cool drinks——

In her bed at night Rosalind put down the book she had been reading. 'The worship of the Virgin is a form of sex expression,' she read.

'Well, what of it? If it be true what does it matter?'

She got out of bed and took off her nightgown. She was herself a virgin. What did that matter? She turned herself slowly about, looking at her strong young woman's body. It was a thing in which sex lived. It was a thing upon which sex in others might express itself. What did it matter?

There was her brother sleeping with his wife in another room near at hand. In Willow Springs, Iowa, her father was at just this moment pumping a pail of water at the well by the kitchen door. In a moment he would carry it into the kitchen to set it on the box by the kitchen sink.

Rosalind's cheeks were flushed. She made an odd and lovely figure standing nude before the glass in her room there in Chicago. She was so much alive and yet not alive. Her eyes shone with excitement. She continued to turn slowly round and round, twisting her head to look at her naked back. 'Perhaps I am learning to think,' she decided. There was some sort of essential mistake in people's conception of life. There was something she knew and it was of as much importance as the things the wise men knew and put into books. She also had found out something about life. Her body was still the body of what was called a virgin. What of it? 'If the sex impulse within it had been gratified, in what way would my problem be solved? I am lonely now. It is evident that after that had happened, I would still be lonely.'

III

Rosalind's life in Chicago had been like a stream that apparently turns back toward its source. It ran forward, then stopped, turned, twisted. At just the time when her awakening became a half-realized thing, she went to work at a new place, a piano factory on the Northwest Side facing a branch of the Chicago River. She became secretary to a man who was treasurer of the company. He was a slender, rather small man of thirty-eight with thin white restless hands and with gray eyes that were clouded and troubled. For the first time she became really interested in the work that ate up her days. Her employer was charged with the responsibility of passing upon the credit of the firm's customers and was unfitted for the task. He was not shrewd, and within a short time had made two costly mistakes by which the company had lost money. 'I have too much to do. My time is too much taken up with details. I need help here,' he had explained, evidently irritated, and Rosalind had been engaged to relieve him of details.

Her new employer, named Walter Sayers, was the only son of a man who in his time had been well known in Chicago's social and club life. Everyone had thought him wealthy and he had tried to live up to people's estimate of his fortune. His son Walter had wanted to be a singer and had expected to inherit a comfortable fortune. At thirty he had married and three years later when his father died he was already the father of two children.

And then suddenly he had found himself quite penniless. He could sing, but his voice was not large. It wasn't an instrument with which one could make money in any dignified way. Fortunately his wife had some money of her own. It was her money, invested in the piano manufacturing business, that had secured him the position as treasurer of the company. With his wife he withdrew from social life and they went to live in a comfortable house in a suburb.

Walter Sayers gave up music, apparently surrendered even his interest in it. Many men and women from his suburb went to hear the orchestra on Friday afternoons, but he did not go. 'What's the use of torturing myself and thinking of a life I cannot lead?' he said to himself. To his wife he pretended a growing interest in his work at the factory. 'It's really fascinating. It's a game, like moving men back and forth on a chessboard. I shall grow to love it,' he said.

He had tried to build up interest in his work, but had not been successful. Certain things would not get into his consciousness. Although he tried hard, he could not make the fact that profit or loss to the company depended upon his judgment, seem important to himself. It was a matter of money lost or gained and money meant nothing to him. 'It's father's fault,' he thought. 'While he lived money never meant anything to me. I was brought up wrong. I am ill prepared for the battle of life.' He became too timid and lost business that should have come to the company quite naturally. Then he became too bold in the extension of credit and other losses followed.

His wife was quite happy and satisfied with her life. There were four or five acres of land about the suburban house and she became absorbed in the work of raising flowers and vegetables. For the sake of the children she kept a cow. With a young Negro gardener she puttered about all day, digging in the earth, spreading manure about the roots of bushes and shrubs, planting and transplanting. In the evening when he had come home from his office in his car, she took him by the arm and led him eagerly about. The two children trotted at their heels. She talked glowingly. They stood at a low spot at the foot of the garden and she spoke of the necessity of putting in tile. The prospect seemed to excite her. 'It will be the best land on the place when it's drained,' she said. She stooped and with a trowel turned over the soft black soil. An odor arose. 'See! Just see how rich and black it is!' she exclaimed eagerly. 'It's a little sour now because water has stood on it.' She seemed to be apologizing as for a wayward child. 'When it's drained I shall use lime to sweeten it,' she added. She was like a mother leaning over the cradle of a sleeping babe. Her enthusiasm irritated him.

When Rosalind came to take the position in his office, the slow fires of hatred that had been burning beneath the surface of Walter Sayers' life had already eaten away much of his vigor and energy. His body sagged in the office chair and there were heavy sagging lines at the corners of his mouth. Outwardly he remained always kindly and cheerful, but back of the clouded, troubled eyes the fires of hatred burned slowly, persistently. It was as though he was trying to awaken from a troubled dream that gripped him, a dream that frightened a little, that was unending. He had contracted little physical habits. A sharp papercutter lay on his desk. As he read a letter from one of the firm's customers, he took it up and jabbed little holes in the leather cover of his desk. When he had several letters to sign, he took up his pen and jabbed it almost viciously into the inkwell. Then before signing he jabbed it in again. Sometimes he did the thing a dozen times in succession.

Sometimes the things that went on beneath the surface of Walter Sayers frightened him. In order to do what he called 'putting in his Saturday afternoons and Sundays,' he had taken up photography. The camera took him away from his own house and the sight of the garden where his wife and the Negro were busy digging, and into the fields and into stretches of woodland at the edge of the suburban village. Also it took him away from his wife's talk, from her eternal planning for the garden's future. Here by the house tulip bulbs were to be put in in the fall. Later there would be a hedge of lilac bushes shutting off the house from the road. The men who lived in the other houses along the suburban street spent their Saturday afternoons and Sunday mornings tinkering with motor cars. On Sunday afternoons they took their families driving, sitting up very straight and silent at the driving wheel. They consumed the afternoon in a swift dash over country roads. The car ate up the hours. Monday morning and the work in the city was there, at the end of the road. They ran madly toward it.

For a time the use of the camera made Walter Sayers almost happy. The study of light, playing on the trunk of a tree or over the grass in a field, appealed to some instinct within. It was an uncertain delicate business. He fixed himself a darkroom upstairs in the house and spent his evenings there. One dipped the films into the developing liquid, held them to the light and then dipped them again. The little nerves that controlled the eyes were aroused. One felt oneself being enriched, a little ——

One Sunday afternoon he went to walk in a strip of woodland and came out upon the slope of a low hill. He had read somewhere that the low hill country southwest of Chicago, in which his suburb lay, had once been the shore of Lake Michigan. The low hills sprang out of the flat land and were covered with forests. Beyond them the flat lands began again. The prairies went on indefinitely, into infinity. People's lives went on so. Life was too long. It was to be spent in the endless doing over and over of an unsatisfactory task. He sat on the slope and looked out across the land.

He thought of his wife. She was back there, in the suburb in the hills, in her garden making things grow. It was a noble sort of thing to be doing. One shouldn't be irritated.

Well, he had married her expecting to have money of his own. Then he would have worked at something else. Money would not have been involved in the matter and success would not have been a thing one must seek. He had expected his own life would be motivated. No matter how much or how hard he worked, he would not have been a great singer. What did that matter? There was a way to live — a way of life in which such things did not matter. The delicate shades of things might be sought after. Before his eyes, there on the grass-covered flat lands, the afternoon light was playing. It was like a breath, a vapor of color blown suddenly from between red lips out over the gray dead burned grass. Song might be like that. The beauty might come out of himself, out of his own body.

Again he thought of his wife and the sleeping light in his eyes flared up, it became a flame. He felt himself being mean, unfair. It didn't matter. Where did the truth lie? Was his wife, digging in her garden, having always a succession of small triumphs, marching forward with the seasons — well, was she becoming a little old, lean and sharp, a little vulgarized?

It seemed so to him. There was something smug in the way in which she managed to fling green growing flowering things over the black land. It was obvious the thing could be done and that there was satisfaction in doing it. It was a little like running a business and making money by it. There was a deep-seated vulgarity involved in the whole matter. His wife put her hands into the black ground. They felt about, caressed the roots of the growing things. She laid hold of the slender trunk of a young tree in a certain way — as though she possessed it.

One could not deny that the destruction of beautiful things was involved. Weeds grew in the garden, delicate shapely things. She plucked them out without thought. He had seen her do it.

As for himself, he also had been pulled out of something. Had he not surrendered to the fact of a wife and growing children? Did he not spend his days doing work he detested? The anger within him burned bright. The fire came into his conscious self. Why should a weed that is to be destroyed pretend to a vegetable existence? As for puttering about with a camera — was it not a form of cheating? He did not want to be a photographer. He had once wanted to be a singer.

He arose and walked along the hillside, still watching the shadows play over the plains below. At night — in bed with his wife — well, was she not sometimes with him as she was in the garden? Something was plucked out of him and another thing grew in its place — something she wanted to have grow. Their love-making was like his puttering with a camera — to make the weekends pass. She came at him a little too determinedly — sure. She was plucking delicate weeds in order that things she had determined upon — 'vegetables,' he exclaimed in disgust — in order that vegetables might grow. Love was a fragrance, the shading of a tone over the lips, out of the throat. It was like the afternoon light on the burned grass. Keeping a garden and making flowers grow had nothing to do with it.

Walter Sayers' fingers twitched. The camera hung by a strap over his shoulder. He took hold of the strap and walked to a tree. He swung the box above his head and brought it down with a thump against the tree trunk. The sharp breaking sound — the delicate parts of the machine being broken — was sweet to his ears. It was as though a song had come suddenly from between his lips. Again he swung the box and again brought it down against the tree trunk.

IV

Rosalind at work in Walter Sayers' office was from the beginning something different, apart from the young woman from Iowa who had been drifting from office to office, moving from rooming house to rooming house on Chicago's North Side, striving feebly to find out something about life by reading books, going to the theater and walking alone in the streets. In the new place her life at once began to have point and purpose, but at the same time the perplexity that was later to send her running to Willow Springs and to the presence of her mother began to grow in her.

Walter Sayers' office was a rather large room on the third floor of the factory whose walls went straight up from the river's edge. In the morning Rosalind arrived at eight and went into the office and closed the door. In a large room across a narrow hallway and shut off from her retreat by two thick, clouded-glass partitions was the company's general office. It contained the desks of salesmen, several clerks, a bookkeeper, and two stenographers. Rosalind avoided becoming acquainted with these people. She was in a mood to be alone, to spend as many hours as possible alone with her own thoughts.

She got to the office at eight and her employer did not arrive until nine-thirty or ten. For an hour or two in the morning and in the late afternoon she had the place to herself. Immediately she shut the door into the hallway and was alone, she felt at home. Even in her father's house it had never been so. She took off her wraps and walked about the room touching things, putting things to rights. During the night a Negro woman had scrubbed the floor and wiped the dust off her employer's desk, but she got a cloth and wiped the desk again. Then she opened the letters that had come in and after reading arranged them in little piles. She wanted to spend a part of her wages for flowers and imagined clusters of flowers arranged in small hanging baskets along the gray walls. 'I'll do that later, perhaps,' she thought.

The walls of the room enclosed her. 'What makes me so happy here?' she asked herself. As for her employer — she felt she scarcely knew him. He was a shy man, rather small ——

She went to a window and stood looking out. Near the factory a bridge crossed the river and over it went a stream of heavily loaded wagons and motor trucks. The sky was gray with smoke. In the afternoon, after her employer had gone for the day, she would stand again by the window. As she stood thus, she faced westward and in the afternoon saw the sun fall down the sky. It was glorious to be there alone during the late hours of the afternoon. What a tremendous thing this city in which she had come to live! For some reason, after she went to work for Walter Sayers, the city seemed, like the room in which she worked, to have accepted her, taken her into itself. In the late afternoon the rays of the departing sun fell across great banks of clouds. The whole city seemed to reach upward. It left the ground and ascended into the air. There was an illusion produced. Stark grim factory chimneys, that all day were stiff cold formal things sticking up into the air and belching forth black smoke, were now slender upreaching pencils of light and wavering color. The tall chimneys detached themselves from the buildings and sprang into the air. The factory in which Rosalind stood had such a chimney. It also was leaping upward. She felt herself being lifted, an odd floating sensation was achieved. With what a stately tread the day went away, over the city! The city, like the factory chimney, yearned after it, hungered for it.

In the morning gulls came in from Lake Michigan to feed on the sewage floating in the river below. The river was the color of chrysoprase. The gulls floated above it as sometimes in the evening the whole city seemed to float before her eyes. They were graceful, living, free things. They were triumphant. The getting of food, even the eating of sewage, was done thus gracefully, beautifully. The gulls turned and twisted in the air. They wheeled and floated and then fell downward to the river in a long curve, just touching, caressing the surface of the water, and then rising again.

Rosalind raised herself on her toes. At her back beyond the two glass partitions were other men and women, but there, in that room, she was alone. She belonged there. What an odd feeling she had! She also belonged to her employer, Walter Sayers. She scarcely knew the man and yet she belonged to him. She threw her arms above her head, trying awkwardly to imitate some movement of the birds.

Her awkwardness shamed her a little and she turned and walked about the room. 'I'm twenty-five years old and it's a little late to begin trying to be a bird, to be graceful,' she thought. She resented the slow stupid heavy movements of her father and mother, the movements she had imitated as a child. 'Why was I not taught to be graceful and beautiful in mind and body, why in the place I came from did no one think it worth while to try to be graceful and beautiful?' she whispered to herself.

How conscious of her own body Rosalind was becoming! She walked across the room, trying to go lightly and gracefully. In the office beyond the glass partitions someone spoke suddenly and she was startled. She laughed foolishly. For a long time after she went to work in the office of Walter Sayers, she thought the desire in herself to be physically more graceful and beautiful and to rise also out of the mental stupidity and sloth of her young womanhood was due to the fact that the factory windows faced the river and the western sky, and that in the morning she saw the gulls feeding and in the afternoon the sun going down through the smoke clouds in a riot of colors.

v

On the August evening, as Rosalind sat on the porch before her father's house in Willow Springs, Walter Sayers came home from the factory by the river and to his wife's suburban garden. When the family had dined, he came out to walk in the paths with the two children, boys, but they soon tired of his silence and went to join their mother. The young Negro came along a path by the kitchen door and joined the party. Walter went to sit on a garden seat that was concealed behind bushes. He lighted a cigarette, but did not smoke. The smoke curled quietly up through his fingers as it burned itself out.

Closing his eyes, Walter sat perfectly still and tried not to think. The soft evening shadows began presently to close down and around him. For a long time he sat thus motionless, like a carved figure placed on the garden bench. He rested. He lived and did not live. The intense body, usually so active and alert, had become a passive thing. It was thrown aside, onto the bench, under the bush, to sit there, waiting to be reinhabited.

This hanging suspended between consciousness and unconsciousness was a thing that did not happen often. There was something to be settled between himself and a woman and the woman had gone away. His whole plan of life had been disturbed. Now he wanted to rest. The details of his life were forgotten. As for the woman, he did not think of her, did not want to think of her. It was ridiculous that he needed her so much. He wondered if he had ever felt that way about Cora, his wife. Perhaps he had. Now she was near him, but a few yards away. It was almost dark, but she with the Negro remained at work, digging in the ground — somewhere near — caressing the soil, making things grow.

When his mind was undisturbed by thoughts and lay like a lake in the hills on a quiet summer evening, little thoughts did come. 'I want you as a lover — far away. Keep yourself far away.' The words trailed through his mind as the smoke from the cigarette trailed slowly upward through his fingers. Did the words refer to Rosalind Wescott? She had been gone from him three days. Did he hope she would never come back, or did the words refer to his wife.

His wife's voice spoke sharply. One of the children, in playing about, had stepped on a plant. 'If you are not careful I shall have to make you stay out of the garden altogether.' She raised her voice and called, 'Marian!' A maid came from the house and took the children away. They went along the path toward the house protesting. Then they ran back to kiss their mother. There was a struggle and then acceptance. The kiss was acceptance of their fate — to obey. 'O, Walter,' the mother's voice called, but the man on the bench did not answer. Tree toads began to cry. 'The kiss is acceptance. Any physical contact with another is acceptance,' he reflected.

The little voices within Walter Sayers were talking away at a great rate. Suddenly he wanted to sing. He had been told that his voice was small, not of much account, that he would never be a singer. It was quite true, no doubt, but here, in the garden on the quiet summer night, was a place and a time for a small voice. It would be like the voice within himself that whispered sometimes when he was quiet, relaxed. One evening when he had been with the woman, Rosalind, when he had taken her into the country in his car, he had suddenly felt as he did now. They sat together in the car that he had run into a field. For a long time they had remained silent. Some cattle came and stood near-by, their figures soft in the night. Suddenly he had felt like a new man in a new world and had begun to sing. He sang one song over and over, then sat in silence for a time, and after that drove out of the field and through a gate into the road. He took the woman back to her place in the city.

In the quiet of the garden on the summer evening, he opened his lips to sing the same song. He would sing with the tree toad hidden away in the fork of a tree somewhere. He would lift his voice up from the earth, up into the branches of trees, away from the ground in which people were digging, his wife and the young Negro.

The song did not come. His wife began speaking and the sound of her voice took away the desire to sing. Why had she not, like the other woman, remained silent?

He began playing a game. Sometimes, when he was alone, the thing happened to him that had now happened. His body became like a tree or a plant. Life ran through it unobstructed. He had dreamed of being a singer, but at such a moment he wanted also to be a dancer. That would have been sweetest of all things — to sway like the tops of young trees when a wind blew, to give himself as gray weeds in a sunburned field gave themselves to the influence of passing shadows, changing color constantly, becoming every moment something new, to live in life and in death too, always to live, to be unafraid of life, to let it flow through his body, to let the blood flow through his body, not to struggle, to offer no resistance, to dance.

Walter Sayers' children had gone into the house with the nursegirl, Marian. It had become too dark for his wife to dig in the garden. It was August, and the fruitful time of the year for farms and gardens had come, but his wife had forgotten fruitfulness. She was making plans for another year. She came along the garden path followed by the Negro. 'We will set out strawberry plants there,' she was saying. The soft voice of the young Negro murmured his assent. It was evident the young man lived in her conception of the garden. His mind sought out her desire and gave itself.

The children Walter Sayers had brought into life through the body of his wife Cora had gone into the house and to bed. They bound him to life, to his wife, to the garden where he sat, to the office by the riverside in the city.

They were not his children. Suddenly he knew that quite clearly. His own children were quite different things. 'Men have children just as women do. The children come out of their bodies. They play about,' he thought. It seemed to him that children, born of his fancy, were at that very moment playing about the bench where he sat. Living things that dwelt within him and that had at the same time the power to depart out of him were now running along paths, swinging from the branches of trees, dancing in the soft light.

His mind sought out the figure of Rosalind Wescott. She had gone away, to her own people in Iowa. There had been a note at the office saying she might be gone for several days. Between himself and Rosalind the conventional relationship of employer and employee had long since been swept quite away. It needed something in a man he did not possess to maintain that relationship with either men or women.

At the moment he wanted to forget Rosalind. In her there was a struggle going on. The two people had wanted to be lovers and he had fought against that. They had talked about it. 'Well,' he said, 'it will not work out. We will bring unnecessary unhappiness upon ourselves.'

He had been honest enough in fighting off the intensification of
their relationship. 'If she were here now, in this garden with me,
it wouldn't matter. We could be lovers and then forget about being
lovers,' he told himself.

His wife came along the path and stopped near-by. She continued
talking in a low voice, making plans for another year of gardening.
The Negro stood near her, his figure making a dark wavering mass
against the foliage of a low-growing bush. His wife wore a white
dress. He could see her figure quite plainly. In the uncertain light it
looked girlish and young. She put her hand up and took hold of the
body of a young tree. The hand became detached from her body.
The pressure of her leaning body made the young tree sway a little.
The white hand moved slowly back and forth in space.

Rosalind Wescott had gone home to tell her mother of her love. In
her note she had said nothing of that, but Walter Sayers knew that
was the object of her visit to the Iowa town. It was an odd sort of
thing to try to do — to tell people of love, to try to explain it to others.

The night was a thing apart from Walter Sayers, the male being
sitting in silence in the garden. Only the children of his fancy understood it. The night was a living thing. It advanced upon him, en-
folded him. 'Night is the sweet little brother of Death,' he thought.

His wife stood very near. Her voice was soft and low, and the voice
of the Negro when he answered her comments on the future of the
garden was soft and low. There was music in the Negro's voice, perhaps a dance in it. Walter remembered about him.

The young Negro had been in trouble before he came to the Sayers.
He had been an ambitious young black and had listened to the voices
of people, to the voices that filled the air of America, rang through
the houses of America. He had wanted to get on in life and had tried
to educate himself. The black had wanted to be a lawyer.

How far away he had got from his own people, from the blacks of
the African forests! He had wanted to be a lawyer in a city in America. What a notion!

Well, he had got into trouble. He had managed to get through college and had opened a law office. Then one evening he went out to
walk and chance led him into a street where a woman, a white
woman, had been murdered an hour before. The body of the woman
was found and then he was found walking in the street. Mrs. Sayers'

brother, a lawyer, had saved him from being punished as a murderer, and after the trial and the young Negro's acquittal, had induced his sister to take him as gardener. His chances as a professional man in the city were no good. 'He has had a terrible experience and has just escaped by a fluke,' the brother had said. Cora Sayers had taken the young man. She had bound him to herself, to her garden.

It was evident the two people were bound together. One cannot bind another without being bound. His wife had no more to say to the Negro, who went away along the path that led to the kitchen door. He had a room in a little house at the foot of the garden. In the room he had books and a piano. Sometimes in the evening he sang. He was going now to his place. By educating himself he had cut himself off from his own people.

Cora Sayers went into the house and Walter sat alone. After a time the young Negro came silently down the path. He stopped by the tree where a moment before the white woman had stood talking to him. He put his hand on the trunk of the young tree where her hand had been and then went softly away. His feet made no sound on the garden path.

An hour passed. In his little house at the foot of the garden the Negro began to sing softly. He did that sometimes in the middle of the night. What a life he had led too! He had come away from his black people, from the warm brown girls with the golden colors playing through the blue black of their skins, and had worked his way through a Northern college, had accepted the patronage of impertinent people who wanted to uplift the black race, had listened to them, had bound himself to them, had tried to follow the way of life they had suggested.

Now he was in the little house at the foot of the Sayers' garden. Walter remembered little things his wife had told him about the man. The experience in the courtroom had frightened him horribly and he did not want to go off the Sayers' place. Education, books had done something to him. He could not go back to his own people. In Chicago, for the most part, the blacks lived crowded into a few streets on the South Side. 'I want to be a slave,' he had said to Cora Sayers. 'You may pay me money if it makes you feel better, but I shall have no use for it. I want to be your slave. I would be happy if I knew I would never have to go off your place.'

The black sang a low-voiced song. It ran like a little wind on the surface of a pond. It had no words. He had remembered the song from his father who had got it from his father. In the South, in Alabama and Mississippi, the blacks sang it when they rolled cotton bales onto the steamers in the rivers. They had got it from other rollers of cotton bales long since dead. Long before there were any cotton bales to roll, black men in boats on rivers in Africa had sung it. Young blacks in boats floated down rivers and came to a town they intended to attack at dawn. There was bravado in singing the song then. It was addressed to the women in the town to be attacked, and contained both a caress and a threat. 'In the morning your husbands and brothers and sweethearts we shall kill. Then we shall come into your town to you. We shall hold you close. We shall make you forget. With our hot love and our strength we shall make you forget.' That was the old significance of the song.

Walter Sayers remembered many things. On other nights, when the Negro sang, and when he lay in his room upstairs in the house, his wife came to him. There were two beds in their room. She sat upright in her bed. 'Do you hear, Walter?' she asked. She came to sit on his bed, sometimes she crept into his arms. In the African villages long ago when the song floated up from the river, men arose and prepared for battle. The song was a defiance, a taunt. That was all gone now. The young Negro's house was at the foot of the garden, and Walter with his wife lay upstairs in the larger house situated on high ground. It was a sad song, filled with race sadness. There was something in the ground that wanted to grow, buried deep in the ground. Cora Sayers understood that. It touched something instinctive in her. Her hand went out and touched, caressed her husband's face, his body. The song made her want to hold him tight, possess him.

The night was advancing and it grew a little cold in the garden. The Negro stopped singing. Walter Sayers arose and went along the path toward the house, but did not enter. Instead he went through a gate into the road and along the suburban streets until he got into the open country. There was no moon, but the stars shone brightly. For a time he hurried along, looking back as though afraid of being followed, but when he got out into a broad flat meadow he went more slowly. For an hour he walked and then stopped and sat on a tuft of dry grass. For some reason he knew he could not return to his house in the suburb that night. In the morning he would go to the office and wait there until Rosalind came. Then? He did not know what he would do then. 'I shall have to make up some story. In the morning I shall have to telephone Cora and make up some silly story,' he thought. It was an absurd thing that he, a grown man, could not spend a night abroad, in the fields, without the necessity of explanations. The thought irritated him and he arose and walked again. Under the stars in the soft night and on the wide flat plains the irritation soon went away and he began to sing softly, but the song he sang was not the one he had repeated over and over on that other night when he sat with Rosalind in the car and the cattle came. It was the song the Negro sang, the river song of the young black warriors that slavery had softened and colored with sadness. On the lips of Walter Sayers the song had lost much of its sadness. He walked almost gaily along, and in the song that flowed from his lips there was a taunt, a kind of challenge.

VI

At the end of the short street on which the Wescotts lived in Willow Springs, there was a corn field. When Rosalind was a child, it was a meadow and beyond was an orchard.

On summer afternoons the child often went there to sit alone on the banks of a tiny stream that wandered away eastward toward Willow Creek, draining the farmers' fields on the way. The creek had made a slight depression in the level contour of the land, and she sat with her back against an old apple tree and with her bare feet almost touching the water. Her mother did not permit her to run barefooted through the streets, but when she got into the orchard she took her shoes off. It gave her a delightful naked feeling.

Overhead and through the branches the child could see the great sky. Masses of white clouds broke into fragments and then the fragments came together again. The sun ran in behind one of the cloud masses and gray shadows slid silently over the face of distant fields. The world of her child life, the Wescott household, Melville Stoner sitting in his house, the cries of other children who lived in her street, all the life she knew went far away. To be there in that silent place was like lying awake in bed at night, only in some way sweeter and better. There were no dull household sounds and the air she breathed was sweeter, cleaner. The child played a little game. All the apple trees in the orchard were old and gnarled and she had given all the trees names. There was one fancy that frightened her a little, but was delicious too. She fancied that at night when she had gone to bed and was asleep and when all the town of Willow Springs had gone to sleep, the trees came out of the ground and walked about. The grasses beneath the trees, the bushes that grew beside the fence — all came out of the ground and ran madly here and there. They danced wildly. The old trees, like stately old men, put their heads together and talked. As they talked, their bodies swayed slightly — back and forth, back and forth. The bushes and flowering weeds ran in great circles among the little grasses. The grasses hopped straight up and down.

Sometimes, when she sat with her back against the tree on warm bright afternoons, the child Rosalind had played the game of dancing life until she grew afraid and had to give it up. Near-by in the fields men were cultivating corn. The breasts of the horses and their wide strong shoulders pushed the young corn aside and made a low rustling sound. Now and then a man's voice was raised in a shout. 'Hi, there, you Joe! Get in there, Frank!' The widow of the hens owned a little woolly dog that occasionally broke into a spasm of barking, apparently without cause, senseless, eager barking. Rosalind shut all the sounds out. She closed her eyes and struggled, trying to get into the place beyond human sounds. After a time her desire was accomplished. There was a low sweet sound like the murmuring of voices far away. Now the thing was happening. With a kind of tearing sound the trees came up to stand on top of the ground. They moved with stately tread toward each other. Now the mad bushes and the flowering weeds came running, dancing madly, now the joyful grasses hopped. Rosalind could not stay long in her world of fancy. It was too mad, too joyful. She opened her eyes and jumped to her feet. Everything was all right. The trees stood solidly rooted in the ground, the weeds and bushes had gone back to their places by the fence, the grasses lay asleep on the ground. She felt that her father and mother, her brother, everyone she knew, would not approve of her being there among them. The world of dancing life was a lovely but a wicked world. She knew. Sometimes she was a little mad herself, and then she was whipped or scolded. The mad world of her fancy had to be put away. It frightened her a little. Once after the thing appeared she cried, went down to the fence crying. A man who was cultivating corn came along and stopped his horses. 'What's the matter?' he asked sharply. She couldn't tell him, so she told a lie. 'A bee stung me,' she said. The man laughed. 'It'll get well. Better put on your shoes,' he advised.

The time of the marching trees and the dancing grasses was in Rosalind's childhood. Later, when she had graduated from the Willow Springs High School and had the three years of waiting about the Wescott house before she went to the city, she had other experiences in the orchard. Then she had been reading novels and had talked with other young women. She knew many things that, after all, she did not know. In the attic of her mother's house there was a cradle in which she and her brother had slept when they were babies. One day she went up there and found it. Bedding for the cradle was packed away in a trunk and she took it out. She arranged the cradle for the reception of a child. Then after she did it she was ashamed. Her mother might come up the attic stairs and see it. She put the bedding quickly back into the trunk and went downstairs, her cheeks burning with shame.

What a confusion! One day she went to the house of a schoolgirl friend who was about to be married. Several other girls came in and they were all taken into a bedroom where the bride's trousseau was laid out on a bed. What soft lovely things! All the girls went forward and stood over them, Rosalind among them. Some of the girls were shy, others bold. There was one, a thin girl who had no breasts. Her body was flat like a door and she had a thin sharp voice and a thin sharp face. She began to cry out strangely. 'How sweet, how sweet, how sweet,' she cried over and over. The voice was not like a human voice. It was like something being hurt, an animal in the forest, far away somewhere by itself, being hurt. Then the girl dropped to her knees beside the bed and began to weep bitterly. She declared she could not bear the thought of her schoolgirl friend being married. 'Don't do it! O Mary, don't do it!' she pleaded. The other girls laughed, but Rosalind couldn't stand it. She hurried out of the house.

That was one thing that had happened to Rosalind and there were other things. Once she saw a young man on the street. He clerked in a store and Rosalind did not know him. However, her fancy played with the thought that she had married him. Her own thoughts made her ashamed.

Everything shamed her. When she went into the orchard on summer afternoons, she sat with her back against the apple tree and took off her shoes and stockings just as she had when she was a child, but the world of her childhood fancy was gone, nothing could bring it back.

Rosalind's body was soft, but all her flesh was firm and strong. She moved away from the tree and lay on the ground. She pressed her body down into the grass, into the firm hard ground. It seemed to her that her mind, her fancy, all the life within her, except just her physical life, went away. The earth pressed upward against her body. Her body was pressed against the earth. There was darkness. She was imprisoned. She pressed against the walls of her prison. Everything was dark and there was in all the earth silence. Her fingers clutched a handful of the grasses, played in the grasses.

Then she grew very still, but did not sleep. There was something that had nothing to do with the ground beneath her or the trees or the clouds in the sky, that seemed to want to come to her, come into her, a kind of white wonder of life.

The thing couldn't happen. She opened her eyes and there was the sky overhead and the trees standing silently about. She went again to sit with her back against one of the trees. She thought with dread of the evening coming on and the necessity of going out of the orchard and to the Wescott house. She was weary. It was the weariness that made her appear to others a rather dull stupid young woman. Where was the wonder of life? It was not within herself, not in the ground. It must be in the sky overhead. Presently it would be night and the stars would come out. Perhaps the wonder did not really exist in life. It had something to do with God. She wanted to ascend upward, to go at once up into God's house, to be there among the light strong men and women who had died and left dullness and heaviness behind them on the earth. Thinking of them took some of her weariness away and sometimes she went out of the orchard in the late afternoon walking almost lightly. Something like grace seemed to have come into her tall strong body.

Rosalind had gone away from the Westcott house and from Willow Springs, Iowa, feeling that life was essentially ugly. In a way she hated life and people. In Chicago sometimes it was unbelievable how ugly the world had become. She tried to shake off the feeling, but it clung to her. She walked through the crowded streets and the buildings were ugly. A sea of faces floated up to her. They were the faces of dead people. The dull death that was in them was in her also. They, too, could not break through the walls of themselves to the white wonder of life. After all, perhaps there was no such thing as the white wonder of life. It might be just a thing of the mind. There was something essentially dirty about life. The dirt was on her and in her. Once as she walked at evening over the Rush Street Bridge to her room on the North Side, she looked up suddenly and saw the chrysoprase river running inland from the lake. Near at hand stood a soap factory. The men of the city had turned the river about, made it flow inland from the lake. Someone had erected a great soap factory there near the river's entrance to the city, to the land of men. Rosalind stopped and stood looking along the river toward the lake. Men and women, wagons, automobiles rushed past her. They were dirty. She was dirty. 'The water of an entire sea and millions of cakes of soap will not wash me clean,' she thought. The dirtiness of life seemed a part of her very being, and an almost overwhelming desire to climb upon the railing of the bridge and leap down into the chrysoprase river swept over her. Her body trembled violently, and putting down her head and staring at the flooring of the bridge she hurried away.

And now Rosalind, a grown woman, was in the Westcott house at the supper table with her father and mother. None of the three people ate. They fussed about with the food Ma Westcott had prepared. Rosalind looked at her mother and thought of what Melville Stoner had said.

'If I wanted to write, I'd do something. I'd tell what everyone thought. It would startle people, frighten them a little, eh? I would tell what you have been thinking this afternoon while you walked here on this railroad track with me. I would tell what your mother has been thinking at the same time and what she would like to say to you.'

What had Rosalind's mother been thinking all through the three days since her daughter had so unexpectedly come home from Chicago? What did mothers think in regard to the lives led by their daughters? Had mothers something of importance to say to daughters, and if they did, when did the time come when they were ready to say it?

She looked at her mother sharply. The older woman's face was heavy and sagging. She had gray eyes like Rosalind's, but they were dull like the eyes of a fish lying on a slab of ice in the window of a city meat market. The daughter was a little frightened by what she saw in her mother's face and something caught in her throat. There was an embarrassing moment. A strange sort of tenseness came into the air of the room and all three people suddenly got up from the table.

Rosalind went to help her mother with the dishes and her father sat in a chair by a window and read a paper. The daughter avoided looking again into her mother's face. 'I must gather myself together if I am to do what I want to do,' she thought. It was strange — in fancy she saw the lean birdlike face of Melville Stoner and the eager tired face of Walter Sayers floating above the head of her mother who leaned over the kitchen sink, washing the dishes. Both of the men's faces sneered at her. 'You think you can, but you can't. You are a young fool,' the men's lips seemed to be saying.

Rosalind's father wondered how long his daughter's visit was to last. After the evening meal he wanted to clear out of the house, go uptown, and he had a guilty feeling that in doing so he was being discourteous to his daughter. While the two women washed the dishes, he put on his hat and going into the back yard began chopping wood. Rosalind went to sit on the front porch. The dishes were all washed and dried, but for a half-hour her mother would putter about in the kitchen. She always did that. She would arrange and rearrange. Pick up dishes and put them down again. She clung to the kitchen. It was as though she dreaded the hours that must pass before she could go upstairs and to bed and asleep, to fall into the oblivion of sleep.

When Henry Wescott came around the corner of the house and confronted his daughter, he was a little startled. He did not know what was the matter, but he felt uncomfortable. For a moment he stopped and looked at her. Life radiated from her figure. A fire burned in her eyes, in her gray intense eyes. Her hair was yellow like cornsilk. She was, at the moment, a complete, a lovely daughter of the cornlands, a being to be loved passionately, completely, by some son of the cornlands — had there been in the land a son as alive as this daughter it had thrown aside. The father had hoped to escape from the house unnoticed. 'I'm going uptown a little while,' he said hesitatingly. Still he lingered a moment. Some old sleeping thing awoke in him, was awakened in him by the startling beauty of his daughter. A little fire flared up among the charred rafters of the old house that was his body. 'You look pretty, girly,' he said sheepishly, and then turned his back to her and went along the path to the gate and the street.

Rosalind followed her father to the gate and stood looking as he went slowly along the short street and around a corner. The mood induced in her by her talk with Melville Stoner had returned. Was it possible that her father also felt as Melville Stoner sometimes did? Did loneliness drive him to the door of insanity, and did he also run through the night seeking some lost, some hidden and half-forgotten loveliness?

When her father had disappeared around the corner, she went through the gate and into the street. 'I'll go sit by the tree in the orchard until mother has finished puttering about the kitchen,' she thought.

Henry Wescott went along the streets until he came to the square about the courthouse and then went into Emanuel Wilson's Hardware Store. Two or three other men presently joined him there. Every evening he sat among these men of his town saying nothing. It was an escape from his own house and his wife. The other men came for the same reason. A faint perverted kind of male fellowship was achieved. One of the men of the party, a little old man who followed the house painter's trade, was unmarried and lived with his mother. He was himself nearing the age of sixty, but his mother was still alive. It was a thing to be wondered about. When in the evening the house painter was a trifle late at the rendezvous, a mild flurry of speculation arose, floated in the air for a moment, and then settled like dust in an empty house. Did the old house painter do the house-work in his own house, did he wash the dishes, cook the food, sweep and make the beds, or did his feeble old mother do these things? Emanuel Wilson told a story he had often told before. In a town in Ohio where he had lived as a young man he had once heard a tale.

There was an old man like the house painter whose mother was also still alive and lived with him. They were very poor and in the winter had not enough bedclothes to keep them both warm. They crawled into a bed together. It was an innocent enough matter, just like a mother taking her child into her bed.

Henry Wescott sat in the store listening to the tale Emanuel Wilson told for the twentieth time and thought about his daughter. Her beauty made him feel a little proud, a little above the men who were his companions. He had never before thought of his daughter as a beautiful woman. Why had he never before noticed her beauty? Why had she come from Chicago, there by the lake, to Willow Springs, in the hot month of August? Had she come home from Chicago because she really wanted to see her father and mother? For a moment he was ashamed of his own heavy body, of his shabby clothes and his unshaven face, and then the tiny flame that had flared up within him burned itself out. The house painter came in and the faint flavor of male companionship to which he clung so tenaciously was re-established.

In the orchard Rosalind sat with her back against the tree in the same spot where her fancy had created the dancing life of her childhood and where as a young woman graduate of the Willow Springs High School she had come to try to break through the wall that separated her from life. The sun had disappeared and the gray shadows of night were creeping over the grass, lengthening the shadows cast by the trees. The orchard had long been neglected and many of the trees were dead and without foliage. The shadows of the dead branches were like long lean arms that reached out, felt their way forward over the gray grass. Long lean fingers reached and clutched. There was no wind and the night would be dark and without a moon, a hot dark starlit night of the plains.

In a moment more it would be black night. Already the creeping shadows on the grass were barely discernible. Rosalind felt death all about her, in the orchard, in the town. Something Walter Sayers had once said to her came sharply back into her mind. 'When you are in the country alone at night sometime, try giving yourself to the night, to the darkness, to the shadows cast by trees. The experience, if you really give yourself to it, will tell you a startling story. You will find that, although the white men have owned the land for several generations now and although they have built towns everywhere, dug coal out of the ground, covered the land with railroads, towns and cities, they do not own an inch of the land in the whole continent. It still belongs to a race who in their physical life are now dead. The red men, although they are practically all gone, still own the American continent. Their fancy has peopled it with ghosts, with gods and devils. It is because in their time they loved the land. The proof of what I say is to be seen everywhere. We have given our towns no beautiful names of our own because we have not built the towns beautifully. When an American town has a beautiful name, it was stolen from another race, from a race that still owns the land in which we live. We are all strangers here. When you are alone at night in the country, anywhere in America, try giving yourself to the night. You will find that death only resides in the conquering whites and that life remains in the red men who are gone.'

The spirits of the two men, Walter Sayers and Melville Stoner, dominated the mind of Rosalind. She felt that. It was as though they were beside her, sitting beside her on the grass in the orchard. She was quite certain that Melville Stoner had come back to his house and was now sitting within sound of her voice, did she raise her voice to call. What did they want of her? Had she suddenly begun to love two men, both older than herself? The shadows of the branches of trees made a carpet on the floor of the orchard, a soft carpet spun of some delicate material on which the footsteps of men could make no sound. The two men were coming toward her, advancing over the carpet. Melville Stoner was near at hand and Walter Sayers was coming from far away, out of the distance. The spirit of him was creeping toward her. The two men were in accord. They came bearing some male knowledge of life, something they wanted to give her.

She arose and stood by the tree, trembling. Into what a state she had got herself! How long would it endure? Into what knowledge of life and death was she being led? She had come home on a simple mission. She loved Walter Sayers, wanted to offer herself to him, but before doing so had felt the call to come home to her mother. She had thought she would be bold and would tell her mother the story of her love. She would tell her and then take what the older woman offered. If her mother understood and sympathized, well, that would be a beautiful thing to have happen. If her mother did not understand — at any rate she would have paid some old debt, would have been true to some old, unexpressed obligation.

The two men — what did they want of her? What had Melville Stoner to do with the matter? She put the figure of him out of her mind. In the figure of the other man, Walter Sayers, there was something less aggressive, less assertive. She clung to that.

She put her arm about the trunk of the old apple tree and laid her cheek against its rough bark. Within herself she was so intense, so excited, that she wanted to rub her cheeks against the bark of the tree until the blood came, until physical pain came to counteract the tenseness within that had become pain.

Since the meadow between the orchard and the street end had been planted to corn, she would have to reach the street by going along a lane, crawling under a wire fence, and crossing the yard of the widowed chicken-raiser. A profound silence reigned over the orchard, and when she had crawled under the fence and reached the widow's back yard, she had to feel her way through a narrow opening between a chicken house and a barn by running her fingers forward over the rough boards.

Her mother sat on the porch waiting and on the narrow porch before his house next door sat Melville Stoner. She saw him as she hurried past and shivered slightly. 'What a dark vulture-like thing he is! He lives off the dead, off dead glimpses of beauty, off dead old sounds heard at night,' she thought. When she got to the Wescott house, she threw herself down on the porch and lay on her back with her arms stretched above her head. Her mother sat on a rocking chair beside her. There was a street lamp at the corner at the end of the street and a little light came through the branches of trees and lighted her mother's face. How white and still and death-like it was! When she had looked, Rosalind closed her eyes. 'I mustn't. I shall lose courage,' she thought.

There was no hurry about delivering the message she had come to deliver. It would be two hours before her father came home. The silence of the village street was broken by a hubbub that arose in the house across the street. Two boys playing some game ran from room to room through the house, slamming doors, shouting. A baby began to cry and then a woman's voice protested. 'Quit it! Quit it!' the voice called. 'Don't you see you have wakened the baby? Now I shall have a time getting him to sleep again.'

Rosalind's fingers closed and her hands remained clenched. 'I came home to tell you something. I have fallen in love with a man and can't marry him. He is a good many years older than myself and is already married. He has two children. I love him and I think he loves me — I know he does. I want him to have me, too. I wanted to come home and tell you before it happened,' she said, speaking in a low clear voice. She wondered if Melville Stoner could hear her declaration.

Nothing happened. The chair in which Rosalind's mother sat had been rocking slowly back and forth and making a slight creaking sound. The sound continued. In the house across the street the baby stopped crying. The words Rosalind had come from Chicago to say to her mother were said and she felt relieved and almost happy. The silence between the two women went on and on. Rosalind's mind wandered away. Presently there would be some sort of reaction from her mother. She would be condemned. Perhaps her mother would say nothing until her father came home and would then tell him. She would be condemned as a wicked woman, ordered to leave the house. It did not matter.

Rosalind waited. Like Walter Sayers, sitting in his garden, her mind seemed to float away, out of her body. It ran away from her mother to the man she loved.

One evening, on just such another quiet summer evening as this one, she had gone into the country with Walter Sayers. Before that he had talked to her, at her, on many other evenings and during long hours in the office. He had found in her someone to whom he could talk, to whom he wanted to talk. What doors of life he had opened for her! The talk had gone on and on. In her presence the man was relieved, he relaxed out of the tenseness that had become the habit of his body. He had told her of how he had wanted to be a singer and had given up the notion. 'It isn't my wife's fault nor the children's fault,' he had said. 'They could have lived without me. The trouble is I could not have lived without them. I am a defeated man, was intended from the first to be a defeated man, and I needed something to cling to, something with which to justify my defeat. I realize that now. I am a dependent. I shall never try to sing now because I am one who has at least one merit. I know defeat. I can accept defeat.'

That is what Walter Sayers had said, and then, on the summer evening in the country as she sat beside him in his car, he had suddenly
begun to sing. He had opened a farm gate and had driven the car
silently along a grass-covered lane and into a meadow. The lights had
been put out and the car crept along. When it stopped, some cattle
came and stood near-by.

Then he began to sing, softly at first and with increasing boldness
as he repeated the song over and over. Rosalind was so happy she had
wanted to cry out. 'It is because of myself he can sing now,' she had
thought proudly. How intensely at the moment she loved the man,
and yet perhaps the thing she felt was not love after all. There was
pride in it. It was for her a moment of triumph. He had crept up to
her out of a dark place, out of the dark cave of defeat. It had been her
hand reached down that had given him courage.

She lay on her back, at her mother's feet, on the porch of the Wescott house trying to think, striving to get her own impulses clear in
her mind. She had just told her mother that she wanted to give herself to the man, Walter Sayers. Having made the statement, she already wondered if it could be quite true. She was a woman and her
mother was a woman. What would her mother have to say to her?
What did mothers say to daughters? The male element in life —
what did it want? Her own desires and impulses were not clearly
realized within herself. Perhaps what she wanted in life could be got
in some sort of communion with another woman, with her mother.
What a strange and beautiful thing it would be if mothers could suddenly begin to sing to their daughters, if out of the darkness and
silence of old women song could come!

Men confused Rosalind, they had always confused her. On that
very evening her father for the first time in years had really looked at
her. He had stopped before her as she sat on the porch and there had
been something in his eyes. A fire had burned in his old eyes as it
had sometimes burned in the eyes of Walter. Was the fire intended to
consume her quite? Was it the fate of women to be consumed by men
and of men to be consumed by women?

In the orchard, an hour before, she had distinctly felt the two men,
Melville Stoner and Walter Sayers, coming toward her, walking silently on the soft carpet made of the dark shadows of trees.

They were again coming toward her. In their thoughts they approached nearer and nearer to her, to the inner truth of her. The street and the town of Willow Springs were covered with a mantle of silence. Was it the silence of death? Had her mother died? Did her mother sit there now a dead thing in the chair beside her.

The soft creaking of the rocking chair went on and on. Of the two men whose spirits seemed hovering about, one, Melville Stoner, was bold and cunning. He was too close to her, knew too much of her. He was unafraid. The spirit of Walter Sayers was merciful. He was gentle, a man of understanding. She grew afraid of Melville Stoner. He was too close to her, knew too much of the dark, stupid side of her life. She turned on her side and stared into the darkness toward the Stoner house, remembering her girlhood. The man was too physically close. The faint light from the distant street lamp that had lighted her mother's face crept between branches of trees and over the tops of bushes and she could see dimly the figure of Melville Stoner sitting before his house. She wished it were possible with a thought to destroy him, wipe him out, cause him to cease to exist. He was waiting. When her mother had gone to bed and when she had gone upstairs to her own room to lie awake, he would invade her privacy. Her father would come home, walking with dragging footsteps along the sidewalk. He would come into the Wescott house and through to the back door. He would pump the pail of water at the pump and bring it into the house to put it on the box by the kitchen sink. Then he would wind the clock. He would——

Rosalind stirred uneasily. Life in the figure of Melville Stoner had her, it gripped her tightly. She could not escape. He would come into her bedroom and invade her secret thoughts. There was no escape for her. She imagined his mocking laughter ringing through the silent house, the sound rising above the dreadful commonplace sounds of everyday life there. She did not want that to happen. The sudden death of Melville Stoner would bring sweet silence. She wished it possible with a thought to destroy him, to destroy all men. She wanted her mother to draw close to her. That would save her from the men. Surely, before the evening had passed, her mother would have something to say, something living and true.

Rosalind forced the figure of Melville Stoner out of her mind. It was as though she had got out of her bed in the room upstairs and had taken the man by the arm to lead him to the door. She had put him out of the room and had closed the door.

Her mind played her a trick. Melville Stoner had no sooner gone out of her mind than Walter Sayers came in. In imagination she was with Walter in the car on the summer evening in the pasture and he was singing. The cattle, with their soft broad noses and the sweet grass-flavored breaths, were crowding in close.

There was sweetness in Rosalind's thoughts now. She rested and waited, waited for her mother to speak. In her presence Walter Sayers had broken his long silence and soon the old silence between mother and daughter would also be broken.

The singer who would not sing had begun to sing because of her presence. Song was the true note of life, it was the triumph of life over death.

What sweet solace had come to her that time when Walter Sayers sang! How life had coursed through her body! How alive she had suddenly become! It was at that moment she had decided definitely, finally, that she wanted to come closer to the man, that she wanted with him the ultimate physical closeness — to find in physical expression through him what in his song he was finding through her.

It was in expressing physically her love of the man she would find the white wonder of life, the wonder of which, as a clumsy and crude girl, she had dreamed as she lay on the grass in the orchard. Through the body of the singer she would approach, touch the white wonder of life. 'I shall willingly sacrifice everything else on the chance that may happen,' she thought.

How peaceful and quiet the summer night had become! How clearly now she understood life! The song Walter Sayers had sung in the field, in the presence of the cattle, was in a tongue she had not understood, but now she understood everything, even the meaning of the strange foreign words.

The song was about life and death. What else was there to sing about? The sudden knowledge of the content of the song had not come out of her own mind. The spirit of Walter was coming toward her. It had pushed the mocking spirit of Melville Stoner aside. What things had not the mind of Walter Sayers already done to her mind, to the awakening woman within her! Now it was telling her the story of the song. The words of the song itself seemed to float down the silent street of the Iowa town. They described the sun going down in the smoke clouds of a city and the gulls coming from a lake to float over the city.

Now the gulls floated over a river. The river was the color of chrysoprase. She, Rosalind Wescott, stood on a bridge in the heart of the city and she had become entirely convinced of the filth and ugliness of life. She was about to throw herself into the river, to destroy herself in an effort to make herself clean.

It did not matter. Strange sharp cries came from the birds. The cries of the birds were like the voice of Melville Stoner. They whirled and turned in the air overhead. In a moment more she would throw herself into the river and then the birds would fall straight down in a long graceful line. The body of her would be gone, swept away by the stream, carried away to decay, but what was really alive in herself would arise with the birds, in the long graceful upward line of the flight of the birds.

Rosalind lay tense and still on the porch at her mother's feet. In the air above the hot sleeping town, buried deep in the ground beneath all towns and cities, life went on singing, it persistently sang. The song of life was in the humming of bees, in the calling of tree toads, in the throats of Negroes rolling cotton bales on a boat in a river.

The song was a command. It told over and over the story of life and of death, life forever defeated by death, death forever defeated by life.

The long silence of Rosalind's mother was broken and Rosalind tried to tear herself away from the spirit of the song that had begun to sing itself within her — The sun sank down into the western sky over a city——

Life defeated by death
Death defeated by life.

The factory chimneys had become pencils of light——

Life defeated by death,
Death defeated by life.

The rocking chair in which Rosalind's mother sat kept creaking. Words came haltingly from between her white lips. The test of Ma Wescott's life had come. Always she had been defeated. Now she must triumph in the person of Rosalind, the daughter who had come out of her body. To her she must make clear the fate of all women. Young girls grew up dreaming, hoping, believing. There was a conspiracy. Men made words, they wrote books and sang songs about a thing called love. Young girls believed. They married or entered into close relationships with men without marriage. On the marriage night there was a brutal assault and after that the woman had to try to save herself as best she could. She withdrew within herself, further and further within herself. Ma Wescott had stayed all her life hidden away within her own house, in the kitchen of her house. As the years passed and after the children came, her man had demanded less and less of her. Now this new trouble had come. Her daughter was to have the same experience, to go through the experience that had spoiled life for her.

How proud she had been of Rosalind, going out into the world, making her own way! Her daughter dressed with a certain air, walked with a certain air. She was a proud, upstanding, triumphant thing. She did not need a man.

'God, Rosalind, don't do it, don't do it!' she muttered over and over.

How much she had wanted Rosalind to keep clear and clean! Once she also had been a young woman, proud, upstanding. Could anyone think she had ever wanted to become Ma Wescott, fat, heavy, and old? All through her married life she had stayed in her own house, in the kitchen of her own house, but in her own way she had watched, she had seen how things went with women. Her man had known how to make money, he had always housed her comfortably. He was a slow, silent man, but in his own way he was as good as any of the men of Willow Springs. Men worked for money, they ate heavily, and then at night they came home to the women they had married.

Before she married, Ma Wescott had been a farmer's daughter. She had seen things among the beasts, how the male pursued the female. There was a certain hard insistence, cruelty. Life perpetuated itself that way. The time of her own marriage was a dim, terrible time. Why had she wanted to marry? She tried to tell Rosalind about it. 'I saw him on the Main Street of town here, one Saturday evening when I had come to town with father, and two weeks after that I met him again at a dance out in the country,' she said. She spoke like one who has been running a long distance and who has some important, some immediate message to deliver. 'He wanted me to marry him and I did it. He wanted me to marry him and I did it.'

She could not get beyond the fact of her marriage. Did her daughter think she had no vital thing to say concerning the relationship of men and women? All through her married life she had stayed in her husband's house, working as a beast might work, washing dirty clothes, dirty dishes, cooking food.

She had been thinking, all through the years she had been thinking. There was a dreadful lie in life, the whole fact of life was a lie.

She had thought it all out. There was a world somewhere unlike the world in which she lived. It was a heavenly place in which there was no marrying or giving in marriage, a sexless quiet windless place where mankind lived in a state of bliss. For some unknown reason mankind had been thrown out of that place, had been thrown down upon the earth. It was a punishment for an unforgivable sin, the sin of sex.

The sin had been in her as well as in the man she had married. She had wanted to marry. Why else did she do it? Men and women were condemned to commit the sin that destroyed them. Except for a few rare sacred beings, no man or woman escaped.

What thinking she had done! When she had just married and after her man had taken what he wanted of her, he slept heavily, but she did not sleep. She crept out of bed and going to a window looked at the stars. The stars were quiet. With what a slow stately tread the moon moved across the sky. The stars did not sin. They did not touch one another. Each star was a thing apart from all other stars, a sacred inviolate thing. On the earth, under the stars everything was corrupt, the trees, flowers, grasses, the beasts of the field, men and women. They were all corrupt. They lived for a moment and then fell into decay. She herself was falling into decay. Life was a lie. Life perpetuated itself by the lie called love. The truth was that life itself came out of sin, perpetuated itself only by sin.

'There is no such thing as love. The word is a lie. The man you are telling me about wants you for the purpose of sin,' she said, and getting heavily up went into the house.

Rosalind heard her moving about in the darkness. She came to the screen door and stood looking at her daughter lying tense and waiting on the porch. The passion of denial was so strong in her that she felt choked. To the daughter it seemed that her mother standing in the darkness behind her had become a great spider, striving to lead her down into some web of darkness. 'Men only hurt women,' she said, 'they can't help wanting to hurt women. They are made that way. The thing they call love doesn't exist. It's a lie.

'Life is dirty. Letting a man touch her dirties a woman.' Ma Wescott fairly screamed forth the words. They seemed torn from her, from some deep inner part of her being. Having said them, she moved off into the darkness and Rosalind heard her going slowly toward the stairway that led to the bedroom above. She was weeping in the peculiar half-choked way in which old fat women weep. The heavy feet that had begun to mount the stair stopped and there was silence. Ma Wescott had said nothing of what was in her mind. She had thought it all out, what she wanted to say to her daughter. Why would the words not come? The passion for denial within her was not satisfied. 'There is no love. Life is a lie. It leads to sin, to death and decay,' she called into the darkness.

A strange, almost uncanny thing happened to Rosalind. The figure of her mother went out of her mind and she was in fancy again a young girl and had gone with other young girls to visit a friend about to be married. With the others she stood in a room where white dresses lay on a bed. One of her companions, a thin, flat breasted girl, fell on her knees beside the bed. A cry arose. Did it come from the girl or from the old tired defeated woman within the Wescott house? 'Don't do it! O Rosalind, don't do it!' pleaded a voice broken with sobs.

The Wescott house had become silent like the street outside and like the sky sprinkled with stars into which Rosalind gazed. The tenseness within her relaxed and she tried again to think. There was a thing that balanced, that swung backward and forward. Was it merely her heart beating? Her mind cleared.

The song that had come from the lips of Walter Sayers was still singing within her —

> Life the conqueror over death,
> Death the conqueror over life.

She sat up and put her head into her hands. 'I came here to Willow Springs to put myself to a test. Is it the test of life and death?' she asked herself. Her mother had gone up the stairway, into the darkness of the bedroom above.

The song singing within Rosalind went on —

                    Life the conqueror over death,
                    Death the conqueror over life.

Was the song a male thing, the call of the male to the female, a lie, as her mother had said? It did not sound like a lie. The song had come from the lips of the man Walter and she had left him and had come to her mother. Then Melville Stoner, another male, had come to her. In him also was singing the song of life and death. When the song stopped singing within one, did death come? Was death but denial? The song was singing within herself. What a confusion!

After her last outcry Ma Wescott had gone weeping up the stairs and to her own room and to bed. After a time Rosalind followed. She threw herself onto her own bed without undressing. Both women lay waiting. Outside in the darkness before his house sat Melville Stoner, the male, the man who knew of all that had passed between mother and daughter. Rosalind thought of the bridge over the river near the factory in the city and of the gulls floating in the air high above the river. She wished herself there, standing on the bridge. 'It would be sweet now to throw my body down into the river,' she thought. She imagined herself falling swiftly and the swifter fall of the birds down out of the sky. They were swooping down to pick up the life she was ready to drop, sweeping swiftly and beautifully down. That was what the song Walter had sung was about.

Henry Wescott came home from his evening at Emanuel Wilson's store. He went heavily through the house to the back door and the pump. There was the slow creaking sound of the pump working, and then he came into the house and put the pail of water on the box by the kitchen sink. A little of the water spilled. There was a soft little slap — like a child's bare feet striking the floor ——

Rosalind arose. The dead cold weariness that had settled down upon her went away. Cold dead hands had been gripping her. Now they were swept aside. Her bag was in a closet, but she had forgotten it. Quickly she took off her shoes and holding them in her hands went out into the hall in her stockinged feet. Her father came heavily up the stairs past her as she stood breathless with her body pressed against the wall in the hallway.

How quick and alert her mind had become! There was a train eastward bound toward Chicago that passed through Willow Springs at two in the morning. She would not wait for it. She would walk the eight miles to the next town to the east. That would get her out of town. It would give her something to do. 'I need to be moving now,' she thought, as she ran down the stairs and went silently out of the house.

She walked on the grass beside the sidewalk to the gate before Melville Stoner's house and he came down to the gate to meet her. He laughed mockingly. 'I fancied I might have another chance to walk with you before the night was gone,' he said, bowing. Rosalind did not know how much of the conversation between herself and her mother he had heard. It did not matter. He knew all Ma Wescott had said, all she could say, and all Rosalind could say or understand. The thought was infinitely sweet to Rosalind. It was Melville Stoner who lifted the town of Willow Springs up out of the shadow of death. Words were unnecessary. With him she had established the things beyond words, beyond passion — the fellowship in living, the fellowship in life.

They walked in silence to the town's edge and then Melville Stoner put out his hand. 'You'll come with me?' she asked, but he shook his head and laughed. 'No,' he said, 'I'll stay here. My time for going passed long ago. I'll stay here until I die. I'll stay here with my thoughts.'

He turned and walked away into the darkness beyond the round circle of light cast by the last street lamp on the street that now became a country road leading to the next town to the east. Rosalind stood to watch him go, and something in his long loping gait again suggested to her mind the figure of a gigantic bird. 'He is like the gulls that float above the river in Chicago,' she thought. 'His spirit floats above the town of Willow Springs. When the death in life comes to the people here, he swoops down, with his mind, plucking out the beauty of them.'

She walked at first slowly along the road between corn fields. The night was a vast quiet place into which she could walk in peace. A little breeze rustled the corn blades, but there were no dreadful significant human sounds, the sounds made by those who lived physically, but who in spirit were dead, had accepted death, believed only in death. The corn blades rubbed against each other and there was a low sweet sound as though something was being born, old dead physical

life was being torn away, cast aside. Perhaps new life was coming
into the land.

Rosalind began to run. She had thrown off the town and her father
and mother as a runner might throw off a heavy and unnecessary garment. She wished also to throw off the garments that stood between
her body and nudity. She wanted to be naked, newborn. Two miles
out of town a bridge crossed Willow Creek. It was now empty and
dry, but in the darkness she imagined it filled with water, swift-running water, water the color of chrysoprase. She had been running
swiftly, and now she stopped and stood on the bridge, her breath
coming in quick little gasps.

After a time she went on again, walking until she had regained her
breath and then running again. Her body tingled with life. She did
not ask herself what she was going to do, how she was to meet the
problem she had come to Willow Springs half-hoping to have solved
by a word from her mother. She ran. Before her eyes the dusty road
kept coming up to her out of darkness. She ran forward, always forward into a faint streak of light. The darkness unfolded before her.
There was joy in the running and with every step she took she
achieved a new sense of escape. A delicious notion came into her
mind. As she ran, she thought the light under her feet became more
distinct. It was, she thought, as though the darkness had grown afraid
in her presence and sprang aside, out of her path. There was a sensation of boldness. She had herself become something that within itself
contained light. She was a creator of light. At her approach darkness
grew afraid and fled away into the distance. When that thought came,
she found herself able to run without stopping to rest and half-wished
she might run on forever, through the land, through towns and cities,
driving darkness away with her presence.

V. LYRICAL

The Man with the Trumpet

I STATED it as definitely as I could.

I was in a room with them.

They had tongues like me, and hair and eyes.

I got up out of my chair and said it as definitely as I could.

Their eyes wavered. Something slipped out of their grasp. Had I been white and strong and young enough I might have plunged through walls, gone outward into nights and days, gone into prairies, into distances — gone outward to the doorstep of the house of God, gone to God's throne room with their hands in mine.

What I am trying to say is this ——

By God, I made their minds flee out of them.

Their minds came out of them as clear and straight as anything could be.

I said they might build temples to their lives.

I threw my words at faces floating in a street.

I threw my words like stones, like building stones.

I scattered words in alleyways like seeds.

I crept at night and threw my words into empty rooms of houses in a street.

I said that life was life, that men in streets and cities might build temples to their souls.

I whispered words at night into a telephone.

I told my people life was sweet, that men might live.

I said a million temples might be built, that doorsteps might be cleansed.

At their fleeing harried minds I hurled a stone.

I said they might build temples to themselves.

My city is very strange. It is tired and nervous. My city has become a woman whose mother is ill. She creeps in the hallway of a house and listens in the darkness at the door of a room.

I cannot tell what my city is like.

My city is a kiss from the feverish lips of many tired people.

My city is a murmur of voices coming out of a pit.

The Lame One

A<small>T</small> NIGHT, when there are no lights, my city is a man who arises from a bed to stare into darkness.

In the daytime my city is the son of a dreamer. He has become the companion of thieves and prostitutes. He has denied his father.

My city is a thin old man who lives in a rooming house in a dirty street. He wears false teeth that have become loose and make a sharp clicking noise when he eats. He cannot find himself a woman and indulges in self-abuse. He picks cigar ends out of the gutter.

My city lives in the roofs of houses, in the eaves. A woman came into my city and he threw her far down out of the eaves on a pile of stones. Nobody knew. Those who live in my city declare she fell.

There is an angry man whose wife is unfaithful. He is my city. My city is in his hair, in his eyes. When he breathes his breath is the breath of my city.

There are many cities standing in rows. There are cities that sleep, cities that stand in the mud of a swamp.

I have come here to my city.

I have walked with my city.

I have limped slowly forward at night with my city.

213

My city is very strange. It is tired and nervous. My city has become a woman whose mother is ill. She creeps in the hallway of a house and listens in the darkness at the door of a room.

I cannot tell what my city is like.

My city is a kiss from the feverish lips of many tired people.

My city is a murmur of voices coming out of a pit.

The Dumb Man

THERE IS A STORY. — I cannot tell it. — I have no words.
The story is almost forgotten, but sometimes I remember.

The story concerns three men in a house in a street.
If I could say the words I would sing the story.
I would whisper it into the ears of women, of mothers.
I would run through the streets saying it over and over.
My tongue would be torn loose — it would rattle against my teeth.

The three men are in a room in the house.
One is young and dandified.
He continually laughs.

There is a second man who has a long white beard.
He is consumed with doubt, but occasionally his doubt leaves him and
   he sleeps.

A third man there is who has wicked eyes and who moves nervously
   about the room rubbing his hands together.
The three men are waiting — waiting.

Upstairs in the house there is a woman standing with her back to a
   wall, in half darkness by a window.

That is the foundation of my story and everything I will ever know
   is distilled in it.

215

I remember that a fourth man came to the house, a white silent man.
Everything was as silent as the sea at night.
His feet on the stone floor of the room where the three men were
    made no sound.

The man with the wicked eyes became like a boiling liquid — he ran
    back and forth like a caged animal.
The old gray man was infected by his nervousness — he kept pulling
    at his beard.

The fourth man, the white one, went upstairs to the woman.

There she was — waiting.

How silent the house was — how loudly all the clocks in the neighbor-
    hood ticked.
The woman upstairs craved love. That must have been the story. She
    hungered for love with her whole being. She wanted to create
    in love.
When the white silent man came into her presence she sprang forward.
Her lips were parted.
There was a smile on her lips.

The white one said nothing.
In his eyes there was no rebuke, no question.
His eyes were as impersonal as stars.

Downstairs the wicked one whined and ran back and forth like a little
    lost hungry dog.
The gray one tried to follow him about, but presently grew tired and
    lay down on the floor to sleep.
He never woke again.

The dandified fellow lay on the floor too.
He laughed and played with his tiny black mustache.

I have no words to tell what happened in my story.
I cannot tell the story.

The white silent one may have been Death.

The waiting eager woman may have been Life.

Both the old gray-bearded man and the wicked one puzzle me.
I think and think, but cannot understand them.
Most of the time, however, I do not think of them at all.
I keep thinking about the dandified man who laughed all through
my story.

If I could understand him I could understand everything.
I could run through the world telling a wonderful story.
I would no longer be dumb.

Why was I not given words?
Why am I dumb?

I have a wonderful story to tell, but know no way to tell it.

Brothers

I AM AT MY HOUSE in the country and it is late October. It rains. Back of my house is a forest and in front there is a road and beyond that open fields. The country is one of low hills, flattening suddenly into plains. Some twenty miles away, across the flat country, lies the huge city Chicago.

On this rainy day the leaves of the trees that line the road before my window are falling like rain, the yellow, red, and golden leaves fall straight down heavily. The rain beats them brutally down. They are denied a last golden flash across the sky. In October leaves should be carried away, out over the plains, in a wind. They should go dancing away.

Yesterday morning I arose at daybreak and went for a walk. There was a heavy fog and I lost myself in it. I went down into the plains and returned to the hills, and everywhere the fog was as a wall before me. Out of it trees sprang suddenly, grotesquely, as in a city street late at night people come suddenly out of the darkness into the circle of light under a street lamp. Above there was the light of day forcing itself slowly into the fog. The fog moved slowly. The tops of trees moved slowly. Under the trees the fog was dense, purple. It was like smoke lying in the streets of a factory town.

An old man came up to me in the fog. I know him well. The people here call him insane. 'He is a little cracked,' they say. He lives alone in a little house buried deep in the forest and has a small dog he carries always in his arms. On many mornings I have met him walking on the road and he has told me of men and women who are his brothers and sisters, his cousins, aunts, uncles, brothers-in-law. It is confusing. He cannot draw close to people near at hand, so he gets hold of a name out of a newspaper and his mind plays with it. On one morning he told me he was a cousin to the man named Cox who at the time when I write is a candidate for the presidency. On another morning he told me that Caruso the singer had married a woman who was his sister-in-law. 'She is my wife's sister,' he said, holding the little dog close. His gray watery eyes looked appealing up to me. He wanted me to believe. 'My wife was a sweet slim girl,' he declared. 'We lived together in a big house and in the morning walked about arm in arm. Now her sister has married Caruso the singer. He is of my family now.'

As someone had told me the old man had never married, I went away wondering. One morning in early September I came upon him sitting under a tree beside a path near his house. The dog barked at me and then ran and crept into his arms. At that time the Chicago newspapers were filled with the story of a millionaire who had got into trouble with his wife because of an intimacy with an actress. The old man told me that the actress was his sister. He is sixty years old and the actress whose story appeared in the newspapers is twenty, but he spoke of their childhood together. 'You would not realize it to see us now, but we were poor then,' he said. 'It's true. We lived in a little house on the side of a hill. Once when there was a storm, the wind nearly swept our house away. How the wind blew! Our father was a carpenter and he built strong houses for other people, but our own house he did not build very strong!' He shook his head sorrowfully. 'My sister the actress has got into trouble. Our house is not built very strongly,' he said, as I went away along the path.

For a month, two months, the Chicago newspapers, that are delivered every morning in our village, have been filled with the story of a murder. A man there has murdered his wife and there seems no reason for the deed. The tale runs something like this:

The man, who is now on trial in the courts and will no doubt be hanged, worked in a bicycle factory where he was a foreman and lived with his wife and his wife's mother in an apartment in Thirty-Second Street. He loved a girl who worked in the office of the factory where he was employed. She came from a town in Iowa and when she first came to the city lived with her aunt who has since died. To the foreman, a heavy stolid-looking man with gray eyes, she seemed the most beautiful woman in the world. Her desk was by a window at an angle of the factory, a sort of wing of the building, and the foreman, down in the shop, had a desk by another window. He sat at his desk making out sheets containing the record of the work done by each man in his department. When he looked up, he could see the girl sitting at work at her desk. The notion got into his head that she was peculiarly lovely. He did not think of trying to draw close to her or of winning her love. He looked at her as one might look at a star across a country of low hills in October when the leaves of the trees are all red and yellow gold. 'She is a pure, virginal thing,' he thought vaguely. 'What can she be thinking about as she sits there by the window at work?'

In fancy the foreman took the girl from Iowa home with him to his apartment in Thirty-Second Street and into the presence of his wife and his mother-in-law. All day in the shop and during the evening at home he carried her figure about with him in his mind. As he stood by a window in his apartment and looked out toward the Illinois Central railroad tracks and beyond the tracks to the lake, the girl was there beside him. Down below women walked in the street and in every woman he saw there was something of the Iowa girl. One woman walked as she did, another made a gesture with her hand that reminded of her. All the women he saw except his wife and his mother-in-law were like the girl he had taken inside himself.

The two women in his own house puzzled and confused him. They became suddenly unlovely and commonplace. His wife in particular was like some strange unlovely growth that had attached itself to his body.

In the evening after the day at the factory he went home to his own place and had dinner. He had always been a silent man and when he did not talk no one minded. After dinner he with his wife went to a picture show. There were two children and his wife expected another. They came into the apartment and sat down. The climb up two flights of stairs had wearied his wife. She sat in a chair beside her mother groaning with weariness.

The mother-in-law was the soul of goodness. She took the place of a servant in the home and got no pay. When her daughter wanted to go to a picture show, she waved her hand and smiled. 'Go on,' she said. 'I don't want to go. I'd rather sit here.' She got a book and sat reading. The little boy of nine awoke and cried. He wanted to sit on the po-po. The mother-in-law attended to that.

After the man and his wife came home the three people sat in silence for an hour or two before bedtime. The man pretended to read a newspaper. He looked at his hands. Although he had washed them carefully, grease from the bicycle frames left dark stains under the nails. He thought of the Iowa girl and of her white quick hands playing over the keys of a typewriter. He felt dirty and uncomfortable.

The girl at the factory knew the foreman had fallen in love with her and the thought excited her a little. Since her aunt's death she had gone to live in a rooming house and had nothing to do in the evening. Although the foreman meant nothing to her, she could in a way use him. To her he became a symbol. Sometimes he came into the office and stood for a moment by the door. His large hands were covered with black grease. She looked at him without seeing. In his place in her imagination stood a tall slender young man. Of the foreman she saw only the gray eyes that began to burn with a strange fire. The eyes expressed eagerness, a humble and devout eagerness. In the presence of a man with such eyes she felt she need not be afraid.

She wanted a lover who would come to her with such a look in his eyes. Occasionally, perhaps once in two weeks, she stayed a little late at the office, pretending to have work that must be finished. Through the window she could see the foreman waiting. When everyone had gone, she closed her desk and went into the street. At the same moment the foreman came out at the factory door.

They walked together along the street a half-dozen blocks to where she got aboard her car. The factory was in a place called South Chicago and as they went along evening was coming on. The streets were lined with small unpainted frame houses and dirty-faced children ran screaming in the dusty roadway. They crossed over a bridge. Two abandoned coal barges lay rotting in the stream.

He went by her side walking heavily and striving to conceal his hands. He had scrubbed them carefully before leaving the factory, but they seemed to him like heavy dirty pieces of waste matter hanging at his side. Their walking together happened but a few times and during one summer. 'It's hot,' he said. He never spoke to her of anything but the weather. 'It's hot,' he said. 'I think it may rain.'

She dreamed of the lover who would some time come, a tall fair young man, a rich man owning houses and lands. The workingman who walked beside her had nothing to do with her conception of love. She walked with him, stayed at the office until the others had gone, to walk unobserved with him because of his eyes, because of the eager thing in his eyes that was at the same time humble, that bowed down to her. In his presence there was no danger, could be no danger. He would never attempt to approach too closely, to touch her with his hands. She was safe with him.

In his apartment in the evening the man sat under the electric light with his wife and his mother-in-law. In the next room his two children were asleep. In a short time his wife would have another child. He had been with her to a picture show and in a short time they would get into bed together.

He would lie awake thinking, would hear the creaking of the springs of a bed where, in another room, his mother-in-law was crawling between the sheets. Life was too intimate. He would lie awake eager, expectant — expecting what?

Nothing. Presently one of the children would cry. It wanted to get out of bed and sit on the po-po. Nothing strange or unusual or lovely would or could happen. Life was too close, intimate. Nothing that could happen in the apartment could in any way stir him; the things his wife might say, her occasional half-hearted outbursts of passion, the goodness of his mother-in-law who did the work of a servant without pay ——

He sat in the apartment under the electric light pretending to read a newspaper — thinking. He looked at his hands. They were large, shapeless, a workingman's hands.

The figure of the girl from Iowa walked about the room. With her he went out of the apartment and walked in silence through miles of streets. It was not necessary to say words. He walked with her by a sea, along the crest of a mountain. The night was clear and silent and the stars shone. She also was a star. It was not necessary to say words.

Her eyes were like stars and her lips were like soft hills rising out of dim, starlit plains. 'She is unattainable, she is far off like the stars,' he thought. 'She is unattainable like the stars, but unlike the stars she breathes, she lives, like myself she has being.'

One evening, some six weeks ago, the man who worked as foreman in the bicycle factory killed his wife and he is now in the courts being tried for murder. Every day the newspapers are filled with the story. On the evening of the murder he had taken his wife as usual to a picture show and they started home at nine. In Thirty-Second Street, at a corner near their apartment building, the figure of a man darted suddenly out of an alleyway and then darted back again. The incident may have put the idea of killing his wife into the man's head.

They got to the entrance to the apartment building and stepped into a dark hallway. Then quite suddenly and apparently without thought the man took a knife out of his pocket. 'Suppose that man who darted into the alleyway had intended to kill us,' he thought. Opening the knife he whirled about and struck at his wife. He struck twice, a dozen times — madly. There was a scream and his wife's body fell.

The janitor had neglected to light the gas in the lower hallway. Afterwards, the foreman decided, that was the reason he did it, that and the fact that the dark slinking figure of a man darted out of an alleyway and then darted back again. 'Surely,' he told himself, 'I could never have done it had the gas been lighted.'

He stood in the hallway thinking. His wife was dead and with her had died her unborn child. There was a sound of doors opening in the apartments above. For several minutes nothing happened. His wife and her unborn child were dead — that was all.

He ran upstairs, thinking quickly. In the darkness on the lower stairway he had put the knife back into his pocket and, as it turned out later, there was no blood on his hands or on his clothes. The knife he later washed carefully in the bathroom, when the excitement had died down a little. He told everyone the same story. 'There has been a holdup,' he explained. 'A man came slinking out of an alleyway and followed me and my wife home. He followed us into the hallway of the building and there was no light. The janitor had neglected to light the gas.' Well — there had been a struggle and in the darkness his wife had been killed. He could not tell how it had happened. 'There was no light. The janitor had neglected to light the gas,' he kept saying.

For a day or two they did not question him specially and he had time to get rid of the knife. He took a long walk and threw it away into the river in South Chicago where the two abandoned coal barges lay rotting under the bridge, the bridge he had crossed when on the summer evenings he walked to the streetcar with the girl who was virginal and pure, who was far off and unattainable, like a star and yet not like a star.

And then he was arrested and right away he confessed — told everything. He said he did not know why he had killed his wife and was careful to say nothing of the girl at the office. The newspapers tried to discover the motive for the crime. They are still trying. Someone had seen him on the few evenings when he walked with the girl and she was dragged into the affair and had her picture printed in the papers. That has been annoying for her, as of course she has been able to prove she had nothing to do with the man.

Yesterday morning a heavy fog lay over our village here at the edge of the city and I went for a long walk in the early morning. As I returned out of the lowlands into our hill country, I met the old man whose family has so many and such strange ramifications. For a time he walked beside me holding the little dog in his arms. It was cold and the dog whined and shivered. In the fog the old man's face was indistinct. It moved slowly back and forth with the fog banks of the upper air and with the tops of trees. He spoke of the man who had killed his wife and whose name is being shouted in the pages of the city newspapers that come to our village each morning. As he walked beside me, he launched into a long tale concerning a life he and his brother, who has now become a murderer, once lived together. 'He is my brother,' he said over and over, shaking his head. He seemed afraid I would not believe. There was a fact that must be established. 'We were boys together, that man and I,' he began again. 'You see we played together in a barn back of our father's house. Our father went away to sea in a ship. That is the way our names became confused. You understand that. We have different names, but we are brothers. We had the same father. We played together in a barn back of our father's house. For hours we lay together in the hay in the barn and it was warm there.'

In the fog the slender body of the old man became like a little gnarled tree. Then it became a thing suspended in air. It swung back and forth like a body hanging on the gallows. The face beseeched me to believe the story the lips were trying to tell. In my mind everything concerning the relationship of men and women became confused, a muddle. The spirit of the man who had killed his wife came into the body of the little old man there by the roadside. It was striving to tell me the story it would never be able to tell in the courtroom in the city, in the presence of the judge. The whole story of mankind's loneliness, of the effort to reach out to unattainable beauty tried to get itself expressed from the lips of a mumbling old man, crazed with loneliness, who stood by the side of a country road on a foggy morning holding a little dog in his arms.

The arms of the old man held the dog so closely that it began to whine with pain. A sort of convulsion shook his body. The soul seemed striving to wrench itself out of the body, to fly away through the fog, down across the plain to the city, to the singer, the politician, the millionaire, the murderer, to its brothers, cousins, sisters, down in the city. The intensity of the old man's desire was terrible and in sympathy my body began to tremble. His arms tightened about the body of the little dog so that it cried with pain. I stepped forward and tore the arms away and the dog fell to the ground and lay whining. No doubt it had been injured. Perhaps ribs had been crushed. The old man stared at the dog lying at his feet as in the hallway of the apartment building the worker from the bicycle factory had stared at his dead wife. 'We are brothers,' he said again. 'We have different names, but we are brothers. Our father, you understand, went off to sea.'

I am sitting in my house in the country and it rains. Before my eyes the hills fall suddenly away and there are the flat plains and beyond the plains the city. An hour ago the old man of the house in the forest went past my door and the little dog was not with him. It may be that as we talked in the fog he crushed the life out of his companion. It may be that the dog, like the workman's wife and her unborn child, is now dead. The leaves of the trees that line the road before my window are falling like rain — the yellow, red, and golden leaves fall straight down, heavily. The rain beat them brutally down. They are denied a last golden flash across the sky. In October leaves should be carried away, out over the plains, in a wind. They should be dancing away.

One Throat

I WAS ON A TRAIN in lower Arkansas. It was a slow day train. At a certain little lumber town the engine broke down. I went to walk in the wood.

It was really a cypress swamp. A road had been made through it by putting logs down. I walked along the road a long way — had indeed forgotten my train.

I came finally to a river, a slow yellow sluggish stream. Negroes were rafting logs in the stream. I stood in the wood watching them. They had not seen me.

What great strong brown fellows there were! On the bank of the stream there was a row of Negro cabins. Evening was coming on. They had still not seen me. I sat on a log behind a tree to look and listen.

The Negroes, on the log rafts on the yellow river, began to sing.

A woman came out of one of the houses on the river bank and began singing. It went on for some time like that, song full of strangeness, sadness, race feeling.

Then, from somewhere in the wood came another voice. It was a woman's voice, very tender, high, with tremendous carrying power.

Well, alas, I am a poet. It is the nature of the poet to have something primitive in him. The poet is in some odd way akin to the savage. It cannot be denied. When he is a true poet he is tender, cruel, isolated from others, intensely a part of others in a way the generality of men will never understand.

And so there was I sitting in a cypress swamp in Arkansas listening

to this Negro singing, the most real, the most tender, the most significant singing I have ever heard.

As I sat thus the Negro woman with the high tender voice came in
a small skiff out of a bayou into the yellow river. She had been row-
ing, but dropped her paddles and let the skiff float toward us.

How shall I describe this scene? There had been a constantly changing light on the river and the cypress forest. Gray patches of clouds
floated across the face of the late afternoon sun and then passed and
the sun shone again.

I sat watching, drunk with all this as I have seldom been drunk.
Long, long I had felt something of the soil in the Negro I had wanted
in myself too.

I mean a sense of earth and skies and trees and rivers, not as a thing
thought about, but as a thing in me. I wanted earth in me and skies
and fields and rivers and people. I wanted these things to come out of
me, as song, as singing prose, as poetry even.

What else have I ever cared for as I have cared to have this happen,
what woman, what possessions, what promise of life after death, all
that? I have wanted this unity of things, this song, this earth, this sky,
this human brotherhood.

I have felt it often in Negroes as I felt it that afternoon in Arkansas.
Of course my train, with my bags on a seat, went away and left me
sitting there. The Negroes sang for a time and then stopped singing.
All the educated Negro singing and white man's singing I have ever
heard in America was as nothing to what I heard that day.

There was the woman in the boat. She was a young yellow Negress,
with white blood in her. The woman on the bank was old and black,
the men rafting the logs were black.

The song came first out of the red throats of the blacks and then
out of her young throat. She was leaning a little forward in the skiff.
The yellow of her skin was as the yellow of the river. I dare say I
loved her at that moment as I have never loved any other woman.

Because of the sky in her voice, the yellow river, the cypress trees,
with their strange knees protruding from the black swamp muck.

Because of something long submerged in her and the others set free
in song.

Have I not myself been submerged, by need of money, possessions,
women, what not?

A race for a moment singing thus out of one throat. Is it not what I also have wanted?

For that would I not give, freely and gladly, all hope of such things as a future life, duty to society, to wife, to family, to all the white man's shibboleths?

When We Care

I GOT INTO A GROUP OF PEOPLE one evening in Paris. It was at a house belonging to some wealthy Frenchman, but leased to an American woman. I was taken there to dine by an American writer, a verp popular and successful writer.

We were shown into a large, expensively furnished room. There were several men and women. Where they came from, I do not know. Ours is a money civilization and there are these men and women sometimes suddenly shot up into prominent positions and aristocratic conditions of life.

The men were all popular and successful writers or painters. The women were all beautiful. At least they had what most men mean when they speak of beauty in women.

They were handsomely clad. How much money is spent trying to enhance the beauty of women! There are all these wonderful gowns. Men devote their lives to making them, little fat men with keen eyes. They think of women impersonally. I have been to establishments where they assemble their creations. Outdoors and in, these workmen study the lines of women, and in the rooms where they work there are adjustable figures. There is this long suave line here, down across the hip. You accentuate it a bit here, flatten it there. Something to please the eye.

If you are a woman who has money or can get a man who is a money-maker, you may have their services and the services of innumerable people all at work to enhance your beauty. You may have experts working upon your body, even changing it. They will accentuate this or that good point. The line of your mouth may be changed, the color of your hair. There is no need of your making any effort.

But what does make beauty in a woman anyhow? Is it her clothes, her carriage, her figure, her hair, her eyes, her features? I should say that beauty is a thing you cannot localize, tie down to any one feature. It is something mysteriously present, showing itself almost involuntarily in unexpected spots, through unexpected motions, turns of the head, gestures of hand or arm, radiance of an inner light. And the women in this room in the Parisian house were not beautiful. I do not know why. I only know that all that evening all the people present hurt and kept hurting each other and me.

I kept thinking of an old mountain woman, seen over in Grayson County, Virginia, one day. She was the wife of a small farmer over there and had lived with him for forty years. He had died. When I saw that old woman, she was coming home along a mountain road afoot from the funeral.

There were several people in the road. I happened to be standing in a stream. I was trout-fishing. The people came silently along the road. I had stepped behind an overhanging bush. I could see along the road. There was the old mountain-woman, two grown daughters and a troop of grandchildren. They were all dressed in the cheap Sunday clothes poor people wear on such occasions. The old wife walked alone behind them all. She had got her a cheap black dress for the occasion.

The sun was shining. It was late afternoon. The old mountain woman was small and slender. Why had all of her own people left her to walk alone like that?

The reason was pretty obvious. There are times when every human being who has experienced life at all keenly must be alone.

Someone very, very near to you has died.

Or, if you get life that way, it may be someone not near you, someone you may never have seen. For example, I myself remember what happened to me when I was told one day that the writer D. H. Lawrence had died. I had never met Lawrence, had never seen him, did not know he was ill.

'He's dead,' someone said.

'What?'

'Yes, D. H. Lawrence. He died. Hadn't you heard? He died. He's dead.'

So, a sudden blackout of the skies. A queer feeling of emptiness, all life being empty. Why should I try to describe the feeling? Innumerable people have felt it. Have you ever gone into a house or a room in a house where someone you once loved formerly lived? It may have been a man or a woman. It doesn't matter. She or he is there no longer.

Why did I think of the poor thin little old mountain woman once seen walking in a road? The point is, she was beautiful, and if I speak of her now it is only to show that beauty can exist in the aged, in the tired, in the defeated.

I knew the old woman's story, knew it vaguely. It was simple enough. As a young girl, the daughter of a poor mountain family, she had married a poor and perhaps, as we in the modern world think of education, an uneducated mountain-man. He couldn't read or write. He had a little bit of mountain land.

They lived there, they raised their children there. In some way they managed.

Their children grew up and married. They lived in other little farms scattered about over the Virginia mountains. For years the old couple lived alone together. Every year they raised and fattened a pig; they kept a cow; they worked a few poor fields. On Sunday afternoons sometimes their children and their grandchildren came to see them. Now he was dead. On the day I saw her walking in the road she and the others had just come from the burial.

The old woman was alone, walking behind the others in the mountain road that day. The others of her people walked ahead of her in silence in the road. Even the children were silent. There was one of the daughters had a tiny babe in her arms. As she walked she suckled it.

The beauty of the old woman flamed. She had braced her shoulders and thrown her head back. Her watery little old eyes were fixed and staring.

As everyone knows, there is a beauty of grief as well as of laughter, and it was in her. It was in her and came out of her. It seemed to me, that day standing in the water of that creek, near a bridge, near a turn of a mountain road, it seemed to me suddenly that coming out of her her beauty of grief ran through trees. It ran through the cold waters of the mountain stream that washed my legs. It climbed in my legs. It sang in distant hills. It sang in every particle of dust in the lithe fields on the sides of the hills . . .

This beauty of which I am speaking in this rather disconnected way can exist in men as well as in women. You go into a certain room or office. A man you have known and loved for years works there. You have gone there often to sit and talk with him. He has left his marks everywhere in the room. Let's say he is a cigarette smoker. There is a mark at his desk, at the edge of his desk. He had put his cigarette down there. He was talking. He was absorbed. In fact there is a little row of black marks. He was thinking perhaps of his work. It doesn't make much difference what his work is.

So there is your friend, standing in his room. Once again he has put his burning cigarette down at the edge of his desk. He is trying to tell you something. He stands there struggling let us say for words. Now the cigarette has begun burning the wood. The desk is varnished, the hot end of the cigarette melts the varnish a little, there is a faint stench in the room. You do not mind. He is beautiful at that moment, because of work, because of absorption in some kind of work. He is doing something he cares about doing. He cares rather tremendously. I think most men I have thought beautiful as I looked at them have been so because they cared.

And all about them there is this 'singing.' Silently and still musically it is in the furniture, the desks and bookshelves, and in the window-frames and walls. It is as if in straight lines of these objects there were a flow and a rejoicing. They stream with it. I am talking about inanimate things. It is something it seems we do to them.

We do it to each other. All of us go about all the time doing something to others. When, for example, you go to a friend's house, you take something there with you. You take health, the gift of beauty in yourself, give that to your friend. Or you take ill health, you take poison. Friends you have, people you love, die and are born again. You know what I mean. There are little deaths as well as the final thing we habitually think of as death. It is always happening to everyone you love. Some quality that made you love your friend dies in him or is born again perhaps through you.

So likewise in the objects. I am in a certain room. I work there. It doesn't matter much whether what I am trying to do in the room ever comes off or not. I do something to everyone who comes into that room, but that isn't all. There are the things. The room has walls. There are chairs, a couch over here, a table yonder. On the walls hang paintings. The paintings, if they are the living work of living men — I mean if they are the work of men alive when they did the painting — they do something to me all the time — but I do something to them, too. They sing like the objects in my friend's office at the moment he was speaking, give forth the melody of their lines and their colors, or are silent.

It all comes down to a terrific responsibility in life. Something our scientists have called to the attention of us poets and other men. They have been breaking all of life up into something very minute — atoms, electrons, molecules. As I understand the whole thing, it is something like this:

In the palm of my hand here there are certain tiny specks of what is called dirt. There probably are a good many of them. I have been out walking in the streets.

The scientists tell us that each particle of this so-called dirt — to my not young eyes invisible particle — is a little world. There are suns and moons, there are planets, moving at incredible speed, there are vast empty spaces all within that speck of so-called inanimate matter.

You see, there isn't any such thing as inanimate matter. Here is a bit of wood. Over there a piece of steel or iron. Here is the cloth of my coat. This piece of wood, that piece of steel, this coat I wear, are masses of tiny, terrifically active worlds. Life is going on down inside there, swimming, revolving, speeding, an intense life. They are all alive as I am when I live. It is but another step to say there is music down in the wood of this desk, in the wool of this coat — music I may never hear any more than I may ever see the world the scientists have described. Still it is there.

I may be bungling this. But recently a scientist told me — he was a bit embarrassed and shy in telling me — scientists are not like us brash men who dare go about talking, lecturing, writing — they hate to commit themselves — at any rate, this man told me about certain experiments he and others working with him had been making.

It was his idea that there is a real music of the molecules present in every form of matter living or dead. While incapable of being heard directly by the ear, this music can be recorded on the spectrographic plate and 'translated' into musical chords which can be played on the piano. If a beam of light is passed through a glass of water, it is possible to discover each molecule of H_2O vibrating much like a violin string and emitting three tones. The frequency of these tones being about one hundred trillion vibrations per second, they are much too high for us to hear, but by dividing the frequency by the velocity of light it is possible to transpose these tones to lower frequencies. The spectrograph, it seems, had revealed even more. It showed the atoms in constant motion, moving in three different ways, and each motion corresponded to a note in a chord formed by the ensemble. The experiment this man and his colleagues were trying to make was that of turning the wave lengths — varied as they are — long and short — long and swinging, abrupt and sudden — trying to turn these activities in gasoline, in metal and woven stuff, by simplification into actual audible music notes and harmonies.

The actual song of this table, then, the song of this coat, the song of these walls!

I had best stop all this. The actual music of which the scientist spoke may never be heard. It may be too faint, too far away. But I am poet enough to know that it exists. What the scientists say clicks with something I have always felt. I know my clothes incessantly sing, the timbers in the floor on which I am walking sing, every speck of dust in every field sings — as the distant hills sang while the poor little old woman passed.

I spoke of the new responsibility. Is it not the tremendousness of caring, in people, in myself, that makes us hear the music? We are beautiful when we care tremendously, and when we are beautiful the 'harmony of the spheres' is audible.

Perhaps this sounds like preaching. It doesn't matter. I am like the man I have tried to describe to you, struggling to find words to say some subtle and difficult thing while his cigarette burned the varnish on his desk.

A memory of a 'dead' house in Paris, where I met certain rich, successful men and 'beautiful' women, started me speaking.

VI. THE LIFE OF ART

Song of Theodore

O MY BELOVED — men and women — I come into your presence. It is night and I am alone and I come to you. I open the window of my room so that you may come in. I am a lover and I would touch you with the fingers of my hands. In my eyes a fire burns. The strength of my imaginings is beyond words to record. I see the loveliness in you that is hidden away. I take something from you. See, I embrace you. I take you in my arms and I run away.

I am alone in my room at night and in me is the spirit of the old priests. What cunning fingers I have. They make intricate designs on the white paper. See, the designs are words and sentences. I am not a priest, but a lover, a new kind of lover, one who is of the flesh and not of the flesh. My cunning fingers are of the flesh. They are like me and I would make love always, to all people — men and women — here — in Chicago — in America — everywhere — always — forever — while my life lasts.

I am afraid. Do you not understand, O my beloved, that I am afraid? In me is the old inheritance. The fires that burn have not burned me. I have not suffered enough.

Now, my beloved, I am not pure and I dare not come to you. I run away and hide. I am a priest and my head is not shaven. I sit in my room and my doors are bolted. I tremble and am afraid.

It is then that you come to me, O my beloved. Men and women you crowd in upon me. Through the walls and the bolted doors you

236

come crowding, hurrying. I was afraid and trembled, but I have
become unafraid.

I cannot tell how many things there are that I understand. I understand all, everything. The words of the men and women who have
come in to me are without meaning, but the air of my room has
brought health to me.

I was determined to withdraw from the world, to be a priest with a
shaven head. In fancy I saw myself go into the forest, into the
dense silence. For days I lay like a stone in the midst of the silence.

My body was bathed in a cold stream. Again and again my body was
bathed. The cold water ran over my body and chilled the warm
blood that runs beneath the surface of the skin.

The inside of my body was made clean. My body was fed on the
white meat of nuts that fell from the trees. I crunched the nuts with
my white teeth. How powerful my body had become!

In the rain in the streets of my city I stood. My clothes were foul. In
the woven cloth that covered my body the dust of my city had
lodged. The dust of my civilization was in my soul. I was a murderer — a weeping prostitute standing by a wall. I was a strong man
with strong arms. In a jail they had lodged me. I was one condemned to be hanged. There was filth on my shoes — my shoes
were filthy.

It was night and I had come into my room. I was cold and my body
trembled. I was afraid. The pencil was gripped in my cunning fingers. Words came. Over the paper my pencil ran — making the
words — saying the words.

There is a song in the pencil that is held in my cunning fingers. Out
— out — out — dear words. The words have saved me. There is
rhythm in the pencil. It sings and swings. It sings a great song. It
is singing the song of my life. It is bringing life in to me, into my
close place.

Out—out—out—out of the room I go. I am become pure. To the homes of the people I go. Here in these words I am become a man. The passions and lusts of men have taken hold of me.

I have gone into the woman's chamber, into the secret places of all women and all men I have gone. I have made love to them. Before me in the chamber lies the naked body of a woman. She is strong and young.

Do you not see, O my beloved, that I am become strong to caress the woman! I caress all men and all women. I make myself naked. I am unafraid. I am a pure thing. I bind and heal. By the running of the pencil over the white paper I have made myself pure. I have made myself whole. I am unafraid. The song of the pencil has done it.

What cunning fingers I have! They make intricate designs on the white paper. My cunning fingers are of the flesh. They are like me and I would make love always—to all people—men and women—here—in Chicago—in America—everywhere—always—forever—while my life lasts.

The Book of the Grotesque

T HE WRITER, an old man with a white mustache, had some difficulty in getting into bed. The windows of the house in which he
lived were high and he wanted to look at the trees when he awoke
in the morning. A carpenter came to fix the bed so that it would be
on a level with the window.

Quite a fuss was made about the matter. The carpenter, who had
been a soldier in the Civil War, came into the writer's room and sat
down to talk of building a platform for the purpose of raising the
bed. The writer had cigars lying about and the carpenter smoked.

For a time the two men talked of the raising of the bed and then
they talked of other things. The soldier got on the subject of the
war. The writer, in fact, led him to that subject. The carpenter had
once been a prisoner in Andersonville Prison and had lost a brother.
The brother had died of starvation, and whenever the carpenter got
upon that subject he cried. He, like the old writer, had a white mustache, and when he cried he puckered up his lips and the mustache
bobbed up and down. The weeping old man with the cigar in his
mouth was ludicrous. The plan the writer had for the raising of his
bed was forgotten and later the carpenter did it in his own way, and
the writer, who was past sixty, had to help himself with a chair when
he went to bed at night.

In his bed the writer rolled over on his side and lay quite still.
For years he had been beset with notions concerning his heart. He
was a hard smoker and his heart fluttered. The idea had got into his
mind that he would sometime die unexpectedly, and always when
he got into bed he thought of that. It did not alarm him. The effect

in fact was quite a special thing and not easily explained. It made him more alive, there in bed, than at any other time. Perfectly still he lay and his body was old and not of much use any more, but something inside him was altogether young. He was like a pregnant woman, only that the thing inside him was not a baby but a youth. No, it wasn't a youth, it was a woman, young, and wearing a coat of mail like a knight. It is absurd, you see, to try to tell what was inside the old writer as he lay on his high bed and listened to the fluttering of his heart. The thing to get at is what the writer, or the young thing within the writer, was thinking about.

The old writer, like all of the people in the world, had got, during his long life, a great many notions in his head. He had once been quite handsome and a number of women had been in love with him. And then, of course, he had known people, many people, known them in a peculiarly intimate way that was different from the way in which you and I know people. At least that is what the writer thought and the thought pleased him. Why quarrel with an old man concerning his thoughts?

In the bed the writer had a dream that was not a dream. As he grew somewhat sleepy, but was still conscious, figures began to appear before his eyes. He imagined the young indescribable thing within himself was driving a long procession of figures before his eyes.

You see, the interest in all this lies in the figures that went before the eyes of the writer. They were all grotesques. All of the men and women the writer had ever known had become grotesques.

The grotesques were not all horrible. Some were amusing, some almost beautiful, and one, a woman all drawn out of shape, hurt the old man by her grotesqueness. When she passed, he made a noise like a small dog whimpering. Had you come into the room you might have supposed the old man had unpleasant dreams or perhaps indigestion.

For an hour the procession of grotesques passed before the eyes of the old man, and then, although it was a painful thing to do, he crept out of bed and began to write. Some one of the grotesques had made a deep impression on his mind and he wanted to describe it.

At his desk the writer worked for an hour. In the end he wrote a book which he called 'The Book of the Grotesque.' It was never published, but I saw it once and it made an indelible impression on my mind. The book had one central thought that is very strange and has always remained with me. By remembering it I have been able to understand many people and things that I was never able to understand before. The thought was involved, but a simple statement of it would be something like this:

That in the beginning when the world was young there were a great many thoughts but no such thing as a truth. Man made the truths himself and each truth was a composite of a great many vague thoughts. All about in the world were the truths and they were all beautiful.

The old man had listed hundreds of the truths in his book. I will not try to tell you of all of them. There was the truth of virginity and the truth of passion, the truth of wealth and of poverty, of thrift and of profligacy, of carelessness and abandon. Hundreds and hundreds were the truths and they were all beautiful.

And then the people came along. Each as he appeared snatched up one of the truths, and some who were quite strong snatched up a dozen of them.

It was the truths that made the people grotesques. The old man had quite an elaborate theory concerning the matter. It was his notion that the moment one of the people took one of the truths to himself, called it his truth, and tried to live his life by it, he became a grotesque and the truth he embraced became a falsehood.

You can see for yourself how the old man, who had spent all of his life writing and was filled with words, would write hundreds of pages concerning this matter. The subject would become so big in his mind that he himself would be in danger of becoming a grotesque. He didn't, I suppose, for the same reason that he never published the book. It was the young thing inside him that saved the old man.

Concerning the old carpenter who fixed the bed for the writer, I only mentioned him because he, like many of what are called very common people, became the nearest thing to what is understandable and lovable of all the grotesques in the writer's book.

Alfred Stieglitz

Old man — perpetually young — we salute you.
Young man — who will not grow old — we salute you.

I DO NOT KNOW, cannot know, when the thing happened to Alfred Stieglitz that made him a man beloved of many men. It may have been when he was a young fellow, but, as he is an American, it perhaps did not happen with him within him — until he had come into middle life. In any event, any man going into the presence of Alfred Stieglitz knows that, on a day long ago, something did happen that has sweetened the man's nature, made him a lover of life and a lover of men. It has come about that many men go gladly and freely in and out of this man's presence. Knowing the man you may not agree with his judgments on this or that piece of work, you may say to yourself that he talks too much, is too much, and sometimes too consciously, the prophet of the new age, but in a moment, and after you have gone out of his physical presence, something happens within you too.

You are walking in a city street and suddenly you walk more gladly and lightly. Weariness goes out of you. You are in a street lined with buildings, for the most part ugly and meaningless, but something within is now telling you that a breath can blow even this colossal stone and brick ugliness away. Again, and now quite definitely and permanently, you know that, although men have blundered terribly in building up the physical world about themselves and although most men have been incurably poisoned by the ugliness created by men, there is at the very heart of humanity a something sweet and sound that has always found and always will find among men, here and there, an individual to strive all his life to give voice to man's inner sweetness and health.

242

As for myself, I have quite definitely come to the conclusion that there is in the world a thing one thinks of as maleness that is represented by such men as Alfred Stieglitz. It has something to do with the craftman's love of his tools and his materials. In an age when practically all men have turned from that old male love of good work well done and have vainly hoped that beauty might be brought into the world wholesale, as Mr. Ford manufactures automobiles, there has always been, here in America, this one man who believed in no such nonsense, who perhaps often stood utterly alone, without fellows, fighting man's old fight for man's old inheritance — the right to his tools, his materials, and the right to make what is sound and sweet in himself articulate through his handling of tools and materials.

There is something definite to be said in this matter, something very important to be said. Whether or not I am clear-headed enough to say it, I can't be sure. What I do know is that in some way the figure of Alfred Stieglitz stands at the heart of the matter. What I think, I believe, is that we Americans, in the age that has just passed, have been a very sick people. Let me speak of that for a moment. To me it seems that the outward signs of that impotence that is the natural result of long illness are all about us in America. It is to be seen in our architecture, in the cowboy plays in our moving-picture theaters, and in our childish liking of the type of statesman who boasts of walking softly and carrying a big stick. True maleness does not boast of its maleness. Only truly strong men can be gentle, tender, patient, and kindly; and sentimental male strutting is perhaps always but an outpouring of poison from the bodies of impotent men. Might it not be that, with the coming into general use of machinery, men did lose the grip of what is perhaps the most truly important of man's functions in life — the right every man has always before held dearest of all his human possessions, the right, in short, to stand alone in the presence of his tools and his materials and with those tools and materials to attempt to twist, to bend, to form something that will be the expression of his inner hunger for the truth that is his own and that is beauty? A year ago Mr. Gilbert Cannan made this dark and threatening comment on our modern life. 'Befoul the workman's tools and materials long enough,' said Mr. Cannan, 'and in the end the workman will turn on you and kill you.'

I myself think we have gone rather far on the road of befouling. To me it seems that the Ford automobile is about the final and absolute expression of our mechanical age — and is not the Ford car an ugly and ill-smelling thing? And against the Ford car and the vast Ford factories out in Detroit I would like to put for a moment the figure of Alfred Stieglitz as the craftsman of genius, in short, the artist. Born into a mechanical age and having lived in an age when practically all American men followed the false gods of cheapness and expediency, he has kept the faith. To me his life is a promise that the craftsmen, who are surely to be reborn into the world, will not have to kill in order to come back into their old inheritance. Against the day of their coming again, Alfred Stieglitz has held to the old faith with an iron grip. Through perhaps almost the single strength of this man, something has been kept alive here in America that we had all come near to forgetting.

I have been walking in the streets of New York and thinking of my friend Alfred Stieglitz and suddenly he no longer stands alone. Certain other figures appear and in them I understand in him certain impulses I have not always understood. I have myself come into the years of manhood in an age of Ford factories, and often enough I have run with the pack. Too often in my own work I have not been patient enough. I have stopped halfway, have not gone all the way. Shame comes to me and suddenly memories appear. I remember that when I was a lad in Ohio there were in my town certain fine old workmen come down into our new age out of an older time. In fancy now I see again two such men and hear them speaking of their work as they stand idling in the evening before one of the stores of my town. The lad, who was myself, is fascinated by their talk and stands behind them, listening. And now suddenly one of the workmen has remembered something he wants to explain to his fellow. They are both wagonmakers and each, in his young manhood, has served his long years of apprenticeship and has gone on his workman's journey. The workman who is talking is trying to explain to his fellow how, in a certain shop where he once worked in the State of Vermont, they made a wagon felloe.

'You come on,' he says, and the two old men go away together along the street in the dusk of a summer evening with a boy tagging at their heels. How sharply their figures remain in my mind, the two old lovers filled with a man's love we moderns have almost forgotten!

And now they have gone to one of the two wagon shops in the town and one of them has lighted a lamp and has opened his chest of tools. How affectionately he handles them and how bright and clean and sharp the tools are! He begins fitting two pieces of wood together. 'At that place I was telling you about we did it like this. Afterward I found out a quicker way, but I believe the harder way is the best. It makes a better joint, stands up better in all kinds of weather; that's what I mean,' the old workman says—and how sharply his figure comes back to me now as I think of Alfred Stieglitz, the prophet of the old workmen who by the intensity of his love of tools and materials has made himself such an outstanding American artist.

There is another man in my mind of the Stieglitz sort. He lives now at Cleveland, Ohio, where he runs a bookstore, but some twenty years ago he came to America from Germany as a workman, as a church-organ builder. On an evening last summer he walked and talked with me and as he walked and talked his mind went back to his boyhood in a German town. He spoke of the workmen in his father's shop and their treatment of him when he was a lad, learning his trade. When he had grown careless the workman, whose assistant he was, did not report the matter to the superintendent, but took the blame on himself. Then the old workman and the boy looked into each other's eyes. 'I didn't cut up any more monkey-shines after that,' said the bookseller of Cleveland.

On Sundays, when he was a lad, my friend at Cleveland walked in the state forest with his father. Other workmen also came with their sons. One of them went to touch one of the trees with his fingers. Soon now that particular tree would be offered for sale and already the workman had put his hand on his materials. He intended to be on hand and to be a bidder when that particular tree was offered for sale. 'After my father died,' my friend at Cleveland said, 'I went to a sale in the forest and bought a tree just because I had once seen my father look long and hungrily at it and because I knew he would want me to get my hands on it and work it up.'

And this man of Cleveland came to America to be a foreman in one of our church-organ factories. He didn't last long. He quit because they used nails instead of wooden pegs in the factory where he was employed. The owner of the factory tried to reason with him, but he quit. 'Here you have to do things in a hurry, in the American way. What's the difference? No one knows. They can't tell the difference.'

But my friend quit. The fact that nails were used instead of wooden pegs seemed to him a quite sufficient explanation of his inability to stay. He thought the nails affected, in a quite poisonous way, the tone of the instruments. He seemed to care about that. 'Every time I drove one of the nails it hurt my arm,' he said, and there was something that hurt him too when he heard the other workmen driving the nails. The sound hurt him. He winced when he spoke of it, and quite suddenly one saw that the sound of the nails being driven into the materials he loved was to him what the sound of the nails being driven into the cross of Christ might have meant in the ears of a primitive Christian.

It is just the spirit of these men that has always been alive and has always been kept alive in the person of Alfred Stieglitz, the photographer. In a peculiar way he has made himself an outstanding figure in the lives of innumerable American artists. In the beginning of this article I said that something must have happened to him long ago. He saw something we others haven't often seen. To me and to many other men I know his figure has been sharply defined, and as the years pass is becoming more and more sharply defined, as the type of the old workman whose love of his tools and his materials has been so passionate that he has emerged out of the workman to become the artist.

And perhaps that he is a photographer is significant too. It may well be the most significant thing of all. For has he not fought all of his life to make machinery the tool and not the master of man? Surely Alfred Stieglitz has seen a vision we may all some day see more and more clearly because of the fight he has made.

Foreword

D<small>ID YOU EVER</small> have a notion of this kind — there is an orange, or say an apple, lying on a table before you. You put out your hand to take it. Perhaps you eat it, make it a part of your physical life. Have you touched? Have you eaten? That's what I wonder about.

The whole subject is only important to me because I want the apple. What subtle flavors are concealed in it — how does it taste, smell, feel? Heavens, man, the way the apple feels in the hand is something — isn't it?

For a long time I thought only of eating the apple. Then later its fragrance became something of importance, too. The fragrance stole out through my room, through a window and into the streets. It made itself a part of all the smells of the streets. The devil! — in Chicago or Pittsburgh, Youngstown or Cleveland, it would have had a rough time.

That doesn't matter.

The point is that after the form of the apple began to take my eye, I often found myself unable to touch it at all. My hands went toward the object of my desire and then came back.

There I sat, in the room with the apple before me, and hours passed. I had pushed myself off into a world where nothing has any existence. Had I done that, or had I merely stepped, for the moment, out of the world of darkness into the light?

It may be that my eyes are blind and that I cannot see.

It may be I am deaf.

My hands are nervous and tremble. How much do they tremble? Now, alas, I am absorbed in looking at my own hands.

With these nervous and uncertain hands may I really feel for the form of things concealed in the darkness?

247

The Man's Story

During his trial for murder and later, after he had been cleared through the confession of that queer little bald chap with the nervous hands, I watched him, fascinated by his continued effort to make something understood.

He was persistently interested in something, having nothing to do with the charge that he had murdered the woman. The matter of whether or not, and by due process of law, he was to be convicted of murder and hanged by the neck until he was dead didn't seem to interest him. The law was something outside his life and he declined to have anything to do with the killing as one might decline a cigarette. 'I thank you, I am not smoking at present. I made a bet with a fellow that I could go along without smoking cigarettes for a month.'

That is the sort of thing I mean. It was puzzling. Really, had he been guilty and trying to save his neck, he couldn't have taken a better line. You see, at first, everyone thought he had done the killing; we were all convinced of it, and then, just because of that magnificent air of indifference, everyone began wanting to save him. When news came of the confession of the crazy little stage hand, everyone broke out into cheers.

He was clear of the law after that but his manner in no way changed. There was, somewhere, a man or a woman who would understand just what he understood, and it was important to find that person and talk things over. There was a time, during the trial and immediately afterward, when I saw a good deal of him, and I had this sharp sense of him, feeling about in the darkness trying to find something like a needle or a pin lost on the floor. Well, he was like an old man who cannot find his glasses. He feels in all his pockets and looks helplessly about.

There was a question in my own mind too, in everyone's mind — 'Can a man be wholly casual and brutal, in every outward way, at a moment when the one nearest and dearest to him is dying, and at the same time, and with quite another part of himself, be altogether tender and sensitive?'

Anyway, it's a story, and once in a while a man likes to tell a story straight out, without putting in any newspaper jargon about beautiful heiresses, cold-blooded murderers, and all that sort of tommyrot.

As I picked the story up, the sense of it was something like this:

The man's name was Wilson — Edgar Wilson — and he had come to Chicago from some place to the westward, perhaps from the mountains. He might once have been a sheepherder or something of the sort in the Far West, as he had the peculiar abstract air acquired only by being a good deal alone. About himself and his past he told a good many conflicting stories, and so, after being with him for a time, one instinctively discarded the past.

'The devil — it doesn't matter — the man can't tell the truth in that direction. Let it go,' one said to oneself. What was known was that he had come to Chicago from a town in Kansas and that he had run away from the Kansas town with another man's wife.

As to her story, I knew little enough of it. She had been at one time, I imagine, a rather handsome thing, in a big strong upstanding sort of way, but her life, until she met Wilson, had been rather messy. In those dead flat Kansas towns lives have a way of getting ugly and messy without anything very definite having happened to make them so. One can't imagine the reasons — Let it go. It just is so and one can't at all believe the writers of Western tales about the life out there.

To be a little more definite about this particular woman — in her young girlhood her father had got into trouble. He had been some sort of a small official, a traveling agent or something of the sort for an express company, and got arrested in connection with the disappearance of some money. And then, when he was in jail and before his trial, he shot and killed himself. The girl's mother was already dead.

Within a year or two she married a man, an honest enough fellow, but from all accounts rather uninteresting. He was a drug clerk and a frugal man and after a short time managed to buy a drugstore of his own.

The woman, as I have said, had been strong and well-built, but now grew thin and nervous. Still she carried herself well with a sort of air, as it were, and there was something about her that appealed strongly to men. Several men of the seedy little town were smitten by her and wrote her letters, trying to get her to creep out with them at night. You know how such things are done. The letters were unsigned. 'You go to such and such a place on Friday evening. If you are willing to talk things over with me, carry a book in your hand.'

Then the woman made a mistake and told her husband about the receipt of one of the letters, and he grew angry and tramped off to the trysting place at night with a shotgun in his hand. When no one appeared, he came home and fussed about. He said little mean tentative things. 'You must have looked — in a certain way — at the man when he passed you on the street. A man don't grow so bold with a married woman unless an opening has been given him.'

The man talked and talked after that, and life in the house must have been gay. She grew habitually silent, and when she was silent the house was silent. They had no children.

Then the man Edgar Wilson came along, going eastward, and stopped over in the town for two or three days. He had at that time a little money and stayed at a small workingmen's boarding house, near the railroad station. One day he saw the woman walking in the street and followed her to her home and the neighbors saw them standing and talking together for an hour by the front gate, and on the next day he came again.

That time they talked for two hours, and then she went into the house; got a few belongings and walked to the railroad station with him. They took a train for Chicago and lived there together, apparently very happy, until she died — in a way I am about to try to tell you about. They, of course, could not be married, and during the three years they lived in Chicago he did nothing toward earning their common living. As he had a very small amount of money when they came, barely enough to get them here from the Kansas town, they were miserably poor.

They lived, when I knew about them, over on the North Side, in that section of old three- and four-story brick residences that were once the homes of what we call our nice people, but that had afterward gone to the bad. The section is having a kind of rebirth now, but for a good many years it rather went to seed. There were these old residences, made into boarding houses, and with unbelievably dirty lace curtains at the windows, and now and then an utterly disreputable old tumbledown frame house — in one of which Wilson lived with his woman.

The place is a sight! Someone owns it, I suppose, who is shrewd enough to know that in a big city like Chicago no section gets neglected always. Such a fellow must have said to himself, 'Well, I'll let the place go. The ground on which the house stands will some day be very valuable, but the house is worth nothing. I'll let it go at a low rental and do nothing to fix it up. Perhaps I will get enough out of it to pay my taxes until prices come up.'

And so the house had stood there unpainted for years and the windows were out of line and the shingles nearly all off the roof. The second floor was reached by an outside stairway with a handrail that had become just the peculiar gray greasy black that wood can become in a soft-coal-burning city like Chicago or Pittsburgh. One's hand became black when the railing was touched; and the rooms above were altogether cold and cheerless.

At the front there was a large room with a fireplace, from which many bricks had fallen, and back of that were two small sleeping rooms.

Wilson and his woman lived in the place, at the time when the thing happened I am to tell you about, and as they had taken it in May, I presume they did not too much mind the cold barrenness of the large front room in which they lived. There was a sagging wooden bed with a leg broken off — the woman had tried to repair it with sticks from a packing box — a kitchen table, that was also used by Wilson as a writing desk, and two or three cheap kitchen chairs.

The woman had managed to get a place as wardrobe woman in a theater in Randolph Street and they lived on her earnings. It was said she had got the job because some man connected with the theater, or a company playing there, had a passion for her, but one can always pick up stories of that sort about any woman who works about the theater — from the scrubwoman to the star.

Anyway, she worked there and had a reputation in the theater of being quiet and efficient.

As for Wilson, he wrote poetry of a sort I've never seen before, although, like most newspaper men, I've taken a turn at verse-making myself now and then — both of the rhymed kind and the newfangled vers libre sort. I rather go in for the classical stuff myself.

About Wilson's verse — it was Greek to me. Well, now, to get right down to hardpan in this matter, it was and it wasn't.

The stuff made me feel just a little bit woozy when I took a whole sheaf of it and sat alone in my room reading it at night. It was all about walls, and deep wells, and great bowls with young trees standing erect in them — and trying to find their way to the light and air over the rim of the bowl.

Queer crazy stuff, every line of it, but fascinating too — in a way. One got into a new world with new values, which, after all, is, I suppose, what poetry is all about. There was the world of fact — we all know or think we know — the world of flat buildings and Middle-Western farms with wire fences about the fields and Fordson tractors running up and down, and towns with high schools and advertising billboards, and everything that makes up life — or that we think makes up life.

There was this world we all walk about in, and then there was this other world that I have come to think of as Wilson's world — a dim place, to me, at least — of faraway near places — things taking new and strange shapes, the insides of people coming out, the eyes seeing new things, the fingers feeling new and strange things.

It was a place of walls mainly. I got hold of the whole lot of Wilson's verse by a piece of luck. It happened that I was the first newspaper man who got into the place on the night when the woman's body was found, and there was all his stuff, carefully written out in a sort of child's copy-book, and two or three stupid policemen standing about. I just shoved the book under my coat, when they weren't looking, and later, during Wilson's trial, we published some of the more intelligible ones in the paper. It made pretty good newspaper stuff — the poet who killed his mistress,

> 'He did not wear his purple coat,
> For blood and wine are red —'

and all that. Chicago loved it.

To get back to the poetry itself for a moment. I just wanted to explain that all through the book there ran this notion, that men had erected walls about themselves and that all men were perhaps destined to stand forever behind the walls — on which they constantly beat with their fists, or with whatever tools they could get hold of. Wanted to break through to something, you understand. One couldn't quite make out whether there was just one great wall or many little individual walls. Sometimes Wilson put it one way, sometimes another. Men had themselves built the walls and now stood behind them, knowing dimly that beyond the walls there was warmth, light, air, beauty, life in fact — while at the same time, and because of a kind of madness in themselves, the walls were constantly being built higher and stronger.

The notion gives you the fantods a little, doesn't it? Anyway, it does me.

And then there was that notion about deep wells — men everywhere constantly digging and digging themselves down deeper and deeper into deep wells. They not wanting to do it, you understand, and no one wanting them to do it, but all the time the thing going on just the same, that is to say, the wells getting constantly deeper and deeper, and the voices growing dimmer and dimmer in the distance — and again the light and the warmth of life going away and going away, because of a kind of blind refusal of people to try to understand each other, I suppose.

It was all very strange to me — Wilson's poetry, I mean — when I came to it. Here is one of his things. It is not directly concerned with the walls, the bowl or the deep-well theme, as you will see, but it is one we ran in the paper during the trial and a lot of folks rather liked it — as I'll admit I do myself. Maybe putting it in here will give a kind of point to my story, by giving you some sense of the strangeness of the man who is the story's hero. In the book it was called merely 'Number Ninety-Seven,' and it went as follows:

> The firm grip of my fingers on the thin paper of this cigarette is a sign that I am very quiet now. Sometimes it is not so. When I am unquiet, I am weak, but when I am quiet, as I am now, I am very strong.
>
> Just now I went along one of the streets of my city and in at a door and came up here, where I am now, lying on a bed and looking out at a window. Very suddenly and completely the knowledge has come

to me that I could grip the sides of tall buildings as freely and as easily as I now grip this cigarette. I could hold the building between my fingers, put it to my lips and blow smoke through it. I could blow confusion away. I could blow a thousand people out through the roof of one tall building into the sky, into the unknown. Building after building I could consume, as I consume the cigarettes in this box. I could throw the burning ends of cities over my shoulder and out through a window.

It is not often I get in the state I am now in — so quiet and sure of myself. When the feeling comes over me there is a directness and simplicity in me that makes me love myself. To myself at such times I say strong sweet words.

I am on a couch by this window and I could ask a woman to come here to lie with me, or a man either for that matter.

I could take a row of houses standing on a street, tip them over, empty the people out of them, squeeze and compress all the people into one person and love that person.

Do you see this hand? Suppose it held a knife that could cut down through all the falseness in you. Suppose it could cut down through the sides of buildings and houses where thousands of people now lie asleep.

It would be something worth thinking about if the fingers of this hand gripped a knife that could cut and rip through all the ugly husks in which millions of lives are enclosed.

Well, there is the idea, you see, a kind of power that could be tender too. I will quote you just one more of his things, a more gentle one. It is called in the book, 'Number Eighty-Three.'

I am a tree that grows beside the wall. I have been thrusting up and up. My body is covered with scars. My body is old, but still I thrust upward, creeping toward the top of the wall.

It is my desire to drop blossoms and fruit over the wall.

I would moisten dry lips.

I would drop blossoms on the heads of children, over the top of the wall.

I would caress with falling blossoms the bodies of those who live on the further side of the wall.

My branches are creeping upward and new sap comes into me out of the dark ground under the wall.

My fruit shall not be my fruit until it drops from my arms, into the arms of the others, over the top of the wall.

And now as to the life led by the man and woman in the larger upper room in that old frame house. By a stroke of luck I have recently got rather a line on that by a discovery I have made.

After they had moved into the house — it was only last spring — the theater in which the woman was employed was dark for a long time and they were more than usually hard up, so the woman tried to pick up a little extra money — to help pay the rent, I suppose — by sub-letting the two little back rooms of that place of theirs.

Various people lived in the dark tiny holes, just how I can't make out, as there was no furniture. Still there are places in Chicago called 'flops' where one may sleep on the floor for five or ten cents and they are more patronized than respectable people know anything about.

What I did discover was a little woman — she wasn't so young, but she was hunchbacked and small, and it is hard not to think of her as a girl — who once lived in one of the rooms for several weeks. She had a job as ironer in a small hand-laundry in the neighborhood and someone had given her a cheap folding cot. She was a curiously sentimental creature, with the kind of hurt eyes deformed people often have, and I have a fancy she had herself a romantic attachment of a sort for the man Wilson. Anyway, I managed to find out a lot from her.

After the other woman's death and after Wilson had been cleared on the murder charge, by the confession of the stage hand, I used to go over to the house where he had lived, sometimes in the late afternoon after our paper had been put to bed for the day. Ours is an afternoon paper and after two o'clock most of us are free.

I found the hunchback girl standing in front of the house one day and began talking with her. She was a gold mine.

There was that look in her eyes I've told you of, the hurt sensitive look. I just spoke to her and we began talking of Wilson. She had lived in one of the rooms at the back. She told me of that at once.

On some days she found herself unable to work at the laundry because her strength suddenly gave out, and so, on such days, she stayed in the room, lying on the cot. Blinding headaches came that lasted for hours during which she was almost entirely unconscious of everything going on about her. Then afterward she was quite conscious, but for a long time very weak. She wasn't one who is destined to live very long, I suppose, and I presume she didn't much care.

Anyway, there she was in the room, in that weak state after the times of illness, and she grew curious about the two people in the front room, so she used to get off her couch and go softly in her stockinged feet to the door between the rooms and peek through the keyhole. She had to kneel on the dusty floor to do it.

The life in the room fascinated her from the beginning. Sometimes the man was in there alone, sitting at the kitchen table and writing the stuff he afterward put into the book I collared, and from which I have quoted; sometimes the woman was with him, and again sometimes he was in there alone, but wasn't writing. Then he was always walking and walking up and down.

When both people were in the room, and when the man was writing, the woman seldom moved, but sat in a chair by one of the windows with her hands crossed. He would write a few lines and then walk up and down talking to himself or to her. When he spoke, she did not answer except with her eyes, the crippled girl said. What I gathered of all this from her talk with me, and what is the product of my own imaginings, I confess I do not quite know.

Anyway, what I got and what I am trying, in my own way, to transmit to you is a sense of a kind of strangeness in the relationship of the two. It wasn't just a domestic household, a little down on its luck, by any means. He was trying to do something very difficult — with his poetry, I presume — and she in her own way was trying to help him.

And of course, as I have no doubt you have gathered from what I have quoted of Wilson's verse, the matter had something to do with the relationships between people — not necessarily between the particular man and woman who happened to be there in that room, but between all peoples.

The fellow had some half-mystic conception of all such things, and before he found his own woman had been going aimlessly about the world looking for a mate. Then he had found the woman in the Kansas town and — he at least thought — things had cleared, for him.

Well, he had the notion that no one in the world could think or feel anything alone, and that people only got into trouble and walled themselves in by trying it, or something of the sort. There was a discord. Things were jangled. Someone, it seems, had to strike a pitch that all voices could take up before the real song of life could begin.

Mind you, I'm not putting forth any notions of my own. What I am trying to do is to give you a sense of something I got from having read Wilson's stuff, from having known him a little, and from having seen something of the effect of his personality upon others.

He felt, quite definitely, that no one in the world could feel or even think alone. And then there was the notion that, if one tried to think with the mind without taking the body into account, one got all balled-up. True, conscious life built itself up like a pyramid. First the body and mind of a beloved one must come into one's thinking and feeling and then, in some mystic way, the bodies and minds of all the other people in the world must come in, must come sweeping in like a great wind — or something of the sort.

Is all this a little tangled up to you, who read my story of Wilson? It may not be. It may be that your minds are more clear than my own and that what I take to be so difficult will be very simple to you.

However, I have to bring up to you just what I can find, after diving down into this sea of motives and impulses — I admit I don't rightly understand.

The hunchback girl felt (or is it my own fancy coloring what she said?) — it doesn't really matter. The thing to get at is what the man Edgar Wilson felt.

He felt, I fancy, that in the field of poetry he had something to express that could never be expressed until he had found a woman who could, in a peculiar and absolute way, give herself in the world of the flesh — and that then there was to be a marriage out of which beauty would come for all people. He had to find the woman who had that power, and the power had to be untainted by self-interest, I fancy. A profound egotist, you see — and he thought he had found what he needed in the wife of the Kansas druggist.

He had found her and had done something to her. What it was I can't quite make out, except that she was absolutely and wholly happy with him, in a strangely inexpressive sort of way.

Trying to speak of him and his influence on others is rather like trying to walk on a tightrope stretched between two tall buildings above a crowded street. A cry from below, a laugh, the honk of an automobile horn, and down one goes into nothingness. One simply becomes ridiculous.

He wanted, it seems, to condense the flesh and the spirit of himself and his woman into his poems. You will remember that in one of the things of his I have quoted he speaks of condensing, of squeezing all the people of a city into one person and of loving that person.

One might think of him as a powerful person, almost hideously powerful. You will see, as you read, how he has got me in his power and is making me serve his purpose.

And he had caught and was holding the woman in his grip. He had wanted her — quite absolutely, and had taken her — as all men, perhaps, want to do with their women, and don't quite dare. Perhaps, too, she was in her own way greedy and he was making actual love to her always day and night, when they were together and when they were apart.

I'll admit I am confused about the whole matter myself. I am trying to express something I have felt, not in myself, nor in the words that came to me from the lips of the hunchback girl whom, you will remember, I left kneeling on the floor in that back room and peeking through a keyhole.

There she was, you see, the hunchback, and in the room before her were the man and woman and the hunchback girl also had fallen under the power of the man Wilson. She also was in love with him — there can be no doubt of that. The room in which she knelt was dark and dusty. There must have been a thick accumulation of dust on the floor.

What she said — or, if she did not say the words, what she made me feel — was that the man Wilson worked in the room, or walked up and down in there before his woman, and that, while he did that, his woman sat in the chair, and that there was in her face, in her eyes, a look ——

He was all the time making love to her, and his making love to her in just that abstract way was a kind of love-making with all people, and that was possible because the woman was as purely physical as he was something else. If all this is meaningless to you, at least it wasn't to the hunchback girl — who certainly was uneducated and never would have set herself up as having any special powers of understanding. She knelt in the dust, listening, and looking in at the keyhole, and in the end she came to feel that the man, in whose presence she had never been and whose person had never in any way touched her person, had made love to her also.

She had felt that and it had gratified her entire nature. One might say it had satisfied her. She was what she was and it had made life worth living for her.

Minor things happened in the room and one may speak of them.

For example, there was a day in June, a dark warm rainy day. The hunchback girl was in her room, kneeling on the floor, and Wilson and his woman were in their room.

Wilson's woman had been doing a family washing, and as it could not be dried outdoors she had stretched ropes across the room and had hung the clothes inside.

When the clothes were all hung, Wilson came from walking outside in the rain and going to the desk sat down and began to write.

He wrote for a few minutes and then got up and went about the room, and in walking a wet garment brushed against his face.

He kept right on walking and talking to the woman, but as he walked and talked he gathered all the clothes in his arms and going to the little landing at the head of the stairs outside, threw them down into the muddy yard below. He did that and the woman sat without moving or saying anything until he had gone back to his desk, then she went down the stairs, got the clothes and washed them again — and it was only after she had done that and when she was again hanging them in the room above that he appeared to know what he had done.

While the clothes were being rewashed, he went for another walk and when she heard his footsteps on the stairs the hunchback girl ran to the keyhole. As she knelt there, and as he came into the room, she could look directly into his face. 'He was like a puzzled child for a moment and then, although he said nothing, the tears began to run down his cheeks,' she said. That happened, and then the woman, who was at the moment rehanging the clothes, turned and saw him. She had her arm filled with clothes, but dropped them on the floor and ran to him. She half-knelt, the hunchback girl said, and putting her arms about his body and looking up into his face pleaded with him. 'Don't. Don't be hurt. Believe me, I know everything. Please don't be hurt,' was what she said.

And now as to the story of the woman's death. It happened in the fall of that year.

In the place where she was sometimes employed — that is to say, in the theater — there was this other man, the little half-crazed stage hand who shot her.

He had fallen in love with her and, like the men in the Kansas town from which she came, had written her several silly notes of which she said nothing to Wilson. The letters weren't very nice and some of them, the most unpleasant ones, were by some twist of the fellow's mind, signed with Wilson's name. Two of them were afterwards found on her person and were brought in as evidence against Wilson during his trial.

And so the woman worked in the theater and the summer had passed, and on an evening in the fall there was to be a dress rehearsal at the theater and the woman went there, taking Wilson with her. It was a fall day, such as we sometimes have in Chicago, cold and wet and with a heavy fog lying over the city.

The dress rehearsal did not come off. The star was ill, or something of the sort happened, and Wilson and his woman sat about, in the cold empty theater, for an hour or two, and then the woman was told she could go for the night.

She and Wilson walked across the city, stopping to get something to eat at a small restaurant. He was in one of the abstract silent moods common to him. No doubt he was thinking of the things he wanted to express in the poetry I have tried to tell you about. He went along, not seeing the woman beside him, not seeing the people drifting up to them and passing them in the streets. He went along in that way and she ——

She was, no doubt, then, as she always was in his presence — silent and satisfied with the fact that she was with him. There was nothing he could think or feel that did not take her into account. The very blood flowing up through his body was her blood too. He had made her feel that, and she was silent and satisfied as he went along, his body walking beside her, but his fancy groping its way through the land of high walls and deep walls.

They had walked from the restaurant, in the Loop District, over a bridge to the North Side, and still no words passed between them.

When they had almost reached their own place, the stage hand, the small man with the nervous hands who had written the notes, appeared out of the fog, as though out of nowhere, and shot the woman.

That was all there was to it. It was as simple as that.

They were walking, as I have described them, when a head flashed up before the woman in the midst of the fog, a hand shot out, there was the quick abrupt sound of a pistol shot and then the absurd little stage hand, he with the wrinkled impotent little old woman's face — then he turned and ran away.

All that happened just as I have written it, and it made no impression at all on the mind of Wilson. He walked along as though nothing had happened, and the woman, after half-falling, gathered herself together and managed to continue walking beside him, still saying nothing.

They went thus for perhaps two blocks, and had reached the foot of the outer stairs that led up to their place when a policeman came running, and the woman told him a lie. She told him some story about a struggle between two drunken men, and after a moment of talk the policeman went away, sent away by the woman in a direction opposite to the one taken by the fleeing stage hand.

They were in the darkness and the fog now and the woman took her man's arm while they climbed the stairs. He was as yet — as far as I will ever be able to explain logically — unaware of the shot, and of the fact that she was dying, although he had seen and heard everything. What the doctors said, who were put on the case afterward, was that a cord or muscle, or something of the sort that controls the action of the heart, had been practically severed by the shot.

She was dead and alive at the same time, I should say.

Anyway, the two people marched up the stairs and into the room above, and then a really dramatic and lovely thing happened. One wishes that the scene, with just all its connotations, could be played out on a stage instead of having to be put down in words.

The two came into the room, the one dead, but not ready to acknowledge death without a flash of something individual and lovely, that is to say, the one dead while still alive and the other alive, but at the moment dead to what was going on.

The room into which they went was dark, but, with the sure instinct of an animal, the woman walked across the room to the fireplace, while the man stopped and stood some ten feet from the door — thinking and thinking in his peculiarly abstract way. The fireplace was filled with an accumulation of waste matter, cigarette ends — the man was a hard smoker — bits of paper on which he had scribbled —

the rubbishy accumulation that gathers about all such fellows as Wilson. There was all of this quickly combustible material, stuffed into the fireplace, on this — the first cold evening of the fall.

And so the woman went to it, and found a match somewhere in the darkness, and touched the pile off.

There is a picture that will remain with me always — just that — the barren room and the blind unseeing man standing there, and the woman kneeling and making a little flare of beauty at the last. Little flames leaped up. Lights crept and danced over the walls. Below, on the floor of the room, there was a deep well of darkness in which the man, blind with his own purpose, was standing.

The pile of burning papers must have made, for a moment, quite a glare of light in the room and the woman stood for a moment, beside the fireplace, just outside the glare of light.

And then, pale and wavering, she walked across the light, as across a lighted stage, going softly and silently toward him. Had she also something to say? No one will ever know. What happened was that she said nothing.

She walked across to him and, at the moment she reached him, fell down on the floor and died at his feet, and at the same moment the little fire of papers died. If she struggled before she died, there on the floor, she struggled in silence. There was no sound. She had fallen and lay between him and the door that led out to the stairway and to the street.

It was then Wilson became altogether inhuman — too much so for my understanding.

The fire had died and the woman he had loved had died.

And there he stood looking into nothingness, thinking — God knows — perhaps of nothingness.

He stood a minute, five minutes, perhaps ten. He was a man who, before he found the woman, had been sunk far down into a deep sea of doubt and questionings. Before he found the woman, no expression had ever come from him. He had perhaps just wandered from place to place, looking at people's faces, wondering about people, wanting to come close to others and not knowing how. The woman had been able to lift him up to the surface of the sea of life for a time, and with her he had floated on the surface of the sea, under the sky, in the sunlight. The woman's warm body — given to him in love — had been as a boat in which he had floated on the surface of the sea, and now the boat had been wrecked and he was sinking again, back into the sea.

All of this had happened and he did not know — that is to say, he did not know, and at the same time he did know.

He was a poet, I presume, and perhaps at the moment a new poem was forming itself in his mind.

At any rate, he stood for a time, as I have said, and then he must have had a feeling that he should make some move, that he should if possible save himself from some disaster about to overtake him.

He had an impulse to go to the door, and by way of the stairway, to go downstairs and into the street — but the body of the woman was between him and the door.

What he did and what, when he later told of it, sounded so terribly cruel to others, was to treat the woman's dead body as one might treat a fallen tree in the darkness in a forest. First he tried to push the body aside with his foot, and then, as that seemed impossible, he stepped awkwardly over it.

He stepped directly on the woman's arm. The discolored mark where his heel landed was afterward found on the body.

He almost fell, and then his body righted itself and he went walking, marched down the rickety stairs and went walking in the streets.

By chance the night had cleared. It had grown colder and a cold wind had driven the fog away. He walked along, very nonchalantly, for several blocks. He walked along as calmly as you, the reader, might walk, after having had lunch with a friend.

As a matter of fact he even stopped to make a purchase at a store. I remember that the place was called 'The Whip.' He went in, bought himself a package of cigarettes, lighted one and stood a moment, apparently listening to a conversation going on among several idlers in the place.

And then he strolled again, going along smoking the cigarette and thinking of his poem, no doubt. Then he came to a moving-picture theater.

That perhaps touched him off. He also was an old fireplace, stuffed with old thoughts, scraps of unwritten poems — God knows what rubbish! Often he had gone at night to the theater, where the woman was employed, to walk home with her, and now the people were coming out of a small moving-picture house. They had been in there seeing a play called *The Light of the World*.

Wilson walked into the midst of the crowd, lost himself in the crowd, smoking his cigarette, and then he took off his hat, looked anxiously about for a moment, and suddenly began shouting in a loud voice.

He stood there, shouting and trying to tell the story of what had happened in a loud voice, and with the uncertain air of one trying to remember a dream. He did that for a moment, and then, after running a little way along the pavement, stopped and began his story again. It was only after he had gone thus, in short rushes, back along the street to the house and up the rickety stairway to where the woman was lying — the crowd following curiously at his heels — that a policeman came up and arrested him.

He seemed excited at first, but was quiet afterward, and he laughed at the notion of insanity when the lawyer who had been retained for him tried to set up the plea in court.

As I have said, his action, during his trial, was confusing to us all, as he seemed wholly uninterested in the murder and in his own fate. After the confession of the man who had fired the shot he seemed to feel no resentment toward him either. There was something he wanted, having nothing to do with what had happened.

There he had been, you see, before he found the woman, wandering about in the world, digging himself deeper and deeper into the deep wells he talked about in his poetry, building the wall between himself and all us others constantly higher and higher.

He knew what he was doing, but he could not stop. That's what he kept talking about, pleading with people about. The man had come up out of the sea of doubt, had grasped for a time the hand of the woman, and with her hand in his had floated for a time upon the surface of life — but now he felt himself again sinking down into the sea.

His talking and talking, stopping people in the street and talking, going into people's houses and talking, was, I presume, but an effort, he was always afterward making, not to sink back forever into the sea; it was the struggle of a drowning man, I dare say.

At any rate, I have told you the man's story — have been compelled to try to tell you his story. There was a kind of power in him, and the power has been exerted over me as it was exerted over the woman from Kansas and the unknown hunchback girl, kneeling on the floor in the dust and peering through a keyhole.

Ever since the woman died, we have all been trying and trying to drag the man Wilson back out of the sea of doubt and dumbness into which we feel him sinking deeper and deeper — and to no avail.

It may be I have been impelled to tell his story in the hope that by writing of him I may myself understand. Is there not a possibility that with understanding would come also the strength to thrust an arm down into the sea and drag the man Wilson back to the surface again?

Milk-Bottles

I LIVED, during that summer, in a large room on the top floor of an old house on the North Side in Chicago. It was August and the night was hot. Until after midnight I sat — the sweat trickling down my back — under a lamp, laboring to feel my way into the lives of the fanciful people who were trying also to live in the tale on which I was at work.

It was a hopeless affair.

I became involved in the efforts of the shadowy people and they in turn became involved in the fact of the hot uncomfortable room, in the fact that, although it was what the farmers of the Middle West call 'good corn-growing weather,' it was plain hell to be alive in Chicago. Hand in hand the shadowy people of my fanciful world and myself groped our way through a forest in which the leaves had all been burned off the trees. The hot ground burned the shoes off our feet. We were striving to make our way through the forest and into some cool beautiful city. The fact is, as you will clearly understand, I was a little off my head.

When I gave up the struggle and got to my feet, the chairs in the room danced about. They also were running aimlessly through a burning land and striving to reach some mythical city. 'I'd better get out of here and go for a walk or go jump into the lake and cool myself off,' I thought.

I went down out of my room and into the street. On a lower floor of the house lived two burlesque actresses who had just come in from their evening's work and who now sat in their room talking. As I reached the street, something heavy whirled past my head and broke

266

on the stone pavement. A white liquid spurted over my clothes, and the voice of one of the actresses could be heard coming from the one lighted room of the house. "Oh, hell! We live such damned lives, we do, and we work in such a town! A dog is better off! And now they are going to take booze away from us too! I come home from working in that hot theater on a hot night like this and what do I see — a half-filled bottle of spoiled milk standing on a window-sill! I won't stand it! I got to smash everything!' she cried.

I walked eastward from my house. From the northwestern end of the city, great hordes of men, women, and children had come to spend the night out-of-doors, by the shore of the lake. It was stifling hot there, too, and the air was heavy with a sense of struggle. On a few hundred acres of flat land, that had formerly been a swamp, some two million people were fighting for the peace and quiet of sleep and not getting it. Out of the half darkness, beyond the little strip of park land at the water's edge, the huge empty houses of Chicago's fashionable folk made a grayish-blue blot against the sky. 'Thank the gods,' I thought, 'there are some people who can get out of here, who can go to the mountains or the seashore or to Europe.' I stumbled in the half darkness over the legs of a woman who was lying and trying to sleep on the grass. A baby lay beside her and when she sat up it began to cry. I muttered an apology and stepped aside, and as I did so my foot struck a half-filled milk bottle and I knocked it over, the milk running out on the grass. 'Oh, I'm sorry. Please forgive me,' I cried. 'Never mind,' the woman answered, 'the milk is sour.'

He is a tall stoop-shouldered man with prematurely grayed hair and works as a copy-writer in an advertising agency in Chicago — an agency where I also have sometimes been employed — and on that night in August I met him, walking with quick eager strides along the shore of the lake and past the tired petulant people. He did not see me at first, and I wondered at the evidence of life in him when everyone else seemed half dead; but a street lamp hanging over a near-by roadway threw its light down upon my face and he pounced. 'Here, you, come up to my place!' he cried sharply. 'I've got something to show you. I was on my way down to see you. That's where I was going,' he lied as he hurried me along.

We went to his apartment on a street leading back from the lake and the park. German, Polish, Italian, and Jewish families, equipped with soiled blankets and the ever-present half-filled bottles of milk, had come prepared to spend the night out-of-doors; but the American families in the crowd were giving up the struggle to find a cool spot and a little stream of them trickled along the sidewalks, going back to hot beds in the hot houses.

It was past one o'clock and my friend's apartment was disorderly as well as hot. He explained that his wife, with their two children, had gone home to visit her mother on a farm near Springfield, Illinois.

We took off our coats and sat down. My friend's thin cheeks were flushed and his eyes shone. 'You know — well — you see,' he began and then hesitated and laughed like an embarrassed schoolboy. 'Well, now,' he began again, 'I've long been wanting to write something real, something besides advertisements. I suppose I'm silly, but that's the way I am. It's been my dream to write something stirring and big. I suppose it's the dream of a lot of advertising writers, eh? Now look here — don't you go laughing. I think I've done it.'

He explained that he had written something concerning Chicago, the capital and heart, as he said, of the whole Central West. He grew angry. 'People come here from the East or from farms, or from little holes of towns like I came from, and they think it smart to run Chicago into the ground,' he declared. 'I thought I'd show 'em up,' he added, jumping up and walking nervously about the room.

He handed me many sheets of paper covered with hastily scrawled words, but I protested and asked him to real it aloud. He did, standing with his face turned away from me. There was a quiver in his voice. The thing he had written concerned some mythical town I had never seen. He called it Chicago, but in the same breath spoke of great streets flaming with color, ghostlike buildings flung up into night skies, and a river, running down a path of gold into the boundless West. It was the city, I told myself, I and the people of my story had been trying to find earlier on that same evening, when because of the heat I went a little off my head and could not work any more. The people of the city he had written about were a cool-headed, brave people, marching forward to some spiritual triumph, the promise of which was inherent in the physical aspects of the town.

Now I am one who, by the careful cultivation of certain traits in my character, have succeeded in building up the more brutal side of my nature, but I cannot knock women and children down in order to get aboard Chicago streetcars, nor can I tell an author to his face that I think his work is rotten.

'You're all right, Ed. You're great. You've knocked out a regular sockdolager of a masterpiece here. Why, you sound as good as Henry Mencken writing about Chicago as the literary center of America, and you've lived in Chicago and he never did. The only thing I can see you've missed is a little something about the stockyards, and you can put that in later,' I added, and prepared to depart.

'What's this?' I asked, picking up a half-dozen sheets of paper that lay on the floor by my chair. I read it eagerly. And when I had finished reading it, he stammered and apologized, and then, stepping across the room, jerked the sheets out of my hand and threw them out at an open window. 'I wish you hadn't seen that. It's something else I wrote about Chicago,' he explained. He was flustered.

'You see, the night was so hot, and, down at the office, I had to write a condensed-milk advertisement, just as I was sneaking away to come home and work on this other thing, and the streetcar was so crowded and the people stank so, and when I finally got home here —the wife being gone — the place was a mess. Well, I couldn't write and I was sore. It's been my chance, you see, the wife and kids being gone and the house being quiet. I went for a walk. I think I went a little off my head. Then I came home and wrote that stuff I've just thrown out of the window.'

He grew cheerful again. 'Oh, well — it's all right. Writing that fool thing stirred me up and enabled me to write this other stuff, this real stuff I showed you first, about Chicago.'

And so I went home and to bed, having in this odd way stumbled upon another bit of the kind of writing that is — for better or worse — really presenting the lives of the people of these towns and cities — sometimes in prose, sometimes in stirring colorful song. It was the kind of thing Mr. Sandburg or Mr. Masters might have done after an evening's walk on a hot night in, say, West Congress Street in Chicago.

The thing I had read of Ed's centered about a half-filled bottle of spoiled milk standing dim in the moonlight on a window-sill. There had been a moon earlier on that August evening, a new moon, a thin crescent golden streak in the sky. What had happened to my friend, the advertising writer, was something like this — I figured it all out as I lay sleepless in bed after our talk.

I am sure I do not know whether or not it is true that all advertising writers and newspaper men want to do other kinds of writing, but Ed did all right. The August day that had preceded the hot night had been a hard one for him to get through. All day he had been wanting to be at home in his quiet apartment producing literature, rather than sitting in an office and writing advertisements. In the late afternoon, when he had thought his desk cleared for the day, the boss of the copy-writers came and ordered him to write a page advertisement for the magazines on the subject of condensed milk. 'We got a chance to get a new account if we can knock out some crackerjack stuff in a hurry,' he said. 'I'm sorry to have to put it up to you on such a rotten hot day, Ed, but we're up against it. Let's see if you've got some of the old pep in you. Get down to hardpan now and knock out something snappy and unusual before you go home.'

Ed had tried. He put away the thoughts he had been having about the city beautiful — the glowing city of the plains — and got right down to business. He thought about milk, milk for little children, the Chicagoans of the future, milk that would produce a little cream to put in the coffee of advertising writers in the morning, sweet fresh milk to keep all his brother and sister Chicagoans robust and strong. What Ed really wanted was a long cool drink of something with a kick in it, but he tried to make himself think he wanted a drink of milk. He gave himself over to thoughts of milk, milk condensed and yellow, milk warm from the cows his father owned when he was a boy — his mind launched a little boat and he set out on a sea of milk.

Out of it all he got what is called an original advertisement. The sea of milk on which he sailed became a mountain of cans of condensed milk, and out of that fancy he got his idea. He made a crude sketch for a picture showing wide rolling green fields with white farm houses. Cows grazed on the green hills, and at one side of the picture a barefooted boy was driving a herd of Jersey cows out of the sweet fair land and down a lane into a kind of funnel at the small end of which was a tin of the condensed milk. Over the picture he put a heading: 'The health and freshness of a whole countryside is condensed into one can of Whitney-Wells Condensed Milk.' The head copy-writer said it was a humdinger.

And then Ed went home. He wanted to begin writing about the city beautiful at once and so didn't go out to dinner, but fished about in the ice chest and found some cold meat out of which he made himself a sandwich. Also, he poured himself a glass of milk, but it was sour. 'Oh, damn!' he said, and poured it into the kitchen sink.

As Ed explained to me later, he sat down and tried to begin writing his real stuff at once, but he couldn't seem to get into it. The last hour in the office, the trip home in the hot smelly car, and the taste of the sour milk in his mouh had jangled his nerves. The truth is that Ed has a rather sensitive, finely balanced nature, and it had got mussed up.

He took a walk and tried to think, but his mind wouldn't stay where he wanted it to. Ed is now a man of nearly forty and on that night his mind ran back to his young manhood in the city — and stayed there. Like other boys who had become grown men in Chicago, he had come to the city from a farm at the edge of a prairie town, and like all such town and farm boys, he had come filled with vague dreams.

What things he had hungered to do and be in Chicago! What he had done you can fancy. For one thing he had got himself married and now lived in the apartment on the North Side. To give a real picture of his life during the twelve or fifteen years that had slipped away since he was a young man would involve writing a novel, and that is not my purpose.

Anyway, there he was in his room — come home from his walk — and it was hot and quiet and he could not manage to get into his masterpiece. How still it was in the apartment with the wife and children away! His mind stayed on the subject of his youth in the city.

He remembered a night of his young manhood when he had gone out to walk, just as he did on that August evening. Then his life wasn't complicated by the fact of the wife and children and he lived alone in his room; but something had got on his nerves then, too. On that evening long ago he grew restless in his room and went out to walk. It was summer, and first he went down by the river where ships were being loaded and then to a crowded park where girls and young fellows walked about.

He grew bold and spoke to a woman who sat alone on a park bench. She let him sit beside her and, because it was dark and she was silent, he began to talk. The night had made him sentimental. 'Human beings are such hard things to get at. I wish I could get close to someone,' he said. 'Oh, you go on! What you doing? You ain't trying to kid someone?' asked the woman.

Ed jumped up and walked away. He went into a long street lined with dark silent buildings and then stopped and looked about. What he wanted was to believe that in the apartment buildings were people who lived intense eager lives, who had great dreams, who were capable of great adventures. 'They are really only separated from me by the brick walls,' was what he told himself on that night.

It was then that the milk-bottle theme first got hold of him. He went into an alleyway to look at the backs of the apartment buildings and, on that evening also, there was a moon. Its light fell upon a long row of half-filled bottles standing on window-sills.

Something within him went a little sick and he hurried out of the alleyway and into the street. A man and woman walked past him and stopped before the entrance to one of the buildings. Hoping they might be lovers, he concealed himself in the entrance to another building to listen to their conversation.

The couple turned out to be a man and wife and they were quarreling. Ed heard the woman's voice saying: 'You come in here. You can't put that over on me. You say you just want to take a walk, but I know you. You want to go out and blow in some money. What I'd like to know is why you don't loosen up a little for me.'

That is the story of what happened to Ed, when, as a young man, he went to walk in the city in the evening, and when he had become a man of forty and went out of his house wanting to dream and to think of a city beautiful, much the same sort of thing happened again. Perhaps the writing of the condensed milk advertisement and the taste of the sour milk he had got out of the icebox had something to do with his mood; but, anyway, milk bottles, like a refrain in a song, got into his brain. They seemed to sit and mock at him from the windows of all the buildings in all the streets, and when he turned to look at people, he met the crowds from the West and the Northwest Sides going to the park and the lake. At the head of each little group of people marched a woman who carried a milk bottle in her hand.

And so, on that August night, Ed went home angry and disturbed, and in anger wrote of his city. Like the burlesque actress in my own house, he wanted to smash something, and, as milk bottles were in his mind, he wanted to smash milk bottles. 'I could grasp the neck of a milk bottle. It fits the hand so neatly. I could kill a man or woman with such a thing,' he thought desperately.

He wrote, you see, the five or six sheets I had read in that mood and then felt better. And after that he wrote about the ghostlike buildings flung into the sky by the hands of a brave adventurous people and about the river that runs down a path of gold, and into the boundless West.

As you have already concluded, the city he described in his masterpiece was lifeless, but the city he, in a queer way, expressed in what he wrote about the milk bottle could not be forgotten. It frightened you a little, but there it was, and in spite of his anger, or perhaps because of it, a lovely singing quality had got into the thing. In those few scrawled pages the miracle had been worked. I was a fool not to have put the sheets into my pocket. When I went down out of his apartment that evening, I did look for them in a dark alleyway, but they had become lost in a sea of rubbish that had leaked over the tops of a long row of tin ash cans that stood at the foot of a stairway leading from the back doors of the apartments above.

A Meeting South

HE TOLD ME THE STORY of his ill fortune — a crack-up in an airplane — with a very gentlemanly little smile on his very sensitive, rather thin, lips. Such things happened. He might well have been speaking of another. I liked his tone and I liked him.

This happened in New Orleans, where I had gone to live. When he came, my friend, Fred, for whom he was looking, had gone away, but immediately I felt a strong desire to know him better and so suggested we spend the evening together. When we went down the stairs from my apartment, I noticed that he was a cripple. The slight limp, the look of pain that occasionally drifted across his face, the little laugh that was intended to be jolly, but did not quite achieve its purpose, all these things began at once to tell me the story I have now set myself to write.

'I shall take him to see Aunt Sally,' I thought. One does not take every caller to Aunt Sally. However, when she is in fine feather, when she has taken a fancy to her visitor, there is no one like her. Although she has lived in New Orleans for thirty years, Aunt Sally is Middle-Western, born and bred.

However, I am plunging a bit too abruptly into my story.

First of all I must speak more of my guest, and for convenience sake I shall call him David. I felt at once that he would be wanting a drink and in New Orleans — dear city of Latins and hot nights — even in prohibition times such things can be managed. We achieved several and my own head became somewhat shaky, but I could see that what we had taken had not affected him. Evening was coming, the abrupt waning of the day and the quick smoky soft-footed coming

274

of night, characteristic of the semi-tropic city, when he produced a
bottle from his hip pocket. It was so large that I was amazed. How
had it happened that the carrying of so large a bottle had not made
him look deformed? His body was very small and delicately built.
'Perhaps, like the kangaroo, his body has developed some kind of a
natural pouch for taking care of supplies,' I thought. Really he walked
as one might fancy a kangaroo would walk when out for a quiet evening stroll. I went along thinking of Darwin and the marvels of prohibition. 'We are a wonderful people, we Americans,' I thought. We
were both in fine humor and had begun to like each other immensely.

He explained the bottle. The stuff, he said, was made by a Negro
man on his father's plantation somewhere over in Alabama. We sat
on the steps of a vacant house deep down in the old French Quarter
of New Orleans — the Vieux Carré — while he explained that his
father had no intention of breaking the law — that is to say, in so far
as the law remained reasonable.

'Our nigger just makes whiskey for us,' he said. 'We keep him
for that purpose. He doesn't have anything else to do, just makes
the family whiskey, that's all. If he went selling any, we'd raise hell
with him. I dare say Dad would shoot him if he caught him up to
any such unlawful trick, and you bet, Jim, our nigger I'm telling
you of, knows it too.

'He's a good whiskey-maker, though, don't you think?' David
added. He talked of Jim in a warm friendly way. 'Lord, he's been
with us always, was born with us. His wife cooks for us and Jim
makes our whiskey. It's a race to see which is best at his job, but I
think Jim will win. He's getting a little better all the time and all of
our family — well, I reckon we just like and need our whiskey more
than we do our food.'

Do you know New Orleans? Have you lived there in the summer
when it is hot, in the winter when it rains, and through the glorious
late fall days? Some of its own, more progressive, people scorn it now.
In New Orleans there is a sense of shame because the city is not more
like Chicago or Pittsburgh.

It, however suited David and me. We walked slowly, on account
of his bad leg, through many streets of the Old Town, Negro women
laughing all around us in the dusk, shadows playing over old buildings, children with their shrill cries dodging in and out of old hall-

ways. The old city was once almost altogether French, but now it is becoming more and more Italian. It, however, remains Latin. People live out-of-doors. Families were sitting down to dinner within full sight of the street — all doors and windows open. A man and his wife quarreled in Italian. In a patio back of an old building a Negress sang a French song.

We came out of the narrow little streets and had a drink in front of the dark cathedral and another in a little square in front. There is a statue of General Jackson, always taking off his hat to Northern tourists who in winter come down to see the city. At his horse's feet an inscription — 'The Union must and will be preserved.' We drank solemnly to that declaration and the general seemed to bow a bit lower. 'He was sure a proud man,' David said, as we went over toward the docks to sit in the darkness and look at the Mississippi. All good New Orleanians go to look at the Mississippi at least once a day. At night it is like creeping into a dark bedroom to look at a sleeping child — something of that sort — gives you the same warm nice feeling, I mean. David is a poet and so in the darkness by the river we spoke of Keats and Shelley, the two English poets all good Southern men love.

All of this, you are to understand, was before I took him to see Aunt Sally.

Both Aunt Sally and myself are Middle-Westerners. We are but guests down here, but perhaps we both in some queer way belong to this city. Something of the sort is in the wind. I don't quite know how it has happened.

A great many Northern men and women come down our way and, when they go back North, write things about the South. The trick is to write nigger stories. The North likes them. They are so amusing. One of the best-known writers of nigger stories was down here recently and a man I know, a Southern man, went to call on him. The writer seemed a bit nervous. 'I don't know much about the South or Southerners,' he said. 'But you have your reputation,' my friend said. 'You are widely known as a writer about the South and about Negro life.' The writer had a notion he was being made sport of. 'Now look here,' he said, 'I don't claim to be a high-brow. I'm a business man myself. At home, up North, I associate mostly with business men and when I am not at work I go out to the country club.

I want you to understand I am not setting myself up as a high-brow. I give them what they want,' he said.

My friend said he appeared angry. 'About what now, do you fancy?' he asked innocently.

However, I am not thinking of the Northern writer of Negro stories. I am thinking of the Southern poet, with the bottle clasped firmly in his hands, sitting in the darkness beside me on the docks facing the Mississippi.

He spoke at some length of his gift for drinking. 'I didn't always have it. It is a thing built up,' he said. The story of how he chanced to be a cripple came out slowly. You are to remember that my own head was a bit unsteady. In the darkness the river, very deep and very powerful off New Orleans, was creeping away to the Gulf. The whole river seemed to move away from us and then to slip noiselessly into the darkness like a vast moving sidewalk.

When he had first come to me, in the late afternoon, and when we had started for our walk together, I had noticed that one of his legs dragged as we went along and that he kept putting a thin hand to an equally thin cheek.

Sitting over by the river he explained, as a boy would explain when he has stubbed his toe running down a hill.

When the World War broke out, he went over to England and managed to get himself enrolled as an aviator, very much, I gathered, in the spirit in which a countryman, in a city for a night, might take in a show.

The English had been glad enough to take him on. He was one more man. They were glad enough to take anyone on just then. He was small and delicately built, but after he got in he turned out to be a first-rate flyer, serving all through the War with a British flying squadron, but at the last got into a crash and fell.

Both legs were broken, one of them in three places, the scalp was badly torn, and some of the bones of the face had been splintered.

They had put him into a field hospital and had patched him up. 'It was my fault if the job was rather bungled,' he said. 'You see, it was a field hospital, a hell of a place. Men were torn all to pieces, groaning and dying. Then they moved me back to a base hospital and it wasn't much better. The fellow who had the bed next to mine had shot himself in the foot to avoid going into a battle. A lot of them did that, but why they picked on their own feet that way is beyond me. I's a nasty place, full of small bones. If you're ever going to shoot yourself, don't pick on a spot like that. Don't pick on your feet. I tell you it's a bad idea.

'Anyway, the man in the hospital was always making a fuss and I got sick of him and the place too. When I got better I faked, said the nerves of my leg didn't hurt. It was a lie, of course. The nerves of my leg and of my face have never quit hurting. I reckon maybe, if I had told the truth, they might have fixed me up all right.'

I got it. No wonder he carried his drinks so well. When I understood, I wanted to keep on drinking with him, wanted to stay with him until he got tired of me as he had of the man who lay beside him in the base hospital over there somewhere in France.

The point was that he never slept, could not sleep, except when he was a little drunk. 'I'm a nut,' he said, smiling.

It was after we got over to Aunt Sally's that he talked most. Aunt Sally had gone to bed when we got there, but she got up when we rang the bell and we all went to sit together in the little patio back of her house. She is a large woman with great arms and rather a paunch, and she had put on nothing but a light flowered dressing-gown over a thin, ridiculously girlish nightgown. By this time the moon had come up and, outside, in the narrow street of the Vieux Carré, three drunken sailors from a ship in the river were sitting on a curb and singing a song,

> 'I've got to get it,
> You've got to get it,
> We've all got to get it
> In our own good time.'

They had rather nice boyish voices, and every time they sang a verse and had done the chorus, they all laughed together heartily.

In Aunt Sally's patio there are many broad-leafed banana plants and a Chinaberry tree throwing its soft purple shadows on a brick floor.

As for Aunt Sally, she is as strange to me as he was. When we came and when we were all seated at a little table in the patio, she ran into her house and presently came back with a bottle of whiskey. She, it seemed, had understood him at once, had understood without unnecessary words that the little Southern man lived always in the black house of pain, that whiskey was good to him, that it quieted his throbbing nerves, temporarily at least. 'Everything is temporary, when you come to that,' I can fancy Aunt Sally saying.

We sat for a time in silence, David having shifted his allegiance and taken two drinks out of Aunt Sally's bottle. Presently he rose and walked up and down the patio floor, crossing and recrossing the network of delicately outlined shadows on the bricks. 'It's really all right, the leg,' he said; 'something just presses on the nerves, that's all.' In me there was a self-satisfied feeling. I had done the right thing. I had brought him to Aunt Sally. 'I have brought him to a mother.' She has always made me feel that way since I have known her.

And now I shall have to explain her a little. It will not be so easy. That whole neighborhood in New Orleans is alive with tales concerning her.

Aunt Sally came to New Orleans in the old days, when the town was wild, in the wide-open days. What she had been before she came no one knew, but anyway she opened a place. That was very, very long ago when I was myself but a lad, up in Ohio. As I have already said, Aunt Sally came from somewhere up in the Middle-Western country. In some obscure subtle way it would flatter me to think she came from my state.

The house she had opened was one of the older places in the French Quarter down here, and when she had got her hands on it, Aunt Sally had a hunch. Instead of making the place modern, cutting it up into small rooms, all that sort of thing, she left it just as it was and spent her money rebuilding falling old walls, mending winding broad old stairways, repairing dim high-ceilinged old rooms, soft-colored old marble mantels. After all, we do seem attached to sin, and there are so many people busy making sin unattractive. It is good to find someone who takes the other road. It would have been so very much to Aunt Sally's advantage to have made the place modern, that is to say, in the business she was in at that time. If a few old rooms, wide old stairways, old cooking ovens built into the walls — if all these things did not facilitate the stealing in of couples on dark nights, they at least did something else. She had opened a gambling and drinking house, but one can have no doubt about the ladies stealing in. 'I was on the make all right,' Aunt Sally told me once.

She ran the place and took in money, and the money she spent on the place itself. A falling wall was made to stand up straight and fine again, the banana plants were made to grow in the patio, the Chinaberry tree got started and was helped through the years of adolescence. On the wall the lovely Rose of Montana bloomed madly. The fragrant Lantana grew in a dense mass at a corner of the wall.

When the Chinaberry tree, planted at the very center of the patio, began to get up into the light, it filled the whole neighborhood with fragrance in the spring.

Fifteen, twenty years of that, with Mississippi River gamblers and race-horse men sitting at tables by windows in the huge rooms upstairs in the house that had once, no doubt, been the town house of some rich planter's family — in the boom days of the forties. Women stealing in, too, in the dusk of evenings. Drinks being sold. Aunt Sally raking down the kitty from the game, raking in her share, quite ruthlessly.

At night, getting a good price, too, from the lovers. No questions asked, a good price for drinks. Moll Flanders might have lived with Aunt Sally. What a pair they would have made! The Chinaberry tree beginning to be lusty. The Lantana blossoming — in the fall the Rose of Montana.

Aunt Sally getting hers. Using the money to keep the old house in fine shape. Salting some away all the time.

A motherly soul, good, sensible Middle-Western woman, eh? Once a race-horse man left twenty-four thousand dollars with her and disappeared. No one knew she had it. There was a report the man was dead. He had killed a gambler in a place down by the French Market, and while they were looking for him he managed to slip into Aunt Sally's and leave his swag. Some time later a body was found floating in the river and it was identified as the horseman, but in reality he had been picked up in a wire-tapping haul in New York City and did not get out of his Northern prison for six years.

When he did get out, naturally, he skipped for New Orleans. No doubt he was somewhat shaky. She had him. If he squealed, there was a murder charge to be brought up and held over his head. It was night when he arrived and Aunt Sally went at once to an old brick oven built into the wall of the kitchen and took out a bag. 'There it is,' she said. The whole affair was part of the day's work for her in those days.

Gamblers at the tables in some of the rooms upstairs, lurking couples, from the old patio below the fragrance of growing things.

When she was fifty, Aunt Sally had got enough and had put them all out. She did not stay in the way of sin too long and she never went in too deep, like that Moll Flanders, and so she was all right and sitting pretty. 'They wanted to gamble and drink and play with the ladies. The ladies liked it all right. I never saw none of them come in protesting too much. The worst was in the morning when they went away. They looked so sheepish and guilty. If they felt that way, what made them come? If I took a man, you bet I'd want him and no monkey-business or nothing doing.

'I got a little tired of all of them, that's the truth,' Aunt Sally laughed. 'But that wasn't until I had got what I went after. Oh, pshaw, they took up too much of my time, after I got enough to be safe.'

Aunt Sally is now sixty-five. If you like her and she likes you, she will let you sit with her in her patio gossiping of the old times, of the old river days. Perhaps — well, you see there is still something of the French influence at work in New Orleans, a sort of matter-of-factness about life — what I started to say is that if you know Aunt Sally and she likes you, and if, by chance, your lady likes the smell of flowers growing in a patio at night — really, I am going a bit too far. I only meant to suggest that Aunt Sally at sixty-five is not harsh. She is a motherly soul.

We sat in the garden talking, the little Southern poet, Aunt Sally, and myself — or rather they talked and I listened. The Southerner's great-grandfather was English, a younger son, and he came over here to make his fortune as a planter, and did it. Once he and his sons owned several great plantations with slaves, but now his father had but a few hundred acres left, about one of the old houses — somewhere over in Alabama. The land is heavily mortgaged and most of it has not been under cultivation for years. Negro labor is growing more and more expensive and unsatisfactory since so many Negroes have run off to Chicago, and the poet's father and the one brother at home are not much good at working the land. 'We aren't strong enough and we don't know how,' the poet said.

The Southerner had come to New Orleans to see Fred, to talk with Fred about poetry, but Fred was out of town. I could only walk about with him, help him drink his home-made whiskey. Already I had taken nearly a dozen drinks. In the morning I would have a headache.

I drew within myself, listening while David and Aunt Sally talked. The Chinaberry tree had been so and so many years growing — she spoke of it as she might have spoken of a daughter. 'It had a lot of different sicknesses when it was young, but it pulled through.' Someone had built a high wall on one side of her patio so that the climbing plants did not get as much sunlight as they needed. The banana plants, however, did very well and now the Chinaberry tree was big and strong enough to take care of itself. She kept giving David drinks of whiskey and he talked.

He told her of the place in his leg where something, a bone, perhaps, pressed on the nerve, and of the place on his left cheek. A silver plate had been set under the skin. She touched the spot with her fat old fingers. The moonlight fell softly down on the patio floor. 'I can't sleep except somewhere out-of-doors,' David said.

He explained how that, at home on his father's plantation, he had to be thinking all day whether or not he would be able to sleep at night.

'I go to bed and then I get up. There is always a bottle of whiskey on the table downstairs and I take three or four drinks. Then I go outdoors.' Often very nice things happened.

'In the fall it's best,' he said. 'You see the niggers are making molasses.' Every Negro cabin on the place had a little clump of ground back of it where cane grew and in the fall the Negroes were making their 'lasses. 'I take the bottle in my hand and go into the fields, unseen by the niggers. Having the bottle with me, that way, I drink a good deal and then lie down on the ground. The mosquitoes bite me some, but I don't mind much. I reckon I get drunk enough not to mind. The little pain makes a kind of rhythm for the great pain — like poetry.

'In a kind of shed the niggers are making the 'lasses, that is to say, pressing the juice out of the cane and boiling it down. They keep singing as they work. In a few years now I reckon our family won't have any land. The banks could take it now if they wanted it. They don't want it. It would be too much trouble for them to manage, I reckon.

'In the fall, at night, the niggers are pressing the cane. Our niggers live pretty much on 'lasses and grits.

'They like working at night and I'm glad they do. There is an old mule going round and round in a circle and beside the press a pile of the dry cane. Niggers come, men and women, old and young. They build a fire outside the shed. The old mule goes round and round.

'The niggers sing. They laugh and shout. Sometimes the young niggers with their gals make love on the dry cane pile. I can hear it rattle.

'I have come out of the big house, me and my bottle, and I creep along, low on the ground, 'til I get up close. There I lie. I'm a little drunk. It all makes me happy. I can sleep some, on the ground like that, when the niggers are singing, when no one knows I'm there.

'I could sleep here, on these bricks here,' David said, pointing to where the shadows cast by the broad leaves of the banana plants were broadest and deepest.

He got up from his chair and went limping, dragging one foot after the other, across the patio and lay down on the bricks.

For a long time Aunt Sally and I sat looking at each other, saying nothing, and presently she made a sign with her fat finger and we crept away into the house. 'I'll let you out at the front door. You let him sleep, right where he is,' she said. In spite of her huge bulk and her age, she walked across the patio floor as softly as a kitten. Beside her I felt awkward and uncertain. When we had got inside, she whispered to me. She had some champagne left from the old days, hidden away somewhere in the old house. 'I'm going to send a magnum up to his dad when he goes home,' she explained.

She, it seemed, was very happy, having him there, drunk and asleep on the brick floor of the patio. 'We used to have some good men come here in the old days too,' she said. As we went into the house through the kitchen door, I had looked back at David, asleep now in the heavy shadows at a corner of the wall. There was no doubt he also was happy, had been happy ever since I had brought him into the presence of Aunt Sally. What a small huddled figure of a man he looked, lying thus on the brick, under the night sky, in the deep shadows of the banana plants.

I went into the house and out at the front door and into a dark narrow street, thinking. Well, I was, after all, a Northern man. It was possible Aunt Sally had become completely Southern, being down here so long.

I remembered that it was the chief boast of her life that once she had shaken hands with John L. Sullivan and that she had known P. T. Barnum.

'I knew Dave Gears. You mean to tell me you don't know who Dave Gears was? Why he was one of the biggest gamblers we ever had in this city.'

As for David and his poetry — it is in the manner of Shelley. 'If I could write like Shelley I would be happy. I wouldn't care what happened to me,' he had said during our walk of the early part of the evening.

I went along enjoying my thoughts. The street was dark and occasionally I laughed. A notion had come to me. It kept dancing in my head and I thought it very delicious. It had something to do with aristocrats, with such people as Aunt Sally and David. 'Lordy,' I thought, 'maybe I do understand them a little. I'm from the Middle West myself, and it seems we can produce our aristocrats too.' I kept thinking of Aunt Sally and of my native state, Ohio. 'Lordy, I hope she comes from up there, but I don't think I had better inquire too closely into her past,' I said to myself, as I went smiling away into the soft smoky night.

The Return

EIGHTEEN YEARS. Well, he was driving a good car, an expensive
roadster. He was well clad, a rather solid, fine-looking man, not too
heavy. When he had left the Middle-Western town to go live in New
York City, he was twenty-two and now, on his way back, he was forty.
He drove toward the town from the East, stopping for lunch at
another town ten miles away.

When he went away from Caxton, after his mother died, he used
to write letters to friends at home, but after several months the replies
began to come with less and less frequency. On the day when he sat
eating his lunch at a small hotel in the town ten miles east of Caxton,
he suddenly thought of the reason, and was ashamed. 'Am I going
back there on this visit for the same reason I wrote the letters?' he
asked himself. For a moment he thought he might not go on. There
was still time to turn back.

Outside, in the principal business street of the neighboring town,
people were walking about. The sun shone warmly. Although he
had lived for so many years in New York, he had always kept, buried
away in him somewhere, a hankering for his own country. All the
day before he had been driving through the eastern Ohio country,
crossing many small streams, running down through small valleys,
seeing the white farmhouses set back from the road, and the big red
barns.

The elders were still in bloom along the fences, boys were swimming in a creek, the wheat had been cut, and now the corn was shoulder-high. Everywhere the drone of bees; in patches of woodland along
the road, a heavy, mysterious silence.

Now, however, he began thinking of something else. Shame crept over him. 'When I first left Caxton, I wrote letters back to my boyhood friends there, but I wrote always of myself. When I had written a letter telling what I was doing in the city, what friends I was making, what my prospects were, I put, at the very end of the letter, perhaps, a little inquiry: "I hope you are well. How are things going with you?" Something of that sort.'

The returning native — his name was John Holden — had grown very uneasy. After eighteen years it seemed to him he could see, lying before him, one of the letters written eighteen years before, when he had first come into the strange Eastern city. His mother's brother, a successful architect in the city, had given him such and such an opportunity: he had been at the theater to see Mansfield as Brutus; he had taken the night boat up-river to Albany with his aunt; there were two very handsome girls on the boat.

Everything must have been in the same tone. His uncle had given him a rare opportunity, and he had taken advantage of it. In time he had also become a successful architect. In New York City there were certain great buildings, two or three skyscrapers, several huge industrial plants, any number of handsome and expensive residences, that were the products of his brain.

When it came down to scratch, John Holden had to admit that his uncle had not been excessively fond of him. It had just happened that his aunt and uncle had no children of their own. He did his work in the office well and carefully, had developed a certain rather striking knack for design. The aunt had liked him better. She had always tried to think of him as her own son, had treated him as a son. Sometimes she called him son. Once or twice, after his uncle died, he had a notion. His aunt was a good woman, but sometimes he thought she would rather have enjoyed having him, John Holden, go in a bit more for wickedness, go a little on the loose, now and then. He never did anything she had to forgive him for. Perhaps she hungered for the opportunity to forgive.

Odd thoughts, eh? Well, what was a fellow to do? You had but the one life to live. You had to think of yourself.

Botheration! John Holden had rather counted on the trip back to Caxton, had really counted on it more than he realized. It was a bright summer day. He had been driving over the mountains of

Pennsylvania, through New York State, through eastern Ohio. Gertrude, his wife, had died during the summer before, and his one son, a lad of twelve, had gone away for the summer to a boys' camp in Vermont.

The idea had just come to him. 'I'll drive the car along slowly through the country, drinking it in. I need a rest, time to think. What I really need is to renew old acquaintances. I'll go back to Caxton and stay several days. I'll see Herman and Frank and Joe. Then I'll go call on Lillian and Kate. What a lot of fun, really!' It might just be that when he got to Caxton, the Caxton ball team would be playing a game, say, with a team from Yerington. Lillian might go to the game with him. It was in his mind faintly that Lillian had never married. How did he know that? He had heard nothing from Caxton for many years. The ball game would be in Heffler's field, and he and Lillian would go out there, walking under the maple trees along Turner Street, past the old stave factory, then in the dust of the road, past where the sawmill used to stand, and on into the field itself. He would be carrying a sunshade over Lillian's head, and Bob French would be standing at the gate where you went into the field and charging the people twenty-five cents to see the game.

Well, it would not be Bob; his son, perhaps. There would be something very nice in the notion of Lillian's going off to a ball game that way with an old sweetheart. A crowd of boys, women and men, going through a cattle gate into Heffler's field, tramping through the dust, young men with their sweethearts, a few gray-haired women, mothers of boys who belonged to the team, Lillian and he sitting in the rickety grandstand in the hot sun.

Once it had been — how they had felt, he and Lillian, sitting there together! It had been rather hard to keep the attention centered on the players in the field. One couldn't ask a neighbor, 'Who's ahead now, Caxton or Yerington?' Lillian's hands lay in her lap. What white, delicate, expressive hands they were! Once — that was just before he went away to live in the city with his uncle and but a month after his mother died — he and Lillian went to the ball field together at night. His father had died when he was a young lad, and he had no relatives left in the town. Going off to the ball field at night was maybe a risky thing for Lillian to do — risky for her reputation if anyone found it out — but she had seemed willing enough. You know how small-town girls of that age are.

Her father owned a retail shoe store in Caxton, and was a good, respectable man; but the Holdens — John's father had been a lawyer.

After they got back from the ball field that night — it must have been after midnight — they went to sit on the front porch before her faher's house. He must have known. A daughter cavorting about half the night with a young man that way! They had clung to each other with a sort of queer, desperate feeling neither understood. She did not go into the house until after three o'clock, and went then only because he insisted. He hadn't wanted to ruin her reputation. Why, he might have . . . She was like a little frightened child at the thought of his going away. He was twenty-two then, and she must have been about eighteen.

Eighteen and twenty-two make forty. John Holden was forty on the day when he sat at lunch at the hotel in the town ten miles from Caxton.

Now, he thought, he might be able to walk through the streets of Caxton to the ball park with Lillian with a certain effect. You know how it is. One has to accept the fact that youth is gone. If there should turn out to be such a ball game and Lillian would go with him, he would leave the car in the garage and ask her to walk. One saw pictures of that sort of thing in the movies — a man coming back to his native village after twenty years; a new beauty taking the place of the beauty of youth — something like that. In the spring the leaves on maple trees are lovely, but they are even more lovely in the fall — a flame of color — manhood and womanhood.

After he had finished his lunch, John did not feel very comfortable. The road to Caxton — it used to take nearly three hours to travel the distance with a horse and buggy, but now, and without any effort, the distance might be made in twenty minutes.

He lit a cigar and went for a walk, not in the streets of Caxton, but in the streets of the town ten miles away. If he got to Caxton in the evening, just at dusk, say, now . . .

With an inward pang John realized that he wanted darkness, the kindliness of soft evening lights. Lillian, Joe, Herman, and the rest. It had been eighteen years for the others as well as for himself. Now he had succeeded, a little, in twisting his fear of Caxton into fear for the others, and it made him feel somewhat better; but at once he realized what he was doing and again felt uncomfortable. One had to look out for changes, new people, new buildings, middle-aged people grown old, youth grown middle-aged. At any rate, he was thinking of the other now. He wasn't, as when he wrote letters home eighteen years before, thinking only of himself. 'Am I?' it *was* a question.

An absurd situation, really. He had sailed along so gaily through upper New York State, through western Pennsylvania, through eastern Ohio. Men were at work in the fields and in the towns, farmers drove into towns in their cars, clouds of dust rose on some distant road, seen across a valley. Once he had stopped his car near a bridge and had gone for a walk along the banks of a creek where it wound through a wood.

He was liking people. Well, he had never before given much time to people, to thinking of them and their affairs. 'I hadn't time,' he told himself. He had always realized that, while he was a good enough architect, things move fast in America. New men were coming on. He couldn't take chances of going on forever on his uncle's reputation. A man had to be always on the alert. Fortunately, his marriage had been a help. It had made valuable connections for him.

Twice he had picked up people on the road. There was a lad of sixteen from some town of eastern Pennsylvania, working his way westward toward the Pacific coast by picking up rides in cars — a summer's adventure. John had carried him all of one day and had listened to his talk with keen pleasure. And so this was the younger generation. The boy had nice eyes and an eager, friendly manner. He smoked cigarettes, and once, when they had a puncture, he was very quick and eager about changing the tire. 'Now, don't you soil your hands, Mister, I can do it like a flash,' he said, and he did. The boy said he intended working his way overland to the Pacific coast, where he would try to get a job of some kind on an ocean freighter, and that, if he did, he would go on around the world. 'But do you speak any foreign languages?' The boy did not. Across John Holden's mind flashed pictures of hot Eastern deserts, crowded Asiatic towns, wild half-savage mountain countries. As a young architect, and before his uncle died, he had spent two years in foreign travel, studying buildings in many countries; but he said nothing of this thought to the boy. Vast plans entered into with eager, boyish abandon, a world tour undertaken as he, when a young man, might have undertaken to find his way from his uncle's house in East Eighty-First Street downtown to the Battery. 'How do I know — perhaps he will do it?' John thought. The day in company with the boy had been very pleasant, and he had been on the alert to pick him up again the next morning; but the boy had gone on his way, had caught a ride with some earlier riser. Why hadn't John invited him to his hotel for the night? The notion hadn't come to him until too late.

Youth, rather wild and undisciplined, running wild, eh? I wonder why I never did it, never wanted to do it.

If he had been a bit wilder, more reckless — that night, that time when he and Lillian . . . 'It's all right being reckless with yourself, but when someone else is involved, a young girl in a small town, you yourself lighting out . . .' He remembered sharply that on the night, long before, as he sat with Lillian on the porch before her father's house, his hand . . . It had seemed as though Lillian, on that evening, might not have objected to anything he wanted to do. He had thought — well, he had thought of the consequences. Women must be protected by men, all that sort of thing. Lillian had seemed rather stunned when he walked away, even though it was three o'clock in the morning. She had been rather like a person waiting at a railroad station for the coming of a train. There is a blackboard, and a strange man comes out and writes on it, 'Train Number 287 has been discontinued' — something like that.

Well, it had been all right.

Later, four years later, he had married a New York woman of good family. Even in a city like New York, where there are so many people, her family had been well known. They had connections.

After marriage, sometimes, it is true, he had wondered. Gertrude used to look at him sometimes with an odd light in her eyes. That boy he picked up in the road — once during the day when he said something to the boy, the same queer look came into his eyes. It would be rather upsetting if you knew that the boy had purposely avoided you next morning. There had been Gertrude's cousin. Once after his marriage, John heard a rumor that Gertrude had wanted to marry that cousin, but of course he had said nothing to her. Why should he have? She was his wife. There had been, he had heard, a good deal of family objection to the cousin. He was reputed to be wild, a gambler and drinker.

Once the cousin came to the Holden apartment at two in the morning, drunk and demanding that he be allowed to see Gertrude, and she slipped on a dressing-gown and went down to him. That was in the hallway of the apartment, downstairs, where almost anyone might have come in and seen her. As a matter of fact, the elevator boy and janitor did see her. She had stood in the hallway below talking for nearly an hour. What about? He had never asked Gertrude directly, and she had never told him anything. When she came upstairs again and had got into her bed, he lay in his own bed trembling, but remained silent. He had been afraid that if he spoke he might say something rude; better keep still. The cousin had disappeared. John had a suspicion that Gertrude later supplied him with money. He went out West somewhere.

Now Gertrude was dead. She had always seemed very well, but suddenly she was attacked by a baffling kind of slow fever that lasted nearly a year. Sometimes she seemed about to get better, and then suddenly the fever grew worse. It might be that she did not want to live. What a notion! John had been at the bedside with the doctor when she died. There was something of the same feeling he had that night of his youth when he went with Lillian to the ball field, an odd sense of inadequacy. There was no doubt that in some subtle way both women had accused him.

Of what? There had always been, in some vague, indefinable way, a kind of accusation in the attitude toward him of his uncle, the architect, and of his aunt. They had left him their money, but . . . It was as though the uncle had said, as though Lillian during that night long ago had said . . .

Had they all said the same thing, and was Gertrude his wife saying it as she lay dying? A smile. 'You have always taken such good care of yourself, haven't you, John dear? You have observed the rules. You have taken no chances for yourself or the others.' She had actually said something of that sort to him once in a moment of anger.

II

In the small town ten miles from Caxton there wasn't any park to which a man could go to sit. If one stayed about the hotel, someone from Caxton might come in. 'Hello, what are you doing here?'

It would be inconvenient to explain. He had wanted the kindliness of soft evening light, both for himself and the old friends he was to see again.

He began thinking of his son, now a boy of twelve. 'Well,' he said to himself, 'his character has not begun to form yet.' There was, as yet, in the son an unconsciousness of other people, a rather casual selfishness, an unawareness of others, an unhealthy sharpness about getting the best of others. It was a thing that should be corrected in him and at once. John Holden had got himself into a small panic. 'I must write him a letter at once. Such a habit gets fixed in a boy and then in the man, and it cannot later be shaken off. There are such a lot of people living in the world! Every man and woman has his own point of view. To be civilized, really, is to be aware of the others, their hopes, their gladnesses, their illusions about life.'

John Holden was now walking along a residence street of a small Ohio town, composing in fancy a letter to his son in the boys' camp in Vermont. He was a man who wrote to his son every day. 'I think a man should,' he told himself. 'He should remember that now the boy has no mother.'

He had come to an outlying railroad station. It was neat with grass and flowers growing in a round bed in the very center of a lawn. Some man, the station agent and telegraph operator, perhaps, passed him and went inside the station. John followed him in. On the wall of the waiting-room there was a framed copy of the time-table, and he stood studying it. A train went to Caxton at five. Another train came from Caxton and passed through the town he was now in at seven-forty-three, the seven-nineteen out of Caxton. The man in the small business section of the station opened a sliding-panel and looked at him. The two men just stared at each other without speaking, and then the panel was slid shut again.

John looked at his watch. Two-twenty-eight. At about six he could drive over to Caxton and dine at the hotel there. After he had dined, it would be evening and people would be coming into the main street. The seven-nineteen would come in. When John was a lad, some-times, he, Joe, Herman, and often several other lads had climbed on the front of the baggage or mail car and had stolen a ride to the very town he was now in. What a thrill, crouched down in the gathering darkness on the platform as the train ran the ten miles, the car rocking from side to side! When it got a little dark, in the fall or spring, the fields beside the track were lighted up when the fireman opened his fire box to throw in coal. Once John saw a rabbit running along in the glare of light beside the track. He could have reached down and caught it with his hand. In the neighboring town the boys went into saloons and played pool and drank beer. They could depend upon catching a ride back home on the local freight that got to Caxton at about ten-thirty. On one of the adventures John and Herman got drunk and Joe had to help them into an empty coal car and later get them out at Caxton. Herman got sick, and when they were getting off the freight at Caxton, he stumbled and came very near falling under the wheels of the moving train. John wasn't as drunk as Herman. When the others weren't looking, he had poured several of the glasses of beer into a spittoon. In Caxton he and Joe had to walk about with Herman for several hours, and when John finally got home, his mother was still awake and was worried. He had to lie to her. 'I drove out into the country with Herman, and a wheel broke. We had to walk home.' The reason Joe could carry his beer so well was because he was German. His father owned the town meat market and the family had beer on the table at home. No wonder it did not knock him out as it did Herman and John.

There was a bench at the side of the railroad station, in the shade, and John sat there for a long time — two hours, three hours. Why hadn't he brought a book? In fancy he composed a letter to his son and in it he spoke of the fields lying beside the road outside the town of Caxton, of his greeting old friends there, of things that had happened when he was a boy. He even spoke of his former sweetheart, of Lillian. If he now thought out just what he was going to say in the letter, he could write it in his room at the hotel over in Caxton in a few minutes without having to stop and think what he was going to say. You can't always be too fussy about what you say to a young boy. Really, sometimes, you should take him into your confidence, into your life, make him a part of your life.

It was six-twenty when John drove into Caxton and went to the hotel, where he registered and was shown to a room. On the streets as he drove into town he saw Billy Baker, who, when he was a young man, had a paralyzed leg that dragged along the sidewalk when he walked. Now he was getting old; his face seemed wrinkled and faded, like a dried lemon, and his clothes had spots down the front. People, even sick people, live a long time in small Ohio towns. It is surprising how they hang on.

John had put his car, of a rather expensive make, into a garage beside the hotel. Formerly, in his day, the building had been used as a livery barn. There used to be pictures of famous trotting and pacing horses on the walls of the little office at the front. Old Dave Grey, who owned race-horses of his own, ran the livery barn then, and John occasionally hired a rig there. He hired a rig and took Lillian for a ride into the country, along moonlit roads. By a lonely farmhouse a dog barked. Sometimes they drove along a little dirt road lined with elders and stopped the horse. How still everything was! What a queer feeling they had! They couldn't talk. Sometimes they sat in silence thus, very near each other, for a long, long time. Once they got out of the buggy, having tied the horse to the fence, and walked in a newly cut hay field. The cut hay lay all about in little cocks. John wanted to lie on one of the haycocks with Lillian, but did not dare suggest it.

At the hotel John ate his dinner in silence. There wasn't even a traveling salesman in the dining room, and presently the proprietor's wife came and stood by his table to talk with him. The hotel had a good many tourists, but this just happened to be a quiet day. Dull days came that way in the hotel business. The woman's husband was a traveling man and had bought the hotel to give his wife something to keep her interested while he was on the road. He was away from home so much! They had come to Caxton from Pittsburgh.

After he had dined, John went up to his room, and presently the woman followed. The door leading into the hall had been left open, and she came and stood in the doorway. Really, she was rather handsome. She only wanted to be sure that everything was all right, that he had towels and soap and everything he needed.

For a time she lingered by the door talking of the town.

'It's a good little town. General Hurst is buried here. You should drive out to the cemetery and see the statue.' He wondered who General Hurst was. In what war had he fought? Odd that he hadn't remembered about him. The town had a piano factory, and there was a watch company from Cincinnati talking of putting up a plant. 'They figure there is less chance of labor trouble in a small town like this.'

The woman went reluctantly away. As she was going along the hallway, she stopped once and looked back. There was something a little queer. They were both self-conscious. 'I hope you'll be comfortable,' she said. At forty a man did not come home to his own home town to start . . . A traveling man's wife, eh? Well! Well!

At seven-forty-five John went out for a walk on Main Street and almost at once he met Tom Ballard, who at once recognized him, a fact that pleased Tom. He bragged about it. 'Once I see a face, I never forget. Well! Well!' When John was twenty-two, Tom must have been about fifteen. His father was the leading doctor of the town. He took John in tow, walked back with him toward the hotel. He kept exclaiming: 'I knew you at once. You haven't changed much, really.'

Tom was in his turn a doctor, and there was about him something . . . Right away John guessed what it was. They went up into John's room, and John, having in his bag a bottle of whiskey, poured Tom a drink, which he took somewhat too eagerly, John thought. There was talk. After Tom had taken the drink, he sat on the edge of the bed, still holding the bottle John had passed to him. Herman was running a dray now. He had married Kit Small and had five kids. Joe was working for the International Harvester Company. 'I don't know whether he's in town now or not. He's a trouble-shooter, a swell mechanic, a good fellow,' Tom said. He drank again.

As for Lillian, mentioned with an air of being casual by John, he, John, knew of course that she had been married and divorced. There was some sort of trouble about another man. Her husband married again later, and now she lived with her mother, her father, the shoe merchant, having died. Tom spoke somewhat guardedly, as though protecting a friend.

'I guess she's all right now, going straight and all. Good thing she never had any kids. She's a little nervous and queer; has lost her looks a good deal.'

The two men went downstairs and, walking along Main Street, got into a car belonging to the doctor.

'I'll take you for a little ride,' Tom said; but as he was about to pull away from the curb where the car had been parked, he turned and smiled at his passenger. 'We ought to celebrate a little, account of your coming back here,' he said. 'What do you say to a quart?'

John handed him a ten-dollar bill, and he disappeared into a near-by drug store. When he came back he laughed.

'I used your name, all right. They didn't recognize it. In the prescription I wrote out I said you had a general breakdown, that you needed to be built up. I recommended that you take a teaspoonful three times a day. Lord! my prescription book is getting almost empty.' The drug store belonged to a man named Will Bennett. 'You remember him, maybe. He's Ed Bennett's son; married Carrie Wyatt.'

The names were but dim things in John's mind. 'This man is going to get drunk. He is going to try to get me drunk, too,' he thought.

When they had turned out of Main Street and into Walnut Street, they stopped midway between two street lights and had another drink, John holding the bottle to his lips, but putting his tongue over the opening. He remembered the evenings with Joe and Herman when he had secretly poured his beer into a spittoon. He felt cold and lonely. Walnut Street was one along which he used to walk, coming home late at night from Lillian's house. He remembered people who then lived along the street, and a list of names began running through his head. Often the names remained, but did not call up images of people. They were just names. He hoped the doctor would not turn the car into the street in which the Holdens had lived. Lillian had lived over in another part of town, in what was called 'The Red House District.' Just why it had been called that, John did not know.

III

They drove silently along, up a small hill, and came to the edge of town, going south. Stopping before a house that had evidently been built since John's time, Tom sounded his horn.

'Didn't the fairgrounds used to stand about here?' John asked.

The doctor turned and nodded his head. 'Yes, just here,' he said. He kept on sounding his horn, and a man and woman came out of the house and stood in the road beside the car.

'Let's get Maud and Alf and all go over to Lysle's Point,' Tom said.

John had indeed been taken in tow. For a time he wondered if he was to be introduced. 'We got some hooch. Meet John Holden; used to live here years ago.' At the fairgrounds, when John was a lad, Dave Grey, the livery man, used to work out his race-horses in the early morning. Herman, who was a horse enthusiast, dreaming of some day becoming a horseman, came often to John's house in the early morning and the two boys went off to the fairgrounds without breakfast. Herman had got some sandwiches made of slices of bread and cold meat out of his mother's pantry. They went 'cross-lots, climbing fences and eating the sandwiches. In a meadow they had to cross there was heavy dew on the grass, and meadowlarks flew up before them. Herman had at least come somewhere near expressing in his life his youthful passion: he still lived about horses; he owned a dray. With a little inward qualm John wondered. Perhaps Herman ran a motor truck.

The man and woman got into the car, the woman on the back seat with John, the husband in front with Tom, and they drove away to another house. John could not keep track of the streets they passed through. Occasionally he asked the woman, 'What street are we in now?' They were joined by Maud and Alf, who also crowded into the back seat. Maud was a slender woman of twenty-eight or thirty, with yellow hair and blue eyes, and at once she seemed determined to make up to John. 'I don't take more than an inch of room,' she said, laughing and squeezing herself in between John and the first woman, whose name he could not later remember.

He had rather liked Maud. When the car had been driven some eighteen miles along a gravel road, they came to Lysle's farmhouse, which had been converted into a roadhouse, and got out. Maud had been silent most of the way, but she sat very close to John, and as he felt cold and lonely, he was grateful for the warmth of her slender body. Occasionally she spoke to him in a half-whisper: 'Ain't the night swell! Gee! I like it out in the dark this way.'

Lysle's Point was at a bend of the Samson River, a small stream to which John as a lad had occasionally gone on fishing excursions with his father. Later he went out there several times with crowds of young fellows and their girls. They drove out then in Grey's old bus, and the trip out and back took several hours. On the way home at night, they had great fun singing at the top of their voices and waking the sleeping farmers along the road. Occasionally some of the party got out and walked for a way. It was a chance for a fellow to kiss his girl when the others could not see. By hurrying a little, they could easily enough catch up with the bus.

A rather heavy-faced Italian named Francisco owned Lysle's, and it had a dance hall and dining room. Drinks could be had if you knew the ropes, and it was evident the doctor and his friends were old acquaintances. At once they declared John should not buy any-thing, the declaration, in fact, being made before he had offered. 'You're our guest now; don't you forget that. When we come some-time to your town, then it will be all right,' Tom said. He laughed. 'And that makes me think. I forgot your change,' he said, handing John a five-dollar bill. The whiskey got at the drug store had been consumed on the way out, all, except John and Maud, drinking heart-ily. 'I don't like the stuff. Do you, Mr. Holden?' Maud said, and giggled. Twice during the trip out, her fingers had crept over and touched lightly his fingers, and each time she had apologized. 'Oh, do excuse me!' she said. John felt a little as he had felt earlier in the evening when the woman of the hotel had come to stand at the door of his room and had seemed reluctant about going away.

After they got out of the car at Lysle's, he felt uncomfortably old and queer. 'What am I doing here with these people?' he kept asking himself. When they had got into the light, he stole a look at his watch. It was not yet nine o'clock. Several other cars, most of them, the doctor explained, from Yerington, stood before the door, and when they had taken several drinks of rather mild Italian red wine, all of the party except Maud and John went into the dance hall to dance. The doctor took John aside and whispered to him: 'Lay off Maud,' he said. He explained hurriedly that Alf and Maud had been having a row and that for several days they had not spoken to each other, although they lived in the same house, ate at the same table, and slept in the same bed. 'He thinks she gets too gay with men,' Tom explained. 'You better look out a little.'

The woman and man sat on a bench under a tree on the lawn be-fore the house, and when the others had danced, they came out, bring-ing more drinks. Tom had got some more whiskey. 'It's moon, but pretty good stuff,' he declared. In the clear sky overhead stars were shining, and when the others were dancing, John turned his head and saw across the road and between the trees that lined its banks the stars reflected in the waters of the Samson. A light from the house fell on Maud's face, a strikingly lovely face in that light, but when looked at closely, rather petulant. 'A good deal of the spoiled child in her,' John thought.

She began asking him about life in the city of New York.

'I was there once, but for only three days. It was when I went to school in the East. A girl I knew lived there. She married a lawyer named Trigan, or something like that. You didn't know him, I guess.'

And now there was a hungry, dissatisfied look on her face.

'God! I'd like to live in a place like that, not in this hole! There hadn't no man better tempt me.' When she said that she giggled again. Once during the evening they walked across the dusty road and stood for a time by the river's edge, but got back to the bench before the others finished their dance. Maud persistently refused to dance.

At ten-thirty, all of the others having got a little drunk, they drove back to town. Maud again sitting beside John. On the drive Alf went to sleep. Maud pressed her slender body against John's, and after two or three futile moves to which he made no special response, she boldly put her hand into his. The second woman and her husband talked with Tom of people they had seen at Lysle's. 'Do you think there's anything up between Fanny and Joe?' 'No; I think she's on the square.'

They got to John's hotel at eleven-thirty, and, bidding them all good night, he went upstairs. Alf had awakened. When they were parting, he leaned out of the car and looked closely at John. 'What did you say your name was?' he asked.

John went up a dark stairway and sat on the bed in his room. Lillian had lost her looks. She had married, and her husband had divorced her. Joe was a trouble-shooter. He worked for the International Harvester Company, a swell mechanic. Herman was a drayman. He had five kids.

Three men in a room next to John's were playing poker. They laughed and talked, and their voices came clearly to John. 'You think so, do you? Well, I'll prove you're wrong.' A mild quarrel began. As it was summer, the windows of John's room were open, and he went to one to stand, looking out. A moon had come up, and he could see down into an alleyway. Two men came out of a street and stood in the alleyway, whispering. After they left, two cats crept along a roof and began a love-making scene. The game in the next room broke up. John could hear voices in the hallway.

'Now, forget it. I tell you, you're both wrong.' John thought of his son at the camp up in Vermont. 'I haven't written him a letter to-day.' He felt guilty.

Opening his bag, he took out paper and sat down to write; but after two or three attempts gave it up and put the paper away again. How fine the night had been as he sat on the bench beside the woman at Lysle's! Now the woman was in bed with her husband. They were not speaking to each other.

'Could I do it?' John asked himself, and then, for the first time that evening, a smile came to his lips.

'Why not?' he asked himself.

With his bag in his hand he went down the dark hallway and into the hotel office and began pounding on a desk. A fat old man with thin red hair and sleep-heavy eyes appeared from somewhere. John explained.

'I can't sleep. I think I'll drive on. I want to get to Pittsburgh and as I can't sleep, I might as well be driving.' He paid his bill.

Then he asked the clerk to go and arouse the man in the garage, and gave him an extra dollar. 'If I need gas, is there any place open?' he asked, but evidently the man did not hear. Perhaps he thought the question absurd.

He stood in the moonlight on the sidewalk before the door of the hotel and heard the clerk pounding on a door. Presently voices were heard, and the headlights of his car shone. The car appeared, driven by a boy. He seemed very alive and alert.

'I saw you out to Lysle's,' he said, and, without being asked, went to look at the tank. 'You're all right; you got 'most eight gallons,' he assured John, who had climbed into the driver's seat.

How friendly the car, how friendly the night! John was not one who enjoyed fast driving, but he went out of town at very high speed. 'You go down two blocks, turn to your right, and go three. There you hit the cement. Go right straight to the east. You can't miss it.'

John was taking the turns at racing speed. At the edge of town someone shouted to him from the darkness, but he did not stop. He hungered to get into the road going east.

'I'll let her out,' he thought. 'Lord! It will be fun! I'll let her out.'

Meeting Ring Lardner

A LONG SOLEMN-FACED MAN. The face was wonderful. It was a mask. All the time when you were with him, you kept wondering . . . 'What is going on back there?'

I was in New Orleans, at the Mardi Gras time, and he telephoned. I had long admired but had never seen the man. He had come to New Orleans for the Mardi Gras, accompanied by his friend Grantland Rice, and it developed that Rice had been afraid that Ring, whom he admired with something like adoration, would not get the attention he deserved. He had got Ring in up to his neck and the voice on the 'phone was a pleading one.

'Please, Sherwood,' it said, 'you do not know me, you have never met me, you do not even know that you have invited me to dinner tonight?'

'Yes,' I said. 'I know. I even know where.' There was a little place, upstairs, down in the French Quarter. It had just been opened by a Frenchman who had been, until a few months before, the chef at Antoine's. 'It is a little place and dark,' I said. 'We could get eight or ten into the room. Good wine. Good food,' I said.

'O.K.,' he said. 'I'll bring my wife and Mr. Fixit and his wife. I hope it is very dark and very dirty. If it isn't very dirty, have them shovel a little dirt into the place. I'll be there.'

And so we dined and Ring talked. I think the mask dropped away for that evening. The man was surrounded by a little halo of something like worship. It was in the eyes of the women in the room, in the men's eyes. I had hurried down in the late morning to see the French chef. 'What!' he said, 'Ring Lardner? You wait. You'll see.'

301

So he too knew about Ring, had a feeling about him. During the dinner and afterwards, over the wine, he kept tiptoeing down a little dark hallway. He put his head in at the door and made a sign to me and I slid out to him. 'Is it all right? Does he like it? Does he like the wine?' He slipped another bottle into my hand. 'Try this one on him.'

There was something loose and free in the little room. How shall I describe it? It was Ring. What we all felt for him was warm affection. I had never known anyone just like him writing in America. He awoke a certain feeling. You wanted him not to be hurt, perhaps to have some freedom he did not have. There was a feeling . . . 'If anyone hurts this man, I'd like to punch him on the jaw.' Almost always, when one of your friends gets kicked downstairs, you're glad. It is a nasty fact, but it is a truth.

I dare say that the tragedy of Ring Lardner . . . that gorgeous talent of his so often smeared . . . is our common tragedy, the tragedy of every creative man, big or little, in our day. No one of us escapes it. How can he?

Just the same, Ring Lardner did often escape. He had a marvelous technique. He could always get behind the mask, and then, too, he must always have had a great deal of what he was getting that night at the dinner; that is to say, warm affection from many people. We poured it over him as we poured the wine down our throats. We loved him. I cannot help thinking it was a rare and a rich evening in his life. He laughed. He talked. He drank the wine. He told stories. It was a good evening for him. It was something more than that for the rest of us. Two years later, I was in the same little restaurant, and the chef, that fat Frenchman, came to my table. I was alone and he brought a bottle of wine. He had come in from the kitchen and had on his white apron. He stood beside my table and poured wine for us both. 'To that man you brought here that time . . . to Ring Lardner,' he said, lifting his glass.

And there was another evening two days later. He and Grantland Rice must have been going it hard, any number of people would have been wanting to meet Ring, to entertain him. He was at the top of his fame then. I don't blame them. He could make a party go, put life and fun into it. Both the high- and the low-brows loved him. He 'phoned me on his way from one party to another. I was to come and get him. The party to which he was bound was in a swell house in a swell part of town.

When I arrived, there was a swarm of people and Ring was busy. He was putting on a show. He sat in the middle of a big room at a piano and they were all gathered about him and he was singing and making them sing with him. He sang 'Two Little Girls in Blue' ... 'Just Tell Her that You Saw Me and that I Was Looking Well' ... 'There'll Be a Hot Time in the Old Town Tonight,' and several others. He made them sing. There were drinks aplenty. A little river of liquor flowed through the room.

There was the expensive furniture, and paintings on the walls. In New Orleans the rich go in for heavily paneled walls, heavy uncomfortable French furniture.

The people were crowded in close about Ring, who sat at the piano wearing his mask. He could look at a man or woman with strangely impersonal eyes. 'Sing,' he said and the person so looked at sang. They were the sort of people you see photographs of in the Sunday newspapers, on the society pages. We writers, painters, etc., sweat our heads off trying to do, now and then, a little thing that is worth doing, and then some dame ... enough money in that gown on her back to give one of us a half-year's leisure. At that it doesn't cover her back much. Hail revolution!

There were heavy-faced rich men, young male society swells, horsey men, down from New York for the races, and women ... women and more women.

It was quite a long time before Ring saw me that night, but when he did he made for me, the singing having stopped abruptly ... he had them all going right ... they had been throwing their heads back, drinking the liquor and stepping into it. He pushed me through them, brushing them aside. Now and then he stopped to introduce me to a man or woman. The mask on his face was well adjusted. He introduced me as an author, his fellow author, the author of *The Great Gatsby* ... *The Confessions of a Young Man* ... *Tess of d'Ubervilles* ... the man who wrote *Moby Dick*.

He kept pressing me on and on through the crowd and we got into a hallway. He pointed to a door. 'It's what they call "the butler's pantry,"' he said. 'I don't believe there is anyone in there. They are taking drinks about. Get three or four bottles of their best stuff,' he said, 'and we'll get out.' He told me where to meet him outside.

I did what he told me to do. I went outside and waited. I got a taxi and made it pull in to the curb. I put the bottles on the floor. I had got six quarts. It looked to me like pretty good stuff.

And then, when he came, he came in the host's car and our host was with him. He was a small man and pale, and right away I knew he was a banker. The stuff was in the taxi and I was walking up and down. It was a tough break for us.

I got into the cab for a moment and fixed myself as best I could. Luckily I had on an overcoat. Then I crawled into the back seat of that car. I rattled a good deal, but Ring, on the front seat with that man, that little pale banker, didn't seem to mind. He was wearing the mask. He looked at me and growled. 'Sit still, Sherwood,' he said. 'Don't rattle so much.'

I tried not to rattle, but I had to get out of the car again when we got to his hotel. I crept out and got into the hotel entrance. I got to where I could see without being seen. Ring stood on the sidewalk.

Our host had got out of his car. It was a Rolls-Royce. He was doing his own driving. 'Your friend, your fellow author — where is he?' he said to Ring, looking about. He seemed extraordinarily small and pale, standing there before Ring. It was like a big dog and a little dog and the little dog was wagging his tail. He didn't care a hang about the liquor we had got. He knew we were going somewhere to sit and drink and talk quietly, and I think he wanted to come along, but he was too polite to ask, and I think also that Ring was, for a moment, tempted to ask him to come.

Ring was looking down at the man. I could see it all. There was an overhead light shining on them. I saw something happen. Ring had been wearing his mask all evening, but, for a moment, it dropped. He started to ask the man to come with us, but changed his mind. I saw his lips tremble. I know what happened. He wanted to ask the man to come along, but was afraid I wouldn't like it, and so he said nothing, but stood there, looking down at the man, his lips trembling. This was a different Ring Lardner from the one I had seen in the room with all those people.

This one was a shy man and so was the little banker. The two men stood like that, looking hard at each other, and then, as by a common impulse, they both began to laugh. They laughed like two young boys, or for that matter like two girls, and then the banker ran quickly and got into his car and drove away, but as he did so he took a shot back at Ring. 'I hope your friend got plenty of good stuff . . . I hope he got enough,' he said, but Ring was not looking. He was a man whose habit it was to wear a mask, and it had slipped off, and at the moment I was like a man standing in the dressing-room of a theater and watching an actor at work on his make-up. I saw him put the mask back on his face and he wore it for the rest of the evening.

Brother Death

THERE WERE THE TWO OAK STUMPS, knee-high to a not-too-tall man and cut quite squarely across. They became to the two children objects of wonder. They had seen the two trees cut, but had run away just as the trees fell. They hadn't thought of the two stumps, to be left standing there; hadn't even looked at them. Afterward Ted said to his sister Mary, speaking of the stumps: 'I wonder if they bled, like legs, when a surgeon cuts a man's leg off.' He had been hearing war stories. A man came to the farm one day to visit one of the farmhands, a man who had been in the World War and had lost an arm. He stood in one of the barns talking. When Ted said that, Mary spoke up at once. She hadn't been lucky enough to be at the barn when the one-armed man was there talking, and was jealous. 'Why not a woman or a girl's leg?' she said, but Ted said the idea was silly. 'Women and girls don't get their legs and arms cut off,' he declared. 'Why not? I'd just like to know why not?' Mary kept saying.

It would have been something if they had stayed, that day the trees were cut. 'We might have gone and touched the places,' Ted said. He meant the stumps. Would they have been warm? Would they have bled? They did go and touch the places afterward, but it was a cold day and the stumps were cold. Ted stuck to his point that only men's arms and legs were cut off, but Mary thought of automobile accidents. 'You can't think just about wars. There might be an automobile accident,' she declared, but Ted wouldn't be convinced.

They were both children, but something had made them both in an odd way old. Mary was fourteen and Ted eleven, but Ted wasn't strong and that rather evened things up. They were the children of a well-to-do Virginia farmer named John Grey in the Blue Ridge country in southwestern Virginia. There was a wide valley called the 'Rich Valley,' with a railroad and a small river running through it and high mountains in sight, to the north and south. Ted had some kind of heart disease, a lesion, something of the sort, the result of a severe attack of diphtheria when he was a child of eight. He was thin and not strong, but curiously alive. The doctor said he might die at any moment, might just drop down dead. The fact had drawn him peculiarly close to his sister Mary. It had awakened a strong and determined maternalism in her.

The whole family, the neighbors, on neighboring farms in the valley, and even the other children at the schoolhouse where they went to school, recognized something as existing between the two children. 'Look at them going along there,' people said. 'They do seem to have good times together, but they are so serious. For such young children they are too serious. Still, I suppose, under the circumstances, it's natural.' Of course, everyone knew about Ted. It had done something to Mary. At fourteen she was both a child and a grown woman. The woman side of her kept popping out at unexpected moments.

She had sensed something concerning her brother Ted. It was because he was as he was, having that kind of a heart, a heart likely at any moment to stop beating, leaving him dead, cut down like a young tree. The others in the Grey family, that is to say, the older ones, the mother and father and an older brother, Don, who was eighteen now, recognized something as belonging to the two children, being, as it were, between them, but the recognition wasn't very definite. People in your own family are likely at any moment to do strange, sometimes hurtful things to you. You have to watch them. Ted and Mary had both found that out.

The brother Don was like the father, already at eighteen almost a grown man. He was that sort, the kind people speak of, saying: 'He's a good man. He'll make a good solid dependable man.' The father, when he was a young man, never drank, never went chasing the girls, was never wild. There had been enough wild young ones in the Rich Valley when he was a lad. Some of them had inherited big farms and had lost them, gambling, drinking, fooling with fast horses, and chasing after the women. It had been almost a Virginia tradition, but John Grey was a land man. All the Greys were. There were other large cattle farms owned by Greys up and down the valley.

John Grey, everyone said, was a natural cattle man. He knew beef cattle, of the big so-called export type, how to pick and feed them to make beef. He knew how and where to get the right kind of young stock to turn into his fields. It was blue-grass country. Big beef cattle went directly off the pastures to market. The Grey farm contained over twelve hundred acres, most of it in blue grass.

The father was a land man, land hungry. He had begun, as a cattle farmer, with a small place, inherited from his father, some two hundred acres, lying next to what was then the big Aspinwahl place and, after he began, he never stopped getting more land. He kept cutting in on the Aspinwahls who were a rather horsey, fast lot. They thought of themselves as Virginia aristocrats, having, as they weren't so modest about pointing out, a family going back and back, family tradition, guests always being entertained, fast horses kept, money being bet on fast horses. John Grey getting their land, now twenty acres, then thirty, then fifty, until at last he got the old Aspinwahl house, with one of the Aspinwahl girls, not a young one, not one of the best-looking ones, as wife. The Aspinwahl place was down, by that time, to less than a hundred acres, but he went on, year after year, always being careful and shrewd, making every penny count, never wasting a cent, adding and adding to what was now the Grey place. The former Aspinwahl house was a large old brick house with fireplaces in all the rooms and was very comfortable.

People wondered why Louise Aspinwahl had married John Grey, but when they were wondering they smiled. The Aspinwahl girls were all well educated, had all been away to college, but Louise wasn't so pretty. She got nicer after marriage, suddenly almost beautiful. The Aspinwahls were, as everyone knew, naturally sensitive, really first-class, but the men couldn't hang onto land and the Greys could. In all that section of Virginia, people gave John Grey credit for being what he was. They respected him. 'He's on the level,' they said, 'as honest as a horse. He has cattle sense, that's it.' He could run his big hand down over the flank of a steer and say, almost to the pound, what he would weigh on the scales, or he could look at a calf or a yearling and say, 'He'll do,' and he would do. A steer is a steer. He isn't supposed to do anything but make beef.

There was Don, the oldest son of the Grey family. He was so evidently destined to be a Grey, to be another like his father. He had

long been a star in the 4H Club of the Virginia county and, even as a
lad of nine and ten, had won prizes at steer judging. At twelve he
had produced, no one helping him, doing all the work himself, more
bushels of corn on an acre of land than any other boy in the State.

It was all a little amazing, even a bit queer to Mary Grey, being,
as she was, a girl peculiarly conscious, so old and young, so aware.
There was Don, the older brother, big and strong of body, like the
father, and there was the younger brother Ted. Ordinarily, in the
ordinary course of life, she being what she was — female — it would
have been quite natural and right for her to have given her young
girl's admiration to Don, but she didn't. For some reason, Don barely
existed for her. He was outside, not in it, while for her Ted, the
seemingly weak one of the family, was everything.

Still there Don was, so big of body, so quiet, so apparently sure of
himself. The father had begun, as a young cattle man, with the two
hundred acres, and now he had the twelve hundred. What would
Don Grey do when he started? Already he knew, although he didn't
say anything, that he wanted to start. He wanted to run things, be
his own boss. His father had offered to send him away to college, to
an agricultural college, but he wouldn't go. 'No, I can learn more
here,' he said.

Already there was a contest, always kept under the surface, between
the father and son. It concerned ways of doing things, decisions to be
made. As yet the son always surrendered.

It is like that in a family, little isolated groups formed within the
larger group, jealousies, concealed hatreds, silent battles secretly going
on — among the Greys, Mary and Ted, Don and his father, the
mother and the two younger children, Gladys, a girl child of six now,
who adored her brother Don, and Harry, a boy child of two.

As for Mary and Ted, they lived within their own world, but their
own world had not been established without a struggle. The point
was that Ted, having the heart that might at any moment stop beating, was always being treated tenderly by the others. Only Mary understood that — how it infuriated and hurt him.

'No, Ted, I wouldn't do that.'

'Now, Ted, do be careful.'

Sometimes Ted went white and trembling with anger, Don, the
father, the mother, all keeping at him like that. It didn't matter what

he wanted to do, learn to drive one of the two family cars, climb a tree to find a bird's nest, run a race with Mary. Naturally, being on a farm, he wanted to try his hand at breaking a colt, beginning with him, getting a saddle on, having it out with him. 'No, Ted. You can't.' He had learned to swear, picking it up from the farm-hands and from boys at the country school. 'Hell! Goddam!' he said to Mary. Only Mary understood how he felt, and she had not put the matter very definitely into words, not even to herself. It was one of the things that made her old when she was so young. It made her stand aside from the others of the family, aroused in her a curious determination. 'They shall not.' She caught herself saying the words to herself. 'They shall not.'

'If he is to have but a few years of life, they shall not spoil what he is to have. Why should they make him die, over and over, day after day?' The thoughts in her did not become so definite. She had resentment against the others. She was like a soldier, standing guard over Ted.

The two children drew more and more away, into their own world and only once did what Mary felt come to the surface. That was with the mother.

It was on an early summer day and Ted and Mary were playing in the rain. They were on a side porch of the house, where the water came pouring down from the eaves. At a corner of the porch there was a great stream, and first Ted and then Mary dashed through it, returning to the porch with clothes soaked and water running in streams from soaked hair. There was something joyous, the feel of the cold water on the body, under clothes, and they were shrieking with laughter when the mother came to the door. She looked at Ted. There was fear and anxiety in her voice. 'Oh, Ted, you know you mustn't, you mustn't.' Just that. All the rest implied. Nothing said to Mary. There it was. 'Oh, Ted, you mustn't. You mustn't run hard, climb trees, ride horses. The least shock to you may do it.' It was the old story again, and, of course, Ted understood. He went white and trembled. Why couldn't the rest understand that was a hundred times worse for him? On that day, without answering his mother, he ran off the porch and through the rain toward the barns. He wanted to go hide himself from every one. Mary knew how he felt.

She got suddenly very old and very angry. The mother and daughter stood looking at each other, the woman nearing fifty and the child of fourteen. It was getting everything in the family reversed. Mary felt that but felt she had to do something. 'You should have more sense, Mother,' she said seriously. She also had gone white. Her lips trembled. 'You mustn't do it any more. Don't you ever do it again.'

'What, child?' There was astonishment and half anger in the mother's voice.

'Always making him think of it,' Mary said. She wanted to cry but didn't.

The mother understood. There was a queer tense moment before Mary also walked off, toward the barns, in the rain. It wasn't all so clear. The mother wanted to fly at the child, perhaps shake her for daring to be so impudent. A child like that to decide things — to dare to reprove her mother. There was so much implied — even that Ted be allowed to die, quickly, suddenly, rather than that death, danger of sudden death, be brought again and again to his attention. There were values in life, implied by a child's words: 'Life, what is it worth? Is death the most terrible thing?' The mother turned and went silently into the house while Mary, going to the barns, presently found Ted. He was in an empty horse stall, standing with his back to the wall, staring. There were no explanations. 'Well,' Ted said presently, and, 'Come on, Ted,' Mary replied. It was necessary to do something, even perhaps more risky than playing in the rain. The rain was already passing. 'Let's take off our shoes,' Mary said. Going barefoot was one of the things forbidden Ted. They took their shoes off and, leaving them in the barn, went into an orchard. There was a small creek below the orchard, a creek that went down to the river and now it would be in flood. They went into it and once Mary got swept off her feet so that Ted had to pull her out.

She spoke then. 'I told Mother,' she said, looking serious.

'What?' Ted said. 'Gee, I guess maybe I saved you from drowning,' he added.

'Sure you did,' said Mary. 'I told her to let you alone.' She grew suddenly fierce. 'They've all got to — they've got to let you alone,' she said.

There was a bond. Ted did his share. He was imaginative and could think of plenty of risky things to do. Perhaps the mother spoke to the father and to Don, the older brother. There was a new inclination in the family to keep hands off the pair, and the fact seemed to give the two children new room in life. Something seemed to open out. There was a little inner world created, always, every day, being re-created, and in it there was a kind of new security. It seemed to the two children — they could not have put their feelings into words — that, being in their own created world, feeling a new security there, they could suddenly look out at the outside world and see, in a new way, what was going on out there in the world that belonged also to others.

It was a world to be thought about, looked at, a world of drama too, the drama of human relations, outside their own world, in a family, on a farm, in a farmhouse. . . . On a farm, calves and yearling steers arriving to be fattened, great heavy steers going off to market, colts being broken to work or to saddle, lambs born in the late winter. The human side of life was more difficult, to a child often incomprehensible, but after the speech to the mother, on the porch of the house that day when it rained, it seemed to Mary almost as though she and Ted had set up a new family. Everything about the farm, the house and the barns got nicer. There was a new freedom. The two children walked along a country road, returning to the farm from school in the late afternoon. There were other children in the road but they managed to fall behind or they got ahead. There were plans made. 'I'm going to be a nurse when I grow up,' Mary said. She may have remembered dimly the woman nurse, from the county-seat town, who had come to stay in the house when Ted was so ill. Ted said that as soon as he could — it would be when he was younger yet than Don was now — he intended to leave and go out West . . . far out, he said. He wanted to be a cowboy or a bronco-buster or something, and, that failing, he thought he would be a railroad engineer. The railroad that went down through the Rich Valley crossed a corner of the Grey farm, and, from the road in the afternoon, they could sometimes see trains, quite far away, the smoke rolling up. There was a faint rumbling noise, and, on clear days they could see the flying piston rods of the engines.

As for the two stumps in the field near the house, they were what was left of two oak trees. The children had known the trees. They were cut one day in the early fall.

There was a back porch to the Grey house — the house that had once been the seat of the Aspinwahl family — and from the porch steps a path led down to a stone spring house. A spring came out of the ground just there, and there was a tiny stream that went along the edge of a field, past two large barns and out across a meadow to a creek — called a 'branch' in Virginia — and the two trees stood close together beyond the spring house and the fence.

They were lusty trees, their roots down in the rich, always damp soil, and one of them had a great limb that came down near the ground, so that Ted and Mary could climb into it and out another limb into its brother tree, and in the fall, when other trees, at the front and side of the house, had shed their leaves, blood-red leaves still clung to the two oaks. They were like dry blood on gray days, but on other days, when the sun came out, the trees flamed against distant hills. The leaves clung, whispering and talking when the wind blew, so that the trees themselves seemed carrying on a conversation.

John Grey had decided he would have the trees cut. At first it was not a very definite decision. 'I think I'll have them cut,' he announced. 'But why?' his wife asked. The trees meant a good deal to her. They had been planted, just in that spot, by her grandfather, she said, having in mind just a certain effect. 'You see how, in the fall, when you stand on the back porch, they are so nice against the hills.' She spoke of the trees, already quite large, having been brought from a distant woods. Her mother had often spoken of it. The man, her grandfather, had a special feeling for trees. 'An Aspinwahl would do that,' John Grey said. 'There is enough yard, here about the house, and enough trees. They do not shade the house or the yard. An Aspinwahl would go to all that trouble for trees and then plant them where grass might be growing.' He had suddenly determined, a half-formed determination in him suddenly hardening. He had perhaps heard too much of the Aspinwahls and their ways. The conversation regarding the trees took place at the table, at the noon hour, and Mary and Ted heard it all.

It began at the table and was carried on afterwards out of doors, in the yard back of the house. The wife had followed her husband out. He always left the table suddenly and silently, getting quickly up and going out heavily, shutting doors with a bang as he went. 'Don't, John,' the wife said, standing on the porch and calling to her husband. It was a cold day, but the sun was out and the trees were like great bonfires against gray distant fields and hills. The older son of the family, young Don, the one so physically like the father and apparently so like him in every way, had come out of the house with the mother, followed by the two children, Ted and Mary, and at first Don said nothing, but, when the father did not answer the mother's protest but started toward the barn, he also spoke. What he said was obviously the determining thing, hardening the father.

To the two other children — they had walked a little aside and stood together watching and listening — there was something. There was their own child's world. 'Let us alone and we'll let you alone.' It wasn't as definite as that. Most of the definite thoughts about what happened in the yard that afternoon came to Mary Grey long afterwards, when she was a grown woman. At the moment there was merely a sudden sharpening of the feeling of isolation, a wall between herself and Ted and the others. The father, even then perhaps, seen in a new light, Don and the mother seen in a new light.

There was something, a driving destructive thing in life, in all relationships between people. All of this felt dimly that day — she always believed both by herself and Ted — but only thought out long afterwards, after Ted was dead. There was the farm her father had won from the Aspinwahls — greater persistence, greater shrewdness. In a family, little remarks dropped from time to time, an impression slowly built up. The father, John Grey, was a successful man. He had acquired. He owned. He was the commander, the one having power to do his will. And the power had run out and covered, not only other human lives, impulses in others, wishes, hungers in others . . . he himself might not have, might not even understand . . . but it went far out beyond that. It was, curiously, the power also of life and death. Did Mary Grey think such thoughts at that moment? . . . ? She couldn't have. . . . Still there was her own peculiar situation, her relationship with her brother Ted, who was to die.

Ownership that gave curious rights, dominances — fathers over children, men and women over lands, houses, factories in cities, fields. 'I will have the trees in that orchard cut. They produce apples but not of the right sort. There is no money in apples of that sort any more.'

'But. Sir . . . you see . . . look . . . the trees there against that hill, against the sky.'

'Nonsense. Sentimentality.'

Confusion.

It would have been such nonsense to think of the father of Mary Grey as a man without feeling. He had struggled hard all his life, perhaps, as a young man, gone without things wanted, deeply hungered for. Someone has to manage things in this life. Possessions mean power, the right to say, 'do this' or 'do that.' If you struggle long and hard for a thing it becomes infinitely sweet to you.

Was there a kind of hatred between the father and the older son of the Grey family? 'You are one also who has this thing — the impulse to power, so like my own. Now you are young and I am growing old.' Admiration mixed with fear. If you would retain power it will not do to admit fear.

The young Don was so curiously like the father. There were the same lines about the jaws, the same eyes. They were both heavy men. Already the young man walked like the father, slammed doors as did the father. There was the same curious lack of delicacy of thought and touch — the heaviness that plows through, gets things done. When John Grey had married Louise Aspinwahl he was already a mature man, on his way to success. Such men do not marry young and recklessly. Now he was nearing sixty and there was the son — so like himself, having the same kind of strength.

Both land lovers, possession lovers. 'It is my farm, my house, my horses, cattle, sheep.' Soon now, another ten years, fifteen at the most, and the father would be ready for death. 'See, already my hand slips a little. All of this to go out of my grasp.' He, John Grey, had not got all of these possessions so easily. It had taken much patience, much persistence. No one but himself would ever quite know. Five, ten, fifteen years of work and saving, getting the Aspinwahl farm piece by piece. 'The fools!' They had liked to think of themselves as aristocrats, throwing the land away, now twenty acres, now thirty, now fifty.

Raising horses that could never plow an acre of land.

And they had robbed the land too, had never put anything back, doing nothing to enrich it, build it up. Such a one thinking: 'I'm an Aspinwahl, a gentleman. I do not soil my hands at the plow.'

'Fools who do not know the meaning of land owned, possessions, money — responsibility. It is they who are second-rate men.'

He had got an Aspinwahl for a wife and, as it had turned out, she was the best, the smartest and, in the end, the best-looking one of the lot.

And now there was his son, standing at the moment near the mother. They had both come down off the porch. It would be natural and right for this one — he being what he already was, what he would become — for him, in his turn, to come into possession, to take command.

There would be, of course, the rights of the other children. If you have the stuff in you (John Grey felt that his son Don had) there is a way to manage. You buy the others out, make arrangements. There was Ted — he wouldn't be alive — and Mary and the two younger children. 'The better for you if you have to struggle.'

All of this, the implication of the moment of sudden struggle between a father and son, coming slowly afterwards to the man's daughter, as yet little more than a child. Does the drama take place when the seed is put into the ground or afterwards when the plant has pushed out of the ground and the bud breaks open, or still later, when the fruit ripens? There were the Greys with their ability — slow, saving, able, determined, patient. Why had they superseded the Aspinwahls in the Rich Valley? Aspinwahl blood also in the two children, Mary and Ted.

There was an Aspinwahl man — called 'Uncle Fred,' a brother to Louise Grey — who came sometimes to the farm. He was a rather striking-looking, tall old man with a gray Vandyke beard and a mustache, somewhat shabbily dressed but always with an indefinable air of class. He came from the county-seat town, where he lived now with a daughter who had married a merchant, a polite courtly old man who always froze into a queer silence in the presence of his sister's husband.

The son Don was standing near the mother on the day in the fall, and the two children, Mary and Ted, stood apart.

'Don't, John,' Louise Grey said again. The father, who had started away toward the barns, stopped.

'Well, I guess I will.'

'No, you won't,' said young Don, speaking suddenly. There was a queer fixed look in his eyes. It had flashed into life — something that was between the two men: 'I possess' . . . 'I will possess.' The father wheeled and looked sharply at the son and then ignored him.

For a moment the mother continued pleading.

'But why, why?'

'They make too much shade. The grass does not grow.'

'But there is so much grass, so many acres of grass.'

John Grey was answering his wife, but now again he looked at his son. There were unspoken words flying back and forth.

'I possess. I am in command here. What do you mean by telling me that I won't?'

'Ha! So! You possess now but soon I will possess.'

'I'll see you in hell first.'

'You fool! Not yet! Not yet!'

None of the words, set down above, was spoken at the moment, and afterwards the daughter Mary never did remember the exact words that had passed between the two men. There was a sudden quick flash of determination in Don — even perhaps sudden determination to stand by the mother — even perhaps something else — a feeling in the young Don out of the Aspinwahl blood in him — for the moment tree love superseding grass love — grass that would fatten steers. . . .

Winner of 4H Club prizes, champion young corn-raiser, judge of steers, land lover, possession lover.

'You won't,' Don said again.

'Won't what?'

'Won't cut those trees.'

The father said nothing more at the moment, but walked away from the little group toward the barns. The sun was still shining brightly. There was a sharp cold little wind. The two trees were like bonfires lighted against distant hills.

It was the noon hour and there were two men, both young, employees on the farm, who lived in a small tenant house beyond the barns. One of them, a man with a harelip, was married, and the other, a rather handsome silent young man, boarded with him. They had just come from the midday meal and were going toward one of the barns. It was the beginning of the fall corn-cutting time and they would be going together to a distant field to cut corn.

The father went to the barn and returned with the two men. They brought axes and a long cross-cut saw. 'I want you to cut those two trees.' There was something, a blind, even stupid determination in the man, John Grey. And at that moment his wife, the mother of his children . . . There was no way any of the children could ever know how many moments of the sort she had been through. She had married John Grey. He was her man.

'If you do, Father . . .' Don Grey said coldly.

'Do as I tell you! Cut those two trees!' This addressed to the two workmen. The one who had a harelip laughed. His laughter was like the bray of a donkey.

'Don't,' said Louise Grey, but she was not addressing her husband this time. She stepped to her son and put a hand on his arm.

'Don't.

'Don't cross him. Don't cross my man.' Could a child like Mary Grey comprehend? It takes time to understand things that happen in life. Life unfolds slowly to the mind. Mary was standing with Ted, whose young face was white and tense. Death at his elbow. At any moment. At any moment.

'I have been through this a hundred times. That is the way this man I married has succeeded. Nothing stops him. I married him; I have had my children by him.

'We women choose to submit.

'This is my affair, more than yours, Don, my son.'

A woman hanging onto her thing — the family, created about her.

The son not seeing things with her eyes. He shook off his mother's hand, lying on his arm. Louise Grey was younger than her husband, but, if he was now nearing sixty, she was drawing near fifty. At the moment she looked very delicate and fragile. There was something, at the moment, in her bearing. . . . Was there, after all, something in blood, the Aspinwahl blood?

In a dim way perhaps, at the moment, the child Mary did comprehend. Women and their men. For her then, at that time, there was but one male, the child Ted. Afterwards she remembered how he looked at that moment, the curiously serious old look on his young face. There was even, she thought later, a kind of contempt for both the father and brother, as though he might have been saying to himself — he couldn't really have been saying it — he was too young: 'Well, we'll see. This is something. These foolish ones — my father and my brother. I myself haven't long to live. I'll see what I can, while I do live.'

The brother Don stepped over near to where his father stood.
'If you do, Father . . .' he said again.
'Well?'
'I'll walk off this farm and I'll never come back.'
'All right. Go then.'

The father began directing the two men who had begun cutting the trees, each man taking a tree. The young man with the harelip kept laughing, the laughter like the bray of a donkey. 'Stop that,' the father said sharply, and the sound ceased abruptly. The son Don walked away, going rather aimlessly toward the barn. He approached one of the barns and then stopped. The mother, white now, half ran into the house.

The son returned toward the house, passing the two younger children without looking at them, but did not enter. The father did not look at him. He went hesitatingly along a path at the front of the house and through a gate and into a road. The road ran for several miles down through the valley and then, turning, went over a mountain to the county-seat town.

As it happened, only Mary saw the son Don when he returned to the farm. There were three or four tense days. Perhaps, all the time, the mother and son had been secretly in touch. There was a telephone in the house. The father stayed all day in the fields, and when he was in the house was silent.

Mary was in one of the barns on the day when Don came back and when the father and son met. It was an odd meeting.

The son came, Mary always afterwards thought, rather sheepishly. The father came out of a horse's stall. He had been throwing corn to work horses. Neither the father nor son saw Mary. There was a car parked in the barn and she had crawled into the driver's seat, her hands on the steering wheel, pretending she was driving.

'Well,' the father said. If he felt triumphant, he did not show his feeling.

'Well,' said the son, 'I have come back.'

'Yes, I see,' the father said. 'They are cutting corn.' He walked toward the barn door and then stopped. 'It will be yours soon now,' he said. 'You can be boss then.'

He said no more and both men went away, the father toward the distant fields and the son toward the house. Mary was afterwards quite sure that nothing more was ever said.

What had the father meant?

'When it is yours you can be boss.' It was too much for the child. Knowledge comes slowly. It meant:

'You will be in command, and for you, in your turn, it will be necessary to assert.

'Such men as we are cannot fool with delicate stuff. Some men are meant to command and others must obey. You can make them obey in your turn.

'There is a kind of death.

'Something in you must die before you can possess and command.'

There was, so obviously, more than one kind of death. For Don Grey one kind and for the younger brother Ted, soon now perhaps, another.

Mary ran out of the barn that day, wanting eagerly to get out into the light, and afterwards, for a long time, she did not try to think her way through what had happened. She and her brother Ted did, however, afterwards, before he died, discuss quite often the two trees. They went on a cold day and put their fingers on the stumps, but the stumps were cold. Ted kept asserting that only men got their legs and arms cut off, and she protested. They continued doing things that had been forbidden Ted to do, but no one protested, and, a year or two later, when he died, he died during the night in his bed.

But while he lived, there was always, Mary afterwards thought, a curious sense of freedom, something that belonged to him that made it good, a great happiness, to be with him. It was, she finally thought, because having to die his kind of death, he never had to make the surrender his brother had made — to be sure of possessions, success, his time to command — would never have to face the more subtle and terrible death that had come to his older brother.

A Part of Earth

I HAD GIVEN A BANKER in Chicago a suggestion about a certain business in which he had money and it had worked. Although my intimate friends never will believe it, I have a head for affairs. Theodore Dreiser once laughed at the notion. 'If you have a head for business, then I have one for breeding sheep,' he said. But he was wrong.

The banker had a talk with me. 'Why, what the hell, man, why haven't you money?' He declared he would put me in.

He had heard I was a writer. He had a son in the University of Chicago, and in one of the son's classes a professor had spoken favorably of a book of mine. 'He tells me you are pretty good.' The banker had a friend in New York who had large holdings in one of the movie companies. 'Why not let me speak to him about getting you on? I understand there's big money in it for you writers.'

The son had told him I was something of a high-brow. 'I know it isn't true,' he said, 'but let me think so.' He tried to explain an idea of his to me. He was himself interested in art. He bought paintings. He had married a woman who was somewhat of a high-brow. And he had read things about painters and poets who starved all their lives. That was all nonsense.

From the suggestion I had given him he could see I had a head for business. So if I wanted to write books that wouldn't sell, why not wait?

I could write the stuff the movies wanted for a time, get myself some dough. Then I could cut it out. I remember that when I had this conversation with the banker, we were dining. He had taken me

321

to an expensive restaurant. The idea he was proposing to me had been held up to me by many others.

Physically he was a fine specimen of a man, and he had a passion for race-horses. We had had conversations about them. 'They are such clear fine creatures, not tricky as we are. A good one will give you all he's got. He likes to.'

The conversation drifted back to my own situation. 'There you are working in that advertising agency, in a minor place, at a piker job.'

'Yes. They don't pay me much. For them my salary is a small affair. But just because my salary is comparatively small, I can occasionally get off, waste time in some town. They do not mind.'

'Man, have you no ambition? Don't you want to be something? You could take on this job for a time. Then you could get out.'

'Like you?' I said. He stared at me.

'I see,' he said, 'you mean —— '

He had got it all right. I did not want to be as he was, spending my life working at something I did not care about. He owned a string of race-horses, but hired a man to train them. I had been to his stables with him.

There was the fellow at the stables, the trainer, a man of the banker's own age, a solid-looking quiet man. He was a man of parts, I thought, had his feet on the ground. 'Why not?' I thought. The fellow was taking the beautiful graceful young creatures, training them, watching them from day to day, picking the good ones, those that had it.

A minor man in a minor place, eh? The banker standing there. He owned the horses. For this one he had paid so and so many dollars, etc. The trainer seemed to be reading my thoughts. I had seen something like envy of that other fellow in the banker's eyes; the trainer of his horses, his servant. I had not been able to keep from smiling. As we walked over to a two-year-old, a young stallion, a tall yellow boy, the trainer, turned and looked hard at me. It was as though he had spoken, 'Keep your thoughts to yourself!'

'But you do want money, don't you?' It was the banker speaking that noon in the restaurant.

'God, yes.' How I did want it! I thought. It was that I just didn't want to earn it. I didn't even want to deserve it. I wanted what it

could mean, escape from the advertising agency, from buying and
selling, and other things. My glances went about the restaurant. Beautifully dressed women were sitting at the tables. I was in love at the
time (I always was in love). I saw myself taking the woman loved
into an expensive shop, buying her beautiful clothes, expensive furs,
elegant shoes; saw myself buying beautiful things for myself too.
Whenever I saw rich fabrics, my fingers ached to touch them.

'Sure I want money. Why don't you give me some?'

A laugh. 'Not me,' said the banker. I understood. Spending his
life as he was, doing something he didn't care about for the sake of a
freedom he imagined he would get, but which really would never
come to him, he wanted me to pay for my freedom.

'You won't,' I said. 'You couldn't set me free while you remain in
prison.' We sat staring at one another. There are moments when
men who instinctively like one another also can hate. 'Be careful.
Do not get too close to the truth when talking with the rich,' I was
whispering to myself.

He switched the conversation. 'What do you get out of it?'

'I'll tell you.' And after a minute I began describing to him something which happened to me on a certain day of my life and a certain night in a Chicago rooming house following the day. I began
with the morning. During all of it, I told him, I had sat at my desk
by a window in a room of the advertising agency. It was a little
room, quite crowded with advertising writers. The other offices of the
agency occupied the entire floor of the building. They were big offices,
and men sat in them, one in each office.

These were the business men. They brought advertisers, 'clients'
they were called, into the agency. They went forth, traveled up and
down in fast trains, played golf with manufacturers. Once I had traveled with one of these men, grown rich now, on a train. He was
taking me to see a client, a certain large manufacturer. He boasted
how he had gotten the client for our house. 'I got him with my
little old studbook,' he said, taking a little notebook out of a pocket. It
was filled with the names and addresses of women. He had got the
manufacturer a little drunk, introduced him to one of these women.

'And after that?'

There had been a little case of blackmail, one business man coming
into a hotel room, the other business man in bed there with the

woman. The click of a camera. 'I told him I destroyed the negative, but he won't believe it. Why shouldn't his account be in our house? We have got some pretty smart advertising writers. You know that.'

That morning the man who had shown me his studbook was in one of the big offices at the front of the building. There was an expensive rug on the floor. He was sitting at a big mahogany desk. But no. It had been March, and cold and rainy. He was off with some 'client' playing golf in Florida. But see what muddled creatures people are! The same man who had boasted of his slickness in getting the new big client for our house only two weeks previously had called me to his office. He had heard I had published a book. 'You come home some night with me,' he said. 'You bring a notebook. I'll tell you the story of my life. It is a wonderful story. Often I have wished I could write,' he continued, and began telling me of his wife, what a fine, pure woman she was. He also had a daughter and a son. What plans he had for them. 'I have had to wade through muck,' he said, 'but I have done it to give them all a finer way of life.' He loved his wife, he declared, and had been true to her. 'Of course,' he said, 'sometimes when I have been out with a client, you understand — he wanted a woman. Perhaps we were a little drunk. But my wife is a wonderful person.'

In any case that morning I had been given an assignment. I was to write a series of advertisements for the daily newspapers playing up a new cathartic. I was to spend the day delving in the mysteries of bowels. I had come in through wet streets, some of the other advertising writers were already there. 'Hello, girls.'

I explained to the banker that we in the 'copy department' were making a struggle. 'For God's sake, let us keep trying. It may be we can hold on.' Two or three of us dreamt of some day becoming real writers. This fellow was, in secret, working on a play, that fellow on a novel. Sometimes at lunch in some little saloon we talked it over among ourselves. 'We are little male harlots. We lie with these business men. Let us at least try keeping our minds a little clear. Don't let's fall for this dope that we are doing something worth doing, here.'

'Hello, girls,' I had repeated.

'Good morning, Mabel.' There was a fat copy-man who always addressed me as 'Mabel.' He had already heard of my assignment. 'Mabel, they have got you a new man.'

'Yes. He deals in excretions.' The fat man had worked out a theory of life. He believed in heaven and hell. 'It's as plain as the nose on your face,' he used to say, 'all the people in this life have lived before. They have been sinners in another life and are being punished for it. We might as well face the facts. We are in the advertising department of hell.'

I told the banker who sat listening in silence that several people who had worked in that room with me had committed suicide. Others had become drunkards. Sitting in the little back room we could look across a street into a loft where they made cheap women's dresses. One woman sat over there by her window, never looking up. How her fingers flew! There was a kind of insanity of speed in her fingers. Sometimes at night in my dreams I saw them flying, flying thus. There were many women's fingers flying, flying, flying. Perhaps they were making some man rich.

For possibly an hour or even two hours I had worked at the series of advertisements. Thoughts of my mother came into my mind. Her life had been much like that of the woman over there in the loft across the street. Her fingers also were never quiet. They were flying, flying, trying to earn food to raise five sons. And that day was one of those on which I rebelled. These rebellions were always happening in the advertising place. Our bosses had to allow for them. 'Come on, Little Eva,' I called to the fat man. In recognition of our common harlotry he was 'Little Eva' as I was 'Mabel.' He was a man who might have weighed two hundred and fifty. 'Come on, let's get a drink.' Formerly he had been a newspaper man, but had come into advertising because there was more money in it. He had a growing family, several sons and a daughter. 'I want to give them an education, give them at least a chance at a more cultured life.'

'So that, in the end, they may be ashamed of their father?'

'Yes.'

We started out, went from bar to bar, made our way, not into the busy part of town, but into side streets. Some instinct led us to tough saloons. 'Have another, Mabel?' 'No, Little Eva. This one's on me.' There were down-and-outs hanging about. They leered at us. 'What have we here, a pair of fairies?' All of this was part of our satisfaction. We were getting a little drunk. 'Shall we go back to the office? Maybe now while I'm drunk I can get through that series of advertisements.' 'No. We won't go back today. Hell is there, but it is also here. We are destined to live our lives in hell. It may even be that this place is not hell. It may be purgatory. Let us go about, seeing how other people live in purgatory.'

It might have been five o'clock when I left the fat hell man to go to my hall bedroom. It was on the North Side. For a while I lingered on one of the river bridges. (This was before the great new bridges were built.) It was one of the old rickety wooden bridges that turned to let vessels pass up and down the stream, and beyond lay the crowded noisy place called South Water Street, where most of the food for the millions in the city was sold. It was a crazy hell of a place and today there was a cold rain, but the bridges were nice. The color of the river water was the apple-green of semi-precious stones, and above the moving vessels sea-gulls screamed and circled. A suggestion of a wide freedom, the sea's and the upper air's, both bare of men, somehow reached me. I was trying to write poetry at the time, and people with me on the turning bridge stared at me standing there and muttering words. I searched for ugly words for the ugliness of life, for beautiful words to express its beauty. Once in my room, I did not remove my wet clothes. As ever when I was drunk my imagination played madly. With head awhirl I lay on my bed, staring through my window into the rainy street, and figures began appearing before my eyes. It may be that I slept and wakened. The street lights had been lit. I sat up.

Does all of this seem trivial? I am trying to tell it again as I told it all to the banker at the lunch table.

There I was, sitting at the edge of the bed in that room. It was dark, but on the wall lay a spot of light cast by a street lamp.

'So, this is my life? This is what I am, what has become of me.'

'Never mind your life. It is unimportant what has become of you. It is the disease of the world, questioning what you are or are not.' Almost it seemed as though a voice in the room had spoken the words.

Faces of people kept passing in and out of the fleck of light. Dim shadows of reality, they whirled and danced, some of them parts of myself, others of other people. Again it seemed something was speaking, saying, 'All of life is too much up in my head.' This time I recognized the voice. It was that of one of the people, the woman in our office who had committed suicide. Of an afternoon she had gone to

a department store and bought a revolver. She had sent it with cartridges to the little hotel where she roomed. This was at the lunch
hour, and she went back to her desk and worked during the afternoon. She was, I thought, a rather attractive woman and that day as
she was leaving the office she had spoken to me.

'Walk a little with me,' she said. We went along through the hurrying crowd. I 'missed' her. There was something I should have
sensed, but did not. It must have been one of the days when I soaked
with self-pity. We went through streets, she talking, seemingly very
brightly, very cheerfully. She kept making sarcastic remarks about
herself. 'I'll tell you of an experience I had,' she said, and told me a
tale of going out one night into the street to pick up a man. She had
seen prostitutes doing it and wanted to know what it must be like.
'I'd been another kind so long and wanted to see what it would be
like going the whole way.' But she couldn't, physically or otherwise,
and had to give it up. 'I spoke to two or three men, but they hurried
away.' She thought they might have mistaken her for a detective.
Her failure was due, she thought, to the fact that the whole thing
was too much just up in her head. 'That's the trouble with me. All
my life is too much up in my head,' and that evening when I left her
she went home to her hotel and with the revolver blew her head out
of the picture.

'And so it is also with you.' This had been myself speaking to myself in the dark room. I had got up and lit the light. I had suddenly
become quite sober. In all my writing, I knew, I had been using only
my head. I had never let other people with their lives come into me.
'This is what it is all about,' said I to myself. 'It's got to come down
from your head and meet people.'

Among the figures on the wall there had been one of a little frightened man. Perhaps it came out of some memory of my own, a face
seen sometimes on the street, a story told by some man in a barroom,
as well as out of the experience that very day, the fat man calling me
'Mabel,' me calling him 'Eva,' and our suspiciousness in the eyes of
other men, hangers-on in the cheap barrooms. But something else was
mixed in it. Out of them seemed to speak the passionate desire in all
people to be understood, to have their stories told, perhaps that the
terrible isolation of their lives may break. I went to my table and began writing. The story is called 'Hands'; it is in *Winesburg*. In sud-

den almost terrible joy afterwards I had walked up and down my room. 'It's there, it's solid. No matter if no one understands its implications. It's sound. For once in my life I've been a part of earth.'

All writers, painters, actors, all men of the arts, have had such hours. They are something also known by workmen. Good farmers have the feeling, too. There was a piece of land, neglected, overcropped for too many years, gone to pot, scraggly weeds growing, and it had come into the hands of the good farmer. He had gone to work, was patient, a land-lover. He had fed the field, slowly enriched it, gotten at last a stand of clover, plowed it under. Wait now. He has given all he has. At last a day has come.

'Look.' You are leaning beside him on the fence at the field's edge. 'Look,' he says. His figure straightens. He is even a little embarrassed, boasting to you. 'The finest stand of corn in all this section. You should have seen this field some five years ago when I got it.'

Perhaps race-horses have such hours, too. I remember trying to tell all of this to my banker. 'I hope I've answered your question,' I said, and added, 'Yes, indeed, I want money. I merely do not want to have to earn it, to do what you call deserve it. Will you give it to me?'

'No,' he laughed. It wasn't a very pleasant laugh. 'You think,' he added, 'you have got now and then a thing I cannot get.'

'I don't mean that at all,' I said. 'Everyone can have it. I mean you won't have it.'

He paid the bill. 'You'd better keep your money,' I said. 'You go to hell,' he replied. Later I heard that he had sold his string of race-horses.

The Yellow Gown

I LAUGHED and stretched myself. 'Work now, you slave.'

'Well, what shall I do? Shall I go to work in a factory? In me there is no gift for the factories. I work and work but do not rise. You see I have read all the books. I knew that, in a factory, when a man has done his work well, he is promoted. At night he takes a course in something — well, let us say in mechanical engineering, and then, some day in the factory, there is a problem to solve and he solves it.'

'But I cannot solve any problems. Do you not understand that figures mean nothing to me?'

'But, my dear man, you will have to work. Go then to a store. Get a job as a clerk. Be honest. There must be a way in which you can rise in the world. You should cultivate respectable people.'

When I had got out-of-doors the sun was shining. I lived at that time in a room near a park in the city of Chicago and when I had walked in the park and had eaten my breakfast at a nearby lunch counter I stood for a moment on the street. 'Shall I go look for work or shall I go call on Harold?' The trouble with me is that I cannot solve problems. As I walked along I became suddenly gloomy. 'I'm in for trouble,' I said to myself.

But I never had thought it would come as it did. I had not thought it would come from the woman named Mildred.

For months, I had been Harold's shadow and, I am afraid, half his servant. He was called the prize student of the Art Institute at that time and the girl students all worshiped him, but Mildred had won him. It was even said . . . Well, he had a studio and Mildred went there almost any time. We, who were their friends, did not use the word, but we thought, perhaps we hoped . . . Romance of just that sort is so hard to come at in Chicago.

She also was an art student and very quick and facile at making pleasant little drawings, but no one took her art seriously. Harold was, however, a different matter. He was a Modern. A painting of his had once been accepted and hung at a show of young moderns in New York City. I remember it now as a wild thing of red and white perpendicular lines across which went meandering a river of red and it was called, I believe, 'The Red Laugh,' after something Harold had read by the Russian, Andreyev.

At the moment, however, and just at the time when I had become most intimate with him, Harold was up to something else. He was, in fact, in the act of showing the Chicago art world how a man of talent goes about it to win the prize in the annual fall show.

At the moment I was not working and was consequently happy and contented with life and had been so for a long time, but my money was beginning to give out. I was living in a cheap rooming house, but was living as best I could the life of leisure. In the evening I went to Harold's room or to the room of some other student and in the morning stayed in my bed. And what joy I had of life! Why get up? I had cigarettes and matches on a chair beside the bed.

Harold had a studio in what had once been a small store in the neighborhood and slept on a cot at the back. I dare say Mildred grew tired of always having me about, but Harold seemed glad of my presence in the afternoons. Perhaps I saved him from her too great ardor.

Until — well, until the great scheme had been hatched.

The great scheme was that Harold should paint a perfectly conventional picture for the fall show and win the-prize. It was to be an interior. There was to be a corner of a ladies' dressing room of the old rich days, say of the fifteenth century in Italy, with a window looking out upon a rolling country, hill after hill getting smaller and smaller in the distance, such hills as Titian or Raphael liked to put into the backgrounds of their canvases.

The interior of the room would be somewhat somber, a heavily carved chair sitting before an equally heavily carved table near the window.

And across the back of the chair — ah, there was the point — across the back of the chair would be thrown ... Harold was so excited about the whole matter when I went to him early that afternoon that it took him a long time to talk at all.

Across the back of the chair would be thrown a woman's heavy yellow velvet gown.

At first I could not understand Harold's excitement concerning the gown, but as he talked I began a little to understand. The folds of the gown should be made to fall in just a certain way. Harold had, in fact, got hold of such a gown as he intended painting into the picture in a second-hand store in lower State Street, Chicago, in a place where women's dresses, that had once belonged to members of the fashionable world and later perhaps been given to servants, had now been put on sale. In a place, in fact, where they were likely to catch the best trade for such wares; that is to say, in a street much frequented at that time by the women of the town.

It may have been that seeing the gown in the store window had put the notion of the painting into Harold's head and he had gone into the store and had bought it at once and now had it in the studio. Its presence there was, I could see at once, a queer sort of shock to Mildred. He kept walking across the room and throwing it across the back of a chair (not the heavily carved chair of the picture — that he would get out of a book at the institute or the public library, he explained. It would be, he thought, Spanish and very rococo — but across a kitchen chair he had bought at a nearby furniture store.

He flung the gown over the back of the chair, arranged the folds a little, picked it up again, walked across the room and again pitched it at the chair. 'The thing may have to be carefully arranged, but there is a chance it may fall just right,' he said, while Mildred and I looked on in wonder. The gown, he explained, was to be the central point of his painting. There it would be in the corner of the dark somber room with the dark somber landscape in the distance. Other things in the picture, the chair, the table, the hills, he could paint in quickly enough, saving all the best of himself for the painting of the gown. It was there, in the painting of the gown, he would show the old painters something. He would paint the soft rich velvet lying in folds in such a way that the committee, the men who were to hang and judge the pictures, would be fairly knocked off their feet. Did he not know such fellows? Ah, he would get them. Their feelings, their sensuality, would be worked on without their knowing. There would be brush work, color, the feel for texture. Men who had always painted in the conventional way and whose natures had become dried and half dead were always saying that men like himself, Gauguin, Cézanne, and the others, were only trying to avoid the real challenge of painting, but he would show them. I do not remember that Harold, when he called the roll of the great moderns in his studio that afternoon, put himself among them, but at least he implied something of the sort.

He would so paint the woman's dress that the power women were able to exert over all men, because of men's sensual natures, would unconsciously be felt by everyone who looked at the painting. 'For the time being, for weeks perhaps, while I am doing the painting, I shall be in love, actually and physically in love with an imagined woman of old times who once wore this dress. I am sitting, you see, at the back of the room waiting for her. The dress is lying across the back of the chair, but, as I sit waiting, it, you see, represents her to me. In it I see the gentle but strong mold of her form, all she is to me, all she is to become to me when I have won her. I have not won her yet. Upon the wonder awakened in her by the way I shall paint depends whether or not I shall make her my own.'

Harold had now worked himself into a state and had completely won my own admiration, but Mildred . . . I was not entirely sorry when I looked at Mildred's face. There had been moments when I had thought that — if Harold were not about . . .

And now Harold, having determined to begin blocking in his picture at once, that same evening, ran to prepare his canvas and easel, all the while telling us of his plans. His father was a wholesale merchant at Fort Wayne, Indiana, and had objected to his becoming an artist. It was only the mother's influence that had induced him to support Harold at the school, but after he had painted the canvas he was now about to begin, and had won the prize in the fall show, all would be changed. Money would be forthcoming and with the money got from his father and from the painting, which would be sure to sell at a large price, he would take Mildred and me with him to Paris. There we would live, Mildred and he studying painting, while I . . . . He had stopped his preparations and, turning, had looked at me. 'Well, you'll be all right whatever turns up,' he had said, heartily enough, I am sure.

I had walked out of Harold's studio with Mildred and we had gone to dine at a nearby restaurant. The money that had paid for the weeks of leisure I had just been enjoying was nearly gone. Soon I would have to go to work. At the table d'hôte we spoke of Harold and what a splendid fellow he was. Mildred, I thought, was hanging between anger and tears. She had wanted a man when Harold had caught her fancy and she had got an artist. Now that he had started on his great canvas, she would, for weeks, get nothing from him. I looked at her and wondered.

She had told me, on the way to the table d'hôte, that she was nearly broke. For some time she had been holding a job as secretary to a business man in the Loop district, but Harold was always phoning her in the afternoon and she was always running off with him and now the man had fired her. She had intended telling Harold about it that afternoon, but had found him so absorbed in his grand plans that she had hated to disturb him. As she had talked the hope in me had flared up and after the table d'hôte and while we were still seated at the table, I took a deep breath and unfolded my scheme.

For several weeks, I explained, Harold would be absorbed with his painting. He would not want Mildred about and she had lost her job. It might well be that she, like myself, was nearly broke. Such a painting as Harold had in hand could not be done offhand. He would be absorbed in it, thinking of nothing else. Above all he would not want a woman about. Had not Mildred heard what he had said about the feelings he would be having for some mysterious woman of old times? Such feelings, while they lasted, were often stronger than the feeling for living people. It is a part of the artist nature that this be so.

'We will have to be comrades, now, Mildred,' I said, and then I unfolded my scheme.

All of this was before the days of prohibition and Chicago had within its borders thousands of small saloons. As I had gone about the city I had noted that saloon keepers had a penchant for pictures back of the bars and these were as a rule very stupidly done. Why not have them better done?

To the saloon keepers I would explain how, at Barbazon and other places, paintings on the walls of little out-of-the-way cafés had become famous and had made the places where some great painter had stopped casually in his youth famous. Rich Americans took voyages out from Paris to see such places and spent money lavishly. I had no doubt that, with the tales I could invent, we could get many an order from thirty to fifty dollars. We would divide our takings and while Harold was engaged with his great work we would also be making money. 'A woman wants her independence,' I said and Mildred nodded. I had been somewhat afraid she would break into tears.

And so it had been arranged, and, for me at least, the adventure with Mildred had turned out to be a great success. For weeks, and while Harold was engaged with his great masterpiece, we had tramped about the streets of Chicago, I making engagements for Mildred and she executing them. How charming she was! In the early morning we met and set out on our own mutual adventure and as she stood on a chair behind some bar, with laborers and teamsters standing about, painting on the bar-room looking glass one of the several scenes we had prepared in advance, I moved among the spectators, speaking in whispers of the great future before her when she had got to Paris and had attracted the attention of the big world. 'The day may come when that looking glass, because of the painting now being put on it, may be worth a thousand dollars,' I said solemnly, and often some man in the crowd ordered on the spot a duplicate of the painting to be done on canvas so that it could be framed and hung up in his house.

What days for me, the presence of Mildred, the dollars rolling in, a new suit bought, an overcoat against the winter, new linen, money in my pocket! Occasionally, in the evening, Mildred went to see Harold, but he was absorbed and did not ask what she was doing and she did not tell him. 'The matter may go on for months and it will surely go on until the great canvas is finished,' I thought, and saw myself living for months with my books and no more compelled to go into some factory or to accept a clerkship.

And then one morning it had all come to an end, and I shall remember that morning as long as I live. It may be that I had begun to hope I would win Mildred myself.

I had gone to a place on the West Side, near Garfield Park in Chicago, where I was to meet Mildred and where our day's work was to begin, but when she appeared I knew at once something had happened. She was not wearing the gay little smock that had been a part of our stage property and there was a sad serious look on her face. At once and without words she had led the way into the park and we sat down on a bench. She was dressed in black. What a come-down! I perhaps made a mistake. I took her hand.

That may have broken the flood gates. She may have intended only to tell me she could not carry on our scheme any more. On the evening before she had gone to Harold and the great painting was at last finished. He had wanted her back. 'Where have you been and what have you been doing?' he had asked, and it was then the horror of what she had been doing had for the first time dawned upon Mildred. The thought of it had made her half ill and she had cried all night. While he, Harold, had been doing his great painting, making a real and lasting contribution to the arts, she, betrayed by me, by the baseness in my nature, had been going about to low saloons and had been painting such pictures on the looking glasses back of the bars. Now, if she had her own way, she would go about painting them all out. The common people, such people as came into small Chicago saloons, had also been betrayed. One should be engaged in lifting up, not in casting down into greater and greater vulgarities the common people.

'But, Mildred,' I said. She had taken her hand from mine and was weeping. A man passing along the path had stopped and seemed about to speak. There was an angry look in his eyes. Perhaps he thought we were married and that I had been beating her. In the far distance, across a flat open green space, some golf players, tiny figures against a sea of green, were passing in and out across an opening between trees. It was early fall and in Chicago early fall days can be lovely.

To think that I had been the one who had betrayed Mildred and through her had betrayed Harold's art! 'There is nothing now you can do except one thing and that you must do. Promise me that I will never see you again and that you will never see Harold again,' she said, getting to her feet and preparing to leave me flat there in the park.

Without another word Mildred had left me, sitting disconsolate and alone on the bench. I arose and stretched. As I have already pointed out, I am one who cannot solve problems. 'Work now, you slave,' I had begun saying to myself again, when another thought came. My new overcoat was warm and, as I have said, fall days in Chicago can sometimes be quite lovely. I put the paint box on the bench and stared at the man who had been staring at me. 'Get out,' I thought, although I said nothing to him. 'Perhaps,' I said to myself, 'when there is a new masterpiece to be done ——' I had, you see, not entirely given up the notion of Mildred.

And so I went back again to my room and my books.

As for the masterpiece, as it turned out, I did not see it at all. It was hung in the fall show and, although it did not win the prize, attracted a great deal of attention. It just happened that at that time I had gone off on my travels.

It did not win the fall prize, but that was because the jury was fixed. I had that from a friend who had it from Mildred. And had you been with us during the days of our mutual adventure, you also would have been unable to doubt what Mildred had said.

Mildred was, you see, such a masterpiece in herself.

I am very sure she must have been worthy of Harold.

A Writer's Conception of Realism

I<small>T MUST BE</small> that I am an incurable small-town man. Either that is true or there is something very special going on here at Olivet and, after some ten days here, I have about concluded that it is not the small town in general that has built up in me a kind of feeling of wonder but Olivet in particular. It has seemed to me a little like something out of the past and at the same time something, too, which one looks forward to in the future, and, I must say, not always very hopefully. Just now and in most of the places in which I have been — I should say ever since the World War — I have felt a certain tenseness. It has been rather hard to work in. Everyone seems to be trying to think nationally and internationally. The old human interest of one man in another seems to have got lost somewhere. People seem more and more to be separating themselves into groups and classes. A man like myself, never anything but a somewhat liberal democrat, finds his name put into a book called *The Red Network*, labeled there as a communist writer; in many places the anti-Jewish feeling apparently growing stronger — often, I have noticed, in places where there are no Jews and among men who know personally no Jews; prejudice against the Negro, often stronger in the North now than in the South; and all of these impulses leading to a new suspicion by man of man and making more prevalent and more marked our human loneliness.

Here in Olivet I have seemed to find these impulses that do so much to destroy human relationships strangely absent. I came here, as a man goes into most new places, nowadays, a little afraid. The fear is gone. I may be a bit nervous about trying to speak to you here tonight, but I am not afraid of you. Since I have been here I do not believe I have heard the word 'capitalist' or 'proletariat' used once. What a relief. Here I have heard talk of music, of painting, of the art of living, and even, strangely enough, of education. It is a little like coming, after a long and stormy sea voyage into some quiet bay, and I feel rather like congratulating the young men and women who are here seeking an education that they can live here, for a time, in this atmosphere, before going out to tackle what they will find they must tackle.

I am here tonight to make a public lecture, the first one I have tried to make for two or three years. I am a professional writer with, I admit, a good many marks of the eternal amateur on me, and so I have written out what I want to say. When a man has sat at a desk for as many hours through as many years as I have, he finds that his thoughts, when he has any, run more naturally down through his arms and fingers than up to his mouth and lips.

Just the same, as you have probably been told that I was going to try to tell you something of a writer's conception of realistic fiction, I think I ought to try to keep the talk as much as possible, on the subject of realism. I do not know what reality is. I do not think any of us quite know how much our point of view, and, in fact, all of our touch with life, is influenced by our imaginations.

In my own experience, for example, and in my work as a writer I have always attempted to use materials that came out of my own experiences of life. I have written a good deal about my father, my mother, a certain grandmother who touched my imagination, and about my brothers and sisters, and it has amused me sometimes, in talking with some of my brothers, to see how poorly my conception of our father and mother fitted into their own conceptions. 'Why, I dare say, the woman you have pictured is all right. She is very interesting, but she is not my mother as I knew her,' they say.

This whole matter of what we think of as realism is probably pretty tricky. I have often told myself that, having met some person for the first time, some other human being, man or woman, and having had my first look, I cannot ever even see him or her again.

If this is true, why is it true? It is true because the moment I meet you and if we begin to talk, my imagination begins to play. Perhaps I begin to make up stories about you. This is a trick all writers, and

for that matter, all people, do. The writer may merely be more conscious of it. It is our method of work. Very little of the work of the
writer is done at his desk or at the typewriter. It is done as he walks
about, as he sits in a room with people, and perhaps most of all as he
lies in bed at night.

I myself, for example, have all my life had over and over an experience that some of you may also have had. If I have been working
intensely, I find myself unable to relax when I go to bed. Often I fall
into a half-dream state, and when I do, the faces of people begin to
appear before me. They seem to snap into place before my eyes, stay
there, sometimes for a short period, sometimes longer. There are
smiling faces, leering ugly faces, tired faces, hopeful faces. Almost
always they seem to be faces of people I cannot remember ever having
met.

However, I am quite sure they are faces of people I have seen.

They may be people I have met quite casually in the street. I have
been walking about. At times the faces of people, met thus, quite
casually seem full of a strange significance. To quote Herman Melville, 'Who has ever fathomed the strangeness and wonder of man?'
I get sometimes the illusion that every man and woman I meet is
crying out to me. Sometimes a single glance at a human face seems
to tell a whole life story, and there have been times, when I walked
thus, when I had to go along with bowed head, looking at the sidewalk. I could not bear looking at any more faces.

I have a kind of illusion about this matter. It is, I have no doubt,
due to a story-teller's point of view. I have the feeling that the faces
that appear before me thus at night are those of people who want their
stories told and whom I have neglected. Once I remember that I
wrote a poem on this matter. I think I had better recite it to you. I
called my verses,

THE STORY TELLER [1]

Tales are people who sit on the doorstep of the house of my mind.
It is cold outside and they sit waiting.
I look out at a window.
The tales have cold hands,
Their hands are freezing.

[1] Reprinted from *A New Testament*, by Sherwood Anderson.

A short thickly-built tale arises and threshes his arms about.
His nose is red and he has two gold teeth.
There is an old female tale that sits hunched up in a cloak.
Many tales come to sit for a moment on the doorstep and then go away.
It is too cold for them outside.
The street before the door of the house of my mind is filled with tales.
They murmur and cry out, they are dying of cold and hunger.
I am a helpless man — my hands tremble.
I should be sitting on a bench like a tailor.
I should be weaving warm cloth out of the threads of thought.
The tales should be clothed.
They are freezing on the doorstep of the house of my mind.
I am a helpless man — my hands tremble.
I feel in the darkness but cannot find the doorknob.
I look out at a window.
Many tales are dying in the street before the house of mind.

Now, when it comes to talking about the experiences of a writer, I think I should say something that perhaps most of you realize. The work of any writer, and for that matter of any artist in any of the seven arts, should contain within it the story of his own life. There are certain beliefs I have. One is that every man who writes, writes as well as he can. We are always hearing stories about men writing with their tongues in their cheeks, but the truth is that if, for example, a man devotes his life to writing detective stories, he probably believes in the detectives he puts in his stories. If he writes cowboy stories, he really believes that cowboys in life are like the cowboys of the stories and the movies. They aren't, of course, but he thinks so.

I have myself, I think, been counted among what we call in America the high-brow writers. I am not in the least a high-brow type of man, so I have to ask myself — or did at first when I first began writing — have to ask myself how it came about that I was called a high-brow. And I concluded finally that it was because I happened to be a man who took writing rather seriously and I took it seriously because I enjoyed it so thoroughly.

I remember reading somewhere a sentence by Joseph Conrad. He said that he only lived fully and richly when he was at work writing. I have always thought of myself as a man who came into writing, let us say, by the back door. I had a rather adventurous youth. I was a laborer, a farm hand and a factory hand until I was twenty-two or twenty-three years old. I was as a youth always a passionate reader.

And I did not read in order to learn to write. I had no notion of being a writer, although it is probable that I always instinctively wanted to be a story-teller. My father was a rather famous story-teller in the little town in which we lived, and I very much admired that quality in him.

And there were other good story-tellers about. I sought them out. I think I perhaps instinctively watched their technique. I became more or less a wanderer and have been one all of my life. For a time, for two or three years, I led the life of a wandering vagabond, a tramp, working just enough to live. I speak of this because I think it was for me a time of learning, or at least trying to learn.

And here I would like to speak of something. When I was a lad there was a good deal of something going on that may be rather on the wane now. There was this talk, heard on all sides, of America being the great land of opportunity. At that time, such talk pretty much meant getting on, if possible, growing rich, getting to be something big in the world. A lad heard it on all sides and it was not unkindly meant. The idea of accumulation of possessions got all mixed up with the idea of happiness and it was rather confusing. I know it got me confused and I suffered for it. I think I should say to some of the students here who have heard me talk to smaller groups that, if I have kept emphasizing this idea, there is a reason. I have spoken here a good deal, perhaps too much, of my own particular experiences in life. It may be I am rather a nut on the subject, that I too much resent the years I myself spent trying to be what I did not want to be. Some years ago I was asked to deliver what is called the William Vaughn Moody series of lectures in the University of Chicago, and through all the lectures I tried to emphasize the idea of smallness as opposed to bigness; that is to say, the desirability of being just a man going along rather than something outstanding and special.

The truth probably is that I wanted to get out of the scramble as much as I could for a particular reason. I had a hunch. It may be that I gradually realized, as I grew out of childhood into young manhood, that I was losing something. All of us who are older can remember with what fervor we read when we were younger. What a rich place our imagined world was! As we grew older, it seemed to get less rich. I suppose I wanted to keep it rich.

We all, I dare say, have to face what are called 'the facts of life,' but I do think we are often inclined to call facts what are not necessarily facts.

And I think also that the actual training of the imagination, the learning to use it, has a lot to do with human relations. That has something to do with what I want to try to say here.

There is something you can do. Even if you are not actually practicing writers, you can employ something of the writer's technique. When you are puzzled about your own life, as we all are most of the time, you can throw imagined figures of others against a background very like your own, put these imagined figures through situations in which you have been involved. It is a very comforting thing to do, a great relief at times, this occasionally losing sense of self, living in these imagined figures. This thing we call self, as I said here in a talk the other evening, is often very like a disease. It seems to sap you, take something from you, destroy your relationship with others, while even occasionally losing sense of self seems to give you an understanding that you didn't have before you became absorbed.

May it not be that all the people we know are only what we imagine them to be? If, for example, you are as I was at the time of which I am now speaking, a business man, on the whole spending my time seeking my own advantage, you lose interest, while, as opposed to this, as you lose yourself in others, life immediately becomes more interesting. A new world seems to open out before you. Your imagination becomes constantly more and more alive.

And there is a profound pleasure in all of this. At least I know that when I came to it, I found it the pleasantest experience I had ever had. To be sure, I do not want to discount the difficulty. It is very hard to understand any other human being. It is difficult to tell truly the story of another, but it is, I think, rather a grand challenge. I hope you will pardon me for speaking thus seriously about that which interests me so profoundly. You see, I am interested in writing. I am a man in love with his craft.

But I would like to speak a little more clearly if possible on the subject of what, when we think of writers, we call realists. I have said that I do not know what reality is. I do not think any man knows. I remember that some years ago I wrote a short essay that has often since been reproduced and has even, I believe, been used in college text books. I called it 'A Note on Realism.' I think I will read some extracts from it.

'There is something very confusing to both readers and writers about the notion of realism in fiction. As generally understood it is akin to what is called "representation" in painting. The fact is before you and you put it down, adding a high spot here and there, to be sure. No man can quite make himself a camera. Even the most realistic worker pays some tribute to what is called "art." Where does representation end and art begin? The location of the line is often as confusing to practicing artists as it is to the public.'

Recently a young writer came to talk with me about our mutual craft. He spoke with enthusiastic admiration of a certain book — very popular a year or two ago. 'It is the very life. So closely observed. It is the sort of thing I should like to do. I should like to bring life itself within the pages of a book. If I could do that I would be happy.'

I wondered. The book in question had only seemed to me good in spots and the spots had been far apart. There was too much dependence upon the notebook. The writer had seemed to me to have very little to give out of himself. What had happened, I thought, was that the writer of the book had confused the life of reality with the life of the imagination. Easy enough to get a thrill out of people with reality. A man struck by an automobile, a child falling out at the window of a city office building. Such things stir the emotions. No one, however, confuses them with art.

This confusion of the life of the imagination with the life of reality is a trap into which most of our critics seem to me to fall about a dozen times each year. Do the trick over and over, and in they tumble. 'It is life,' they say. 'Another great artist has been discovered.'

What never seems to come quite clear is the simple fact that art is art. It is not life.

The life of the imagination will always remain separated from the life of reality. It feeds upon the life of reality, but it is not that life — cannot be. Mr. John Marin painting Brooklyn Bridge, Henry Fielding writing Tom Jones, are not trying in the novel and the painting to give us reality. They are striving for a realization in art of something out of their own imaginative experiences, fed, to be sure, upon the life immediately about. A quite different matter from making an actual picture of what they see before them.

And here arises a confusion. For some reason — I myself have never exactly understood very clearly — the imagination must constantly feed upon reality or starve. Separate yourself too much from life and you may at moments be a lyrical poet, but you are not an artist. Something within dries up, starves for the want of food. Upon the fact in nature the imagination must constantly feed in order that the imaginative life remain significant. The workman who lets his imagination drift off into some experience altogether disconnected with reality, the attempt of the American to depict life in Europe, the New Englander writing of cowboy life — all that sort of thing — in ninety-nine cases out of a hundred ends in the work of such a man becoming at once full of holes and bad spots. The intelligent reader, tricked often enough by the technical skill displayed in hiding holes, never in the end accepts it as good work. The imagination of the workman has become confused. He has had to depend altogether upon tricks. The whole job is a fake.

The difficulty, I fancy, is that so few workmen in the arts will accept their own limitations. It is only when the limitation is fully accepted that it ceases to be a limitation. Such men scold at the life immediately about. 'It's too dull and commonplace to make good material,' they declare. Off they sail in fancy to the South Seas, to Africa, to China. What they cannot realize is their own dullness. Life is never dull except to the dull.

The writer who sets himself down to write a tale has undertaken something. He has undertaken to conduct his readers on a trip through the world of his fancy. If he is a novelist, his imaginative world is filled with people and events. If he has any sense of decency as a workman, he can no more tell lies about his imagined people, fake them, than he can sell out real people in real life. The thing is constantly done, but no man I have ever met, having done such a trick, has felt very clean about the matter afterward.

On the other hand, when the writer is rather intensely true to the people of his imaginative world, when he has set them down truly, when he does not fake, another confusion arises. Being square with your people in the imaginative world does not mean lifting them over into life, into reality. There is a very subtle distinction to be made, and upon the writer's ability to make this distinction will in the long run depend his standing as a workman.

Having lifted the reader out of the reality of daily life, it is entirely possible for the writer to do his job so well that the imaginative life becomes to the reader for the time real life. Little real touches are added. The people of the town — that never existed except in the fancy — eat food, live in houses, suffer, have moments of happiness, and die. To the writer, as he works, they are very real. The imaginative world in which he is for the time living has become for him more alive than the world of reality ever can become. His very sincerity confuses. Being unversed in the matter of making the delicate distinction that the writer himself sometimes has such a hard time making, they call him a realist. The notion shocks him. 'The deuce, I am nothing of the kind,' he says. 'But such a thing could not have happened in a Vermont town.' 'Why not? Have you not learned that anything can happen anywhere? If a thing can happen in my imaginative world, it can of course happen in the flesh and blood world. Upon what do you fancy my imagination feeds?'

My own belief is that the writer with a notebook in his hand is always a bad workman, a man who distrusts his own imagination. Such a man describes actual scenes accurately, he puts down actual conversation.

But people do not converse in the book world as they do in life. Scenes of the imaginative world are not real scenes.

The life of reality is confused, disorderly, almost always without apparent purpose, whereas in the artist's imaginative life there is purpose. There is determination to give the tale, the song, the painting, form — to make it true and real to the theme, not to life. Often the better the job is done, the greater the confusion.

I myself remember with what a shock I heard people say that one of my own books, Winesburg, Ohio, was an exact picture of Ohio village life. The book was written in a crowded tenement district of Chicago. The hint for almost every character was taken from my fellow lodgers in a large rooming house, many of whom had never lived in a village. The confusion arises out of the fact that others besides practicing artists have imaginations. But most people are afraid to trust their imaginations and the artist is not.

Would it not be better to have it understood that realism, in so far as the word means reality to life, is always bad art — although it may possibly be very good journalism?

Which is but another way of saying that all of the so-called great realists were not realists at all and never intended being. Madame Bovary did not exist in fact. She existed in the imaginative life of Flaubert and he managed to make her exist in the imaginative life of his readers.

. . . .

I have been writing a story. A man is walking in a street and suddenly turns out of the street into an alleyway. There he meets another man and a hurried whispered conversation takes place. In real life they may be but a pair of rather small bootleggers, but they are not that to me.

When I began writing, the physical aspect of one of the men, the one who walked in the street, was taken rather literally from life. He looked strikingly like a man I once knew, so much like him in fact that there was a confusion. A matter easy enough to correct.

A stroke of my pen saves me from realism. The man I knew in life had red hair; he was tall and thin.

With a few words I have changed him completely. Now he has black hair and a black mustache. He is short and has broad shoulders. And now he no longer lives in the world of reality. He is a denizen of my own imaginative world. He can now begin a life having nothing at all to do with the life of the red-haired man.

If I am to succeed in making him real in this new world, he, like hundreds of other men and women who live only in my own fanciful world, must live and move within the scope of the story or novel into which I have cast him. If I do tricks with him in the imaginative world, sell him out, I become merely a romancer. If, however, I have the courage to let him really live, he will, perhaps, show me the way to a fine story or novel.

But the story or novel will not be a picture of life. I will never have had any intentions of making it that.

And so you will see in this matter of realism what I am trying to say. There is a reality to your book, your story people. They may, in the beginning, be lifted out of life, but once lifted, once become a part of the book, of the story-life — realism, in the sense in which the word is commonly used, no longer exists.

There are, you see, these two kinds of realism, the realism to actual life that is the challenge to the journalist and the realism to the book or the story-life. That I should say is the job of your real story-teller.

We Little Children of the Arts

THE BIG GERMAN MAN came along the river bank to where I was lying on the brown grass at the river's edge. The book I had been reading was on the grass beside me. I had been gazing across the sluggish little river at the distant horizon.

I had hoped to spend the day working. There was a story I wanted to write. This was in a low flat country southwest of the city of Chicago. I had come there that morning by train with the others, Joe and George and Jerry, the big German.

They all wanted to be painters. They were striving. The Sundays were very precious to the others and to me. We were all working during the week and looking forward to the week-ends. There were certain canvases the others wanted to paint. If one of them could get a painting hung in the Chicago Art Institute, it might be a beginning.

We used to speak of it at the lunch hours during the week.

There was a certain story that had been in my mind for weeks, even months. We were all living about in little rooming houses. We were clerks. Jerry, the big German, had been a truck-driver. Now he had a job as a shipping clerk in a cold-storage warehouse.

I had tried time and again to write the particular story that was in my mind. I told the others about it. I didn't tell them the story. That would bring bad luck. I spoke instead of how I wanted the words and sentences to march.

'Like soldiers marching across a field,' I said.

'Like a plow turning up its ribbon of earth across a field.'

Fine phrases about work not done. There had been too much of that. You can kill any job so. Just keep talking about the great thing you are to do some time in the future. That will kill it.

'Yes, and it is so also that paint should go on a canvas.'

This would be one of the others, one of the painters speaking.

There was this big talk, plenty of that, words, too many words. Sometimes, after the day's work, in the hot Chicago summers, we all got together to dine in some cheap place. There was a chop-suey joint to which we went often, soft-footed, soft-voiced Chinamen trotting up and down. Chop suey and then a couple of bottles of beer each. We lingered long over that. Then a walk together along the lake front on the near North Side. There was a little strip of park up there facing the lake, a bathing beach; working men with wives and children came there to escape the heat; newspapers spread on the grass, whole families huddled together in the heat; even the moon, looking down, seeming to give forth heat.

We would be full of literary phrases, culled out of books.

Only Jerry, the big German, was a little different. He had a wife and children.

'What's it all about? Why do I want to paint? Why can't I be satisfied driving a truck and working in my warehouse?'

'Going home at night to the wife and kids?'

'What is it keeps stirring in a man, making him want to do something out of just himself?'

He grew profane. He would be describing a scene. He had come to the Chinese place from his warehouse across the Chicago River; this before the river was beautified, in the days of the old wooden bridges over the river.

He had stood for a time on one of the bridges, seeing a lake boat pass, lake sailors standing on the deck of the boat and looking up at him standing there above on the moving bridge, the curiously lovely chrysoprase color of the river, the gulls floating over the river.

He would begin speaking of all that, the beauty of the smoky sky over buildings off to the west. Sometimes he pounded with his fists on the table in the chop-suey joint. A string of oaths flowed from his lips. Sometimes tears came into his eyes.

He was, to be sure, ridiculous. There was in him something I knew so well later in another friend, Tom Wolfe — a determination, half-physical, all his big body in it, like a man striving to push his way through a stone wall.

Out into what?

He couldn't have said what any more than I could of my own hopes, my own passionate desires, of which I was always half-ashamed.

To get it in some way down, something felt.

A man was too much in a cage — in some way trapped.

A man got himself trapped. All of this business of making a living. There were Jerry and Joe, both married. They both had children.

Joe had been a farmer boy, on his father's farm, somewhere in Iowa. He had come to Chicago filled with hope.

He was like Jerry, the German. He wanted to paint.

'That's what I want.

'I want something.'

And why the hell did a man get married? They spoke of that. They weren't complaining of the particular women they had married. You knew they were both fond of their children.

A man got stuck on some dame. A man was made that way. When it got him, when it gripped him, he thought, he convinced himself, that in her, in that particular one, was the thing he sought.

Then the kids coming.

They trap you that way.

Joe speaking up. He wasn't as intense as Jerry. He said we couldn't blame them, the women, his own or any other man's woman.

How'd we know they weren't trapped too? They were wanting to be beautiful in some man's eyes, that was it. They had, Joe declared, as much right to want their thing as we had to want ours.

But what was it we were all wanting, the little group of us, there in that vast Chicago, who had in some way found each other?

Comradeship in hungers we couldn't express.

Anyway, it wasn't really success. We knew that. We had got that far.

George said we ought to be skunks. 'A man should be a skunk,' he said. George wasn't married, but had an old mother and father he was supporting. He was laying down a law he couldn't obey.

'So I'm a clerk, eh?

'And whose fault is it?

'Mine, I tell you.

'I ought to walk out on them, on everyone, let 'em go to hell.

'What I want is to wander up and down for a long time. Look and look.

'People think of it as a virtue, a man like me, sticking to a clerk's job, supporting my old father and mother, when it's just cowardice, that's all.

'If I had the courage to walk out on them, be a skunk.'

It was something he couldn't do. We all knew that.

By the river bank, on the Sunday afternoon, after a morning trying to write the story I had for weeks been trying to write, I had torn up what I had written. There were the pages of meaningless words, that refused to march, thrown into the sluggish river, floating slowly away.

White patches on a background of yellow, sluggish river.

'Patience, patience.'

White clouds floating in a hot sky, over a distant corn field.

'Oh, to hell with patience.'

How many men like me, over the world, everywhere, all over America, in big towns like Chicago and New York, small towns or farms.

Trying for it.

For what?

There was something beyond money to be made, fame got, a big name. I was already past thirty. There were the others, Joe, Jerry, and George, none of them any longer young.

The World War had not yet come. It was to scatter us, shatter us.

The big German Jerry came down to where I lay on my back on the dry grass by the sluggish stream. He had with him the canvas on which he had been working all day. Now it was growing late. At noon, when we had together eaten our lunches, he had been hopeful.

'I think I'll get something. By the gods, I think I will.'

Now he sat beside me on the grass at the stream's edge. He had thrown his wet canvas aside. Across the stream from us we could see stretched away the vast corn fields.

The corn was ripening now. The stalks grew high, the long ears hanging down. Soon it would be corn-cutting time.

It was a fat rich land — the Middle West. At noon Jerry, the German — son of a German immigrant — who had been a city man all his life, had suddenly begun talking.

He had been trying to paint the corn field. For the time he had forgotten to be profane. We others had all come from farms or from country towns of the Middle West. He had said that he wanted to paint a corn field in such a way that everyone looking at his painting would begin to think of the fatness and richness of all Middle-Western America.

It would be something to give men new confidence in life. He had grown serious. He was the son of a German immigrant who had fled to America to escape military service. Germany believed in the army, in the brute power of arms, but he, Jerry, wanted by his painting to make people believe in the land.

I remembered that, in his earnestness, he had shaken a big finger under our noses. 'You fellows, your fathers and grandfathers were born on the land. You can't see how rich it all is, how gloriously men might live here.' He had spoken of his father, the immigrant, now an old man. We others couldn't understand how hard and meager life had become for the peasants in all the European lands. We didn't know our own richness, what a foundation the land, on which to build.

But he would show them through the richness of the fields. The skyscrapers in the cities, money piled in banks, men owning great factories, they were not the significant things.

The real significance was in the tall corn growing. There was the real American poetry.

He'd show them.

He sat beside me on the grass, by the stream. We sat a long time in silence. There was a grim look on his face and I knew that he had failed as, earlier in the day, I had. I did not want to embarrass him by speaking. I stayed silent, occasionally looking up at him.

He sat staring at the sluggish stream and looking across the stream to where the corn fields began and I thought I saw tears in his eyes.

He didn't want me to see.

Suddenly he jumped up. Profane words flew from his lips. He began to dance up and down on the canvas lying on the grass. I remember that the sun was going down over the tops of the tall corn stalks and he shook his fists at it. He cursed the sun, the corn, himself. What was the use? He had wanted to say something he'd never be able to say. 'I'm a shipping clerk in a lousy warehouse and I'll always be just that, nothing else.' It was a child's rage in a grown man. He picked up the canvas on which he had been at work all day and threw it far out into the stream.

We were on our way to the suburban station where we would get our train into the city. All the others, Joe, George, and Jerry, had their painting traps, their easels, boxes of color, palettes. They had little canvas stools on which they sat while painting and Joe and George carried the wet canvases they had done during the day.

We went along in silence, Joe and George ahead while I walked with Jerry. Did he want me to carry some of his traps?

'Oh, to hell with them, and you too.'

He was in this grim mood. Fighting back something in himself. We went along a dusty road beside a wood and cut across a field in which tall weeds grew. We were getting near the station where we were to take the train.

Back to the city.

To our clerkships.

To his being a shipping clerk in his warehouse.

To little hot and cold Chicago flats where some of us had wives and children waiting.

To be fed, clothed, housed.

'A man can't just live in his children. He can't, I tell you.'

Something rebellious in all of us.

What is it a man wants, to be of some account in the world, in himself, in his own manhood?

The attempts to write, to paint, these efforts only a part of something we wanted.

All of us half-knowing all our efforts would end in futility.

I am very sure the same thoughts were in all our minds that evening, in the field of tall weeds, in the half darkness, as we drew near the little prairie railroad station, the lights of the train already seen far off, across the flat prairies.

And then the final explosion from Jerry. He had suddenly put his painting traps down. He began to throw his tubes of paint about, hurling them into the tall weeds in the field.

'You get out of here, damn you! Go on about your business.'

He had thrown his easel, his stool, his paint brushes. He stood there dancing among the tall weeds.

'Go on! Go away! I'll kill you if you don't.'

I moved away from him and joined the others on the platform by the station. It was still light enough to see the man out there in the field where the tall weeds grew waist-high. He was still dancing with rage, his hands raised, no doubt still cursing his fate.

He was expressing something for us all. He was going through something we had all been through and before we died would all go through again and again.

And then the train came and we got silently aboard, but already we could see happening what I think we all knew would happen. We saw Jerry, that brusque, profane German, already down on his knees among the weeds in the field.

We knew what he was doing, but, when our train arrived in the city and we separated at the station, Joe and George still clinging to the canvases they both knew were no good — when the others had gone, I hung about the station.

I had been a farm boy, an American small-town boy like Joe and George. I was curious. Jerry, the big German, had spoken of the land. We had, all of us, been thinking of ourselves as rather special human beings, men with a right to that curious happiness that comes sometimes, fleetingly enough, with accomplishment.

Forgetting the millions like us on farms, holding minor jobs in cities.

What old Abe Lincoln meant when he spoke of 'the people.'

I was remembering bad years when I was a small-town boy, working about on farms, farmers working all through the year, from daylight until dark.

Big Jerry wanted to express something out of the American land.

Droughts coming, hailstorms destroying crops, disease among the cattle, often a long year's work come to nothing.

Something else remembered out of my own boyhood.

Springs coming, after such disastrous years, and the farmers near my own Middle-Western town out again in their fields, again plowing the land.

A kind of deep patient heroism in millions of men, on the land, in cities, too.

The government pensioning men who went out to kill other men, but no pensions for men who spent long lives raising food to feed men.

Killers become heroes, the millions of others never thinking of themselves as heroes.

There would be another train in an hour and I wanted to see what I did see, keeping myself unseen, the arrival of Jerry, most of his painting traps again collected.

Knowing, as I did know, that on another week-end he would be trying again.

The Sound of the Stream

I HAVE ALREADY MENTIONED that my house stands by a mountain stream. It is a stream of sounds, and at night, ever since I had completed the building of my house and had moved into it, the stream has talked to me.

On how many nights have I lain in my bed in my house, the doors and windows that faced the stream all open and the sounds coming in.

The stream runs over rocks. It runs under a bridge, and somewhere I have written telling how, on dark nights, the sounds change and become strangely significant.

There was the sound of the feet of children running on the floor of the bridge. A horse galloped, soldiers marched. I heard at night the footsteps of old friends, the voices of women I had loved.

There was a crippled girl I have spoken of to whom I had once made love, in the rain, under a bush in a city park. She had cried, and I heard the haunting sound of her feet, the curious broken rhythm on the bridge over the stream by my house at night . . . the voices of Fred, of Mary, of Tom, of Esther, and a hundred others, loved and lost in what I called my real life, and always, above these voices, the sound also of the footsteps and the voices of those of my imaginative world.

The long slow stride of Hugh McVey. These mingled let us say with the footsteps of Carl Sandburg or Ben Hecht. My friend John Emerson or Maurice Long walking beside my Doctor Parcival. The footsteps of the naked man in the room with his daughter in *Many Marriages,* soft beside the footsteps of some dear one in the life I had led away from my desk.

These sounds from the stream whispering to me, sometimes crying out, through many nights, making nights alive . . .

It was in the early summer and I had gotten a letter from my literary agent. It may be that I had been writing to him. He had certain stories I had sent him to sell.

'Can't you, sir, sell one of the stories to some magazine? I am needing money.'

He answered my letter. He is a sensible man, knows his business.

'I admit that the stories you have sent me are good stories. But,' he said, 'you are always getting something into all of your stories that spoils the sale.'

He did not go further, but I know what he meant.

'Look here,' he once said to me, 'why don't you, for the time at least, drop this rather intimate style of yours?'

He smiled when he said it and I also smiled.

'Let us say, now, that you are yourself the editor of one of our big American magazines. You have yourself been in business. When you first began to write, even after you had published some of your earlier books, you had to go on for years, working in an advertising place. You must know that all of our large American magazines are business ventures. It costs a great deal of money to print and distribute hundreds of thousands of copies. Often, as you know, the price received for the magazine, when sold on the newsstand, does not pay for the paper on which it is printed.'

'Yes, I know.'

'They have to have stories that please people.'

'Yes. I know.'

We had stopped to have a drink at a bar. But a few weeks before he had written me a letter. 'There is a certain large magazine that would like to have a story from you. It should be, let us say, a story of about ten thousand words. Do not attempt to write the story. Make an outline, I should say a three- or four-page outline. I can sell the story for you.'

I made the outline and sent it to him.

'It is splendid,' he wrote. 'Now you can go ahead. I can get such and such a sum.'

'Oh!' the sum mentioned would get me out of my difficulties.

'I will get busy,' I said to myself. 'In a week I will dash off the story.'

Some two or three weeks before, a man friend had come to me one evening. He is a man to whom I am deeply attached.

'Come and walk with me,' he said, and we set out afoot, leaving the town where he lived. I had gone to the town to see him, but, when I got to his town, there was a sudden illness in his house. The man has children and two of them were in bed with a contagious disease.

I stayed at a hotel. He came there. We walked beyond the town, got into a dirt road, passed farmhouses, dogs barked at us. We got into a moonlit meadow.

We had walked for a long time in silence. At the hotel I had noticed that my friend was in a tense, excited mood.

'You are in some sort of trouble. Is it the children? Has the disease taken a turn for the worse?'

'No,' he said, 'the children are better. They are all right.'

We were in the moonlit meadow, standing by a fence, some sheep grazing nearby and it was a delicious night of the early summer.

'There is something I have to tell to someone,' he said. 'I wrote to you, begged you to come here.'

My friend is a highly respected man in his town.

He began talking. He talked for hours. He told me a story of a secret life he had been living.

My friend is a man of fifty. He is employed as an experimental scientist by a large manufacturing company.

But I might as well confess at once that I am, as you the reader may have guessed, covering the trail of my friend. I am a man rather fortunate in life. I have a good many men friends. If I make this one an experimental scientist working for a large manufacturing company, it will do.

His story was, on the whole, strange. It was like so many stories, not invented but coming directly out of life. It was a story having in it certain so-called sordid touches, strange impulses come to a man of fifty in the grip of an odd passion.

'I have been doing this.

'I have been doing that.

'I have to unload, to tell someone.

'I have been suffering.'

My friend did unload his story, getting a certain relief talking to me of a turn in his life that threatened to destroy the position he had achieved in his community. He had got a sudden passion for a woman of his town, the sort of thing always happening in towns. 'Three years ago,' he said to me, 'there was another man here, a friend, a man, as I am, of standing in our community, who did what I am doing now. He became enamored of a woman here, the wife of a friend, and began to meet her secretly.

'At least he thought, or hoped, he was meeting her secretly.

'He did as I have been doing. In the evening when darkness came, he got into his car. She had walked out along a street and in some dark place along the street he picked her up. He drove with her out along little side roads, went to distant towns, but soon everyone knew.

'And how I blamed him. I went to him. "What a fool you are being," I said to him.

'"Yes, but I cannot help it. This is the great love of my life."

'"What nonsense," I said. I pled with him, quarreled with him, but it did no good. I thought him an utter fool and now I am being just such another.'

I had taken the man with whom I talked in the field, and his story, as the basis for the story I was to write for one of the popular magazines, had made an outline that was pronounced splendid by my agent.

But what rough places I had smoothed out.

'No, I cannot say that such a figure holding such a respectable place in my life did that. There must not be anything unpleasant. There must be nothing that will remind readers of certain sordid moments, thoughts, passions, acts, in their own lives if I am to get this money — and, oh, how I need it.'

I am no Shakespeare, but did not even Shakespeare write a play he called *As You Like It*?

'When you are writing to please people you must not touch certain secret, often dark little recesses, that are in all humans.

'Keep in the clear, man. Go gaily along.

'It will be all right to startle them a little.

'You must get a certain dramatic force into your story.'

But that night the man, upon whose story I have based the story I am about to write, was, as he talked, simply broken. He even put his face down upon the top rail of the fence, there in that moonlit meadow, and cried. I went to him. I put my arms about his shoulders, said words to him.

'This passion that has come to you at this time in your life, that now threatens to tear down all you have so carefully built up, that threatens to destroy the lives of others you love, will pass.

'At our age everything passes.'

I do not remember just what I did say to him.

And so I began to write, but alas . . .

Our difficulty is that as we write we become interested, absorbed, often a little in love with these characters of our stories that seem to be growing here, under our hand.

I have begun this story, taking off, as it were, from the story told me in the meadow by my friend; but now, as I write, he has disappeared.

There is a new man, coming to life, here. He seems to be here in this room where I work.

'You must do me right now,' he seems to be saying to me.

'There is a certain morality involved,' he says.

'Now you must tell everything, put it all down. Do not hesitate. I want it all put down.'

At this point there was a series of letters concerning a story to be written that lay on my desk. I had had them brought to me from my files.

'If you are to write the story for us, it would be well for you to keep certain things in mind.

'The story should be concerned with the lives of people who are in what might be called comfortable circumstances.

'Above all, it should not be too gloomy.

'We want you to understand that we do not wish, in any way, to dictate to you.'

I had sat down to write the tale, for which I had made an outline, in bitter need of the money it might bring. After twenty-five years of writing, some twenty to twenty-five books published, my name up as one of the outstanding American writers of my day, my books translated into many languages, after all of this, I was always in need of money, always just two jumps ahead of the sheriff.

'Well, I will do it. I will. I will.'

For two days, three, a week, I wrote doggedly, with dogged determination.

'I will give them just what they want. I had been told, it had been impressed deeply upon my mind, that, above all things, to be popular, successful, I must first of all observe the "don'ts." '

A friend, another American writer, came to see me. He mentioned a certain, at present, very popular woman writer.

'Boy, she is cleaning up,' he said.

However it seemed that she, one who knew her trade and was safe, occasionally slipped.

It may be that here, in telling of this incident, I have got the story of what happened to the woman writer confused with many such stories I have heard.

However, it lies in my mind that the writer was making, for the movies, an adaptation of a very popular novel of a past generation. In it there was a child who, eating candy before breakfast, was reproved by his mother.

'Put that stuff aside. It will ruin your health.'

Something of that sort must have been written. It was unnoticed, got by. What, and with the candy people spending millions in advertising! What, the suggestion that candy could ruin the health of a child, candy called 'stuff'!

My friend told some tale of a big damage suit, of indignant candy manufacturers.

'Why, there must be thousands of these "don'ts," ' I said to myself.

'It would be better, in your story, if your people be in what might be called comfortable positions in life.'

I had got that sentence from someone. I wrote it out, tucked it up over my desk.

And so I wrote for a week, and there was a great sickness in me. I who had always loved the pile of clean white sheets on my desk, who had been for years obsessed with the notion that some day, by chance, I would find myself suddenly overtaken by a passion for writing and would find myself without paper, pencils, pens, or ink so that I was always stealing fountain pens and pencils from my friends, storing them away as a squirrel stores nuts, who, upon going for even a short trip away from home, always put into my car enough paper to write at least five long novels, who kept bottles of ink stored in all sorts of odd places about the house, found myself suddenly hating the smell of ink.

There were the white sheets and I wanted to throw them all out of the window.

Days of this, a week. It may have gone on for two weeks. There were the days, something strangely gone out of life, and there were the nights. Why, I dare say that to those who do not write or paint or in any way work in the arts, all of this will seem nonsense indeed.

'When it comes to that,' they will be saying, 'our own work is not always so pleasant. Do you think it's always a joy to be a lawyer, wrangling over other people's ugly quarrels in courts, or being a doctor, always and forever with the sick, or a factory owner, with all this new unrest among workers, or a worker, getting nowhere working your life out for the profit of others?'

But there I was, having what is called literary fame. And I was no longer young. 'Presently I will be old. The pen will fall from my hand. There will come the time of long afternoons sitting in the sun, or under the shade of a tree. I will no longer want to write. It may be that I will have my fill of people, their problems, the tangle of life, and will want only to look at sheep grazing on distant hillsides, to watch the waters of a stream rolling over rocks, or just follow with my aging eyes the wandering of a country road winding away among hills,' I thought.

'It would be better for me to turn aside, make money now. I must. I must.'

I remembered the advice always being given me when I was a young writer. 'Go in for it,' my friends said. At that time the movies had just become a gold mine for writers.

'Take it on for a time,' my friends were saying to me. 'You can change. Get yourself a stake. Make yourself secure and then, when you are quite safe, you can go abroad. Then you can write as you want to write.'

'It may not have been good advice then but it is now,' I said to myself. Formerly when I was writing all of my earlier books, I was very strong. I could work all day in the advertising place or in the factory I once owned. I could go home to my rooms. I took a cold plunge. Always, it seemed to me there was something that had to be washed away. When I was writing the Winesburg tales and, later, the novel, *Poor White,* I couldn't get tired, and often after working all day wrote all night. I have never been one who can correct, fill in, rework his stories. I must try, and when I fail must throw away. Some of my best stories have been written ten or twelve times.

An odd thing happens to a man, a writer. Perhaps I am saying all of this, not at all for those who do not write but for the young American writers. Nowadays they are always coming to me. They write me letters. 'You are our father,' they say to me.

'One day I picked up a book of stories of yours, or it was one of your novels, and a great door seemed to swing open for me.'

There are such sentences written to me by young writers in letters. Sometimes they even put such sentences into the autobiographical novels with which almost all new writers begin.

And it is so they should begin too. First the learning to use the experiences, the words and hungers of their own lives and then, gradually, the reaching out into other lives.

And so I am addressing here our young American writers, the beginners, but what am I trying to say to them?

Perhaps I am only trying to say that the struggle in which we are engaged has no end; that we in America have, all of us, been led into a blind alley. We have always before us, we keep before us, the mythical thing we call 'success,' but for us there is, there can be, no success, for while this belief in the mythical thing called success remains among us, always in the minds of others about us, we shall be in danger of infection. I am trying to prove all of this to you by showing here how I, a veteran now among you, for a long time thinking myself safe from the contagion, was also taken with the disease.

And so I sat in my room, trying and trying.

I was in one of my frightened moods. Soon now my money would all be gone. I am a man who has always had, in the matter of finance, a line that, when crossed, made me begin to tremble. Anything above five hundred dollars in the bank has always seemed to me riches, but when my bank account goes below that amount, the fears come.

Soon I shall have but four hundred dollars, then three, two, one. I live in the country on a farm and in the house built by my one successful book. Bills come, so many pounds of grass seed for a field, a ton of lime, a new plow. Great God, will I be compelled to return to the advertising agency?

I have three or four short stories in my agent's hands. Once a magazine called *Pictorial Review* paid me seven hundred and fifty dollars for a short story. I had given the story the title, 'There She is, She is Taking Her Bath,' but after the story had been got into type and illustrations made for it, the editor of the magazine grew doubtful. 'We are doubtful about the title,' he wired. 'Can't you suggest another?' and I replied, saying, 'Roll Your Own,' but got from him a second wire, saying that he didn't think that that title fitted the story, and in the end he never published it.

'Will he be demanding back my seven hundred and fifty dollars?' I asked myself, knowing nothing of my own legal rights. But then a thought came, a very comforting thought.

'He may demand but how can he get it?' I had spent the money for an automobile, had got a new overcoat, a new suit of clothes.

'Just let him try. What can he do? I am dustproof,' I muttered; but I had misjudged the man. He must really have been a splendid fellow, for in the end and without protest, and after some four or five years, he sent the story back to me, saying nothing at all of all that money given me for it. He said, if I remember correctly, that, while he personally liked the story, in fact thought it splendid, a magnificent achievement, etc., etc., also that he had always greatly admired my work, this story did not really fit into the tone of the magazine. There was in it, as I now remember, a little business man, timid and absurdly jealous of his wife. He had got it into his head that she was having affairs with other men and had determined to have it out with her, but, when he worked himself up to it and rushed home, always fearing he would lose his courage, it happened that invariably she was taking her bath. A man couldn't, of course, stand outside the door of a bathroom, his wife splashing in the tub, and through the door accuse her of unfaithfulness.

In my story the wife was, to be sure, quite innocent. As a detective he hired to watch her assured him, she was as innocent as a little flower . . . if I remember correctly that was the expression used . . . but, also, as in so many of my stories, there was a business man made to appear a little ridiculous.

Why, I am told there are men and women who receive, for a single short story, as much as a thousand, fifteen hundred, even two thousand dollars. I am also told that I have had a profound effect upon the art of short-story writing.

'And so, what's wrong?' I more than a hundred times have asked myself; but at last I have come to a conclusion.

'You are just a little too apt, Sherwood, my boy, to find the business man a little ridiculous,' I have told myself.

'Yes, and there is just your trouble, my boy. The business man, as he is represented in our picture, as he must be represented, is, above all things, a shrewd and knowing man. It would be better to represent him as very resolute, very courageous. He should have really what is called "an iron jaw." This is to indicate resolution, courage, determination.

'And you are to bear in mind that earlier in life he was an athlete. He was a star football player, a triple threat, whatever that is, or he was of the team at Yale.

'He is older now, but he has kept himself in trim. He is like the first Roosevelt, the Teddy one. Every day he goes to his club to box. The man who is to succeed in business cannot . . . keep that in mind . . . let himself grow fat. Do not ever make him fat, watery-eyed, bald. Do not let him have a kidney complaint.

'The trouble with you,' I told myself, 'is just the years you spent in business,' and I began to remember the men, hundreds of them, some of them known internationally, often sensitive fellows, at bottom kindly, who were puzzled as I was puzzled, always breaking out into odd confessions, telling intimate little stories of their loves, their hopes, their disappointments.

'How did I get where I am? What brought me here?'

'This is something I never wanted to do. Why am I doing it?'

Something of that sort and then also, so often, something naïve, often wistful and also a little ridiculous.

I could not shake off the fact that, in the fifteen or twenty years during which I was in business as advertising writer, as manufacturer, five men among my personal acquaintances killed themselves.

So there was tragedy too, plenty of it.

'But, my dear fellow, you must bear in mind that this is a country ruled by business. Only yesterday, when you were driving on the highway, you saw a huge sign. "What is good for business is good for you," the sign said.

'So there, you see, we are one great brotherhood.'

All of this said to myself, over and over. 'Now you are below the line, the five-hundred-dollar line. Keep that in mind.'

There were these days, my struggle to write in a new vein, to keep persistently cheerful, letting nothing reflecting on the uprightness, the good intent, the underlying courage of business, creep into my story.

'Above all do not put into your story a business man who is by chance shy, sensitive, who does occasionally ridiculous things. Even if, at bottom, the fellow is gentle, lovable, do not do that.

'But, you see, my man is not in business. I have made him a judge.

'But, you fool, don't you see . . . my God, man, a judge!

'Is there not also a pattern, a mold made, for the judge?'

And so you see me arguing, fighting with myself, through the days, through the nights. The nights were the worst.

'But can't you sleep, my dear?'

'No, my darling, I cannot sleep.'

'But what is on your mind?'

You see, I cannot tell my wife. She would rebel. She would begin talking about a job. 'We can give up this house, this farm,' she would say. 'You are always spending your money on it,' she would add. She would call attention to the absurd notion I have that, in the end, I can make our farm pay. We would get into an argument, with me pointing out that it is a dishonorable thing to live on land and not work constantly to make it more productive.

'It would be better for me to surrender everything else before my love of the land itself,' I would say, and this would set me off. As she is a Southern woman, I would begin on the South, pointing out to her how the masters of the land and the slaves of the old South, claiming as they did an aristocratic outlook on life, had been, nevertheless, great land destroyers; and from that I would go on, declaring that no man could make claim to aristocracy who destroyed the land under his feet.

It is a favorite subject of mine and it gets us nowhere.

'I think I have been smoking too many cigarettes,' I said, and she agreed with me. She spoke again, as she had so often, of her fear of the habit-forming danger of a certain drug I sometimes take; but —
'You had better take one,' she said.

And so I did, but it did not help.

'But why should you be afraid?' I asked myself. Even after I had taken the drug, I was wide awake and remained so night after night.

But why go on? We story-tellers, and I am writing all of this solely for story-tellers, all know, we must know, it is the beginning of knowledge of our craft, that the unreal is more real than the real, that there is no real other than the unreal; and I say this here because, first of all, I presume to re-establish my own faith — badly shaken recently by an experience — and I say it a little because as a veteran story-teller I want to strengthen the faith in other and younger American men.

Now I have remembered that once, some five or ten years ago . . . I was living in New Orleans at the time . . . I had been in the evening to the movies and had seen a picture, written by a man of talent, who had once been my friend, and having seen it had been shocked by what seemed to me a terrible selling out of all life, and, having got out of the movie theater and into the street, I went along, growing constantly more and more angry, so that when I got to my room I sat down at my desk and wrote for the rest of the night, and what I wrote was a kind of American 'I Accuse.'

I had written the words, 'I Accuse,' at the head of the first of a great pile of sheets on the desk before me and, as I wrote that night, I called the roll. I made a great list of the names, of American actors, American writers, who, having had a quick and often temporary success in New York, or who, having written a novel or a story that had caught the popular fancy, had walked off to Hollywood.

There was the temptation and I knew it must be a terrible one: . . . five hundred, a thousand a week.

'I will do it for a time. I will store up my money.

'When I have got rich I will be free.'

'But, my dear fellow, do you not understand that the complete selling out of the imaginations of the men and women of America, by the artists, of the stage, by the artist story-tellers, is completely and wholly an acceptance of harlotry?'

I had written all of this very bitterly, on a certain night in New Orleans, naming the men who had done it, some of them my personal friends. A good many of them were also radicals. They wanted, or thought they wanted, a new world. They thought that a new world could be made by depending on the economists . . . it was a time when the whole world was, seemingly, dominated by the economists. A new world was to arise, dominated by a new class, the proletariat. A good many of them had turned to the writing of so-called proletarian stories. It was the fashion.

'If I go to Hollywood, write there, get money by it, and if I give that money to the cause?'

'But please, what cause?'

'Why, to the overthrowing of capitalism, the making of a new and better world.'

'But, don't you see that what you are doing . . . the suffering of the world, the most bitter suffering, does not come primarily from physical suffering. It is by the continual selling out of the imaginative lives of people that the great suffering comes. There the most bitter harm is done.'

I accuse.

I accuse.

I had accused my fellow artists of America, had named names. I wrote for hours and hours, and when I had finished writing, had poured out all of the bitterness in me, brought on by the picture I had seen, I leaned back in my chair and laughed at myself.

'How can you accuse others when you yourself have not been tempted?'

Once, being in California, I had gone to Hollywood to see a friend working in one of the great studios; and as we walked through a hallway in one of the buildings, now often a row of little offices like the offices we used to sit in in the advertising agency, I saw the name of a writer I knew; the writer came out to me.

'And have they got you too?'

'No,' I said, 'I am just looking about.'

'Well, they have not got you yet, but they will get to you.'

I had even written two or three times to agents in New York or Hollywood.

'Cannot you sell, to the pictures, such and such a story of mine?'

There had been no offers. I had not been tempted.

'Let us say,' I remarked to myself that night in New Orleans after the outbreak of writing against others, accusations hurled on their heads, 'that you had been offered . . . let us be generous . . . let us say twenty-five thousand for the best of all of your Winesburg stories, or, for that matter, for the whole series.

'Would you have turned the offer down? If you did such a thing, everyone who knew you and who knew of your constant need of money would call you a fool. Would you do it?'

I had to admit that I did not know and so, laughing at myself, I was compelled to tear up, to throw in the wastebasket, the thousands of words of my American 'I Accuse.'

You were, on that night in New Orleans, asking yourself whether you, the pure and holy one, would have the courage to turn down an offer of twenty-five thousand just to let someone sentimentalize one of your stories, twist the characters of the stories about; yet now, because you are again nearly broke, because you are beginning to fear old age, an old age perhaps of poverty, you are at work doing the thing for which you were about to publicly accuse others and doing it for a few hundred dollars.

The above thought jumping into my head at night, I got out of bed. The moon was shining and sending so bright a path of light through an open door into the room that I thought a lamp must have been left burning in a near-by room. I went to look.

I returned to where my wife lay, curled into a little ball at the bed's edge, the light coming through the door falling on her face. I had told her nothing of the new temptation that had come to me. She was one who, like my mother, would have gladly worked herself into the grave, as my mother had done, rather than that I should be trying to do what I had been trying to do.

And what was the fear that had come upon me, the fear of old age, an old age of poverty?

But you will not starve. At the worst you will have more than your mother ever had during her whole life. You will wear better clothes, eat better food. You may be even able to retain this beautiful house a book of yours built.

I stood that night by my wife's bed, having this argument with myself, the whole matter being one that will interest only other artists, realizing dimly, as I stood thus, that the fear in me that night, of which my wife knew nothing . . . it would have shocked her profoundly to be told of it . . . the fear perhaps came up into me from a long line of men and women . . . I remembered that night how my father, in his occasional sad moods . . . he was, most of the time rather a gay dog . . . used to go sit in the darkness of our house in a street of workingmen's houses, and sitting there, the rest of us suddenly silent, sing in a low voice a song called 'Over the Hill to the Poor-House.'

The fear in him, too, perhaps into him from his father and his father's father and on back and back, all perhaps men who had lived, as I had always lived, precariously.

It is what gets a man. In the artist there must always be this terrible contradiction. It is in all of us. We want passionately the luxuries of life, the things we produce — our books, paintings, statues, the songs we make, the music we make — these are all luxuries.

We want luxuries, for who but his fellow artists can really love the work of the artist while at the same time knowing, deep down in us, that if we give way to this passion for the possession of beautiful things about us, getting them by cheapening our own work, all understanding of beauty must go out of us.

'And so why all this silly struggle? Why this absurd fear?'

I left the moonlit room where my wife lay asleep . . . there is something grows very close between people who have lived long together, who have really achieved a marriage . . . as I had stood at the foot of the bed in which my wife lay, I had seen little waves of pain run across her sleeping face as waves run across a lake in a wind. . . .

Barefooted I went out of my house, clad in my pajamas . . . they are of silk . . . my wife insists on buying them for me with money she herself earns . . . she is constantly, persistently buying me expensive shirts, expensive ties, shoes, hats, overcoats . . . I speak here of poverty, but, on a rack in a closet off my sleeping room there are dozens, perhaps even a hundred ties that have cost at least two dollars each.

Absurdity and more absurdity. What children we are. I went and stood by an apple tree in the orchard back of my house and then, going around the house, climbed a little hill where I could see the front of the house.

'It is one of the most beautiful houses in all America,' I said to myself, and for a time that night I sat absorbed, forgetting entirely the absurd struggle that had been going on in me for a week, for two weeks, my eye following the line of the wall rising out of the ground and then following along the roof. 'Oh, how perfect the proportion; and there is where beauty lies.'

Only a few of the many people who had come to visit me had been able to realize the extreme beauty of my achievement in building the house. It was true that there had been an architect who had made the drawings for me, but I had not followed the drawings. For two years and while the house was building, all the money made for me by Horace Liveright going into it, myself once having to stop building for two years while I went delivering silly lectures to get more money, I had done no writing. It didn't matter. A friend had once walked up the hill with me, to sit with me on the top of a cement tank that went down into the ground, where I sat that night in my pajamas, it also being a moonlight night, had said that my house was as beautiful to him as a poem. 'Cling to it,' he said. 'Live all the rest of your days in it.' He went on at length, saying that the house was as beautiful as my story 'Brother Death.' He named those other stories, 'The Untold Lie,' 'The New Englander,' and 'A Man's Story.' 'It has the quality they have.'

He said that and I giggled with pleasure, enjoying his praise of the beauty of my house more than any praise I had ever got from my writing.

On that night I walked down the hill past my house and to a bridge over a stream and stood, still arguing with myself.

'But I have a right now to put money first. I have got to begin now thinking of money. I have got to begin making money. I will — I will. These people of my story shall behave as I wish. For years I have been a slave to these people of my imagination, but I will be a slave no longer. For years I have served them and now they shall serve me.'

Here I was, standing in silence on the bridge over the stream. . . . And there again were the sounds in the stream. They crept into me, invaded me. I heard again the sound of the feet of children, horses galloping, soldiers marching, the sob of that crippled girl. I heard the voices of old friends. The sounds went on for a time. Of a sudden the sounds all changed.

There were no more voices, only laughter. The laughter began. It increased in volume. It seemed to become a roar.

'See, the very stream is laughing at me,' I cried, and began to run along the country road that goes past my house. I ran and ran. I ran until I was exhausted. I ran up hill and down. I hurt my bare feet. I had come out of my house wearing bedroom slippers, but I had lost them. I ran until I was out of breath, exhausted. I had hurt one of my feet on a sharp stone. It bled. I stopped running that night at the brow of a low hill, after all not far from my house . . . a man of my age, who has spent so much of his life at a desk, who has smoked so many hundreds of thousands, it may be near millions, of cigarettes, does not run far.

I ran until I was exhausted and then, hobbling along, as once a cripple girl in Chicago had hobbled sobbing beside me in a rainswept Chicago street, I went back over the road along which I had been running and to my cabin by the creek.

I let myself into my cabin and getting the manuscript on which I had been at work I took it out to a little open grassy place beside the stream and sitting there on the grass I burned it page by page.

The burning took a long time and it was a job. It was, I knew, an absurd performance; and I knew that I was, as all such men as myself must ever be, a child. But later, as you see, I have wanted to write of it, to see if in words I can catch the mood of it.

'It will be a joy to other writers, other artists, to know that I also, a veteran among them, am also as they are, a child,' I thought.

I did all of this — as I have here set it down, going at great length, as you will see, to catch the mood of it, to give it background — and then, being very careful with my cut foot, I went back to my house and to my bed.

However, I went first to the bathroom. I put disinfectant on the cut on my foot and my wife awoke.

'What are you doing?' she asked me, speaking sleepily, and, 'Oh, I just got up to go to the bathroom,' I said. And so she slept again, and before again getting into bed I stood for a time looking at her asleep.

'I dare say that all men, artists and others, are, as I am, children, at bottom,' I thought; and I wondered a little if it were true that only a few women among all the millions of women got, by the pain of living with us, a little mature.

I was again in my bed and I thought that the voices in the stream by my house had stopped laughing at me and that again they talked and whispered to me; and on the next morning my shoe hurt my foot so that, when I was out of my wife's sight, I hobbled painfully along. I went to my cabin and to the black spot on the grass by the creek where I had burned the attempt I had made to impose my own will on the people of my imaginative world. I began to laugh at myself.

It had, I thought, been an absurd and silly experience through which I had passed but, God knows, I told myself, I may have to pass through it again, time after time. I knew as I sat down at my desk that morning, determined again not to impose myself, to let the story I was trying to write write itself, to be again what I had always been, a slave to the people of my imaginary world if they would do it, making their own story of their own loves, my pen merely forming the words on the paper . . . I knew that what I had been through, in such an absurd and childish form, letting myself again be a victim to old fears, was nevertheless the story of like experiences in the life of all artists, no doubt throughout time.

VII. PASTORAL

Morning Roll-Call

People. They parade before you at night. There was Smoky Pete. He was a solidly built man, unmarried, who lived with his old mother. He had been a soldier of sorts, but could not get into the G.A.R. Father and other veterans said he had been a bounty-jumper.

He was a gay, defiant man, always ready for a fight. In the spring he worked in his mother's garden, but he did no other work for the rest of the year. Perhaps his mother had a small income.

He filled a basket with vegetables and came down along the railroad track to our main street. He was intent upon trading the vegetables to some saloon-keeper for a morning drink. He shouted. He laughed loudly. He sang.

'What's the use of being poor when you can own the whole world for ten cents?' he shouted. Ten cents was the prevailing price of a drink of bar whiskey.

It was Smoky Pete who started our morning roll-call. He became a corrector of the morals of the town. He spread terror through the town.

His mother's house was on a street out near the edge of town and in the early morning, intent on his morning drink, he went along the street to the railroad and along the tracks toward Main Street. It was the quiet hour, a spring, summer, or fall morning. Smoky Pete swaggered along. There was a gleam in his eyes. He had a short black General Grant beard and smoked a short-stemmed clay pipe. The smoke lay like a cloud in mountain forests in his beard.

It was a day of meat and potato breakfasts. The wives of the town were old-fashioned friers. There was none of the modern orange juice, toast-and-coffee addicts among the breakfasters of that day.

The women of the town bought cheap cuts of round steak at the local meat market. Somewhere near the outer edge of every Middle-Western town there was a slaughter-house filled with rats and flies and surrounded by a field piled high with bones of old cows. The women took the cheap steaks home and laid them on a board. They beat the steaks with a hammer. They pounded away. There was a drumming sound as of a hundred woodpeckers at work.

Smoky Pete was coming up the railroad track, swaggering along. Some citizen of the town had sinned. It might be a man who worked in the bank, or a merchant. It might even be a man who taught a class in the Sunday School of one of our churches.

There were in our town, as in all towns, certain women and girls. They were known as 'push-overs.' They were 'putting out.' Men met them in the evening on a side street of the town. The automobile had not come yet, but almost every man in town owned a horse and buggy.

The push-over was gotten in. Alas, often she was gathered in by some respectable married man of the town. The push-over was driven off into some quiet country lane. What ho!

But someone had slipped the word to Smoky Pete. The clerks in the stores along Main Street, having swept out the stores, were now sweeping the sidewalks before them. One of them raised his voice. The name of the man who had secretly, he had hoped, met Sally Graves in the dark street, down by the Seventh Day Adventist Church on the night before, who had got Sally into his buggy and had driven off with her into the darkness, was shouted over the roofs of the town.

'John Huntington.'

Alas, poor John.

So you thought no one saw you pick up Sally, eh?

There was some clerk with a malicious streak in his makeup.

'John Huntington.' The name so hurled forth floated through the quiet morning streets of the town and housewives who had been busily beating breakfast steaks quit beating. They ran quickly to kitchen doors. They were waiting for Smoky Pete's answering voice from down the railroad tracks.

It came.

S-s-s-s-l-y 'Graves.'

There was an outburst of laughter from the clerks.

'P. T. Smith.'

A fresh cry, 'Mary Thompson.' Poor Mary had a bad leg. She went hopping about. She hopped into dark corners with men and boys at night.

'P. T. Smith,' yelled the clerks, again.

'Mary Thompson,' came the echo.

It was all very cruel. It got Smoky Pete into endless fights, but he did not mind. Well, the G.A.R. wouldn't take him in. There was something wrong with his war record. He was having a good time. He was getting men. Some man of the town was always slipping him the dirt of the town.

At the county seat there was a certain house run by one Nell Hunter.

Again some respectable man's foot had slipped. He had, on a certain night, gone secretly to that place. He hoped his going would remain unknown.

He was at home now, in his own house, waiting for his breakfast, but at the sound of Smoky Pete's voice — a far-carrying one, floating thus through the quiet morning streets — he trembled.

Had someone seen him slipping into the house in the darkness?

The names of respectable men were being called off. There were twenty or thiry clerks standing now before the Main Street stores with brooms in their hands. If his name was bawled out thus by one of the clerks, it would be difficult, if not impossible, to name the culprit.

A. G. Bottomly. Bottomly had told his wife that he had to go to the county seat on business.

And now, Ye Gods, there it was!

'A. G. Bottomly.' And then the answering cry from Smoky Pete.

'Nell Hunter.'

It was something to drive a man mad. Late that day there would be a fight on Main Street, but what did it matter to Smoky Pete? He enjoyed fighting. He was almost always victorious in fights.

Smoky Pete advanced along the railroad track, past the railroad station, calling off names, connecting thus the names of often respectable citizens with females of ill repute.   If it was spring, he carried the little basket of vegetables on his arm. He was pleased with himself and with life. He was creating trouble. He was stirring up fights. He was getting even with life. He advanced to the middle of Main Street and turned to face the clerks standing along the street before the stores. He put a hand up to his mouth, made a trumpet of his hand. His voice rolled up the street and was followed by a loud outburst of laughter. All the men of the town, whose names had not been called off in Smoky Pete's morning roll-call, laughed. Women whose men were not involved giggled as they went back to their steak-pounding. The old impulse in man to enjoy heartily the discomfiture of others shook the town with laughter.

Smoky Pete was standing erect, like a soldier at the foot of our Main Street. He had made a trumpet of his hand.

'Go-o-o-od Damn!' His voice rolled up the street, as it died away was followed by the outburst of laughter. The morning roll-call was at an end. Three or four more citizens had been thus jerked up to stand trembling under the judgment of the town.

I'm a Fool

I<small>T WAS A HARD JOLT</small> for me, one of the most bitterest I ever had to face. And it all came about through my own foolishness, too. Even yet sometimes, when I think of it, I want to cry or swear or kick myself. Perhaps, even now, after all this time, there will be a kind of satisfaction in making myself look cheap by telling of it.

It began at three o'clock one October afternoon as I sat in the grandstand at the fall trotting and pacing meet at Sandusky, Ohio.

To tell the truth, I felt a little foolish that I should be sitting in the grandstand at all. During the summer before I had left my home town with Harry Whitehead and, with a nigger named Burt, had taken a job as swipe with one of the two horses Harry was campaigning through the fall race meets that year. Mother cried, and my sister Mildred, who wanted to get a job as a school-teacher in our town that fall, stormed and scolded about the house all during the week before I left. They both thought it something disgraceful that one of our family should take a place as a swipe with race-horses. I've an idea Mildred thought my taking the place would stand in the way of her getting the job she'd been working so long for.

But after all, I had to work, and there was no other work to be got. A big lumbering fellow of nineteen couldn't just hang around the house, and I had got too big to mow people's lawns and sell newspapers. Little chaps who could get next to people's sympathies by their sizes were always getting jobs away from me. There was one fellow who kept saying to everyone who wanted a lawn mowed or a cistern cleaned, that he was saving money to work his way through college, and I used to lay awake nights thinking up ways to injure him without being found out. I kept thinking of wagons running over him and bricks falling on his head as he walked along the street. But never mind him.

I got the place with Harry and I liked Burt fine. We got along splendid together. He was a big nigger with a lazy, sprawling body and soft, kind eyes, and when it came to a fight, he could hit like Jack Johnson. He had Bucephalus, a big black pacing stallion that could do 2.09 or 2.10 if he had to, and I had a little gelding named Doctor Fritz that never lost a race all fall when Harry wanted him to win.

We set out from home late in July in a boxcar with the two horses, and after that, until late November, we kept moving along to the race meets and the fairs. It was a peachy time for me, I'll say that. Sometimes now I think that boys who are raised regular in houses, and never have a fine nigger like Burt for best friend, and go to high schools and college, and never steal anything, or get drunk a little, or learn to swear from fellows who know how, or come walking up in front of a grandstand in their shirt-sleeves and with dirty horsey pants on when the races are going on and the grandstand is full of people all dressed up —— What's the use of talking about it? Such fellows don't know nothing at all. They've never had no opportunity.

But I did. Burt taught me how to rub down a horse and put the bandages on after a race and steam a horse out and a lot of valuable things for any man to know. He could wrap a bandage on a horse's leg so smooth that if it had been the same color you would think it was his skin, and I guess he'd have been a big driver, too, and got to the top like Murphy and Walter Cox and the others if he hadn't been black.

Gee whizz, it was fun. You got to a county-seat town, maybe say on a Saturday or Sunday, and the fair began the next Tuesday and lasted until Friday afternoon. Doctor Fritz would be, say in the 2.25 trot on Tuesday afternoon, and on Thursday afternoon Bucephalus would knock 'em cold in the 'free-for-all' pace. It left you a lot of time to hang around and listen to horse talk, and see Burt knock some yap cold that got too gay, and you'd find out about horses and men and pick up a lot of stuff you could use all the rest of your life, if you had some sense and salted down what you heard and felt and saw.

And then at the end of the week when the race meet was over, and Harry had run home to tend up to his livery-stable business, you and Burt hitched the two horses to carts and drove slow and steady across country, to the place for the next meeting, so as to not overheat the horses, etc., etc., you know.

Gee whizz, Gosh amighty, the nice hickory-nut and beech-nut and oaks and other kinds of trees along the roads, all brown and red, and the good smells, and Burt singing a song that was called Deep River, and the country girls at the windows of houses and everything. You can stick your colleges up your nose for all me. I guess I know where I got my education.

Why, one of those little burgs of towns you come to on the way, say now on a Saturday afternoon, and Burt says, 'Let's lay up here.' And you did.

And you took the horses to a livery stable and fed them, and you got your good clothes out of a box and put them on.

And the town was full of farmers gaping, because they could see you were race-horse people, and the kids maybe never see a nigger before and was afraid and run away when the two of us walked down their main street.

And that was before prohibition and all that foolishness, and so you went into a saloon, the two of you, and all the yaps come and stood around, and there was always someone pretended he was horsey and knew things and spoke up and began asking questions, and all you did was to lie and lie all you could about what horses you had, and I said I owned them, and then some fellow said, 'Will you have a drink of whiskey?' and Burt knocked his eye out the way he could say, offhand like, 'Oh, well, all right, I'm agreeable to a little nip. I'll split a quart with you.' Gee whizz.

But that isn't what I want to tell my story about. We got home late in November and I promised mother I'd quit the race-horses for good. There's a lot of things you've got to promise a mother because she don't know any better.

And so, there not being any work in our town any more than when I left there to go to the races, I went off to Sandusky and got a pretty good place taking care of horses for a man who owned a teaming and delivery and storage and coal and real estate business

there. It was a pretty good place with good eats, and a day off each
week, and sleeping on a cot in a big barn, and mostly just shoveling
in hay and oats to a lot of big good-enough skates of horses, that
couldn't have trotted a race with a toad. I wasn't dissatisfied and I
could send money home.

And then, as I started to tell you, the fall races come to Sandusky
and I got the day off and I went. I left the job at noon and had on
my good clothes and my new brown derby hat, I'd just bought the
Saturday before, and a stand-up collar.

First of all I went downtown and walked about with the dudes. I've
always thought to myself, 'Put up a good front,' and so I did it. I had
forty dollars in my pocket and so I went into the West House, a
big hotel, and walked up to the cigar stand. 'Give me three twenty-
five-cent cigars,' I said. There was a lot of horsemen and strangers
and dressed-up people from other towns standing around in the
lobby and in the bar, and I mingled amongst them. In the bar there
was a fellow with a cane and a Windsor tie on, that it made me sick
to look at him. I like a man to be a man and dress up, but not to
go put on that kind of airs. So I pushed him aside, kind of rough, and
had me a drink of whiskey. And then he looked at me, as though
he thought maybe he'd get gay, but he changed his mind and didn't
say anything. And then I had another drink of whiskey, just to show
him something, and went out and had a hack out to the races, all to
myself, and when I got there I bought myself the best seat I could get
up in the grandstand, but didn't go in for any of these boxes. That's
putting on too many airs.

And so there I was, sitting up in the grandstand as gay as you
please and looking down on the swipes coming out with their horses,
and with their dirty horsey pants on and the horse blankets swung
over their shoulders, same as I had been doing all the year before. I
liked one thing about the same as the other, sitting up there and feeling grand and being down there and looking up at the yaps and feeling grander and more important, too. One thing's about as good as
another, if you take it just right. I've often said that.

Well, right in front of me, in the grandstand that day, there was a
fellow with a couple of girls and they was about my age. The young
fellow was a nice guy all right. He was the kind maybe that goes to
college and then comes to be a lawyer or maybe a newspaper editor

or something like that, but he wasn't stuck on himself. There are some of that kind are all right and he was one of the ones.

He had his sister with him and another girl and the sister looked around over his shoulder, accidental at first, not intending to start anything — she wasn't that kind — and her eyes and mine happened to meet.

You know how it is. Gee, she was a peach! She had on a soft dress, kind of a blue stuff and it looked carelessly made, but was well sewed and made and everything. I knew that much. I blushed when she looked right at me and so did she. She was the nicest girl I've ever seen in my life. She wasn't stuck on herself and she could talk proper grammar without being like a school-teacher or something like that. What I mean is, she was O.K. I think maybe her father was well-to-do, but not rich to make her chesty because she was his daughter, as some are. Maybe he owned a drugstore or a drygoods store in their home town, or something like that. She never told me and I never asked.

My own people are all O.K. too, when you come to that. My grandfather was Welsh and over in the old country, in Wales he was —— But never mind that.

The first heat of the first race come off and the young fellow setting there with the two girls left them and went down to make a bet. I knew what he was up to, but he didn't talk big and noisy and let everyone around know he was a sport, as some do. He wasn't that kind. Well, he come back and I heard him tell the two girls what horse he'd bet on, and when the heat was trotted they all half got to their feet and acted in the excited, sweaty way people do when they've got money down on a race, and the horse they bet on is up there pretty close at the end, and they think maybe he'll come on with a rush, but he never does because he hasn't got the old juice in him, come right down to it.

And then, pretty soon, the horses came out for the 2.18 pace and there was a horse in it I knew. He was a horse Bob French had in his string, but Bob didn't own him. He was a horse owned by a Mr. Mathers down at Marietta, Ohio.

This Mr. Mathers had a lot of money and owned some coal mines or something, and he had a swell place out in the country, and he was stuck on race-horses, but was a Presbyterian or something, and I think more than likely his wife was one, too, maybe a stiffer one than himself. So he never raced his horses hisself, and the story round the Ohio race-tracks was that when one of his horses got ready to go to the races, he turned him over to Bob French and pretended to his wife he was sold.

So Bob had the horses and he did pretty much as he pleased and you can't blame Bob, at least, I never did. Sometimes he was out to win and sometimes he wasn't. I never cared much about that when I was swiping a horse. What I did want to know was that my horse had the speed and could go out in front, if you wanted him to.

And, as I'm telling you, there was Bob in this race with one of Mr. Mathers' horses, was named 'About Ben Ahem' or something like that, and was fast as a streak. He was a gelding and had a mark of 2.21, but could step in .08 or .09.

Because when Burt and I were out, as I've told you, the year before, there was a nigger Burt knew, worked for Mr. Mathers and we went out there one day when we didn't have no race on at the Marietta Fair and our boss Harry was gone home.

And so everyone was gone to the fair but just this one nigger and he took us all through Mr. Mathers' swell house and he and Burt tapped a bottle of wine Mr. Mathers had hid in his bedroom, back in a closet, without his wife knowing, and he showed us this Ahem horse. Burt was always stuck on being a driver, but didn't have much chance to get to the top, being a nigger, and he and the other nigger gulped that whole bottle of wine and Burt got a little lit up.

So the nigger let Burt take this About Ben Ahem and step him a mile in a track Mr. Mathers had all to himself, right there on the farm. And Mr. Mathers had one child, a daughter, kinda sick and not very good-looking, and she came home and we had to hustle and get About Ben Ahem stuck back in the barn.

I'm only telling you to get everything straight. At Sandusky, that afternoon I was at the fair, this young fellow with the two girls was fussed, being with the girls and losing his bet. You know how a fellow is that way. One of them was his girl and the other his sister. I had figured that out.

'Gee whizz,' I says to myself, 'I'm going to give him the dope.'

He was mighty nice when I touched him on the shoulder. He and the girls were nice to me right from the start and clear to the end. I'm not blaming them.

And so he leaned back and I give him the dope on About Ben Ahem. 'Don't bet a cent on this first heat because he'll go like an oxen hitched to a plow, but when the first heat is over go right down and lay on your pile.' That's what I told him.

Well, I never saw a fellow treat any one sweller. There was a fat man sitting beside the little girl, that had looked at me twice by this time, and I at her, and both blushing, and what did he do but have the nerve to turn and ask the fat man to get up and change places with me so I could set with his crowd.

Gee whizz, craps amighty. There I was. What a chump I was to go and get gay up there in the West House bar, and just because that dude was standing there with a cane and that kind of a necktie on, to go and get all balled up and drink that whiskey, just to show off.

Of course she would know, me setting right beside her and letting her smell of my breath. I could have kicked myself right down out of that grandstand and all around that race track and made a faster record than most of the skates of horses they had there that year.

Because that girl wasn't any mutt of a girl. What wouldn't I have give right then for a stick of chewing gum to chew, or a lozenger, or some liquorice, or most anything. I was glad I had those twenty-five-cent cigars in my pocket and right away I give that fellow one and lit one myself. Then that fat man got up and we changed places and there I was, plunked right down beside her.

They introduced themselves and the fellow's best girl, he had with him, was named Miss Elinor Woodbury, and her father was a manufacturer of barrels from a place called Tiffin, Ohio. And the fellow himself was named Wilbur Wessen and his sister was Miss Lucy Wessen.

I suppose it was their having such swell names got me off my trolley. A fellow, just because he has been a swipe with a race-horse, and works taking care of horses for a man in the teaming, delivery, and storage business, isn't any better or worse than anyone else. I've often thought that, and said it too.

But you know how a fellow is. There's something in that kind of nice clothes, and the kind of nice eyes she had, and the way she had looked at me, awhile before, over her brother's shoulder, and me looking back at her, and both of us blushing.

I couldn't show her up for a boob, could I?

I made a fool of myself, that's what I did. I said my name was
Walter Mathers from Marietta, Ohio, and then I told all three of
them the smashingest lie you ever heard. What I said was that my
father owned the horse About Ben Ahem and that he had let him
out to this Bob French for racing purposes, because our family was
proud and had never gone into racing that way, in our own name, I
mean. Then I had got started and they were all leaning over and
listening, and Miss Lucy Wessen's eyes were shining, and I went the
whole hog.

I told about our place down at Marietta, and about the big stables
and the grand brick house we had on a hill, up above the Ohio River,
but I knew enough not to do it in no bragging way. What I did was
to start things and then let them drag the rest out of me. I acted just
as reluctant to tell as I could. Our family hasn't got any barrel factory, and, since I've known us, we've always been pretty poor, but not
asking anything of any one at that, and my grandfather, over in Wales
— but never mind that.

We set there talking like we had known each other for years and
years, and I went and told them that my father had been expecting
maybe this Bob French wasn't on the square, and had sent me up to
Sandusky on the sly to find out what I could.

And I bluffed it through I had found out all about the 2.18 pace, in
which About Ben Ahem was to start.

I said he would lose the first heat by pacing like a lame cow and
then he would come back and skin 'em alive after that. And to back
up what I said I took thirty dollars out of my pocket and handed it to
Mr. Wilbur Wessen and asked him, would he mind, after the first
heat, to go down and place it on About Ben Ahem for whatever odds
he could get. What I said was that I didn't want Bob French to see
me and none of the swipes.

Sure enough the first heat come off and About Ben Ahem went off
his stride, up the back stretch, and looked like a wooden horse or a
sick one, and come in to be last. Then this Wilbur Wessen went
down to the betting place under the grandstand and there I was with
the two girls, and when that Miss Woodbury was looking the other

way once, Lucy Wessen kinda, with her shoulder you know, kinda touched me. Not just tucking down, I don't mean. You know how a woman can do. They get close, but not getting gay either. You know what they do. Gee whiz.

And then they give me a jolt. What they had done, when I didn't know, was to get together, and they had decided Wilbur Wessen would bet fifty dollars, and the two girls had gone and put in ten dollars each, of their own money, too. I was sick then, but I was sicker later.

About the gelding, About Ben Ahem, and their winning their money, I wasn't worried a lot about that. It come out O.K. Ahem stepped the next three heats like a bushel of spoiled eggs going to market before they could be found out, and Wilbur Wessen had got nine to two for the money. There was something else eating at me.

Because Wilbur come back, after he had bet the money, and after that he spent most of his time talking to that Miss Woodbury, and Lucy Wessen and I was left alone together like on a desert island. Gee, if I'd only been on the square or if there had been any way of getting myself on the square. There ain't any Walter Mathers, like I said to her and them, and there hasn't ever been one, but if there was, I bet I'd go to Marietta, Ohio, and shoot him tomorrow.

There I was, big boob that I am. Pretty soon the race was over, and Wilbur had gone down and collected our money, and we had a hack downtown, and he stood us a swell supper at the West House, and a bottle of champagne beside.

And I was with that girl and she wasn't saying much, and I wasn't saying much either. One thing I know. She wasn't stuck on me because of the lie about my father being rich and all that. There's a way you know. . . . Craps amighty. There's a kind of girl, you see just once in your life, and if you don't get busy and make hay, then you're gone for good and all, and might as well go jump off a bridge. They give you a look from inside of them somewhere, and it ain't no vamping, and what it means is — you want that girl to be your wife, and you want nice things around her like flowers and swell clothes, and you want her to have the kids you're going to have, and you want good music played and no ragtime. Gee whizz.

There's a place over near Sandusky, across a kind of bay, and it's called Cedar Point. And after we had supper we went over to it in a launch, all by ourselves. Wilbur and Miss Lucy and that Miss Woodbury had to catch a ten-o'clock train back to Tiffin, Ohio, because, when you're out with girls like that, you can't get careless and miss any trains and stay out all night, like you can with some kinds of Janes.

And Wilbur blowed himself to the launch and it cost him fifteen cold plunks, but I wouldn't never have knew if I hadn't listened. He wasn't no tin-horn kind of a sport.

Over at the Cedar Point place, we didn't stay around where there was a gang of common kind of cattle at all.

There was big dance halls and dining places for yaps, and there was a beach you could walk along and get where it was dark, and we went there.

She didn't talk hardly at all and neither did I, and I was thinking how glad I was my mother was all right, and always made us kids learn to eat with a fork at table, and not swill soup, and not be noisy and rough like a gang you see around a race track that way.

Then Wilbur and his girl went away up the beach and Lucy and I sat down in a dark place, where there was some roots of old trees the water had washed up, and after that the time, till we had to go back in the launch and they had to catch their trains, wasn't nothing at all. It went like winking your eye.

Here's how it was. The place we were setting in was dark, like I said, and there was the roots from that old stump sticking up like arms, and there was a watery smell, and the night was like — as if you could put your hand out and feel it — so warm and soft and dark and sweet like an orange.

I most cried and I most swore and I most jumped up and danced, I was so mad and happy and sad.

When Wilbur come back from being alone with his girl, and she saw him coming, Lucy she says, 'we got to go to the train now,' and she was most crying too, but she never knew nothing I knew, and she couldn't be so all busted up. And then, before Wilbur and Miss Woodbury got up to where we was, she put her face up and kissed me quick and put her head up against me and she was all quivering and —— Gee whizz.

Sometimes I hope I have cancer and die. I guess you know what I mean. We went in the launch across the bay to the train like that, and it was dark, too. She whispered and said it was like she and I could get out of the boat and walk on the water, and it sounded foolish, but I knew what she meant.

And then quick we were right at the depot, and there was a big gang of yaps, the kind that goes to the fairs, and crowded and milling around like cattle, and how could I tell her? 'It won't be long because you'll write and I'll write to you.' That's all she said.

I got a chance like a hay barn afire. A swell chance I got.

And maybe she would write me, down at Marietta that way, and the letter would come back, and stamped on the front of it by the U.S.A. 'There ain't any such guy,' or something like that, whatever they stamp on a letter that way.

And me trying to pass myself off for a bigbug and a swell — to her, as decent a little body as God ever made. Craps amighty — a swell chance I got!

And then the train come in, and she got on it, and Wilbur Wessen he come and shook hands with me, and that Miss Woodbury was nice too and bowed to me, and I at her, and the train went and I busted out and cried like a kid.

Gee, I could have run after that train and made Dan Patch look like a freight train after a wreck, but, socks amighty, what was the use? Did you ever see such a fool?

I'll bet you what — if I had an arm broke right now or a train had run over my foot — I wouldn't go to no doctor at all. I'd go set down and let her hurt and hurt — that's what I'd do.

I'll bet you what — if I hadn't a drunk that booze I'd a never been such a boob as to go tell such a lie — that couldn't never be made straight to a lady like her.

I wish I had that fellow right here that had on a Windsor tie and carried a cane. I'd smash him for fair. Gosh darn his eyes. He's a big fool — that's what he is.

And if I'm not another you just go find me one and I'll quit working and be a bum and give him my job. I don't care nothing for working, and earning money, and saving it for no such boob as myself.

A Sentimental Journey

M Y FRIEND DAVID, with his wife, Mildred, came to live in the
hills. She was a delicate little woman. I used to go often to the cabin
they had rented. Although David is a scholar, he and a mountain
man named Joe, a man much older than David, became friends. I sat
in their cabin one evening, after I had first met David, while he told
me the story. Joe was not there and Mildred was in the kitchen at
work.

Joe is a thin mountain man of forty with the straight wiry figure
of a young boy. David spoke of the first time he ever saw the man.
He said:

'I remember that he frightened me. It was a day last fall, when we
had first come in here, and I was on the gray horse riding the hills.

'I was a little nervous. You know how it is. Romantic tales of
mountain men shooting strangers from behind trees or from wooded
mountain-sides floated through my mind. Suddenly, out of an old
timber road, barely discernible, leading off up into the hills, he
emerged.

'He was mounted on a beautifully gaited but bony bay horse, and
while I admired the horse's gait I feared the rider.

'What a fierce-looking man! Stories of men taken for Federal
agents and killed by such fellows on lonely roads became suddenly
real. His face was long and lean and he had a huge nose. His thin
cheeks had not been shaved for weeks. He had on, I remember, an
old wide-brimmed black hat, pulled well down over his eyes, and the
eyes were cold and gray. The eyes stared at me. They were as cold
as the gray sky overhead.

'Out of the thick golden-brown trees, well up the side of the mountain down which Joe had just come, I saw a thin column of smoke floating up into the sky. "He has a still up there," I thought. I felt myself in a dangerous position.

'Joe rode past me without speaking. My horse stood motionless in the road. I did not dare take my eyes off the man. "He will shoot me in the back," I thought. What a silly notion! My hands were trembling. "Well," I thought. "Howdy," said Joe.

'Stopping the bay horse, he waited for me and we rode together down the mountain-side. He was curious about me. As to whether he had a still concealed in the woods I do not now know and I haven't asked. No doubt he had.

'And so Joe, the mountain man, rode with me to my house here. (It was a log cabin built on the bank of a creek.) Mildred was inside cooking dinner. When we got to the little bridge that crosses the creek, I looked at the man who had ridden beside me for half an hour without speaking and he looked at me. "Light," I said, "and come in and eat." We walked across the bridge toward the house. The night was turning cold. Before we entered the house he touched my arm gently with his long bony hand. He made a motion for me to stop and took a bottle from his coat pocket. I took a sip, but it was raw new stuff and burned my throat. It seemed to me that Joe took a half pint in one great gulp. "It's new, he'll get drunk," I thought, "he'll raise hell in the house." I was afraid for Mildred. She had been ill. That was the reason we had come up here, into this country.

'We were sitting here in the house by the fireplace here and could look through that open door. While we ate, Mildred was nervous and kept looking at Joe with frightened eyes. There was the open door there, and Joe looked through it and into his hills. Darkness was coming on fast and in the hills a strong wind blew, but it did not come down into this valley. The air above was filled with floating yellow and red leaves. The room here was heavy with late fall smells and the smell of moon whiskey. That was Joe's breath.

'He was curious about my typewriter and the row of books on the shelves up there along the wall, but the fact that we were living in this old log house put him at his ease. We were not too grand. Mountain men are, as a rule, as you know, uncommunicative, but it turned out that Joe is a talker. He wanted to talk. He said that he had been wanting to come and see us for a long time. Someone had told him we were from distant parts, that we had seen the ocean and foreign lands. He had himself always wanted to go wandering in the big world but had been afraid. The idea of his being frightened of anything seemed absurd. I glanced at Mildred and we both smiled. We were feeling easier.

'And now Joe began to talk to us of his one attempt to go out of these mountains and into the outside world. It hadn't been successful. He was a hill man and could not escape the hills, had been raised in the hills and had never learned to read or write. He got up and fingered one of my books cautiously and then sat down again. "Oh, Lord," I thought, "the man is lucky." I had just read the book he had touched and after the glowing blurb on the jacket it had been a bitter disappointment.

'He told us that he had got married when he was sixteen and suggested vaguely that there was a reason. There often is, I guess, among these mountain people. Although he is yet a young man he is the father of fourteen children. Back in the hills somewhere he owned a little strip of land, some twenty acres, on which he raised corn. Most of the corn, I fancy, goes into whiskey. A man who has fourteen children and but twenty acres of land has to scratch hard to live. I imagined that the coming of prohibition and the rise in the price of moon has been a big help to him.

'That first evening his being with us started his mind reaching out into the world. He began talking of the journey he had once taken —that time he tried to escape from the hills.

'It was when he had been married but a short time and had but six children. Suddenly he decided to go out of the hills and into the broad world. Leaving his wife and five of the children at home in his mountain cabin, he set out —taking with him the oldest, a boy of seven.

'He said he did it because his corn crop had failed and his two hogs had died. It was an excuse. He really wanted to travel. He had a bony horse, and taking the boy on behind him he set out over the hills. I gathered that he had taken the boy because he was fraid he would be too lonely in the big world without some of his family. It was late fall and the boy had no shoes.

'They went through the hills and down into a plain and then on into other hills and came at last to a coal-mining town where there were also factories. It was a large town. Joe got a job in the mines at once and he got good wages. It must have been a good year. He had never made so much money before. He told us, as though it were a breath-taking statement, that he made four dollars a day.

'It did not cost him much to live. He and the boy slept on the floor in a miner's cabin. The house in which they slept must have belonged to an Italian. Joe spoke of the people with whom he lived as "Tallies."

'And there was Joe, the mountain man, in the big world and he was afraid. There were the noises in the house at night. Joe and the boy were accustomed to the silence of the hills. In another room, during the evenings, men gathered and sat talking. They drank and began to sing. Sometimes they fought. They seemed as strange and terrible to Joe and his son as these mountain people had seemed at first to Mildred and myself. At night he came home from the mine, having bought some food at a store, and then he and the boy sat on a bench and ate. There were tears of loneliness in the boy's eyes. Joe hadn't put him in school. None of his children ever went to school. He was ashamed. He was only staying in the mining country to make money. His curiosity about the outside world was quite gone. How sweet these distant hills now seemed to him!

'On the streets of the mining town crowds of men were going along. There was a huge factory with grim-looking walls. What a noise it made! It kept going night and day. The air was filled with black smoke. Freight trains were always switching up and down a siding near the house where Joe and the boy lay on the floor, under the patched quilts they had brought with them from the hills.

'And then winter came. It snowed and froze and then snowed again. In the hills now the snow would be ten feet deep in places. Joe was hungry for its whiteness. He was working in the mines, but he said he did not know how to get his money at the week's end. He was shy about asking. You had to go to a certain office where they had your name on a book. Joe said he did not know where it was.

'At last he found out. What a lot of money he had! Clutching it in his hand he went to the miner's house and got the boy. They had left the horse with a small farmer across the plain at the place where the hills began.

'They went there that evening, wading through the deep snow. It was bitter cold. I asked Joe if he had got shoes for the boy and he said "no." He said that by the time he got ready to start back into the hills it was night and the stores were closed. He figured he had enough money to buy a hog and some corn. He could go back to making whiskey, back to these hills. Both he and the boy were half-insane with desire.

'He cut up one of the quilts and made a covering for the boy's feet. Sitting in our house here, as the darkness came, he described the journey.

'It was an oddly dramatic recital. Joe had the gift. There was really no necessity for his starting off in such a rush. He might have waited until the roads were broken after the great snow.

'The only explanation he could give us was that he could not wait and the boy was sick with loneliness.

'And so, since he had been a boy, Joe had wanted to see the outside world, and now, having seen it, he wanted back his hills. He spoke of the happiness of himself and the boy trudging in the darkness in the deep snow.

'There was his woman in his cabin some eighty miles away in the hills. What of her? No one in the family could read or write. She might be getting out of wood. It was absurd. Such mountain women can fell trees as well as a man.

'It was all sentimentality on Joe's part. He knew that. At midnight he and the boy reached the cabin where they had left the horse and getting on the horse rode all of that night. When they were afraid they would freeze, they got off the horse and struggled forward afoot. Joe said it warmed them up.

'They kept it up like that all the way home. Occasionally they came to a mountain cabin where there was a fire.

'Joe said the trip took three days and three nights and that he lost his way, but he had no desire to sleep. The boy and the horse had, however, to have rest. At one place, while the boy slept on the floor of a mountain house before a fire and the horse ate and rested in a stable, Joe sat up with another mountain man and played cards from after midnight until four in the morning. He said he won two dollars.

'All the people in the mountain cabins on the way welcomed him and there was but one house where he had trouble. Looking at Mildred and myself, Joe smiled when he spoke of that night. It was when he had lost his way and had got down out of the hills and into a valley. The people of that house were outsiders. They were not hill people. I fancy they were afraid of Joe, as Mildred and I had been afraid, and that being afraid they had wanted to close the door on him and the boy.

'When he stopped at the house and called from the road, a man put his head out at a window and told him to go away. The boy was almost frozen. Joe laughed. It was two in the morning.

'What he did was to take the boy in his arms and walk to the front door. Then he put his shoulder to the door and pushed. He got in. There was a little fireplace in a large front room and he went through the house to the back door and got wood.

'The man and his wife, dressed, Joe said, like city folks — that is to say, evidently in night clothes, pajamas, perhaps — came to the door of a bedroom and looked at him. What he looked like, standing there in the firelight with the old hat pulled down over his face — the long lean face and the cold eyes — you may imagine.

'He stayed in the house three hours, warming himself and the boy. He went into a stable and fed the horse. The people in the house never showed themselves again. They had taken the one look at Joe and then, going quickly back into the bedroom, had closed and locked the door.

'Joe was curious. He said it was a grand house. I gathered it was much grander than my place. The whole inside of the house, he said, was like one big grand piece of furniture. Joe went into the kitchen, but would not touch the food he found. He said he reckoned the people of the house were higher-toned than we were. They were, he said, so high and mighty that he would not touch their food. What they were doing with such a house in that country he did not know. In some places, in the valleys among the hills, he said high-toned people like us were now coming in. He looked at Mildred and smiled when he said that.

'And, anyway, as Joe said, the people of the grand house evidently did not have any better food than he sometimes had at home. He had been curious and had gone into the kitchen and the pantry to look. I looked at Mildred. I was glad he had seemed to like our food.

'And so Joe and the boy were warmed and the horse was fed and they left the house as they had found it, the two strange people, who might also have heard or read tales of the dangerous character of mountain people, trembling in the room in which they had locked themselves.

'They got, Joe said, to their own house late on the next evening and they were almost starved. The snow had grown deeper. After the first heavy snow there had been a rain followed by sleet and then came more snow. In some of the mountain passes he and the boy had to go ahead of the horse, breaking the way.

'They got home at last and Joe did nothing but sleep for two days. He said the boy was all right. He also slept. Joe tried to explain to us that he had taken the desperate trip out of the mining country back into his own hills in such a hurry because he was afraid his wife, back in her cabin in the hills, would be out of firewood, but when he said it he had to smile.

'"Pshaw," he said, grinning sheepishly, "there was plenty of wood in the house."'

Justice

F RED'S PLACE, at the edge of our town, is in a little valley in the hills. Fred is a small, quiet man. I am not putting down his real name. He is a well-known writer. A good many writers who go into the country to live are seeking what they call local color, but I do not believe Fred is up to anything of the sort. Once I asked him, 'Did you come here to live among us, did you build your house and settle down here to write us up?'

He smiled. 'I haven't run short of things to write about,' he said. 'Every man and woman I ever saw is a story. There are too many stories. A man is a fool who seeks materials. The thing is to know how to handle materials. That's something.'

When Fred settled here, in our hills, among our Blue Ridge mountain people — 'hillbillies,' I guess you'd call them — he was misunderstood. For one thing, everyone thought he was rich. These mountain people of ours aren't much like the mountain moonshiners you read about in magazine stories. It's true a good many of them can't read or write, but if you think they are stupid, just try to trade horses with one of them.

When Fred built his house, in his upland valley, a few miles out of town, half the mountain men for miles about worked for him. Old Jim Salt was boss on the job, when he wasn't drunk. Fred paid good wages, the best ever paid about here. That may have been a mistake. Folks thought he was easy.

They began laying for him, robbing him a little here, a little there. They thought he didn't know it, but the truth is that he didn't much mind. He isn't a man who has much money sense, and once when I spoke to him of the matter he said to me, 'Pshaw! They haven't enough imagination to rob me much.'

The little sharp tricks some of our mountain men worked on him only amused him.

Once he talked to me a long time about money. It seemed to puzzle him. I guess he talked to me more openly than others in town, because I've been a college professor. He may have thought I was more at home in his book world. He had a mountain man named Felix working for him. Felix was building a stone wall, and he is a great talker. Fred told me that he went and sat for an hour on the wall near where Felix was at work, and that Felix began spinning yarns. What Felix was really doing was loafing, but he told Fred a tale and Fred went into the house and wrote it down — 'word for word as Felix told it,' he said. 'I got three hundred dollars for it and I was paying Felix two dollars a day. I guess if a man understood money, he'd understand a lot.'

Fred had a neighbor named Tom Case, a one-eyed man. Tom's queer. He is both mean and generous. Catch him on one mood and he'll steal the fillings out of your teeth, but the next day when you meet him, he'll give you his shirt.

Tom's farm is in on the hillside, above the valley where Fred built his house, and after Fred moved in, Tom laid for him. Fred had bought himself an old saddle horse to ride about the country, and one day the horse got through a fence into Tom's corn field. It was an accident the first time, but Tom got roaring mad, or pretended to be mad, and went down to Fred's house, raving and swearing and demanding ten dollars' damage. The horse hadn't done fifty cents' worth of damage to the corn, but Fred gave him the ten.

So it happened again, and then a third time. We all thought Tom was letting the horse into the corn. It was a small hillside field, and there wasn't five dollars' worth of corn in it. Thirty dollars for Tom. 'Pretty good, eh,' everyone said. We all knew well enough what Tom was doing, but in all of us there was the same feeling. 'Well, he's a city man. He makes money easy.' We might even have been a little jealous of Tom's easy picking.

And then Tom spoiled it. He went whole-hog on Fred. The horse got in the corn a fourth time and he wanted twenty-five dollars. Jake

Wilson told me he wanted to get his roof fixed. 'Roof fixed?' said Harley Davids. 'He's after a new house and a new farm.'

But he overreached that time. He raved and swore and declared he'd kill Fred, and he took Fred's horse and locked him in his barn. I've noticed that when a man is being dirty mean and crooked with another, he begins to hate the other. Fred kept quiet when all this happened, and came into town and got the sheriff to go get his horse. He had decided to go to law with Tom, and put up a hundred-dollar bond to cover any possible damage Tom might get in court.

Tom was so sore he even threatened to shoot the sheriff when he went for the horse. Fred told me that in the mood Tom was in he was afraid Tom might starve the beast. The business about shooting the sheriff was bluff, of course. He just laughed and made Tom unlock the barn, and took the horse home. 'You're a fool. You've spoiled your own racket,' he said, and Tom, who was standing in the barnyard with a shotgun in his hand, danced with rage. Our sheriff, Sam Hopkins, says that when a man is going to shoot, he doesn't talk. 'He just shoots,' he says.

So there was to be a trial in a Virginia squire's court, and half the town and all the farmers and hill men for miles around turned out. It was a nice day, a Saturday in the fall after the corn was cut. The trial was on the Burleson road, at Squire Wills's house. Squire Wills sat with Squire Grey, from the Flat Ridge. These Virginia squires don't pretend to know much law, and they don't like lawyers around telling them what's what. Get a lawyer, and you lose your case, every time. That's why neither Fred nor Tom got one. The squires are elected, and there may be as many as a dozen in one county. They get three dollars each for sitting a case, and you can have as many as three sittings, if you want.

So we were all fixed for a big day, and we all went. These country courts are our theater, here in the hills. The two squires, both old men, sat solemnly on the front porch of Squire Wills's house and we all gathered on the lawn in front, or in the road.

There was a good deal going on. It was a rare day in the fall, and the horse-traders were out. Men and women had come in cars, and the mountain men ahorseback. There was a good deal of shouting and laughing, some at Tom, some at Fred.

Tom didn't speak to anyone but his brother from Floyd County, who had come over for the trial. The brother stood in the road, and Tom rode up and down on a big black horse. He had his shotgun with him, and he had been drinking a good deal of mountain moon and he was trying to intimidate both Fred and the judges.

It didn't work. So Tom stopped his horse near his brother and leaned over to whisper to him. We were all watching. After all, we thought, although Tom Case never had shot anyone, he might begin.

And then, after Tom had whispered to another man, and he to a third, and he had gone to whisper to Fred, who was sitting on the edge of the porch, and Fred shook his head, we all knew that, anyway, the trial wasn't going to be settled out of court. Fred told me afterward that Tom offered to settle for twelve dollars. 'I wouldn't have settled for ten cents,' he said. He was beginning to get the spirit of the country all right.

So then the trial began, and Fred got up and told how he had given Tom ten dollars three times and he said he might have done it this time but that Tom had been a hog. 'I suggest,' he said, 'that the judges, or Tom and me, select three men and let them go down to Tom's place and look at that corn field.'

'I'll still pay whatever they say is right,' he said.

So that, of course, brought on something new. The two squires put their heads together and whispered and nodded, and finally said that Fred could choose a man, Tom another, and that the judges would choose a third.

Of course Tom objected. He swore, he raved, he rode his big horse up and down the road, he waved his gun, he whispered with his brother, and once one of the judges warned him.

'We could have you up for contempt of court, Tom,' Squire Wills yelled, and everyone, even Tom and the other judge, had to laugh at that. They figured some lawyer must have been talking to Squire Wills.

Finally, anyway, Tom selected his Floyd County brother, and Fred me, and the judges named Jim Wilson, and we drove down to Tom's field. Tom's wife came out while we were looking over the corn. We couldn't see where there had been any damage done you could notice . . . it's pretty hard to damage a hillside corn field much . . . and the wife said she was fair ashamed of Tom and had argued with him, but for us not to tell him what she said. We decided on two dollars because we all thought Fred could spare it, but Tom's brother spoke up and said, 'No, let's make it three.'

He laughed when he said it, and I said three would be all right. 'Fred'll maybe write all this up and get his money back anyway,' I said.

Then we came back, and gave in our decision, and you should have heard Tom roar. He threw his gun on the ground and rode around, and shook his fist under first his brother's nose, then Jim's, and then mine, but, as we say in the hills, we didn't pay him no mind, and the judges gave out their decision and stuck Fred for the costs.

So then Fred got a little sore, the first time I ever saw him bothered much. He got up and protested.

'Look here,' he said, 'I tendered this man ten dollars. You all know I've got thirty dollars invested in that corn field now, and you all know he was after twenty-five dollars from me, and the judges you sent down there only found three dollars' damage.' He turned to us referees. 'Men,' he said, 'how much would the whole crop of corn in the field have been worth if my horse had never got in there?'

'If he got in and wasn't put in?' Fred asked.

'About seven dollars,' Jim Wilson said, and the whole crowd had to laugh.

What was wrong, of course, was with the judges. There was a little shed beside the house and Squire Wills and Squire Grey went in there. They stayed for a while, conferring, I guess, and then Squire Grey came to the door and motioned for Fred to come in. He told me afterward how it was. He said the squires told him that the costs of the trial would be six dollars. 'Three dollars apiece,' they said. 'We don't want to stick you, Fred, but Tom's mad. He won't pay,' they said. They told Fred they thought it wouldn't be fair for them not to get their regular fees for such a big important trial, and Fred told them he thought so, too. 'Only I don't want that Tom to get the best of me in this,' he told them.

Then Fred did some fast thinking. He told me afterward that he was prouder of that moment than of any other in his whole life.

'Look here,' he said to the two Virginia squires, 'I'll tell you what let's do.

'You go out there on the porch and announce that the cost of the trial is to be divided, fifty-fifty,' he said.

'I'll pay the three dollars' damage, and half the costs and that makes six. You two keep it all.

'Tom won't get a red cent,' he said.

And so it was done, and I don't believe Tom quite understands it yet. He got some damage, and he didn't get it. He was madder than ever, but not at Fred now, but at the squires, and he swore he'd run them both out of the country.

So he got his gun up off the ground where he had thrown it, and rode off, swearing, and we all went on home, and afterward Fred told me of something else that happened. He said he didn't see Tom again for as much as two months, and that then, one day in the early winter, when it was raining, he was out for a walk in the rain and met Tom on his black horse, on a narrow mountain road. He said Tom stopped, and he stopped, and they both stood and stared at each other awhile, and then they both began to laugh and Tom got down off his horse.

Fred said they must have talked for two hours, friendly as the devil, about crops and weather and Democrats and Republicans and horses and who'd be a good man for county assessor, old Sylvester Sullivan being dead, but they never mentioned the trial at all.

And after that, Fred had Tom on his hands. He'd come down once a week, looking for some work to do, and when Fred let him do a few chores, now and then, about the place, he wouldn't take a cent.

'I'm only doing this work because I believe in neighbors being good neighbors,' Tom said.

A Dead Dog

Tom Hunt, who told the story of the dog's death, said he thought it was a good story because it had such amazing contradictions in it. Some of his listeners weren't so sure. 'Where are the contradictions?' someone asked.

Tom went on at length about the beauty of the dog that got killed. He was an English setter, a full-blooded thoroughbred one. He didn't belong to the man who shot him, but to a friend.

It happened in Tennessee, in a little county-seat town, the one Tom came from, and the man who shot the dog was the county prosecuting attorney. Tom said they call them 'attorney generals' in Tennessee. That was stepping about among titles everyone thought.

Tom spoke again of contradictions in character. The point being that this prosecuting attorney — his name was John Wilkins — was a regular man-eater. We gathered he was a rampaging bloodhound when it came to going after some poor man or woman he had got up in the courts.

Tom described him thus. He said he was a long, lean man with cold gray eyes and a long jaw and walked with a lope.

There would be a case up in the courts. So there was a man who had made, or they had found on him, let's say, a quart of moon. He had been drinking the stuff. That should have been punishment enough, several men who were sitting about and listening thought and said. They spoke with feeling. Some of them had been in Tennessee and evidently had drunk of the Tennessee moon.

But never mind, Tom said, they had him up. Suppose he was a little hill farmer from up in the hills. He had a wife and three or four scrawny kids. As he had no money, the court had appointed an attorney to defend him and the attorney, really touched by the poverty of the family — the wife sitting there downhearted, her toes sticking out of her shoes, a dirty barefooted babe in her arms — the attorney for the defense, really touched, tried to get down to his job.

Let us say they had asked the man where he got the moon and had even suggested that he tell who sold it to him — if he would tell they would let him off lightly, a suspended sentence, perhaps — but the man had said he did not know.

He didn't want to give his friend away — that is to say, if he did buy the booze, if he didn't make it.

He said he had met a stranger in the road and had got it from him or had found it sitting under a tree or that he had seen two men running and that one of them dropped it. There are some wobbly stories of that kind told nowadays by unimaginative people in liquor cases in the country courts.

The lawyer for the defense would be striding up and down before the jury, occasionally putting his handkerchief to his eyes and pleading. He would be a short fat man with a red nose.

'Let him off this time. Look at that woman there, a mother, gentlemen. Look at that babe. Look at its innocent eyes.

'Have you got a mother? Have you got a wife?'

He tells the jury that the hill woman has told him that there isn't a stick of wood in her house at home. The children are all small. They can't cut wood. 'Look at them. Can babes like that cut wood? Can they chop down trees in the forest recesses of this county?

'Let him go, gentlemen, this time. Let him go. Be easy on him.

'Do you want the babe to freeze? Do you want the little tired mother to freeze?'

So the attorney for the defense gets through and sits down, wiping his eyes, and John Wilkins gets up. His gray eyes are as cold as ice. He sneers. Tom Hunt, when he told this story, walked up and down in his room acting out the parts.

'Do your duty, gentlemen. Stick it to him,' Tom shouted, trying to give us all a picture of this John Wilkins in court.

'S-blood!

'Ah, we've heard this kind of stuff before. Don't think these mountain moonshiners ain't slick.

'They lie.

'We gave him a chance. Why won't he tell where he got that liquor? Likely as not he went and borrowed that woman and those kids. How do we know they are his kids?

'Stick it to him.

'We been bunked enough in this county. We honest men in this community have got to stand together. You let down the bars to this rabble, let a little cheap sentimentality sway you, look at a few cheap tears shed by some lawyer — who has maybe got an onion hid in his handkerchief — you let these fellows off ——

'Very likely this man made the stuff himself. Who's ruining the young men of this town? You know who they are, those being ruined.' (Walking to the poor dumbfounded mountain man) 'He doesn't know whether moon whiskey ruins people or not — he has always drunk it — he has been ruined himself a long time — he was born ruined.' (John Wilkins, the cold, the iron-hearted one, points a shaking finger.)

'There he is — the miscreant, the home-ruiner.

'Stick it to him, gentlemen. Stick it to him.'

Tom said that John Wilkins got an almighty sight of convictions in his Tennessee county. He told about a lot of cases.

There was a little thin-cheeked girl, only sixteen. She had a half-crazy mother and her dad was the town drunkard.

She wanted some silk stockings, like other girls had, and a fur coat, bought on the installment plan. That, Tom said, was why she did what she did do.

'Stick it to her, gentlemen. Don't waver. She is a home-ruiner.'

Suppose, said Tom, there was a woman — this happened in that county in Tennessee — who being what she was, a widow with two or three kids living on a mean little hillside farm near town, so worn out with toil and worry trying to get along, that Tom didn't think she was accountable for anything she did ——

Suppose such a woman, being in her cabin, killed a man.

She did kill one. He was a young man, a young mountain rough.

He came to her cabin one winter afternoon, Tom said, with another young man. They just came along a mountain road and stopping at the house began to annoy the woman. They had been drinking.

'So you're a widow. It's a shame you aren't prettier. If you was prettier I'd kiss you, that's what I'd do.'

'Now you git out of here. You let me alone. You let me alone.'

The woman was getting worked up. Her kids were scared. One of them was crying.

So the young fellows, being full of moon whiskey, being young mountain roughs, wouldn't let her alone and she picked up a stove poker — it was a heavy iron one turned at the end, and sat by a stone fireplace.

She ran at one of the young fellows and swung the poker, not intending to hit him, but the heavy sharp iron entered his head and he fell down dead. Tom Hunt acted that scene out for us, too. First he was the little tired mountain woman and then he was the young rough. Tom was good. Everyone said he should have gone on the stage.

As the mountain woman he made his face look worn and haggard. Fred Sloper was in the room with us and Fred always carries a cane. Tom picked it up and rushed across the room. We all drew back, thinking he was going to hit someone, but fortunately, just as we were all becoming alarmed, he shifted characters again. He became the young rough, threw his hands up to his head, groaned, and fell down dead. He did a very good fall.

That woman was up for trial on a murder charge.

'She killed him, didn't she?'

'It may not be murder. It's manslaughter, though.'

'You got to stick it to her, gentlemen. You got to be firm.'

Tom said it made him sick.

'Stick it to 'em.'

'Stick it to 'em.'

He said that all around that county they called John Wilkins 'old stick it to 'em.' The odd part was that every time he came up for re-election he went in again with a whoop. He got a smashing big majority every time. Even a lot of people, moonshiners and so forth, he had stuck for jail sentences or maybe a turn on the road, went to the polls and voted him in again.

Tom said he couldn't figure it out in any way except that these mountain people said to themselves — 'Well, he's just a fellow trying to do his job. He does it pretty well.

'I guess he don't have no personal feelings. I guess he's just a fellow, doing his job,' they said.

But to return to dogs. Tom explained that there was a lot of good bird-hunting over in his home county, in Tennessee. He said that a good bird dog was something in that country. Once there was a case in the courts in that county. It was about a bird dog that had been shot by a farmer and the owner was suing for the value of the dog. They called another farmer, a young man, as a dog expert.

'What is a good bird dog worth?' a lawyer asked.

'Well, I don't know,' he said. 'It depends on the dog.

'A good one,' he said, 'A really good one is, I guess, worth more than anything else in this world.'

Tom told this story to illustrate, you understand, how they felt about bird dogs in that Tennessee county.

'It is like this,' Tom said, 'You may be a good shot and maybe not. If you are going to hunt, it's nice to be a good shot.

'Because up the birds come and there you are. You are hunting with another fellow over a brace of dogs. They are in a stubble field near a fence.' Tom was acting the part of a hunter now. He had got ahold of Fred Sloper's stick again.

'The dogs are stanch,' he said. 'They are standing rigid.

'So you advance. "First or last bird?" you say to your partner. That's so you won't both of you crack down on the same bird.

'He's a crack shot, let's say. "First one," he says. He'll take the first bird up and leave the last one to you.

'Of course you'll both do what you can in the mass of them.

'The point being that, for the moment, you yourself are something nice. There you stand, not too rigid, not relaxed either. Up the birds go. You draw down on them. Bang! It's something to drop them clean, one after the other.

'Suppose they are at the edge of the fence in that stubble field and there is a hillside, covered with dense laurel, as so many of the hillsides are in Tennessee. You have got to work fast and accurately all right.'

Tom pointed out something else too.

'Suppose now,' he said, 'you aren't such a crack shot. You go out with two fellows that are.

'There's your covey. So you draw a little back. Perhaps you don't shoot at all.

'You take it out of you watching the dogs and the men.'

There is something fine, Tom pointed out, in seeing well-trained men and animals working perfectly together like that, the dogs doing their part, the men their part, everything just right between animal and man, each understanding the other, each depending on the other.

'If you can't shoot much,' Tom said, 'you can get almost as much satisfaction going along and just looking — more maybe.'

He spoke about men and horses.

'Go to the races,' he said. 'You see a horse and his rider working beautifully together.

'Then say the rider is thrown. There is the horse running alone. He runs about as well as he did before, but it doesn't mean anything to you.'

The particular dog that got killed, Tom said, was named in the national setter bird dog book — it seems there is a record kept of all such thoroughbred dogs — 'Windham's Kentucky Lad,' but his owner didn't commonly call him that. He called him 'Bum.'

He belonged, said Tom, to a man named Sam Rierdon and Sam Rierdon was a sawmill man. Tom said he was a bushy, hairy kind of a man, rather stout and short, and that his wife was dead.

Then he had a daughter, and she died.

So he had gone in for dogs, the English setter breed, and had three, all good ones, but this Bum was the best of the lot.

He had been trained right and was right, Tom said.

He was a tail-bleeder.

'You know,' Tom said, 'a good one, not too thick-skinned, fast, with a fine nose —— '

That kind, according to Tom, never do get fat. Some of them, the best of them, he said, were like the sons of the Czar of Russia that got shot up by the Bolshevists. They were easy bleeders, we gathered. If you pointed a finger at one of them, he bled a little right at the place you were pointing at. He was that fine on the trigger, that sensitive, let's say.

This Bum bled at the tail. The end of his swinging tail got blood-red; that is to say, a place at the tail's end, about as big as a shaving brush, got red like that when he had been working five minutes in the field.

The tail was threshing from side to side, sticking up in the gray-brown fall fields of Tennessee like that.

Tom said Bum could scent a covey of birds farther, in all kinds of weather, and go nearer without flushing and would stand stancher and would pick up and bring in dead birds faster than any dog he had ever seen work.

He said that when a covey had been broken up, he seemed to know just where the singles had gone. He would pick them up and stand them, one after another, Tom said, like picking up apples on the ground under a tree.

What happened was that the man John Wilkins — the hard-boiled, cold-hearted prosecuting attorney — borrowed this Bum from his owner for a day's hunting.

So one day he saw this Sam Rierdon on the street.

'Sam,' he said, 'I got a dog all right, but I've been hearing about your Bum.

'I'd like to shoot over him once,' he said.

'All right, John,' said Sam. 'Say when.'

'Tomorrow,' said John.

'All right,' said Sam. 'He's in his kennel back of my house.'

'Won't you come along?' says John.

'I can't,' says Sam. 'I got a car of lumber to get off tomorrow.'

So John Wilkins went hunting alone, taking his own dog and Bum. He drove out to a place called Poorfolk Valley. Tom said it was a long narrow valley between high Tennessee hills and was about fifteen miles out from town.

There were some little flat fields along a creek in that valley. Sometimes the hills pitched right down to the creek's edge and the road, and sometimes they opened out, making the fields.

They were old corn, wheat, and rye fields and the farmers who owned them knew John. He had hunted that valley before, but it hadn't been hunted much that year.

Something had held John up in town and he didn't get started until late afternoon. It was a cold windy day and snow threatened. It was a bad day, Tom said, for birds.

'It was the kind of a day,' he said, 'when the birds are likely to be in the woods or in the thickets on the sides of the mountains where you can't get at them much.

'The birds felt a storm coming,' he explained, 'and were getting ready for it.'

This is what happened after John Wilkins, that icy-eyed Tennessee attorney-general of Tom's home county in Tennessee, got out into the Poorfolk Valley and had begun to hunt.

He got out there and got the dogs, Bum and one of his own, a bitch named Flora, out of the car. The road just there, where he happened to stop the car, ran up out of the valley and climbed the side of a steep bluff.

He went down the side of the bluff through dense laurels, crossed a creek and got into some fields. He didn't expect to do much. It wasn't any kind of a hunting day.

He worked up through the fields and Bum and Flora worked well together, backing each other up just fine, and he got into three coveys and knocked down four birds.

The last covey he shot into was in a narrow little field at the edge of another bluff, where the laurel was pretty thick, and the birds, after he had shot into them, scattered and went up in there.

There wasn't much chance to get at them again, but he thought he might get a single or two.

So with his gun in his hand he crossed the creek and climbed the bluff. He had found a little footing and was going along, working his way up, when, said Tom, he kicked up a bird. Just where the dogs were he didn't know. The bird went off fast, on up the side of the bluff.

Of course, John cracked down on him. He always thought afterward that the dog Bum must have found another single farther up the hillside somewhere and was standing him there, hidden by the bushes, making his point.

John Wilkins missed his bird. It had gone whirling through the top of a young cedar tree some twenty yards away up the bluff. He heard a little sound when that happened, not much of a sound he said afterward, just a tiny little yelp, like the quick, excited yelp of a pup.

John worked on up the hill — it was laborious climbing — keeping his eye out for the dogs and thinking maybe he might find them down on some of the birds. He didn't find anything, so he finally blew his whistle for the dogs to come in and his Flora came. Bum didn't appear.

John had got up to the place where that first bird had disappeared into the tree, thinking he might have got him, after all. 'You know how a good shot is,' Tom said, 'he hates to think he ever misses one.'

There was a little ledge of rock just under the tree. He stood there and looked around and the bird flew out, but he didn't shoot. For, at just that moment, his eye caught something. It was Bum lying on another ledge of rock some twenty feet below where he stood. It had begun to snow now, light hard flurries of snow, and the wind was howling. Bum had been standing a bird and had been shot and knocked down the side of the bluff.

John Wilkins dropped his gun and leaped down. There Bum was. He didn't seem to be bleeding. There were two little flecks of blood on his white sides, but these might well have come from his bloody tail whipping around. The creek that ran through the valley was a hundred yards below and John carried Bum in his arms, half-falling and tumbling down through the brush to the creek's bank. It was a wonder, Tom thought, he didn't break his own neck.

Bum was still alive, but couldn't stand on his hind legs. He kept looking, as under such circumstances a dog will, into John Wilkins's eyes. They were the same eyes, Tom reminded us, into which more than one poor man and woman in that county had looked, hoping to find a little mercy and human sympathy there, and finding none.

John Wilkins took off his hat and dipping up water in it poured it over the dog's head.

That went on for sometime, but didn't seem to do any good.

So he picked the dog up in his arms again, waded the stream, crossed a field, and then, climbing through the laurels, got up the hillside to the road where the car was.

Bum was heavy, of course. It was a steep climb. Every now and then John Wilkins had to put him down for a rest and to get his breath and every time he did Bum looked up at him again, threshing the red shaving brush end of his tail about and trying to get to his feet.

He couldn't make it. Tom thought he must have been shot and had leaped into the air with a little yelp. Falling over the ledge he had broken his back.

Every time he tried to get to his feet like that, John Wilkins gritted his teeth and a little sobbing sound came from between his lips. 'Don't, Bum. For God's sake, don't. Lie still. Don't do it,' he pleaded.

He got up to the road to where the car was. John's own dog, the bitch Flora, was already there. 'Well,' Tom said, 'she was a female. She didn't seem to mind much.' She was hopping around in the road wagging her tail and jumping on her master. She never paid any attention to Bum.

This John Wilkins, Tom said, was pretty sick by now. He felt weak and looked pale and done up. He put Bum on some dry grass beside the road and started toward a distant farmhouse. The road was muddy. Tom said he went a little way along the road and then came back. He had happened to think that poor Bum might try to get to his legs again while he was gone and he couldn't bear the thought. How Tom knew all these details I can't say. He was down there on a visit for the fall shooting when all this happened. I'm just telling it as he told it to us.

He said that John came back along the muddy road and, getting a piece of rope from the car, tied Bum so he couldn't, he hoped, make that effort to get to his feet, Bum looking him in the eyes in that hurt-dog way all the time. Then he went and got the farmer. The farmer was a man he knew. He, the farmer, looked at the dog, felt of him, and said he thought he would be all right. He lifted him up and put him in the front seat of the car. 'I don't believe his back's broke,' he said — he was one of the optimistic kind of men who are always trying to cheer people up — 'if you get him to a veterinarian in town I think he'll be O.K., John,' he said.

So John Wilkins started for town and the dog died on the seat beside him on the way in. My friend Tom Hunt — while he was telling us about it in his room that day acted everything out, even the part of Bum — described all this to us. He spoke at length about the drive home. He said Bum never whimpered. He said John Wilkins couldn't help looking hopefully at him every now and then, but that, every time he did, his eyes met that look in the dog's eyes and he came near running the car off the road and into the ditch.

'It got dark,' Tom said, 'and it snowed and at last John, with the dead Bum on the seat beside him, got to Sam Rierdon's house.' Sam's house was out at the edge of town. He lived alone, but was pretty

well-heeled, Tom said, and had some niggers that waited on him, got
his food, kept his house in order and all. We gathered, from what
Tom said, that he was rather a lonesome man.

A man like that, who had lost his wife and his daughter and really
had nothing but his dogs——

John Wilkins got there after dark and parked the car in the road in
front of the house. He took the dead Bum in his arms and went and
laid him on the front porch of the house, by the front door.

Then he took a turn in the yard, walking around in the dark in the
snow trying to get a grip on himself. This John Wilkins, as you may
well guess, being prosecuting attorney in a mountain county in Tennessee, had been up against things in his life. More than once there
had been threats made to take his life, Tom said, but they hadn't
scared him none.

He was scared now, though. Finally, bracing himself, he went and
knocked on the door.

Sam Rierdon came out. 'I shot your dog,' John Wilkins said. 'Well,
I shot Bum. I killed him. He's dead. There he is.' Tom said that
John Wilkins shot the words at Sam Rierdon. He spoke as though
an injury had been done him and he was sore. 'He had to,' Tom said.

He pointed at Bum lying there dead. The light from inside the
house came out through the open door and lighted up the scene. Tom
said that Sam Rierdon didn't say a word and that John Wilkins didn't
say anything more.

The prosecuting attorney took one look at his friend the lumberman
and then, still acting as though he was sore, went away. He went
out to his car and getting in drove rapidly away. It was snowing
pretty hard. He seemed to want to get away from the sight of his
friend and his friend's house.

That was all of it, Tom said, all of the story.

Except about John Wilkins's icy-gray eyes, about his being so hard-
boiled. Tom said quite a lot about that and about his looking at Sam
Rierdon and Sam looking at him and what each saw in the other's
eyes, but I'll leave all that out.

Tom also talked a lot about the inconsistencies in the character of
John Wilkins. 'It's the inconsistency of the whole thing that makes
the story, that's what makes it interesting,' he said.

'A man like that, who could be so hard-boiled about people and be
like that about a dog.'

Well, I respect Tom all right. I respect his story-telling ability and the way he acts out the parts when he is telling a story, but that day, when he told several of us this story up in his room and after we left and were walking along a street, I asked the rest of the crowd what they thought. They were all men with more or less experience of dogs and horses and men.

'Do you think he was inconsistent, this Wilkins?' I asked.

'Inconsistent?' they all said. 'What are you talking about? I can't see where the inconsistency lies.'

The Death of Bill Graves

T HE HILL PEOPLE of Eastern and Middle America have begun to get into the public consciousness. The hill country runs across America, between the North and the South, taking in great chunks of Virginia, North Carolina, West Virginia, Northern Georgia and Alabama, Tennessee, Kentucky, and Missouri.

There have been plays, stories, magazine articles, and books written about the hill people. Some of the writing has been intelligent and sensible and a lot of it has been foolish, some of it even hurtful.

There is this trick, so many writers have, of working always along broad lines. A tall, lean mountain man stands at a still on a mountain-side, with a rifle in his hand. He has just shot a Federal agent on the road below. Such things happen in the mountains, but not all mountain men are tall, lean, and fierce, and few enough of them own rifles. It is again, as I have found in so many other levels of American life, a matter of just people. Mean ones, generous, tricky, fierce, gentle — there they are.

There still is, however, in the hill country, a way of life that is outside the tone of most America just now. The machine has not penetrated deeply into the hills. There is still hand-weaving being done. There are few self-binders and the grain is still cut with a cradle.

You may see oxen on the hill roads and in the fields, and when a man dies his neighbors come to his house and build his coffin in the yard before his door.

Although they call themselves Southern, the hill men are not to be confused with the men of the great coastal plains, the 'crackers,' so-called, of the hot plains of lower Georgia, South Carolina, Florida,

Alabama, and Mississippi. They are alike only in that the men of the plains are poor as are the hill men.

In the hills there are a good many of men and women who cannot read or write, and that is confusing. There are so many smart, learned men of the richer valley towns who seem foolish enough when they come into the hills.

The hills have, however, their own fools, their beautiful women, their liars, their oversensitive, easily hurt ones.

Oh, the snobbishness of men! There are prosperous towns and cities in some of the wide valleys, and in the towns and cities men live more easily than we do in the hills. They grow proud and snobbish. Because their fields grow bigger corn, because they live in bigger houses, own automobiles and raise bigger cattle, they feel themselves superior.

Let them try living as the hill men must live, on the same sort of poor, often worn-out, land. Let them try to get what the poor hill men often get out of life. Last year a sculptor from New York came to live for some months in our hills and I took him for several long walks. The sculptor knew something.

We were walking on a mountain road near a mountain town and, as it was Saturday, men, women, and children were coming into town for supplies. Even in the broad road they walked in single file, the man followed by his wife, the wife by the children.

'It comes from walking much on mountain trails,' I explained to the sculptor.

There were mountain women and girls, some of them quite dressed up, but as is a habit of the country, many were barefooted. The women carried shoes and stockings in their hands. They were to be put on as the women sat on a creek bank, and after they had washed their feet at the town's edge. Mountain people can't waste shoe leather. It costs too much.

The sculptor kept looking and exclaiming as we passed the women, 'See how beautifully they walk.' I remember one tall, dark woman of thirty. But for the sculptor, I might not have noticed how firmly and beautifully her bare feet met the earth on a mountain road, or how well she carried her slender woman's body.

But I sat down this morning to write the story of the death of an old mountain man named Bill Graves. Bill died, one day last week at the age of seventy-five. He had three wives during his long life, two of them having died of the hard work and the hard living. There had been a good many children.

He got him a new wife, a young one, when he was sixty-eight. His second wife had died two years earlier, leaving several small children on his hands.

A little mountain family — a man with his wife and daughter had come through the hills and had put up one night at his house. The daughter might have been eighteen and she was tall and dark-eyed. There often is a curious pregnant sadness in these mountain girls, a something born in them. It is like the sadness of a late fall evening when the light is fading and winds blow over the hills.

'I gotta go down this lonesome road.'

Bill's new woman's father and mother were drifting through the country. We have a good many such drifters. There is a little family on a mountain farm, and the farm will no longer support it. The man has a bony horse and a wagon. He and his family become drifters — no longer attached to the soil. The man and woman who came to Bill's house were, some of the neighbors said, of the no-account sort. The man was such a fellow as Thomas Lincoln, Abe Lincoln's father. He had drifted out of the same sort of background.

The family stayed for a night with Bill and on the next day the man and woman, with their broken wagon and the bony horse, went on their way. Bill had talked to the tall daughter during the evening. She stayed on with him and the next day they drove to the county-seat town and got married. She had four children by Bill Graves and then he died.

Bill was one of the tall, lean sort and in early life he had been a lumberjack. It was as a lumberjack, when the hill country was being timbered off, that he made the money to buy his mountain farm.

He was a man who impressed himself. None of his neighbors — at least, not the women — were surprised that the young mountain-woman stayed with him and became his wife. More and more, as he had grown older, other mountain-men of his mountain country had been coming to him with their problems. He was the man in his neighborhood who settled quarrels. He had got himself elected a squire and performed marriage ceremonies. With his tongue in his cheek and pen in hand, he wrote wills and agreements. It was laborious work for Bill. Two of his neighbors had got into a quarrel about a line fence, but, although he was a squire, he didn't let them come into his court. He went and looked at the fence. 'Put it here,' he said. He had a way with men. He made his decisions stick.

Bill had been a hard-drinking man all his life. Every morning when he awoke, he took a tin cupful of raw moon whiskey, and he took several more during the day. Just the same, he never got drunk. He kept his little farm in trim and was always ready to lend a hand to others in the seasons when the farm work in the little valleys and hollers grew heavy.

There was the Widow Littlejohn who lived on the mountain above his house. Her man died two years ahead of Bill, and in the late fall, after her man died, just when the snow began to fly, Bill appeared at her house with a load of firewood. He had cut the wood on his own land and had hauled it up the mountain-side to her place. He hauled six loads, enough to keep her fires going for the winter, stopping his team in the road before her house. He threw the wood over the fence into the yard, and when she came to the door to thank him he swore at her. He turned his team and drove away, lashing the horses and swearing.

'What the devil'd you mean, letting your man die on you! A woman ought always to die ahead of her man. That's the way to do it,' he shouted.

There is some grain, mostly rye, raised on hillside land in the hill country, but the hill men do not cut it with the modern self-binders. A self-binder would roll down off most of the fields. Men go into the fields with cradles to cut the grain, and when there are several mountain men working in a grain field it is a sight to see. There is the long sweep of the cradles, the grain cut by the scythe and caught in the cradle. As the swing is completed, the frame of the cradler catches the bunched grain and it is laid on the ground ready for the women and children to tie into bundles. The grain-cutting is something to be remembered. Often there is a group of a half-dozen men swinging across a hillside field, marching forward, the cradles swinging, the women and children following, all the men, women, and children of a neighborhood gathered, the shouting and laughing, each man trying to out-march the others.

There is a jug of moon whiskey in a fence corner at the end of the field.

It is the test of the mountainer's manhood. Can he keep up with the others? Can he lead the others across the field? Can he keep leading them all through a long hot summer day?

The city man, that sculptor, who came to live in the hills one summer, was walking with me past Bill Graves's house on the afternoon when he died.

Bill's house was on a side road, deep in the hills.

There was the long rye field on a hillside and several mountain men, neighbors of Bill's, had come to help in the harvest. Afterwards, a doctor in town told me about Bill. He said that Bill had suffered with cancer of the stomach for two years. He hadn't let anyone know. Even his wife didn't know. There is a good deal of cancer of the stomach among mountain men. It may be the hog-and-hominy diet, and I dare say the raw corn whiskey doesn't help. On the day of Bill's death, the sculptor, a small blond man, walked up the road with me and there on the sloping hillside, beside the road, was Bill leading a half-dozen of his neighbors across the field. We stopped and looked. I'm myself far from a big man and I'm a town man. What we saw in the field gripped the sculptor. There was a rail fence separating the road from the field, and he went and put his hands on the top rail, and stared.

'Look!' he cried. The mountain men were swinging across the field, the sweat pouring from their faces. 'Look at the rhythm of it. It's a dance!' he cried.

It was a sweltering hot day. Bill Graves was swearing at the men, taunting them as he led the march across the field and they were laughing at him. He saw us standing in the road and, dropping his cradle, ran down to us. He must have been full of corn whiskey, had been drinking to keep himself going.

'You, you fellow!' he cried to us. 'I've been waiting for this.'

'You city and town fellows coming in here!' he shouted. 'I'm going to make you come up here into this field.' He stood laughing. 'I want to see what you town fellows can do with a cradle.'

He had got down to the fence and had put his hand on the top rail ready to vault over when something happened. Although Bill had been blustering and swearing, the little sculptor was not alarmed. He also laughed. And then suddenly the laughing died on his lips.

It was late in the afternoon. All day Bill Graves, now seventy-five, had been leading the others in the grain field. He had kept himself going by drinking quantities of the moon whiskey. The laughing threat he threw at us was the end of him. As he stood by the fence in the bright late afternoon sunlight, his hand on the top rail, both the sculptor and I saw the quiver that ran through his body. He died as he stood, but he died laughing at us. 'I am going to get you!' he cried, and laughed; and then he turned and called to his young wife who had been at work among the women.

'Come here, Hallie,' he called to her and she came, tall and bare-footed, down the hillside through the grain stubbles. She was very like that other woman the sculptor and I had seen in the road at the edge of the mountain town. The woman Hallie, Bill Graves's young girl-wife, came down to him as he stood by the fence, his hands behind him tripping the fence rail, as he spoke to her.

'It's come out all wrong, Hallie,' he said, speaking quietly to her. 'A woman should always die before her man, but I was too old when you got me. I'm going, I'm going to die on you,' he said.

He said the words and slumped to the ground, and all the men, women, and children in the field came running toward us. But Hallie, Bill's wife, didn't run.

In the road, some twenty yards beyond where I stood with the sculptor from the city, there was a little bridge that crossed a stream, and while the others, the mountain men, Bill's neighbors, who had been helping him in his rye field, were picking him up and carrying what was left of him over the fence and along the road toward his house, the other women and children following with frightened faces, the city sculptor and I both turned and looked at Bill's Hallie. She had jumped lightly over the fence and had walked to the bridge. She sat on the bridge and turned her back to us. She was a young but a proud woman. Afterward the sculptor told me he would never forget her figure as she sat on the low bridge, her feet in the water of a mountain stream.

Although Bill Graves was an old man when he got his Hallie, he had done what a good many younger men never succeed in doing with their women. He had really got her. She wanted to be alone in the first storm of her grief, and so the city sculptor and I hurried away past the house and around a turn at the road and off into the hills.

Daughters

THERE WERE TWO SHEPARD GIRLS, Kate and Wave. Wave was slender. When she walked, she thrust the upper part of her body slightly forward. She had masses of soft hair always slipping from place and falling down. 'It won't stay where I put it,' said Wave. Her hair was brown, touched with red, and her eyes were brown. Most of the time she wouldn't get up in the morning. She let Kate do all the work about the house, but Kate didn't care if she did.

The Shepards had come to Longville, to live in town. John Shepard got a job working as a section hand on the railroad. He had been a lumberman working in lumber camps ever since he was a boy and didn't like being in town. He came in because of his daughters. Kate, the elder of the girls, wanted to be a school-teacher. To do that you had to go through high school. Afterwards you had to go through normal school. Kate thought she could do it.

Before moving into Longville, they had lived in a small unpainted frame house in a little valley up in the hills. The house lay six miles back in the hills beyond the Bear Creek settlement and the Bear Creek lumber camp where John Shepard had been working when his wife died. His wife was a huge fat woman with a reputation for laziness. 'Look at her house,' people said. Her house always was dirty. It was in disorder. It had remained that way until Kate got old enough to take a hand in the housework.

Kate was a girl who could do everything. She had kept the garden behind the house. She milked the cow. She swept and kept the house. She rose before daylight to put the house in order and be in time for school. The girls had had to walk three miles to reach the one-room country schoolhouse. Often they had to wade through snow and, in the spring, through mud. Whenever the weather was bad, when it was cold or rainy, or snow or mud lay deep on the valley road, which followed the windings of a creek, Wave didn't go.

When she did go, she always played in the boys' games. She threw a ball as if she were a boy. She could outrun the boys and sometimes tore into one of them and licked him. She swore like a boy.

'Hell, I'll not go to school, not in this weather. To hell with it,' she said. Her mother could not get her to obey.

All through their childhood, the two girls saw little of their father, who often worked in lumber camps. Sometimes, coming home at the week-end after a long hard week of heavy work, and finding his wife sitting in a disordered house, dirty clothes lying about on the floor, and the bed in which he was to sleep with her unmade, and hearing her say she couldn't do anything with Wave, John Shepard, who seldom complained, had spoken almost sharply.

'What's the matter with you, Nan?' he asked. 'Can't you run your house? Can't you run your children?'

'I would just like to have you try it, with that Wave,' she said. 'She's a little hell-cat,' she added. She said that if you tried to make Wave do something she didn't want to do, she'd just lay on the floor and scream.

'I got a whip and whipped her, but she just kept screaming, screaming and kicking her heels in the air. She wouldn't give in. You couldn't make her give in.'

He himself, when at home and in a room with his daughter Wave, always felt a little uncomfortable. He spoke to her and, if she didn't want to, she didn't answer. She could look at you and make you feel uncomfortable. There was something a little queer. Sometimes her eyes seemed to be insulting you. 'Don't bother me. Who are you that you should bother me? If I want to answer when you speak to me, I will. If I don't, I won't.'

Wave sat in a chair and put her legs up. She put her feet up on the back of another chair. She left her dress all open at the front. She went about barefooted, barelegged. Her legs were dirty. She could sit for a long, long time, saying nothing, staring at you until you wanted to go and cuff her.

And then, suddenly she could grow nice. There was a soft warm look came into her eyes. You wanted to go and take her into your arms, hold her tight, cuddle her, kiss her, but you'd better not try. She might suddenly hit you with her hard, sharp little fists. Once she had done that to her father, and having taken her into his arms he put her quickly down.

'Your mother can't do anything with you, but I'll show that I can,' he said. 'I was as mad as I ever was in my life,' he said afterwards, talking with George Russell, a man who worked with him in the woods. 'My wife just had two girls,' he said. 'I wish they had been boys.' He explained to the other man how it was about girls. 'They are good or they ain't. You can't make them good.

'When they're little things they're nice, but, as soon as they begin to grow up, they bother you. You get to thinking, "now what's going to happen to them?"

'There are always boys hanging after young girls,' he said. He said that, in the country, girls, when they got to a certain age, were always going into the bushes with boys.

'You can talk to a boy, set him straight, but you can't talk about a thing like that to a girl. How can you?' he asked.

The other man, with whom John Shepard worked, didn't know how you could. He had three sons. He didn't have any girls. 'I don't know how you could. I guess you can't,' he said.

That time, when Wave hit her father in the face with her fists, because, just then, she didn't want to be held by him, didn't at the moment fancy being caressed by him, John went and cut a switch, a good stout one. He went to where there was a thicket beyond his farm, but, when he came back to his house, Wave wasn't there.

She was sitting astride the roof of his house. He told the man in the woods about it.

'The roof of my house is so steep a cat couldn't climb it, but she climbed it,' he said.

She just sat up there, staring down at him.

'Come down,' he said.

'Come down,' his wife said. His wife was alive then. His wife could sit all day without moving. She took a chair out into the yard and sat in it. 'I can sit down here as long as she can sit up there,' John's wife said. He thought probably she could. 'I never saw a woman could sit as long as my wife can,' he said to the man in the woods. He said she could sit anywhere, on a chair, on the ground, even when the ground was wet, on the floor. He said that if his wife, instead of Wave, had been sitting on the roof, he'd have given up at once.

'I gave up, promised I'd never touch her if she came on down, made my wife promise, because Kate, her sister cried so hard.

'She just sobbed and sobbed. She was so scared her sister would fall. She's such a good girl that I couldn't say, "no."

' "Don't touch her, Pa. Please don't touch her. Promise you won't touch her. Make Ma promise," she kept pleading and she kept sobbing like her heart was breaking, so I promised,' he said to the man in the woods. He said he thought that his daughter Wave was just having a good time. 'She was enjoying herself, the little hell-cat,' he said.

It was a year after his wife's death that John Shepard had moved to Longville. He hated it. He didn't want to live in town. He had saved his money and bought a little farm in a nice little valley. Working in the camps he had made plans. A stream ran through the farm, a rapid little stream that came down out of the East Tennessee hills, and he planned to build a dam and run a mill. He would grind corn for people who lived on little farms farther up the valley. A man could get his toll. He could keep enough meal to feed his family and his chickens. He could keep two or three cows, sell the calves, raise hogs. 'A man can get along good,' he said to another man with whom he worked — always in deep woods. 'He can enjoy his family.' He was a quiet, slow-speaking man who, even when a young fellow, hadn't gone off, after pay-day, drinking or whore-hopping like most of the young fellows in the camps.

But he had had a talk with his daughter Kate, one week-end when he was at home, after his wife had died. Kate was nearly fifteen, Wave almost thirteen. It was a Sunday morning and Kate had got his breakfast. She had been up a long time, milked the cow, fed the chickens and the two pigs. She had brought water from the spring. John had shaved. He had put on a clean shirt and a clean pair of overalls. Kate had washed them for him. The little house was all in order, everything swept, the windows washed, nothing lying about on the floor in the front room where the family ate, where they sat.

There was a fireplace and, as the bright spring morning was cold, Kate had brought in wood and built a fire.

She asked him whether the coffee was good. She got him a second cup.

Wave was in bed.

'You've been doing all of the work, ain't you?' he asked, but Kate said, no, she hadn't. She brought him some jelly for his bread and told him Wave had made it. Wave had baked a cake. Kate began bragging about Wave. She could make pies. She could bake the lightest cake you ever ate.

'I can't cook half as good as Wave can,' Kate said. She said Wave could do anything she put her hand to. If she wanted to and when she went to school, she could be the smartest one there. Kate got a little excited when she spoke of her sister. She always did. There was a kind of shine came into her eyes. It was true, said Kate, that, when there was bad weather or when she didn't want to go, she wouldn't go to school, but, you give her a book, a hard one, now, any book, and she could read it right off.

She could read a book or a story and then she could tell about it, make it sound better than when you read it yourself.

And when she wanted to, she could make clothes. 'You just give her some odd scraps,' Kate said. She said that Wave had taken an old dress that had belonged to their mother and had cut it up. She had just slashed right into it. She had made two dresses out of the one dress, one for herself and one for Kate.

Kate came and sat at the table with her father.

'Pa, we ought to move to town,' said she. Her face had got flushed. It was hard for Kate to talk as she did that morning. She wanted her father to sell the farm, to try to get a job in town, and John Shepard thought, listening to her talk, that Wave had put her up to it.

'I'll bet the little hell-cat did put her up to it,' he said to the man who worked with him in the woods. Kate had, however, said nothing of Wave's wishes. She had been bragging her sister up and then she stopped. She took it all on her own shoulders. She said she wanted to be a school-teacher and had to go to high school. She said that, if they lived in town, in Longville . . . it was twenty miles away . . . it was a big town . . . if they lived there she bet she could get a job, maybe in a store. She said she bet she could do something to help earn money. He told the man in the woods that, once she had got on the subject, she didn't let up. She talked that Sunday, and then she talked every time he went home. He said it wasn't like her. His daughter, Wave, he knew was back of it, but what could he do? He said he couldn't say no to Kate, not for long.

'She's such a good girl,' he said. He said he couldn't refuse her anything. 'She works so hard. She does everything. She never complains. I guess I got to give her her chance,' he said, and he said he wouldn't mind, he was getting old, he didn't expect it mattered much where he worked, although he hated living in town, didn't like it at all.

He had hoped to spend his old age on his farm. That was why he had worked and saved to buy it. He expected, if he sold his farm, he'd only get enough to buy a little house in town with no ground at all, not to speak of.

'Maybe just enough for a little scrawny garden and it mighty poor soil,' he said. 'And I've got my place now pretty well built up. I've been buying fertilizer and putting it on. What my land needs is time,' he said.

He said he knew that his youngest daughter was back of Kate's talk about moving to town and being a school-teacher and all, but that he guessed he couldn't refuse.

It was a little yellow house. You went down a sloping, unpaved street that ended in a swamp and the yellow house was at the end of the street. It stood on a high gravelly bank above the low swampy land and there were trees, two hickory trees and a beech, their roots reaching down into the black swamp land. They stood just where the yard of the yellow house shelved off into the swamp and just at the base of the beech — a tree with great spreading limbs, one of its great branches lying against the house wall — a spring bubbled up. People came from other houses along the short little street to get water. There had been a barrel sunk into the ground and a stream ran down from the barrel's edge, spreading out over the low black land.

The low land was covered with little grassy hills surrounded by stagnant water. There was a stream that, sometimes in the spring and fall, got out of its banks, covering the low land, but in the summer it was a mere trickle. The stream came out of the town. It went away across fields. You could stand in the yard before the yellow house and look away to long stretches of farmland. There was a big white farmhouse, standing on a low hill in the distance, and back of it was a big red barn.

John Shepard, the lumberman, had sold his little farm in the valley between high hills and bought the yellow house. He hated it, but 'What's the use of complaining?' he thought. He had got a job working on the railroad that went through Longville, was a section hand. He got a dollar-fifty a day. He had bought the house at the town's edge, because, he thought, 'Anyway, it won't be so crowded.'

There wasn't anyone to talk to in town. He was a man who went cautiously toward others — made friends slowly. He left the house early in the morning, carried his lunch-pail, and was gone all day. It seemed strange and unnatural to him not to be in the deep woods, not to have the smell of the woods in his nostrils. There was that other man with whom he had worked in the woods, the fellow that had sons and no daughters. He missed him. The two men had worked together for a long time. It was a big cutting they had been on. They had kept going forward, into hills, swamping-out roads, getting the logs out. You worked with another man, felling the trees, and others came and trimmed the logs. You could get ahead of them, sit down and rest, talk with the other man who worked with you.

You didn't see much of the boss. You had your life in there, away deep in there, in the deep woods with the other man, your pardner.

John Shepard went along through busy town streets, up and out of the street at the end of which, by the swampy place, he had his house. He had to go through a street where there were big houses set in lawns. His daughter Kate had a job in one of the big houses. She prepared his breakfast, fixed his lunch-pail, and then went to the big house.

She cooked there. She swept out rooms and made beds. She wasn't the first girl in the house. She was the second one. They let her go to school. The woman gave her dresses. She told her father how nice they were to her. She said they wanted her to have her chance. 'I tell you, Pa, they're mighty nice to me,' she said. She stayed up there at night, after school, working sometimes until eight or even nine o'clock, then she came home and got her father's supper. When there was a party or something up where she worked and she knew she'd be late, she'd slip home after school and get something cold ready for him. Regular evenings, when she had everything cleaned up, she'd sit in the kitchen, at the kitchen table, studying.

Wave wasn't there. She was off somewhere, traipsing around with the town boys. She never seemed to want to eat much. She didn't mind missing a meal. Sometimes quite late at night, when Kate had got through studying and had gone to bed and when John Shepard was in bed, a car drove up before the house and Wave got out.

He could hear some man's voice. He could hear the car turn.

Most of the dresses Kate had given her, working up there in the rich people's house, Wave got.

She could take a dress and change it. She could make it something new. If it was out of style, she could put it back in style. She could take two dresses and make one. Wave wasn't afraid of anyone or anything. Kate, when she had time to talk to her father, maybe in the evening after the evening meal, when she was washing dishes and cleaning up and he was on the steps by the kitchen door smoking his pipe before going to bed, continued bragging Wave up.

'I wish I could cook like Wave can.

'She can do anything she sets her hand to.

'If I could fix up dresses as well as she can, I'll bet I'd have a shop.' John said nothing. It made him sore to hear Kate talk so.

'If she can cook so good, why don't she stay home and get my supper?' he thought. Sometimes he thought, 'Kate is away all day and so am I. She's just bound to get herself into trouble and bring disgrace on us.' Sometimes he wanted to spank Wave. He came home from work and there she was, on the front porch, sitting in a chair, her legs up on another chair. She didn't seem to mind what she showed. Shed'd show everything she had. She was always reading. She got books somewhere, Kate said from a free library. She didn't care if there was someone coming along the street. The people on that street were always coming down to the spring, under the trees, at the edge of the bank, right near the front of the house. There were women coming. Men came. There were some of the men who were young fellows. They worked in a factory in town.

Wave didn't care. She'd dress up, like a doll, right in the morning, when she first got up. Sometimes she didn't get up until noon. She

turned night into day. She was there, like that, on the porch, reading
a book, maybe just waiting for some man to come in a car and take
her out, God only knew to where, when John Shepard came home.

He asked her if she had got his supper and she didn't answer. She
didn't even look at him and he wanted to snatch the book out of her
hands. He wanted to take her across his knees. She wasn't very big.
She was slender and not very strong. He wanted to take her on his
knees and spank her behind.

'I'd like to fan her little behind for her,' he thought.

Sometimes when John Shepard came home from his work and
Wave was there sitting maybe on the porch, not answering when he
spoke to her, her feet up on another chair or on the porch rail, reading
a book, and when Kate hadn't got a chance to slip home and get
something ready for him and he got mad, he thought, 'Kate wouldn't
like it. She wouldn't stand for it,' he thought. When that happened,
sometimes he got a headache.

It was because he was so mad and could do nothing. It was because
it was Wave who was behind Kate's wanting to come live in town. It
was because Wave kept putting all the work on Kate.

'I don't know how she got to be like she is,' he told himself. He
hated to think about her. He didn't want to. When he thought about
fanning her little behind, he got excited. It was an odd excitement. It
made his head ache. It made his back ache. When he was in the
woods cutting down trees, he always did heavy work, but he never
had a backache or headache, but when he got mad at Wave and could
do nothing because there was nothing he could do, he did . . .

It wasn't the work he was doing, on the railroad. He knew that.
It wasn't such heavy work.

He hated being alone in the house with Wave. She could make him
furious just looking at him. Sometimes, when he came home from
work, and she was there and Kate wasn't — he couldn't stay. He kept
opening and closing his fists. Even if it was winter and if Wave was
at home and not traipsing around with some man and there was snow
on the ground, he went out of the house.

He went into the back yard. There wasn't much front yard, but the
back yard was long. When he had bought the place, he had thought
that maybe he would raise chickens. He never had. 'I don't seem to
get around to begin,' he said to himself. He thought maybe it was
Wave's fault.

He stood about. He was waiting for Wave to go away or Kate to come home. When it was dark, he sat sometimes on the ground, under one of the hickory trees. The hickory trees were at the back of the yard, where the ground shelved off, down to the swamp. The beech tree was in front, right by the street. He got so mad that he beat the ground with his open hand. One night he beat so hard that the gravelly soil hurt his hand. He didn't mind the hurt. He liked it, but afterwards his back ached and his head ached. It spoiled his supper.

A porch extended along one side of the little yellow house and faced the street. Through a door in the side porch you entered a small parlor, behind which lay a bedroom, where the girls slept. The kitchen was built on. The stairs to the upper story mounted out of the girls' room. There was no door at its head, and the stairs came right into the room where John Shepard had his bed. A wooden railing had been placed beside the stair-pit, there, so that in case you did not light a lamp when you went to bed, or got up in the night or early in winter, you wouldn't in the darkness fall through the opening. There was a second room in the upper story, and to reach it you had to pass through John Shepard's.

He was wandering restlessly about in the back yard. It was evening. A car drove up and Wave got into it. She was 'stepping out.' 'I'm stepping out, Kid,' she would have said to her sister, fixing herself up. Wave, although younger than Kate, always called her sister 'Kid.' It was the assertion of a kind of superiority perhaps in worldly knowledge which Kate didn't mind. Kate never minded anything Wave said or did. John Shepard heard a man's voice out in the road. The fellow had to turn the car and John got behind one of the hickories. He didn't want the car's headlight to search him out, find him wandering there. Anyway, he didn't want Wave to know she could worry him.

He went into the house. Kate was sitting in the kitchen by the table. She was sitting under a kerosene lamp, as the Shepards didn't have electric lights. She had a book open. It was nice and clean in there. When Kate was in the house even for just a little while, she got everything looking and smelling nice. He thought Kate was very pretty. He thought she was beautiful. Sometimes when he admired her he wondered how she had come to be as fine as she was, and was disloyal to his dead wife. 'She isn't much like her Ma or me either,' thought he.

'Where you been, Pa?' Kate asked, and he said he had just stepped outside. He wanted to tell her that he couldn't bear being in the house when Wave was there. He wasn't a swearing man, but he wanted to say, 'Goddam Wave. I wish she'd get the hell out of my house and stay out.' He wanted to say, 'I don't give a goddam what happens to her. I can't bear being in the goddam house when she's here.'

Sometimes he said such things aloud, when he was going to work, in the early morning, hardly anyone in the streets, even in Main Street, through which he had to pass, just maybe a few clerks, opening up and sweeping out stores. He said such things aloud, then or in the evening when he was coming home. But he knew he couldn't say them to Kate.

He said, 'I guess I'll go on to bed.' He didn't want to go to bed, but he didn't want to interrupt her in her studies. He thought, 'Maybe I could just sit down here, near her, and smoke my pipe.

'I like to be near her,' he thought.

He thought, 'I never liked to be near her Ma, even when she was a young girl, before she got so fat, when I was courting her, like I like to be near Kate.

'But maybe it would bother her, me sitting about,' he thought.

'And anyway,' he thought, 'I don't enjoy smoking when I've got a headache.'

He hesitated, standing back of Kate, who was absorbed in her book. She turned and saw him.

She had got a new lampshade on her lamp. 'Look at it, Pa,' she said. 'Ain't it pretty?' She said that Wave had made it. His headache got worse.

'Goddam Wave,' he thought.

'She's sure got fine eyes,' he thought, looking at her. He was always wondering, since he came to live in town, why it was that men and boys all seemed to be crazy to be with Wave and why so few got after Kate. He thought it showed that town men hadn't a bit of sense.

'If I was a young fellow now,' he thought, 'and Kate wasn't my daughter —— '

He had gone to stand near the door that led into Kate's and Wave's room and to the foot of the stairs.

'I'd better not sit down,' he thought. If he sat down he'd be staying. She worked hard. 'She ought to get her studying done and go to bed,' he thought.

Kate had been talking about the room upstairs, the one at the front of the house. She had said that sometimes she thought she'd better put an ad in the paper. 'We could get something for the room and it would be a help.' If, as sometimes happened, she also spoke of wanting to buy something for Wave, speaking maybe of Wave's birthday coming, or maybe Christmas, mentioning maybe a pair of silk stockings, something like that, it spoiled things. But sometimes she didn't mention Wave at all, and when she talked in her intimate way, Wave gone, it seemed to him that his back and head both were feeling better.

Kate began speaking about the roomer for the room above, giving the impression that she had given the matter a lot of thought.

'If it was a young fellow now, a quiet one.'

She was attending the town high school. There were young fellows, also from the country, who came to town to school, some drove into town in cars, but others had no cars.

'If we had a young fellow like that, in the other room, upstairs, he and I could talk over our lessons.'

Kate said that some of the lessons she had to take in school were mighty hard for her. She had to study a thing called Latin.

'What's that?' her father asked, and she said it was a language.

'It's the way people talked, a long time ago,' she explained. She said they wrote books in a language different from the one she and her father talked. She didn't know why you had to learn to read books written in it, but you did. If she was ever going to get a chance as a school-teacher, she had to learn it.

'Even if we got only a dollar a week,' she continued. 'It couldn't be a girl, up there with you, having to go back and forth through your room. If he wanted his breakfast, I could get it while I am getting yours.'

She continued earnestly talking of the possible roomer. Suddenly it occurred to her father that she was describing a real person. She spoke so definitely of him.

John Shepard went upstairs and to bed. For some time a vague resentment against young men had been growing in him. Going to work and coming from it he had begun looking closely at young men he met. Now and then one of them, who came in the evening for Wave — he might be going to take her for a ride in his car — there seemed an endless stream of the men, some younger than others, big ones and little ones — men well dressed, others rather shabbily dressed — now and then one of them sat for a time on the side porch of the house.

He would himself have fled into the back yard. Wrath was rising in him. 'What's she up to?' It must be, he thought, that half the town was talking about his daughter.

'I don't believe all of these men would be after her unless——'

There were thoughts he couldn't finish, didn't want to finish.

If she were going all the way with them, one after another ——

Wrath boiled up in him.

But, lying in bed, it seemed to him that the young roomer was in the house. He was in the room at the front of the house, just beyond his own, behind the closed door. He was in there studying as Kate was studying below in the kitchen. — Now he was below with her, talking their lessons over with her. — He was quietly coming upstairs.

John Shepard had always wanted a son. The young man would be like Kate, not like Wave, a fellow always running around in the streets at night, crazy after girls as Wave was crazy after boys.

The resentment returned. The young fellow who had come for Wave earlier in the evening had returned with her, was sitting down on the porch with her. The two were laughing and talking together.

'Now quit that, smarty,' he heard Wave say to the man.

He would have been grabbing her leg or something like that. It sounded like it.

She wasn't mad, though. She laughed when she told the fellow to quit it. She didn't sound as though she meant it. She had a curiously soft silvery laugh. She began singing.

She could do all sorts of things Kate couldn't do and that was annoying too.

For example she could sing. She had a curiously soft, clear, penetrating voice. Late at night, when she had come home, after an evening spent with some man and had got into bed with Kate and was telling Kate of her adventures and was speaking in a low voice, hardly more than a whisper, her father, in his bed upstairs could hear every word she said.

Kate had a rather husky voice. It sounded as though she were catching cold. Her father was always asking, 'You ain't catching cold, are you, Kate?'

'Why, no,' she said.

Wave knew a lot of songs. She'd sing songs to the men that weren't very nice. She sang a song about a girl who got pregnant by some man she wasn't married to. It was called 'Careless Love.' It was about a girl who got big with child so that she couldn't tie her apron strings. The strings wouldn't go around her swollen belly. The man who did it to her, after he had done it, wouldn't marry her.

It wasn't any song to sing, to just any man, especially when you weren't married to him. Wave sang it in her soft, low, clear voice and John Shepard was sure she could be heard all along the street at the end of which they lived.

God only knew what people thought.

But, just the same, in spite of yourself, when Wave sang like that . . . you just couldn't help yourself . . . you began to like her in spite of yourself.

The singing seemed to carry John Shepard back into his young manhood. He was again a young lumberman. On Saturday night he was in a town near the lumber camp where he worked then. He had gone into town with other young lumbermen.

They were drinking and fighting. They were going whore-hopping, out to raise hell, but he wasn't. He walked about. The town was small, but he got off the main street.

There was a house, halfway up a hill, a half-mile out of town. It had apple trees in the yard.

There was an old man with a gray beard, who walked with a stick. There was an old blind woman.

There was a young girl, very slender, very pretty. They had mosquito netting about the porch of their house.

On warm clear nights they brought a lamp out there and the young girl read aloud to the old white-bearded man and to the blind woman.

Her voice was like a bird singing away off somewhere in the deep woods.

The first time when John Shepard, as a young man, had gone into the town and when wandering about, not wanting to drink and raise hell with the others, not wanting to go whore-hopping . . . he didn't believe in it . . . it was against his principles . . . he had often said to himself, 'I'll wait 'til I get honestly married . . .'

'I'm not just an animal . . .' he had said.

'I'll go clean to her. I'll be asking her to come clean to me and I ought to go clean to her . . .'

There was deep dust in the road and when he went past that house, that was quite near the road. They didn't see him. They didn't hear him. There was a kind of hedge and he sat down under it. He hadn't ever thought that he could get a woman like the one on the porch of that house, reading aloud to the two old people, so beautiful, so evidently refined.

He thought, 'I'll bet she's educated. She reads so well.' He thought maybe she had just come there, to that town, maybe to visit her grandmother and grandfather.

'I'll bet, at home, she's away up in life,' he thought. He imagined all sorts of things about her, creeping back to hide under the hedge, on many Saturday nights, always dreaming and thinking about her all week when he was at work in the woods. Bitterly disappointed when, having gone into town and up there, she wasn't on the porch, reading to the old people, so disappointed that sometimes he cried.

Not that he had ever thought he could get such a woman.

He had never even spoken to her. How could he have gotten a chance, he told himself, and if a chance had come, what could he have said? She had been there with the two old people and then she wasn't there. He guessed she was just visiting there, in that house, in that town. He guessed they were her grandparents. It had been like spring coming after a long hard winter in the woods. Spring comes, and then after a while, it isn't spring any more.

What annoyed John Shepard, though, was that Wave, sitting singing on the porch to a man she had picked up, should rouse a funny feeling in her father. Making him think of his youth when he went creeping up a hillside road, out of a lumber town, hiding under bushes, seeing another young woman on the porch of a house, himself full of a mysterious love that made him sit by the roadside silently crying, just as if, he told himself, a man, certainly a very ordinary man, not educated, one who always had lived with rough uncouth men, drinkers, fighters and whore-hoppers, had fallen in love with an angel sitting on a star up in the sky. As if she herself, the little devil down there, were an angel sitting on a star. The singing carried you up to her. It seemed to float you. Made you as if in a dream, where your feet leave the earth and you float like a bird up in the sky.

It made him angry. God knows he had seen and heard enough of his daughter Wave. In spite of himself, though, he quit wanting to fan her little behind, and went to sleep.

He awoke. Kate was up, getting his breakfast. It was lucky that, at the place where she worked, they didn't have their breakfast early like that. John guessed they stayed in bed. 'How they can, when it's broad daylight, say now in the summer, I don't know,' he thought.

'I like the early part of the day,' he thought. He remembered how, when he was still working in the woods, he went, from where he slept, in a bunk, in a little shack, usually with two or three others to where they all ate their breakfast.

It would be hardly day. It would be a pinkness. You went along a creek and crossed on a log. There was good woods smells and good food smells. In the lumber camp, no one talked while they were eating. It was a rule they had. It wasn't a law. It was a rule. It was in all lumber camps. It made it nice.

You ate and got on a car, a flat one, part of a lumber train, and you went along a creek.

There were some began to talk, but John didn't. He sat silent, at the edge of a flatcar, his legs hanging down.

There was a kingfisher bird, up early and on a limb, a dead limb, hanging out over the stream. There was a quiet above the talk of the men. There was a squirrel went up the trunk of a tree.

It was all nice. It was funny to think there were people in towns who wanted to stay in bed.

'I couldn't. Even if I had a million dollars, I couldn't,' thought John Shepard.

He went downstairs and there was Wave in bed asleep. She had kicked the covers off again. You could see clear up her leg, all of it, and see her little behind.

He was in bed again. He had been talking with Kate again about the roomer for the room next his.

'It gets kind of real,' he thought.

'I guess now he'd be down there with Kate,' he thought. Sometimes, when he was in bed like that, not asleep yet, not wanting to go to sleep, not feeling like sleep, he could almost see the young man.

'He'd have to be a pretty sensible one.' He thought it would be nice if the young man was good-looking but not too good-looking. He might be smart and quick at things, like Wave was . . . at least like Kate was always saying Wave was . . . but, he thought, not too goddam smart. 'Smart enough, though, not to fall for Wave,' he thought.

He thought, 'He'd be down there with Kate, she helping him, he helping her, but she wouldn't be showing her legs. Nothing like that,' he thought.

He thought . . . 'Maybe they'd both be like I was about that one on the porch that time. Like that about each other,' he thought.

It got so that, having these thoughts, night after night, they got more and more real.

Sometimes he thought, when he went upstairs to bed, when he was undressing, he thought . . . 'No, he ain't down there with Kate.

'He's in there. He's in his room.

'He's studying now. I got to be mighty careful.

'I can't make any noise,' he thought.

He argued with himself. 'The fellow can't be down there with Kate, sitting with her, studying with her, liking her, gradually getting more and more stuck on her, because I just came up from there.

'He's in there in his room, studying now,' he thought.

'If he comes through the room here, going down to be with Kate, I'll pretend to be asleep.' He thought of something that gave him a lot of satisfaction. 'There's a lot of men that snore when they sleep, but I don't,' he thought. There had been a fellow at the lumber camp where he worked. He came to bunk in the same shack. He said, 'Thank God, you don't snore.' He said it in the morning after the first night in the shack with John. He said, 'Christ, the bedbugs are as bad here as where I was where I worked last, but thank God, you ain't no snorer.' He said that, in the last camp where he had worked, he had been put in to bunk in a shack with a man who snored so that he raised the goddam roof. He said the fellow made the goddam roof flop up and down like a goddam tent that hadn't, he said, been pegged down.

'You know,' he said, 'like a goddam tent in a goddam storm.' He meant to say that John didn't snore when he slept.

'And I'm glad I don't,' John thought. He thought he'd hate to be bothering the roomer he and Kate were always speaking about. 'Either,' he thought, 'when he's up here in his room or when he's down there sitting with Kate.'

Lying there, arguing with himself in bed, upstairs in his house, John Shepard heard the sound of voices. His daughter Wave had been out with one of her men. She had come home and she and Kate were in bed.

They were talking. They were laughing. There was a fat girl who worked in the house where Kate worked.

She couldn't get any men. Kate was telling Wave a story. The fat girl, who worked at that place where Kate worked, wrote letters to herself. Kate said she had seen one of the letters.

The fat girl had let it fall on the floor. It fell out of the pocket of her apron. Her name was Evelyn. 'Darling Evelyn,' the letter began. The fat girl couldn't spell very well. Kate said the fat girl went down into the town. She went to a florist. She bought a box of roses and sent them to herself. She had, Kate said to Wave, gone somewhere and had some cards printed. There was a man's name on the cards.

She put one of the cards into the box of roses. She had it addressed to herself. She had it sent to the house where she worked. She left the box open. Kate saw the card lying in the box on the roses.

'When she was down in the kitchen, I went into her room. She had got a whole pack of the cards printed. They were in a little paste-board box in there. The name printed on the cards was "Robert Huntington."'

There wasn't any such man. Kate and Wave were lying downstairs. They were laughing at the fat girl. Wave was telling Kate about some man.

'He wanted to kiss me.

'He put his hand on my leg.'

They began talking in lowered voices. Wave was telling Kate what some man had tried to do to her. Occasionally the two girls giggled, and John Shepard silently got out of bed.

He was barefooted. He slept in the same shirt he wore during the day. At night, when he went to bed he just took off his shoes, his socks and his pants. He shivered as he went silently down the stairs. He stood there near the foot of the stairs.

Wave was telling Kate how far she thought it was safe to let the men go. She was saying that there was one man who had almost got her.

'I let him go a little too far.'

'What did you let him do?'

Wave had begun to whisper. It was almost as though she knew someone was listening. Kate was living her life in Wave's life. As Wave whispered, she giggled.

Kate also giggled.

It was all strange. It was in some way terrible to hear. Kate was feeling what Wave had felt. When she giggled, it was not as it was when Wave giggled. There was something in the tone of the low laughter that came from Kate that made her father shiver again.

He got suddenly angry. He wanted to run and choke Wave. He wanted to drag her out of the bed. He wanted to fan her behind, fan it hard.

He went silently back up the stairs and got into the bed.

There was the fat girl who wrote letters to herself. She sent herself flowers. Kate was living her life in Wave's life. Something not nice, he felt, was going on in his house. It seemed to him that Wave, coming into the silent house at night and talking with Kate, had brought something in that spoiled things.

The conversation between his daughters went on. John Shepard was very angry. He was so angry that little beads of sweat stood out on his forehead. He was as he sometimes was in the darkness in the back yard. In the back yard he pounded the ground with his hand. Now he pounded the bedclothes. His head ached and his back hurt.

John Shepard and his daughter Kate got their young man. Kate had put an ad in the paper. The young man had taken the room upstairs in the Shepard house. He was in the house. He was in and out. His feet were on the stairs. He was doing exactly as John Shepard had dreamed he would do.

He was a student in the town high school and, apparently, a very studious, earnest young man. He had his breakfast in the house. Like Kate and John Shepard himself, he got up early in the morning. His name was Ben Hurd and, like John himself, he had come to town from a lumber camp. He was a tall, slender young fellow. He had black hair and dark eyes.

He had got a job in town. He was at a store. He went there in the early morning, opened the store and swept out. Then he hurried off to school and after school, in the late afternoon, he returned to the store.

He stayed at the store until ten o'clock at night and then he came to the Shepard house.

John Shepard waited for his coming. Kate waited. John wondered if he was going to study with her. John would be upstairs in his room. He would be in bed with his light out.

John had become neat. When he went to bed at night, he had always just let his clothes lie on the floor, but now he folded his pants. There was a small chest of drawers and he put socks in a drawer and his shoes under the bed. 'There isn't any light, but a man might as well learn to be neat,' he thought. Kate had got him some pajamas to wear. She said, 'Pa, you'd better put these on at night.' She said that men in town wore them. He said he'd never heard of any such thing.

'It's what the man does where I work,' she said.

'All right,' he said.

And Kate had got so she wished she didn't have to work as a servant. She told her father about that. 'It isn't such hard work, but it's being a servant. They look down on you,' she said.

She said she wished she could get some other work. 'Of course,' she said, 'if I was working, say now in a store, I wouldn't be having clothes and things given to me.' She said she was glad Wave didn't have to be a servant. She said she was determined Wave shouldn't be one. When she got to be a school-teacher, she was going to save her money. She had a plan. She and Wave would have a shop. She thought sometimes it would be a millinery shop and at other times she thought it would be a dressmaking shop.

She thought it would be better even than being a school-teacher. She and Wave could be together. 'You wouldn't have to work so hard, Pa,' she said.

John Shepard said nothing. When she talked like that, dragging Wave in, he kept still. 'To hell with Wave,' he thought, but he didn't say it.

He had to stand and listen to Kate talk. It was Wave this and Wave that. Kate was worried because she thought that, because she had to work as a servant, people would look down on them.

When Wave didn't do a damn thing, just loafed about the house, didn't go to school to improve herself, spent all her time fussing with her clothes and her hair, Kate didn't complain.

'Ain't she got nice hair! Ain't it soft! Ain't it pretty!' Kate said.

When she went on about Wave sometimes John Shepard could hardly stand it. He had to clinch his fist. He had to stand and listen. When, in the evening, after the young fellow came to room in the house and Wave wasn't at home . . . she had a date . . . she wasn't there . . . and John was standing by the door, talking to Kate, who was by the kitchen table, sitting there, her schoolbooks on the table, her lamp on the table, and John was having a little talk with Kate and it got on Wave, he just waited, saying nothing until she got through. Then he said, 'Good night.'

'I guess you want to study. I guess I'll say good night,' he said.

He went upstairs. He got into bed. He didn't sleep.

He wondered if Ben Hurd, when he came, would stop and talk maybe with Kate. He thought, 'I'll bet Wave don't get him.'

'I'll bet he's got more sense than to fool with her,' he thought.

'He looks to me like a sensible young fellow,' he thought.

'They'd make a nice couple,' he thought. Sometimes when Ben Hurd came after ten, and Wave wasn't at home and Kate was down there waiting up . . . no matter how late it was she always stayed up until Wave came . . . she and Ben Hurd would talk a little.

They didn't much at first because the young fellow was shy and Kate was shy, but then they did, more and more.

A little more and a little more. Not studying together as John Shepard had thought maybe they would, but just talking.

Like, 'How do you like it here in town?' or, 'How do you like it working in a store?'

It was a drygoods store. It was a kind of general store. It was owned by a Jew. He didn't have just the one store. He had different stores in different towns.

He came and he went away. Ben Hurd told Kate about the store. He stood by the door downstairs, just as John did himself when he talked to Kate.

'Won't you sit down?' Kate said. She offered him things.

'Won't you have a cup of coffee? I'll make you some.

'Won't you have a glass of milk?'

She offered him a piece of pie. 'I'll bet you're hungry.' She bragged about the pie. She said Wave made it. She'd begin telling him about Wave, what good pies she could make, what good cake, what good fudge.

There'd be some of her fudge, in a dish on the table downstairs. 'Won't you have some?' Kate would say to young Ben Hurd. 'I don't care if I do,' he'd say. He'd go over to where she was and get a piece, but he wouldn't sit down.

'I got to get upstairs,' the young fellow would say to Kate and, instead of sitting awhile, down there with her, he'd come on up. He'd go through John Shepard's room and into his own room.

He'd light his lamp in there. He'd study awhile and then he'd write.

'What the hell's he writing?' John Shepard wondered. The young fellow, Ben Hurd, would write and write. He'd be leaning over his desk. Maybe Wave would come home and she and Kate would go to bed. They'd laugh and talk. Wave would be telling Kate about some man. 'He got pretty gay,' she'd say. She'd swear sometimes.

Sometimes the young fellow, in the room up there, had left his door a little open. Wave called some man she had been out with a son-of-a-bitch.

'The son-of-a-bitch thought he could get me.' She laughed when she said it. It made John Shepard furious. 'I'll bet he can hear,' thought he. It made him mad that, when Wave spoke in this way, Kate didn't mind. 'He'll think Kate's like Wave is,' thought he.

He was glad the young fellow had a job, had to work. If he was around the house when Wave was at home, very likely she'd get him. She'd rope him in. She'd do it just to show she could. Once or twice, after the young man came to room in the house and when he had come upstairs and was in his room . . . but not in bed . . . sitting in there and writing like he did . . . the door into John's room maybe a little open . . . no door downstairs, at the foot of the stairs . . . Wave coming home, talking down there . . . Sometimes she'd ask . . .

'What's this young fellow like?' she asked.

'Is he a live wire or is he dead on his feet?' she asked.

She'd say he looked to her like a goody-goody.

'Why don't you find out about him?' she'd ask Kate.

She'd go on like that, maybe saying that, if Kate didn't want him, maybe she'd take a whirl at him herself.

'Hush. Be careful. He's up there. He'll hear,' Kate would say, but Wave didn't seem to care. She'd go right on.

'He's yours. You saw him first. I don't want to cut in on you,' Wave would say, and then she'd laugh and Kate would laugh, and if the door to the young man's room was even a little open and a streak of light from his lamp falling into John's room, John Shepard would silently get out of bed and shut the door.

He went up into the main street of the town. It was after dark and Wave was at home. He had run out of tobacco for his pipe, and wasn't in a very good mood. He had been sitting at the supper table alone. Kate had got his supper and had put it on the back of the stove. She had set the table. He had to get his own supper, off the stove, and put it on the table.

It had made him sore because Wave was right there. She was in the girls' bedroom.

'I suppose she's dolling up,' he had thought. There would be some man coming for her. 'It gets so that my food doesn't do me any good. I get so I can't digest it,' he thought.

He hadn't anyone to say such things to. 'If a man can talk things over with another man he don't mind so much,' he thought. He had thought that a lot of times since he had been living in town . . .

He had been remembering when he used to work in the woods, most of the time with just that one other man, George Russell.

A man likes to talk about his work. On the section, where John worked after he came to town, there were two Italians. There was a Negro. There was a German.

The foreman was a silent man. On lots of days, except to tell the men what to do, he never said a word. He was a man who didn't believe in getting too friendly with men working for him. You were out in the open. You were on the railroad. You didn't hear nice sounds, far off, like in the woods.

In the woods it was almost like in church. There was a something solemn. There was a close feeling you had with your pardner. When you got ahead of the knot bumpers, you could sit down, have a pipe with him. You spoke about other times, when you were a young fellow, what you did, things you felt.

You talked about your wives and your families. You told about how it was in another camp where you had worked, before you worked with George . . .

On the main street he went into the drug store that kept his brand of tobacco. Some young town boys and girls were sitting in the store, in some little booths, open at the side. There was a girl with her legs crossed, her dress, he thought, pulled pretty far up. There was a man sitting with her and they were having some kind of a drink.

The girl had made him think again of Wave. She probably came into that place with men, sat in there showing herself off as she did sitting on the porch at home. He went out of the drug store . . . and ran into George Russell coming along the street.

There was a gladness. There was a jumping of the heart.

'Why, hello!

'Well, I'm damned. It's you. Hello, John.'

They went walking along together. George Russell was in town to see his oldest boy off on a train.

'He just left, ten minutes ago.'

He was proud. Right away he began telling John about his son.

'Yep,' he said, 'he's going to go to college. He's been a good boy. He's saved up his money.'

He was boy crazy about books. He was smart. He hadn't enough money to pay his way through college, but he was going to start.

He figured maybe he could work his way through, when he got a start.

He wanted to be a lawyer.

I'll bet he makes it too. I'll just bet he does,' George said.

The two men walked along.

'How do you like it in town, John?'

'I don't like it. I did it on account of my girls. Where you staying, George?'

George was staying in a little hotel on a side street and the two went there.

John was ashamed. 'Hell, I'd like to have you at the house, but we ain't got no bed.'

George said he had intended looking John up. 'I didn't rightly know where you live. I was going to ask,' he said.

John thought, 'Ain't it hell I can't ask him to come? I ought to ask him to come stay at my house. But hell, who'd cook for him?' he thought. 'Not Wave. She'd let him starve,' he thought. 'Or sit him down maybe to a cold picked-up supper while she went hell-catting around, riding with men in automobiles, sitting in drug stores with men.'

The two sat in some chairs on the porch before the hotel where George was staying, right across from the station of the railroad on which John worked. George said he knew the young fellow who was rooming in John's house. He was a good boy. He was all right. He thought maybe John knew his mother, but John said he didn't. He hadn't lived near the mill, he had lived on his farm. 'That's right,' George said. He talked about his boys. Two of them were all right and good steady boys, but the youngest one he thought wasn't much good. He said the boy was lazy. 'And he's a damn little liar.' He couldn't account for the boy. He wasn't like George himself and he wasn't like his mother.

The two men talked until quite late, and when George had got through bragging about his son who had gone away to college, John Shepard bragged up his Kate. He wasn't going to say anything about Wave, but then suddenly he did. He told everything, how she was everlasting chasing around with men, how she wouldn't do any work about the house, how she put it all on Kate.

'I'd like to fan her behind. I would, too, if it wasn't for Kate. I don't understand why Kate's like she is about Wave. She takes everything from her. I don't understand it,' he said.

He was thinking how much better it must be to have boys than just girls. 'You just can't understand a girl,' he thought. But he thought, anyway, that George had one boy who wasn't much good. But George was talking about the woods. He was going back to his job in the early morning. There had been a big boundary he and George had worked on together, but now, George said, it was almost cleaned up. George had said he reckoned, pretty soon, he'd be in another camp. 'There isn't much big timber left,' George had said. 'Pretty soon,' George said, 'there'd only be little pickerwood mills.' George had said he wasn't worried. He reckoned his oldest son would get to be a lawyer. He was a good boy. He'd take care of George.

'I don't mean I'd want to go and live with him, not after he gets married.' What George meant was that his son, when he had got to be a lawyer, would maybe, every month, send his father some money.

John didn't start home till nearly eleven. He was a little excited, felt it had done him good to have the talk with his friend. He didn't go right home. Ever since he had come to live in town he had been pretty lonely, but now he felt as he used to feel, when as a young fellow he went off to town with other young lumbermen on a Saturday night. He walked around. He was in quiet residential streets. He was down by the railroad. He was by a dark warehouse. There was a man in there, in his shirt-sleeves, under a light, leaning over a desk. He seemed to be writing. Lots of nights Ben Hurd in his room in the Shepard house also wrote that way under the lighted lamp. Some people worked like that over books, in a warehouse, one studying to be a school-teacher, another to be a lawyer like George Russell's boy. Some of them got rich. They lived in big houses. He thought maybe Ben Hurd and his Kate would get married and be like that.

'I wouldn't want to be like that myself,' he thought. 'I'd rather be a workingman, in a lumber camp, or anyway just go on, until I get too old, just working.'

'But a man does get old,' he thought that night as he walked through streets and past houses. Once he found himself again in front of the little hotel where he had sat and talked with George Russell.

'He don't want to live with them when he's old,' he thought, his mind running on George Russell's boy, grown to be a lawyer and married, George grown old, not able to work any longer, and then on young Ben Hurd, married to his Kate, gotten to be a business man, maybe, owning a warehouse, or a store, or maybe being a lawyer, like George's boy.

He supposed maybe his Wave might get married too. 'If she does, I pity the man. I pity him,' he thought.

He decided he'd better be home. He went through dark streets. 'It must be past midnight,' he thought.

He went along his own street. There was a light in his house, in the kitchen of his house.

He got off the sidewalk. He got into the road. He didn't know afterwards why he did it.

He could see there was a light in the kitchen of his house. He went past in the dusty road. The street ended in the black swamp, but it was summer and the swamp was almost dried up. He went through it. He got into his own gravelly back yard.

He could hear voices.

'It's Wave,' he thought.

He thought, 'She's sitting on the porch. She's got a man out there. Goddam her,' he thought.

He went silently up to the kitchen window and looked in. Kate was sitting in there. She had her book open, but she wasn't studying.

She was crying. She was crying silently, as he once had done, lying under a hedge, by a road, near a house, where there was a young girl sitting with two old people on a porch.

There was a man's voice on the porch. Wave was out there. John went into the shed that was back of his house. When he was in the shed he could see through a crack.

There was light come out from Kate's lamp onto the porch. Young Ben Hurd was there. He was sitting there with Wave. They were sitting close. He had his arm around Wave.

He must have done something with his hand.

'Now you quit,' she said.

She called him a 'smarty.'

'You quit it, smarty,' she said, and then she laughed.

She moved a little away from him. She put her legs up. The way she was sitting, the light coming out from the kitchen, through an open door, and the way young Ben Hurd was sitting, he could see plenty, all right.

'Goddam! She's showing him all she's got,' her father thought.

He felt frozen. He felt cold. He just stood.

And then she began to sing. Her voice was like that of the girl on the porch of another house when he was young. There was the same clearness, the same strange sweetness.

There was tenderness. There was something like a bird singing.

It was something he couldn't stand, that had always made him furious.

She sang, and then she stopped. Ben Hurd tried to kiss her, but she wouldn't let him. She stood by a post. Her soft mass of hair had slipped down. They talked in low tones. 'Good night,' she said. She made him go away. She kept saying, 'Good night.'

She pushed him away, made him go away.

He went upstairs. John Shepard heard him go up the stairs.

Wave just sat on the porch. She put her legs up again. She sang again and John Shepard rushed out of the shed.

He ran to where she was. He got his hand on her throat. He choked her.

She struggled, but he had her down on the floor of the porch. She scratched his face. She kicked him, but he fanned her behind.

He fanned her behind with his open hand. He had her dress up. His palm struck her flesh. He fanned it hard. He kept fanning it. His hand pressed hard on her throat. He had her, she could not make a sound.

'By God, I'd 'a' killed her, I guess I'd 'a' choked her to death, if it hadn't been for Kate.'

Kate had come running out. She had begun hitting him with her fist. She kept pleading. She didn't plead loud. She didn't want Ben Hurd to hear.

Ben was upstairs. He remained silent.

Kate's voice was far off. It was like in a dream. It was far off and then it got a little nearer.

It came in to him. His mind was a house and the door of the house was closed. It came open. Kate's voice pleading and pleading made it come open. He let go of Wave's throat. He quit fanning her flesh. She was very white, lying on the porch, in the light from Kate's lamp.

'Maybe she's dead,' he thought, and he went away. He went into the gravelly back yard. He sat down out there. His head ached and his back hurt.

He could see through a window into the kitchen. He didn't know how long it was, but he saw Kate in there.

He saw Wave. She wasn't dead.

'I didn't kill her, goddam it. I didn't kill her,' he thought. He sat a long time, his head aching and his back hurting.

'I guess they're going to bed,' he thought.

'I'll bet they ain't laughing or talking now,' he thought.

He sat and sat and then he went to bed himself. He went upstairs through their room.

'I got to be quiet,' he thought. That young Ben Hurd was in his room. 'I'm glad I don't snore when I sleep,' he thought. Ben Hurd's door was a little open and he went softly and silently and closed it. He got into bed. He saw the sky through a window in his room. He saw the stars. He wanted to cry, but he didn't. He just stayed still, looking at the stars and wishing his head would quit aching and his back quit hurting, until presently he heard his two daughters in their room downstairs.

They were laughing and talking. They talked in low tones and then they laughed. There was something incomprehensible. His head didn't quit aching and his back didn't quit hurting. They ached and they hurt worse than ever. He thought he wouldn't get any sleep.

'I'll bet I don't,' he thought. 'I'll be tired tomorrow.' He thought of the men in the woods. He wished he was like George Russell, who'd had boys. Girls were something you couldn't understand.

The sound of the whispering continued. Girls were something you couldn't understand. There was something . . . it was hidden from you. How strange it was!

VIII. FANTASY AND SYMBOL

An Ohio Pagan
The Man With a Scar
River Journey

An Ohio Pagan

Tom Edwards was a Welshman, born in Northern Ohio, and a descendant of that Thomas Edwards, the Welsh poet, who was called, in his own time and country, Twn O'r Nant — which in our own tongue means, 'Tom of the dingle or vale.'

The first Thomas Edwards was a gigantic figure in the history of the spiritual life of the Welsh. Not only did he write many stirring interludes concerning life, death, earth, fire, and water, but as a man he was a true brother to the elements and to all the passions of his sturdy and musical race. He sang beautifully, but he also played stoutly and beautifully the part of a man. There is a wonderful tale, told in Wales and written into a book by the poet himself, of how he, with a team of horses, once moved a great ship out of the land into the sea, after three hundred Welshmen had failed at the task. Also he taught Welsh woodsmen the secret of the crane and pulley for lifting great logs in the forests, and once he fought to the point of death the bully of the countryside, a man known over a great part of Wales as 'The Cruel Fighter.' Tom Edwards, the descendant of this man, was born in Ohio near my own native town of Bidwell. His name was not Edwards, but as his father was dead when he was born, his mother gave him the old poet's name out of pride in having such blood in her veins. Then when the boy was six his mother died also and the man for whom both his mother and father had worked, a sporting farmer named Harry Whitehead, took the boy into his own house to live.

They were gigantic people, the Whiteheads. Harry himself weighed two hundred and seventy pounds and his wife twenty pounds more. About the time he took young Tom to live with him, the farmer became interested in the racing of horses, moved off his farms, of which he had three, and came to live in our town.

In the town of Bidwell there was an old frame building that had once been a factory for the making of barrel staves, but that had stood for years vacant, staring with windowless eyes into the streets, and Harry bought it at a low price and transformed it into a splendid stable with a board floor and two long rows of box-stalls. At a sale of blooded horses held in the city of Cleveland, he bought twenty young colts, all of the trotting strain, and set up as a trainer of race-horses.

Among the colts thus brought to our town was one great black fellow named Bucephalus. Harry got the name from John Telfer, our town poetry lover. It was the name of the mighty horse of a mighty man,' Telfer said, and that satisfied Harry.

Young Tom was told off to be the special guardian and caretaker of Bucephalus, and the black stallion, who had in him the mighty blood of the Tennessee Patchins, quickly became the pride of the stables. He was in his nature a great ugly-tempered beast, as given to whims and notions as an opera star, and from the very first began to make trouble. Within a year no one but Harry Whitehead himself and the boy Tom dared go into his stall. The methods of the two people with the great horse were entirely different but equally effective. Once big Harry turned the stallion loose on the floor of the stable, closed all the doors, and with a cruel long whip in his hand, went in to conquer or to be conquered. He came out victorious and ever after the horse behaved when he was about.

The boy's method was different. He loved Bucephalus and the wicked animal loved him. Tom slept on a cot in the barn, and day or night, even when there were mares about, walked into Bucephalus' box-stall without fear. When the stallion was in temper, he sometimes turned at the boy's entrance and with a snort sent his iron-shod heels banging against the sides of the stall, but Tom laughed and, putting a simple rope halter over the horse's head, led him forth to be cleaned or hitched to a cart for his morning's jog on our town's half-mile race-track. A sight it was to see the boy with the blood of Twn O'r Nant in his veins leading by the nose Bucephalus of the royal blood of the Patchens.

When he was six years old, the horse Bucephalus went forth to race and conquer at the great spring race meeting at Columbus, Ohio. He won two heats of the trotting free-for-all — the great race of the meeting — with heavy Harry in the sulky, and then faltered. A gelding named Light o' the Orient beat him in the next heat. Tom, then a lad of sixteen, was put into the sulky and the two of them, horse and boy, fought out a royal battle with the gelding and a little bay mare, that hadn't been heard from before, but that suddenly developed a whirlwind burst of speed.

The big stallion and the slender boy won. From amid a mob of cursing, shouting, whip-slashing men a black horse shot out and a pale boy, leaning far forward, called and murmured to him. 'Go on, boy! Go, boy! Go, boy!' the lad's voice had called over and over all through the race. Bucephalus got a record of 2.06¼, and Tom Edwards became a newspaper hero. His picture was in the Cleveland *Leader* and the Cincinnati *Enquirer,* and when he came back to Bidwell we other boys fairly wept in our envy of him.

Then it was, however, that Tom Edwards fell down from his high place. There he was, a tall boy, almost of man's stature and, except for a few months during the winters when he lived on the Whitehead farms, and between his sixth and thirteenth years, when he had attended a country school and had learned to read and write and do sums, he was without education. And now, during that very fall of the year of his triumph at Columbus, the Bidwell truant officer, a thin man with white hair, who was also superintendent of the Baptist Sunday School, came one afternoon to the Whitehead stables and told him that if he did not begin going to school both he and his employer would get into serious trouble.

Harry Whitehead was furious and so was Tom. There he was, a great tall slender fellow who had been with race-horses to the fairs all over northern Ohio and Indiana, during that very fall, and who had just come home from the journey during which he had driven the winner in the free-for-all trot at a Grand Circuit meeting and had given Bucephalus a mark of 2.06¼.

Was such a fellow to go sit in a schoolroom, with a silly schoolbook in his hand, reading of the affairs of the men who dealt in butter, eggs, potatoes, and apples, and whose unnecessarily complicated business life the children were asked to unravel — was such a fellow to go sit in a room, under the eyes of a woman teacher, and in the company of boys half his age and with none of his wide experience of life?

It was a hard thought and Tom took it hard. The law was all right, Harry Whitehead said, and was intended to keep no-account kids off the streets, but what it had to do with himself Tom couldn't make out. When the truant officer had gone and Tom was left alone in the stable with his employer, the man and boy stood for a long time glumly staring at each other. It was all right to be educated, but Tom felt he had book education enough. He could read, write, and do sums, and what other book-training did a horseman need? As for books, they were all right for rainy evenings when there were no men sitting by the stable door and talking of horses and races. And also when one went to the races in a strange town and arrived, perhaps on Sunday, and the races did not begin until the following Wednesday — it was all right then to have a book in the chest with the horse blankets. When the weather was fine and the work was all done on a fine fall afternoon, and the other swipes, both niggers and whites, had gone off to town, one could take a book out under a tree and read of life in faraway places that was as strange and almost as fascinating as one's own life. Tom had read *Robinson Crusoe, Uncle Tom's Cabin,* and *Tales from the Bible,* all of which he had found in the Whitehead house, and Jacob Friedman, the school superintendent at Bidwell, who had a fancy for horses, had loaned him other books that he intended reading during the coming winter. They were in his chest — one called *Gulliver's Travels* and the other *Moll Flanders.*

And now the law said he must give up being a horseman and go every day to a school and do little foolish sums, he who had already proven himself a man. What other schoolboy knew what he did about life? Had he not seen and spoken to several of the greatest men of this world, men who had driven horses to beat world records, and did they not respect him? When he became a driver of racehorses, such men as Pop Geers, Walter Cox, John Splan, Murphy, and the others would not ask him what books he had read, or how many feet make a rod and how many rods in a mile. In the race at Columbus, where he had won his spurs as a driver, he had already proven that life had given him the kind of education he needed. The driver of the gelding, Light o' the Orient, had tried to bluff him in that third heat and had not succeeded. He was a big man with a black mustache and had lost one eye so that he looked fierce and ugly, and when the two horses were fighting it out, neck and neck, up the back stretch, and when Tom was tooling Bucephalus smoothly and surely to the front, the older man turned in his sulky to glare at him. 'You damned little whipper-snapper,' he yelled, 'I'll knock you out of your sulky if you don't take back.'

He had yelled that at Tom and then had struck at the boy with the butt of his whip — not intending actually to hit him perhaps, but just missing the boy's head, and Tom had kept his eyes steadily on his own horse, had held him smoothly in his stride and at the upper turn, at just the right moment, had begun to pull out in front.

Later he hadn't even told Harry Whitehead of the incident, and that fact, too, he felt vaguely, had something to do with his qualifications as a man.

And now they were going to put him into a school with the kids. He was at work on the stable floor, rubbing the legs of a trim-looking colt, and Bucephalus was in his stall waiting to be taken to a late fall meeting at Indianapolis on the following Monday, when the blow fell. Harry Whitehead walked back and forth swearing at the two men who were loafing in chairs at the stable door. 'Do you call that law, eh, robbing a kid of the chance Tom's got?' he asked, shaking a riding whip under their noses. 'I never see such a law. What I say is, Dod blast such a law.'

Tom took the colt back to its place and went into Bucephalus' box-stall. The stallion was in one of his gentle moods and turned to have his nose rubbed, but Tom went and buried his face against the great black neck and for a long time stood thus, trembling. He had thought perhaps Harry would let him drive Bucephalus in all his races another season and now that was all to come to an end and he was to be pitched back into childhood, to be made just a kid in school. 'I won't do it,' he decided suddenly and a dogged light came into his eyes. His future as a driver of race-horses might have to be sacrificed, but that didn't matter so much as the humiliation of this other, and he decided he would say nothing to Harry Whitehead or his wife, but would make his own move.

'I'll get out of here. Before they get me into that school, I'll skip out of town,' he told himself as his hand crept up and fondled the soft nose of Bucephalus, the son royal of the Patchens.

Tom left Bidwell during the night, going east on a freight train, and no one there ever saw him again. During that winter he lived in the city of Cleveland, where he got work driving a milk wagon in a district where factory workers lived.

Then spring came again and with it the memory of other springs — of thunder-showers rolling over fields of wheat, just appearing, green and vivid, out of the black ground — of the sweet smell of new-plowed fields, and most of all the smell and sound of animals about barns at the Whitehead farms north of Bidwell. How sharply he remembered those days on the farms and the days later when he lived in Bidwell, slept in the stables and went each morning to jog race-horses and young colts round and round the half-mile race-track at the fairgrounds at Bidwell!

That was a life! Round and round the track they went, young colthood and young manhood together, not thinking but carrying life very keenly within themselves and feeling tremendously. The colts' legs were to be hardened and their wind made sound and for the boy long hours were to be spent in a kind of dream-world, and life lived in the company of something fine, courageous, filled with a terrible, waiting surge of life. At the fairgrounds, away at the town's edge, tall grass grew in the enclosure inside the track and there were trees from which came the voices of squirrels, chattering and scolding, accompanied by the call of nesting birds and, down below on the ground, by the song of bees visiting early blossoms and of insects hidden away in the grass.

How different the life of the city streets in the springtime! To Tom it was in a way fetid and foul. For months he had been living in a boarding house with some six, and often eight or ten, other young fellows, in narrow rooms above a foul street. The young fellows were unmarried and made good wages, and on the winter evenings and on Sundays they dressed in good clothes and went forth, to return later, half drunk, to sit for long hours boasting and talking loudly in the rooms. Because he was shy, often lonely and sometimes startled and frightened by what he saw and heard in the city, the others would have nothing to do with Tom. They felt a kind of contempt for him, looked upon him as a 'rube,' and in the late afternoon when his work was done he often went for long walks alone in grim streets of workingmen's houses, breathing the smoke-laden air and listening to the roar and clatter of machinery in great factories. At other times and immediately after the evening meal, he went off to his room and to bed, half sick with fear and with some strange nameless dread of the life about him.

And so in the early summer of his seventeenth year Tom left the city and, going back into his own northern Ohio lake country, found work with a man named John Bottsford who owned a threshing outfit and worked among the farmers of Erie County, Ohio. The slender boy, who had urged Bucephalus to his greatest victory and had driven him the fastest mile of his career, had become a tall strong fellow with heavy features, brown eyes, and big nerveless hands — but in spite of his apparent heaviness there was something tremendously alive in him. He now drove a team of plodding gray farm horses and it was his job to keep the threshing engine supplied with water and fuel and to haul the threshed grain out of the fields and into farmers' barns.

The thresherman Bottsford was a broad-shouldered, powerful old man of sixty and had, besides Tom, three grown sons in his employ. He had been a farmer, working on rented land, all his life and had saved some money, with which he had bought the threshing outfit, and all day the five men worked like driven slaves and at night slept in the hay in the farmers' barns. It was rainy that season in the lake country and at the beginning of the time of threshing things did not go very well for Bottsford.

The old threshman was worried. The threshing venture had taken all of his money and he had a dread of going into debt, and, as he was a deeply religious man, at night when he thought the others asleep, he crawled out of the hayloft and went down onto the barn floor to pray.

Something happened to Tom and for the first time in his life he began to think about life and its meaning. He was in the country, that he loved, in the yellow sun-washed fields, far from the dreaded noises and dirt of city life, and here was a man, of his own type, in some deep way a brother to himself, who was continuously crying out to some power outside himself, some power that was in the sun, in the clouds, in the roaring thunder that accompanied the summer rains — that was in these things and that at the same time controlled all these things.

The young threshing apprentice was impressed. Throughout the rainy days, when no work could be done, he wandered about and waited for night, and then, when they all had gone into the barn loft and the others prepared to sleep, he stayed awake to think and listen. He thought of God and of the possibilities of God's part in the affairs of men. The thresherman's youngest son, a fat jolly fellow, lay beside him and, for a time after they had crawled into the hay, the two boys whispered and laughed together. The fat boy's skin was sensitive and the dry broken ends of grass stalks crept down under his clothes and tickled him. He giggled and twisted about, wriggling and kicking, and Tom looked at him and laughed also. The thoughts of God went out of his mind.

In the barn all became quiet and when it rained a low drumming sound went on overhead. Tom could hear the horses and cattle, down below, moving about. The smells were all delicious smells. The smell of the cows in particular awoke something heady in him. It was as though he had been drinking strong wine. Every part of his body seemed alive. The two older boys, who like their father had serious natures, lay with their feet buried in the hay. They lay very still and a warm musty smell arose from their clothes, that were full of the sweat of toil. Presently the bearded old thresherman, who slept off by himself, arose cautiously and walked across the hay in his stockinged feet. He went down a ladder to the floor below, and Tom listened eagerly. The fat boy snored, but he was quite sure that the older boys were awake like himself. Every sound from below was magnified. He heard a horse stamp on the barn floor and a cow rub her horns against a feed-box. The old thresherman prayed fervently, calling on the name of Jesus to help him out of his difficulty. Tom could not hear all his words, but some of them came to him quite clearly and one group of words ran like a refrain through the thresherman's prayer. 'Gentle Jesus,' he cried, 'send the good days. Let the good days come quickly. Look out over the land. Send us the fair warm days.'

Came the warm fair days and Tom wondered. Late every morning, after the sun had marched far up into the sky and after the machines were set by a great pile of wheat bundles, he drove his tank wagon off to be filled at some distant creek or at a pond. Sometimes he was compelled to drive two or three miles to the lake. Dust gathered in the roads and the horses plodded along. He passed through a grove of trees and went down a lane and into a small valley where there was a spring, and he thought of the old man's words, uttered in the silence and the darkness of the barns. He made himself a figure of Jesus as a young god walking about over the land. The young god went through the lanes and through the shaded covered places. The feet of the horses came down with a thump in the dust of the road and there was an echoing thump far away in the wood. Tom leaned forward and listened and his cheeks became a little pale. He was no longer the growing man, but had become again the fine and sensitive boy who had driven Bucephalus through a mob of angry, determined men to victory. For the first time the blood of the old poet Twn O'r Nant awoke in him.

The water boy for the threshing crew rode the horse Pegasus down through the lanes back of the farmhouses in Erie County, Ohio, to the creeks where the threshing tanks must be filled. Beside him on the soft earth in the forest walked the young god Jesus. At the creek Pegasus, born of the springs of Ocean, stamped on the ground. The plodding farm horses stopped. With a dazed look in his eyes Tom Edwards arose from the wagon seat and prepared his hose and pump for filling the tank. The god Jesus walked away over the land, and with a wave of his hand summoned the smiling days.

A light came into Tom Edwards's eyes and grace seemed to come also into his heavy maturing body. New impulses came to him. As the threshing crew went about, over the roads and through the villages, from farm to farm, women and young girls looked at the young man and smiled. Sometimes as he came from the fields to a farmer's barn, with a load of wheat in bags on his wagon, the daughter of the farmer stepped out of the farmhouse and stood looking at him. Tom looked at the woman and hunger crept into his heart and, in the evenings while the thresherman and his sons sat on the ground by the barns and talked of their affairs, he walked nervously about. Making a motion to the fat boy, who was not really interested in the talk of his father and brothers, the two younger men went to walk in the near-by fields and on the roads. Sometimes they stumbled along a country road in the dusk of the evening and came into the lighted streets of a town. Under the store-lights young girls walked about. The two boys stood in the shadows by a building and watched and later, as they went homeward in the darkness, the fat boy expressed what they both felt. They passed through a dark place where the road wound through a wood. In silence the frogs croaked, and birds roosting in the trees were disturbed by their presence and fluttered about. The fat boy wore heavy overalls and his fat legs rubbed against each other. The rough cloth made a queer creaking sound. He spoke passionately. 'I would like to hold a woman, tight, tight, tight,' he said.

One Sunday the thresherman took his entire crew with him to a church. They had been working near a village called Castalia, but did not go into the town, but to a small white frame church that stood amid trees and by a stream at the side of a road, a mile north of the village. They went on Tom's water wagon, from which they had lifted the tank and placed boards for seats. The boy drove the horses.

Many teams were tied in the shade under the trees in a little grove near the church, and strange men — farmers and their sons — stood about in little groups and talked of the season's crops. Although it was hot, a breeze played among the leaves of the trees under which they stood, and back of the church and the grove the stream ran over stones and made a persistent soft murmuring noise that arose above the hum of voices.

In the church Tom sat beside the fat boy, who stared at the country girls as they came in and who, after the sermon began, went to sleep while Tom listened eagerly to the sermon. The minister, an old man, with a beard and a strong sturdy body, looked, he thought, not unlike his employer Bottsford the thresherman.

The minister in the country church talked of that time when Mary Magdalene, the woman who had been taken in adultery, was being stoned by the crowd of men who had forgotten their own sins and when, in the tale the minister told, Jesus approached and rescued the woman Tom's heart thumped with excitement. Then later the minister talked of how Jesus was tempted by the Devil, as he stood on a high place in the mountain, but the boy did not listen. He leaned forward and looked out through a window across fields and the minister's words came to him but in broken sentences. Tom took what was said concerning the temptation on the mountain to mean that Mary had followed Jesus and had offered her body to him, and that afternoon, when he had returned with the others to the farm where they were to begin threshing on the next morning, he called the fat boy aside and asked his opinion.

The two boys walked across a field of wheat stubble and sat down on a log in a grove of trees. It had never occurred to Tom that a man could be tempted by a woman. It had always seemed to him that it must be the other way, that women must always be tempted by men. 'I thought men always asked,' he said, 'and now it seems that women sometimes do the asking. That would be a fine thing if it could happen to us. Don't you think so?'

The two boys arose and walked under the trees and dark shadows began to form on the ground underfoot. Tom burst into words and continually asked questions and the fat boy, who had been often to church and for whom the figure of Jesus had lost most of its reality, felt a little embarrassed. He did not think the subject should be thus freely discussed and when Tom's mind kept playing with the notion of Jesus pursued and tempted by a woman, he grunted his disapproval.

'Do you think he really refused?' Tom asked over and over.

The fat boy tried to explain. 'He had twelve disciples,' he said. 'It couldn't have happened. They were always about. Well, you see, she wouldn't ever have had no chance. Wherever he went they went with him. They were men he was teaching to preach. One of them later betrayed him to soldiers who killed him.'

Tom wondered. 'How did that come about? How could a man like that be betrayed?' he asked.

'By a kiss,' the fat boy replied.

On the evening of the day when Tom Edwards — for the first and last time in his life — went into a church, there was a light shower, the only one that fell upon John Bottsford's threshing crew during the last three months the Welsh boy was with them and the shower in no way interfered with their work. The shower came up suddenly and in a few minutes was gone. As it was Sunday and as there was no work, the men had all gathered in the barn and were looking out through the open barn doors. Two or three men from the farmhouse came and sat with them on boxes and barrels on the barn floor and, as is customary with country people, very little was said. The men took knives out of their pockets and finding little sticks among the rubbish on the barn floor began to whittle, while the old thresherman went restlessly about with his hands in his trouser pockets. Tom, who sat near the door, where an occasional drop of rain was blown against his cheek, alternately looked from his employer to the open country where the rain played over the fields. One of the farmers remarked that a rainy time had come on and that there would be no good threshing weather for several days and, while the thresherman did not answer, Tom saw his lips move and his gray beard bob up and down. He thought the thresherman was protesting, but did not want to protest in words.

As they had gone about the country, many rains had passed to the north, south, and east of the threshing crew and on some days the clouds hung over them all day, but no rain fell and when they had got to a new place they were told it had rained there three days before. Sometimes when they left a farm, Tom stood up on the seat of his water wagon and looked back. He looked across fields to where they had been at work and then looked up into the sky. 'The rain may come now. The threshing is done and the wheat is all in the barn. The rain can now do no harm to our labor,' he thought.

On the Sunday evening when he sat with the men on the floor of the barn, Tom was sure that the shower that had now come would be but a passing affair. He thought his employer must be very close to Jesus, who controlled the affairs of the heavens, and that a long rain would not come because the thresherman did not want it. He fell into a deep reverie and John Bottsford came and stood close beside him. The thresherman put his hand against the door jamb and looked out and Tom could still see the gray beard moving. The man was praying and was so close to himself that his trouser leg touched Tom's hand. Into the boy's mind came the remembrance of how John Bottsford had prayed at night on the barn floor. On that very morning he had prayed. It was just as daylight came and the boy was awakened because, as he crept across the hay to descend the ladder, the old man's foot had touched his hand.

As always Tom had been excited and wanted to hear every word said in the older man's prayers. He lay tense, listening to every sound that came up from below. A faint glow of light came into the hayloft, through a crack in the side of the barn, a rooster crowed and some pigs, housed in a pen near the barn, grunted loudly. They had heard the thresherman moving about and wanted to be fed and their grunting, and the occasional restless movement of a horse or a cow in the stable below, prevented Tom's hearing very distinctly. He, however, made out that his employer was thanking Jesus for the fine weather that had attended them and was protesting that he did not want to be selfish in asking it to continue. 'Jesus,' he said, 'send, if you wish, a little shower on this day when, because of our love for you, we do not work in the fields. Let it be fine tomorrow, but today, after we have come back from the house of worship, let a shower freshen the land.'

As Tom sat on a box near the door of the barn and saw how aptly the words of his employer had been answered by Jesus, he knew that the rain would not last. The man for whom he worked seemed to him so close to the throne of God that he raised the hand, that had been touched by John Bottsford's trouser leg, to his lips and secretly kissed it — and when he looked again out over the fields the clouds were being blown away by a wind and the evening sun was coming out. It seemed to him that the young and beautiful god Jesus must be right at hand, within hearing of his voice. 'He is,' Tom told himself, 'standing behind a tree in the orchard.' The rain stopped and he went silently out of the barn, towards a small apple orchard that lay beside the farmhouse, but when he came to a fence and was about to climb over he stopped. 'If Jesus is there he will not want me to find him,' he thought. As he turned again toward the barn he could see, across a field, a low grass-covered hill. He decided that Jesus was not after all in the orchard. The long slanting rays of the evening sun fell on the crest of the hill and touched with light the grass stalks, heavy with drops of rain and for a moment the hill was crowned as with a crown of jewels. A million tiny drops of water, reflecting the light, made the hilltop sparkle as though set with gems. 'Jesus is there,' muttered the boy. 'He lies on his belly in the grass. He is looking at me over the edge of the hill.'

John Bottsford went with his threshing crew to work for a large farmer named Barton near the town of Sandusky. The threshing season was drawing near an end and the days remained clear, cool, and beautiful. The country into which he now came made a deep impression on Tom's mind and he never forgot the thoughts and experiences that came to him during the last weeks of that summer on the Barton farms.

The traction engine, puffing forth smoke and attracting the excited attention of dogs and children as it rumbled along and pulled the heavy red grain separator, had trailed slowly over miles of road and had come down almost to Lake Erie. Tom, with the fat Bottsford boy sitting beside him on the water wagon, followed the rumbling, puffing engine, and when they came to the new place, where they were to stay for several days, he could see, from the wagon seat, the smoke of the factories in the town of Sandusky rising into the clear morning air.

The man for whom John Bottsford was threshing owned three farms, one on an island in the bay, where he lived, and two on the mainland, and the larger of the mainland farms had great stacks of wheat standing in a field near the barns. The farm was in a wide basin of land, very fertile, through which a creek flowed northward into Sandusky Bay and, besides the stacks of wheat in the basin, other stacks had been made in the upland fields beyond the creek, where a country of low hills began. From these latter fields the waters of the bay could be seen glistening in the bright fall sunlight and steamers went from Sandusky to a pleasure resort called Cedar Point. When the wind blew from the north or west and when the threshing machinery had been stopped at the noon hour, the men, resting with their backs against a strawstack, could hear a band playing on one of the steamers.

Fall came on early that year, and the leaves on the trees in the forests that grew along the roads that ran down through the low creek bottom lands began to turn yellow and red. In the afternoons when Tom went to the creek for water, he walked beside his horses and the dry leaves crackled and snapped underfoot.

As the season had been a prosperous one, Bottsford decided that his youngest son should attend school in town during the fall and winter. He had bought himself a machine for cutting firewood and with his two older sons intended to take up that work. 'The logs will have to be hauled out of the woodlots to where we set up the saws,' he said to Tom. 'You can come with us if you wish.'

The thresherman began to talk to Tom of the value of learning. 'You'd better go to some town yourself this winter. It would be better for you to get into a school,' he said sharply. He grew excited and walked up and down beside the water wagon, on the seat of which Tom sat listening and said that God had given men both minds and bodies and it was wicked to let either decay because of neglect. 'I have watched you,' he said. 'You don't talk very much, but you do plenty of thinking, I guess. Go into the schools. Find out what the books have to say. You don't have to believe when they say things that are lies.'

The Bottsford family lived in a rented house facing a stone road near the town of Bellevue, and the fat boy was to go to that town — a distance of some eighteen miles from where the men were at work — afoot, and on the evening before he set out, he and Tom went out of the barns intending to have a last walk and talk together on the roads.

They went along in the dusk of the fall evening, each thinking his own thoughts, and coming to a bridge that led over the creek in the valley sat on the bridge rail. Tom had little to say, but his companion wanted to talk about women and, when darkness came on, the embarrassment he felt regarding the subject went quite away and he talked boldly and freely. He said that in the town of Bellevue, where he was to live and attend school during the coming winter, he would be sure to get in with a woman. 'I'm not going to be cheated out of that chance,' he declared. He explained that as his father would be away from home when he moved into town, he would be free to pick his own place to board.

The fat boy's imagination became inflamed and he told Tom his plans. 'I won't try to get in with any young girl,' he declared shrewdly. 'That only gets a fellow in a fix. He might have to marry her. I'll go live in a house with a widow, that's what I'll do. And in the evening the two of us will be there alone. We'll begin to talk and I'll keep touching her with my hands. That will get her excited.'

The fat boy jumped to his feet and walked back and forth on the bridge. He was nervous and a little ashamed and wanted to justify what he had said. The thing for which he hungered had, he thought, become a possibility — an act half-achieved. Coming to stand before Tom, he put a hand on his shoulder. 'I'll go into her room at night,' he declared. 'I'll not tell her I'm coming, but will creep in when she is asleep. Then I'll get down on my knees by her bed and I'll kiss her, hard, hard. I'll hold her tight, so she can't get away, and I'll kiss her mouth till she wants what I want. Then I'll stay in her house all winter. No one will know. Even if she won't have me, I'll only have to move, I'm sure to be safe. No one will believe what she says, if she tells on me. I'm not going to be like a boy any more. I'll tell you what — I'm as big as a man and I'm going to do like men do, that's what I am.'

The two young men went back to the barn where they were to sleep on the hay. The rich farmer for whom they were now at work had a large house and provided beds for the thresherman and his two older sons, but the two younger men slept in the barn loft and on the night before had lain under one blanket. After the talk by the bridge, however, Tom did not feel very comfortable and that stout exponent of manhood, the younger Bottsford, was also embarrassed. In the road the young man, whose name was Paul, walked a little ahead of his companion and when they got to the barn, each sought a separate place in the loft. Each wanted to have thoughts into which he did not want the presence of the other to intrude.

For the first time Tom's body burned with eager desire for a female. He lay where he could see out through a crack, in the side of the barn, and at first his thoughts were all about animals. He had brought a horse blanket up from the stable below and crawling under it lay on his side with his eyes close to the crack and thought about the love-making of horses and cattle. Things he had seen in the stables when he worked for Whitehead, the racing man, came back to his mind and a queer animal hunger ran through him so that his legs stiffened. He rolled restlessly about on the hay and for some reason he did not understand his lust took the form of anger and he hated the fat boy. He thought he would like to crawl over the hay and pound his companion's face with his fists. Although he had not seen Paul Bottsford's face when he talked of the widow, he had sensed in him a flavor of triumph. 'He thinks he has got the better of me,' young Edwards thought.

He rolled again to the crack and stared out into the night. There was a new moon and the fields were dimly outlined and clumps of trees, along the road that led into the town of Sandusky, looked like black clouds that had settled down over the land. For some reason the sight of the land, lying dim and quiet under the moon, took all of his anger away and he began to think, not of Paul Bottsford, with hot eager lust in his eyes, creeping into the room of the widow at Bellevue, but of the god Jesus, going up into a mountain with his woman, Mary.

His companion's notion of going into a room where a woman lay sleeping and taking her, as it were unawares, now seemed to him entirely mean and the hot jealous feeling that had turned into anger and hatred went entirely away. He tried to think what the god, who had brought the beautiful days for the threshing, would do with a woman.

Tom's body still burned with desire and his mind wanted to think lascivious thoughts. The moon that had been hidden behind clouds emerged and a wind began to blow. It was still early evening and in the town of Sandusky pleasure-seekers were taking the boat to the resort over the bay and the wind brought to Tom's ears the sound of music, blown over the waters of the bay and down the creek basin. In a grove near the barn the wind swayed gently the branches of young trees and black shadows ran here and there on the ground.

The younger Bottsford had gone to sleep in a distant part of the barn loft, and now began to snore loudly. The tenseness went out of Tom's legs and he prepared to sleep, but before sleeping he muttered, half timidly, certain words, that were half a prayer, half an appeal to some spirit of the night. 'Jesus, bring me a woman,' he whispered.

Outside the barn, in the fields, the wind, becoming a little stronger, picked up bits of straw and blew them about among the hard up-standing stubble and there was a low gentle whispering sound as though the gods were answering his appeal.

Tom went to sleep with his arm under his head and with his eye close to the crack that gave him a view of the moonlit fields, and in his dream the cry from within repeated itself over and over. The mysterious god Jesus had heard and answered the needs of his em-ployer, John Bottsford, and his own need would, he was quite sure, be understood and attended to. 'Bring me a woman. I need her. Jesus, bring me a woman,' he kept whispering into the night, as conscious-ness left him and he slipped away into dreams.

After the youngest of the Bottsfords had departed, a change took place in the nature of Tom's work. The threshing crew had got now into a country of large farms where the wheat had all been brought in from the fields and stacked near the barns and where there was always plenty of water near at hand. Everything was simplified. The separator was pulled in close by the barn door and the threshed grain was carried directly to the bins from the separator. As it was not a part of Tom's work to feed the bundles of grain into the whirling teeth of the separator — this work being done by John Bottsford's two elder sons — there was little for the crew's teamster to do. Sometimes John Bottsford, who was the engineer, departed, going to make arrangements for the next stop, and was gone for a half-day, and at such times Tom, who had picked up some knowledge of the art, ran the engine.

On other days, however, there was nothing at all for him to do and his mind, unoccupied for long hours, began to play him tricks. In the morning, after his team had been fed and cleaned until the gray coats of the old farm horses shone like racers, he went out of the barn and into an orchard. Filling his pockets with ripe apples he went to a fence and leaned over. In a field young colts played about. As he held the apples and called softly, they came timidly forward, stopping in alarm and then running a little forward, until one of them, bolder than the others, ate one of the apples out of his hand.

All through those bright warm clear fall days a restless feeling, it seemed to Tom, ran through everything in nature. In the clumps of woodland still standing on the farms flaming red spread itself out along the limbs of trees and there was one grove of young maple trees, near a barn, that was like a troop of girls, young girls who had walked together down a sloping field, to stop in alarm at seeing the men at work in the barnyard. Tom stood looking at the trees. A slight breeze made them sway gently from side to side. Two horses standing among the trees drew near each other. One nipped the other's neck. They rubbed their heads together.

The crew stopped at another large farm and it was to be their last stop for the season. 'When we have finished this job, we'll go home and get our own fall work done,' Bottsford said. Saturday evening came and the threshermen and his sons took the horses and drove away, going to their own home for the Sunday, and leaving Tom alone. 'We'll be back early, on Monday morning,' the thresherman said as they drove away. Sunday alone among the strange farm people brought a sharp experience to Tom, and when it had passed, he decided he would not wait for the end of the threshing season but a few days off now — but would quit his job and go into the city and surrender to the schools. He remembered his employer's words, 'Find out what the books have to say. You don't have to believe, when they say things that are lies.'

As he walked in lanes, across meadows and upon the hillsides of the farm, also on the shores of Sandusky Bay, that Sunday morning Tom thought almost constantly of his friend the fat fellow, young Paul Bottsford, who had gone to spend the fall and winter at Bellevue, and wondered what his life there might be like. He had himself lived in such a town, in Bidwell, but had rarely left Harry Whitehead's stable. What went on in such a town? What happened at night in the houses of the towns? He remembered Paul's plan for getting into a house alone with a widow and how he was to creep into her room at night, holding her tightly in his arms until she wanted what he wanted. 'I wonder if he will have the nerve. Gee, I wonder if he will have the nerve,' he muttered.

For a long time, ever since Paul had gone away and he had no one with whom he could talk, things had taken on a new aspect in Tom's mind. The rustle of dry leaves underfoot, as he walked in a forest — the playing of shadows over the open face of a field — the murmuring song of insects in the dry grass beside the fences in the lanes — and at night the hushed contented sounds made by the animals in the barns, were no longer so sweet to him. For him no more did the young god Jesus walk beside him, just out of sight behind low hills or down the dry beds of streams. Something within himself that had been sleeping was now awakening. When he returned from walking in the fields on the fall evenings and, thinking of Paul Bottsford alone in the house with the widow at Bellevue, half wishing he were in the same position, he felt ashamed in the presence of the gentle old thresherman, and afterward did not lie awake listening to the older man's prayers. The men who had come from near-by farms to help with the threshing laughed and shouted to each other as they pitched the straw into great stacks or carried the filled bags of grain to the bins, and they had wives and daughters who had come with them and who were now at work in the farmhouse kitchen, from which also laughter came. Girls and women kept coming out at the kitchen door into the barnyard, tall awkward girls, plump, red-cheeked girls, women with worn, thin faces and sagging breasts. All men and women seemed made for each other.

They all laughed and talked together, understood one another. Only he was alone. He only had no one to whom he could feel warm and close, to whom he could draw close.

On the Sunday when the Bottsfords had all gone away, Tom came in from walking all morning in the fields and ate his dinner with many other people in a big farmhouse dining room. In preparation for the threshing days ahead and the feeding of many people, several women had come to spend the day and to help in preparing food. The farmer's daughter, who was married and lived in Sandusky, came with her husband, and three other women, neighbors, came from farms in the neighborhood. Tom did not look at them, but ate his dinner in silence, and as soon as he could manage got out of the house and went to the barns. Going into a long shed, he sat on the tongue of a wagon that from long disuse was covered with dust. Swallows flew back and forth among the rafters overhead and, in an upper corner of the shed where they evidently had a nest, wasps buzzed in the semi-darkness.

The daughter of the farmer, who had come from town, came from the house with a babe in her arms. It was nursing time, and she wanted to escape from the crowded house and, without having seen Tom, she sat on a box near the shed door and opened her dress. Embarrassed and at the same time fascinated by the sight of a woman's breasts, seen through cracks of the wagon box, Tom drew his legs up and his head down and remained concealed until the woman had gone back to the house. Then he went again to the fields and did not go back to the house for the evening meal.

As he walked on that Sunday afternoon, the grandson of the Welsh poet experienced many new sensations. In a way he came to understand that the things Paul had talked of doing and that had, but a short time before, filled him with disgust were now possible to himself also. In the past when he had thought about women there had always been something healthy and animal-like in his lusts, but now they took a new form. The passion that could not find expression through his body went up into his mind and he began to see visions. Women became to him something different from anything else in nature, more desirable than anything else in nature, and at the same time everything in nature became woman. The trees, in the apple orchard by the barn, were like the arms of women. The apples on the trees were round like the breasts of women. They were the breasts of women — and when he had got onto a low hill the contour of the fences that marked the confines of the fields fell into the forms of women's bodies. Even the clouds in the sky did the same thing.

He walked down along a lane to a stream and crossed the stream by a wooden bridge. Then he climbed another hill, the highest place in all that part of the country, and there the fever that possessed him became more active. An odd lassitude crept over him and he lay down in the grass on the hilltop and closed his eyes. For a long time he remained in a hushed, half-sleeping, dreamless state and then opened his eyes again.

Again the forms of women floated before him. To his left the bay was ruffled by a gentle breeze and far over toward the city of Sandusky two sailboats were apparently engaged in a race. The masts of the boats were fully dressed, but on the great stretch of water they seemed to stand still. The bay itself, in Tom's eyes, had taken on the form and shape of a woman's head and body and the two sailboats were the woman's eyes looking at him.

The bay was a woman with her head lying where lay the city of Sandusky. Smoke arose from the stacks of steamers docked at the city's wharves and the smoke formed itself into masses of black hair. Through the farm, where he had come to thresh, ran a stream. It swept down past the foot of the hill on which he lay. The stream was the arm of the woman. Her hand was thrust into the land and the lower part of her body was lost — far down to the north, where the bay became a part of Lake Erie — but her other arm could be seen. It was outlined in the further shore of the bay. Her other arm was drawn up and her hand was pressing against her face. Her form was distorted by pain, but at the same time the giant woman smiled at the boy on the hill. There was something in the smile that was like the smile that had come unconsciously to the lips of the woman who had nursed her child in the shed.

Turning his face away from the bay, Tom looked at the sky. A great white cloud that lay along the southern horizon formed itself into the giant head of a man. Tom watched as the cloud crept slowly across the sky. There was something noble and quieting about the giant's face and his hair, pure white and as thick as wheat in a rich field in June, added to its nobility. Only the face appeared. Below the shoulders there was just a white shapeless mass of clouds.

And then this formless mass began also to change. The face of a giant woman appeared. It pressed upward toward the face of the man. Two arms formed themselves on the man's shoulders and pressed the woman closely. The two faces merged. Something seemed to snap in Tom's brain.

He sat upright and looked neither at the bay nor at the sky. Evening was coming on and soft shadows began to play over the land. Below him lay the farm with its barns and houses and in the field, below the hill on which he was lying, there were two smaller hills that became at once in his eyes the two full breasts of a woman. Two white sheep appeared and stood nibbling the grass on the woman's breasts. They were like babes being suckled. The trees in the orchards near the barns were the woman's hair. An arm of the stream that ran down to the bay, the stream he had crossed on the wooden bridge when he came to the hill, cut across a meadow beyond the two low hills. It widened into a pond and the pond made a mouth for the woman. Her eyes were two black hollows — low spots in a field where hogs had rooted the grass away, looking for roots. Black puddles of water lay in the hollows and they seemed eyes shining invitingly up at him.

This woman also smiled and her smile was now an invitation. Tom got to his feet and hurried away down the hill and, going stealthily past the barns and the house, got into a road. All night he walked under the stars thinking new thoughts. 'I am obsessed with this idea of having a woman. I'd better go to the city and go to school and see if I can make myself fit to have a woman of my own,' he thought. 'I won't sleep tonight, but will wait until tomorrow when Bottsford comes back and then I'll quit and go into the city.' He walked, trying to make plans. Even a good man like John Bottsford had a woman for himself. Could he do that?

The thought was exciting. At the moment it seemed to him that he had only to go into the city, and go to the schools for a time, to become beautiful and to have beautiful women love him. In his half-ecstatic state he forgot the winter months he had spent in the city of Cleveland, and forgot also the grim streets, the long rows of dark prison-like factories and the loneliness of his life in the city. For the moment and as he walked in the dusty roads under the moon, he thought of American towns and cities as places for beautifully satisfying adventures, for all such fellows as himself.

The Man With a Scar

I WAS AN ADVERTISING MAN in Chicago and sat in a room with some half a dozen others. We had met to discuss some matter of grave importance to, say, a maker of plows or automobile tires. The matter was really of no importance to me. The man had come to Chicago with three or four others and we were to discuss methods of increasing his sales. So many thousands of tires made, so many thousands of plows. There were other makers of tires, other makers of plows too. Could we be more persuasive than they, more bold and daring in statement, more foxy and clever, perhaps?

We sat in a room to talk it over, and near me sat a large man with a beard. Someone had told me that he was the treasurer of the plow company, but that had meant little. Now, as he sat there smoking a cigarette and gazing out at a window, I saw, just when his head was slightly turned, that he had a long scar on his cheek, that he had grown the beard to conceal the scar. The talk went on, but I sat fascinated. 'We must develop the trade in the Southwest, that's what we must do,' said a voice from some far-distant place. Pictures had begun to form in my fancy. Besides the voice in the room, other voices were making themselves heard. Old memories had begun to stir.

There was something, a story within me that had been there a long time, but had never been told, and that the scar under the beard had brought to life. What an unfortunate time for the story to begin asserting itself at just that moment! Now I was to think of the promotion of the sale of plows in the newly opened State of Oklahoma and in Texas.

I sat with some six or eight men by a large table in a room and some man was talking. He had been to Texas and knew things I would later have to know when I wrote advertisements for the plow company. I tried to appear attentive. There was a trick I had cultivated for just such occasions. I leaned a little forward and put my head in my hands, as though lost in deep thought. Some of the men in the room had heard that I wrote stories and had therefore concluded that I had a good brain. Americans have always a kind of tenderness for such cheats as I was being at the moment. Now they gave me credit for thinking deeply on the subject of plows, which was what I wanted. One of my employers — he was president of our company and his name was Barton — tried to cover up my obvious inattention. Already he had decided I would have to write the plow company's advertisements, but later he would tell me of all that had been said in the room. He would take me into his office and scold me gently, like a mother speaking to a badly behaved child. 'Of course you didn't hear a blamed word they said, but here is the gist of it. I had to tell that big man with a beard that you were a genius. My God, what lies do I not tell on your account! When the little man with the glasses was speaking of agricultural conditions in Texas, I was afraid that at any moment you might begin to whistle or sing.'

Voices inside the room and voices inside myself too. Was something coming a bit clear at last?

Now my fancy had taken me quite out of the room where the others talked of plows. One night, years before, when I was a young laborer and was beating my way westward on a freight train, a brakeman had succeeded in throwing me off the train in an Indiana town. I had remembered the place long afterward because of my embarrassment — walking about among people in my dirty torn clothes and with my dirty hands and face. However, I had a little money, and after I had walked through the town to a country road, I found a creek and bathed. Then I went back to town to a restaurant and bought food.

It was a Saturday evening and the streets were filled with people. After it grew dark, my torn clothes were not so much in evidence and by a street light near a church on a side street a girl smiled at me. Half-undecided as to whether or not I had better try to follow and pick up an acquaintance, I stood for some moments by a tree staring after her. Then I bethought me that, when she had seen me more closely and had seen the condition of my clothes, she would in any event have nothing to do with me.

As is natural to man, under such circumstances, I told myself I did not want her, anyway, and went off down another street.

I came to a bridge and stood for a time looking down into the water and then went across the bridge along a road and into a field where long grass grew. It was a summer night and I was sleepy, but after I had slept, perhaps for several hours, I was awakened by something going on in the field and within a few feet of me.

The field was small and two houses stood facing it, the one near where I lay in a fence corner and the other a few hundred yards away. When I had come into the field, lights were lighted in both houses, but now they were both dark and before me — some ten paces away — three men were struggling silently while near them stood a woman who held her hands over her face and who sobbed, not loudly, but with a kind of low, wailing cry. There was something, dimly seen, something white, lying on the ground near the woman, and suddenly by a kind of flash of intuition I understood what had happened. The white thing on the ground was a woman's garment.

The three men were struggling desperately, and even in the dim light it was evident that two of them were trying to overcome the third. He was the woman's lover and lived in the house at the end of the path that crossed the field and the two others were her brothers. They had gone into the town for the evening and had come home late and, as they were walking silently across the grass in the field, they had stumbled upon the love-makers and in a flash there was the impulse to kill their sister's lover. Perhaps they felt the honor of their house had been destroyed.

And now one of them had got a knife out of his pocket and had slashed at the lover, laying his cheek open, and they might have killed the man as the woman and I watched trembling, but at that moment he got away and ran across the field toward his own house, followed by the others.

I was left alone in the field with the woman — we were within a few feet of each other — and for a long time she did not move. 'After all, I am not a man of action. I am a recorder of things, a teller of tales.' It was somewhat thus I excused myself for not coming to the lover's aid, as I lay perfectly still in the fence corner, looking and listening. The woman continued to sob, and now, from across the dark field, there was a shout. The lover had not succeeded in getting into his own house, was really but a step ahead of his pursuers, and perhaps did not dare risk trying to open a door. He ran back across the field, dodging here and there, and passing near us crossed the bridge into the road that led to town. The woman in the field began calling, evidently to her two brothers, but they paid no attention. 'John! Fred!' she called between her sobs. 'Stop! Stop!'

And now again all was silent in the field and I could hear the rapid steps of the three running men in the dusty road in the distance.

Then lights appeared in both the houses facing the field and the woman went into the house near me, still sobbing bitterly, and presently there were voices to be heard. Then the woman — now fully clad — came out and went across the field to the second house and presently came back with another woman. Their skirts almost brushed my face as they passed me.

The three sat on the steps of the house on my side of the field, all crying, and above the sound of their crying I could still hear, far off, the sound of running feet. The lover had got into the town, which was but half a mile away, and was evidently dodging through streets. Was the town aroused? Now and then shouts came from the distance. I had no watch and did not know how long I had slept in the field.

Now all became silent again and there were just the four people, myself lying trembling in the grass and the three women on the steps of the house near me, and all three crying softly. Time passed. What had happened? What would happen? In fancy I saw the running man caught and perhaps killed in some dark little side street of an Indiana farming town into which I had been thrown by the accident that a railroad brakeman had seen me standing on the bumpers between two cars of his train and had ordered me off. 'Well, get off or give me a dollar,' he had said, and I had not wanted to give him a dollar. I had only had three dollars in my pocket. Why should I give one to him? 'There will be other freight trains,' I had said to myself, 'and perhaps I shall see something of interest here in this town.'

Interest, indeed! Now I lay in the grass trembling with fear. In fancy I had become the lover of the younger of the three women sitting on the steps of the house and my sweetheart's brothers with open knives in their hands were pursuing me in a dark street. I felt the knives slashing my body and knew that what I felt the three women also felt. Every few minutes the younger of the three cried out. It was as though a knife had gone into her body. All four of us trembled with fear.

And then, as we waited and shook with dread, there was a stir in the silence. Feet, not running but walking steadily, were heard on the bridge that led into the road that passed the field and four men appeared. Somewhere in the town, in the dark night streets of the town, the two brothers had caught the lover, but it was evident there had been an explanation. The three had gone together to a doctor, the cut cheek had been patched, they had got a marriage license and a preacher, and were now coming home for a marriage.

The marriage took place at once, there before me on the steps of the house, and after the marriage, and after some sort of heavy joke on the part of the preacher, a joke at which no one laughed, the lover with his sweetheart, accompanied by the third woman, the one from the house across the field and who was evidently the lover's mother, went off across the field. Presently the field where I lay was all dark and silent again.

And that had been the scene playing itself out in my fancy as I sat in the advertising office in Chicago, pretending to listen to the man who spoke of agricultural conditions in Texas and looking at the man with the scar on his cheek, the scar that had been partly hidden from the sight of others by growing the beard. I remembered that the plow company, now wanting to sell its plows in greater numbers in the Southwest, was located in an Indiana town. How fine it would be if I could speak to the man of the beard and ask him if by any chance he was the lover of the field! In fancy I saw all the men in the room suddenly talking with the greatest intimacy. Experiences in life were exchanged, everyone laughed. There had been something in the air of the room. The men who had come to us were from a small city in Indiana while we all lived in the great city. They were somewhat suspicious of us while we were compelled to try to allay their suspicions. After the conference there would be a dinner, perhaps at some club, and afterward drinks — but there would still be suspicion. I fancied a scene in which no man suspected another. What tales might then be told! How much we might find out of each other!

And now in fancy the bearded man and I were walking and talking together and I was telling him of the scene in the field and of what I had seen and he had told me of what I had not seen. He told me of how during the running he had become exhausted and had stopped in a dark little alleyway behind stores in the town and of how the brothers had found him there. One of them came toward him threateningly, but he began to talk and an explanation followed. Then they had gone to arouse a doctor and a small official who gave them the marriage license.

'Do you know,' he said, 'neither her mother nor my own knew just what had happened and didn't dare ask. Her mother never asked her and my mother never asked me. We went along later as though nothing had happened at all except that with all of us, her brothers and myself, and even our two mothers, there was a kind of formality. They did not come to our house without being invited and we did not go freely to their house as we always had done before the brothers saw us together in the field that night.

'It was all a little strange, and as soon as I could, I grew the beard to hide the scar on my face that I thought embarrassed all the others.

'As for Molly and myself — well, you see it was somewhat strange to find ourselves suddenly man and wife, but she has been a good wife to me. After the ceremony that night on the porch of the house and after the preacher went away, we all stood for a little time together saying nothing, then my mother started for our house across the field and I took my wife's arm and followed. When we got to our house I took my Molly into my bedroom and we sat on the edge of the bed. There was a window that looked over across the field to the house where she had always lived and after a while the lights went out over there. My own mother kept moving about in our house and, although she made no noise, I knew she was crying. Was she crying because she was glad or sad? Had Molly and I married in the regular way I suppose there would have been rejoicing in both houses and I think there is no doubt we would inevitably have married. Anyway, my mother did things about the house she had already done once that night, opened the door to let out the cat that was already out, tried to wind the clock that was already wound. Then she went off upstairs and our house was dark and silent too.

'We just sat like that, on the edge of the bed, Molly and me, I don't know for how long. Then she did something. The doctor in town had sewed up the wound in my cheek and had covered the place with a soft cloth held in place by pieces of tape. What she did was to reach up and touch the end of the wound, timidly, with the tips of her fingers. She did it several times, and each time a soft little moan came from her lips.

'She did that, as I say, six or eight times and then we both lay down on the bed and took each other's hands. We didn't undress. What we did was to lie there, all night, just as I have described, with our clothes on and holding fast to each other's hands.'

River Journey

OTHER STRANGE MEMORIES for Bruce, walking with Sponge. When he went with his father and mother from Old Harbor to Indianapolis, they went by boat to Louisville. Then Bruce was twelve. His memories of that occasion might be more trustworthy. They got up in the early morning and went in a hack to the boat-landing. There were two other passengers, two young men who were evidently not citizens of Old Harbor. Who were they? Certain figures, seen under certain circumstances, remain sharply in the memory always. A tricky business, though, taking such things too seriously. It might lead to mysticism and an American mystic would be something ridiculous.

That woman in the car by the factory door Bruce and Sponge had just passed. Odd that Sponge had known about there being a passage — of a sort — between her and Bruce. He hadn't been looking.

Odd, too, if Bruce's mother had been one who was always making such contacts, making them and her man — Bruce's father — not knowing.

She, herself, might not have known — not consciously.

That day of his boyhood on the river had undoubtedly been very vivid to Bruce.

To be sure, Bruce was a child then, and to a child the adventure of going to live at a new place is something tremendous.

What will be seen at the new place, what people will be there, what will life be like there?

The two young men who had got on the boat that morning when he, with his father and mother, left Old Harbor, had stood by a railing on an upper deck talking while the boat got out into the stream. One was rather heavy, a broad-shouldered man with black hair and big hands. He smoked a pipe. The other was slender and had a small black mustache which he kept stroking.

Bruce sat with his father and mother on a bench. The morning passed. Landings were made and goods were put off the boat. The two young men passengers kept walking about, laughing and talking earnestly, and the child had a feeling that one of them, the slender man, had some sort of connection with his mother. It was as though the man and the woman had once known each other and were embarrassed finding themselves on the same boat. When they passed the bench where the Stocktons sat, the slender man did not look at them, but out over the river. Bruce had a shy boyish desire to call to him. He became absorbed in the young man and in his mother. How young she looked that day — like a girl!

Bruce's father got into a long talk with the captain of the boat, who bragged of his experiences in the early days on the river. He talked of the black deck-hands. 'We owned them then, like so many horses, but we had to take care of them like horses. It was after the war we began getting the most out of them. They were our property just the same, do you see, but we couldn't sell them and we could always get all we wanted. Niggers love the river. You can't keep a nigger off the river. We used to get 'em for five or six dollars a month, and we didn't pay 'em if we didn't want to. Why should we? If a nigger got gay, we knocked him into the river. No one ever made any inquiry about a missing nigger, them days.'

The boat captain and the school-teacher went away to another part of the boat and Bruce sat alone with his mother. In his memory — after she died — she remained a slender, rather small woman with a sweet, serious face. Almost always she was quiet and reserved, but sometimes — rarely — as on that day on the boat, she became strangely alive and eager. In the afternoon, when the boy had grown tired running about the boat, he went to sit with her again. Evening came. Within an hour they would be tied up at Louisville. The captain had taken Bruce's father up into the pilot-house. Near Bruce and his mother stood the two young men. The boat came to a landing, the last landing it would make before reaching the city.

There was a long sloping shore with cobblestones set in the mud of the river levee and the town at which they had stopped was much like the town of Old Harbor, only somewhat smaller. Many bags of grain were to be put off and the niggers were trotting up and down the landing-stage singing as they worked.

From the throats of ragged black men as they trotted up and down the landing-stage, strange haunting notes. Words were caught up, tossed about, held in the throat. Word-lovers, sound-lovers — the blacks seemed to hold a tone in some warm place, under their red tongues, perhaps. Their thick lips were walls under which the tone hid. Unconscious love of inanimate things lost to the whites — skies, the river, a moving boat — black mysticism — never expressed except in song or in the movements of bodies. The bodies of the black workers belonged to each other as the sky belonged to the river. Far off now, down-river, where the sky was splashed with red, it touched the face of the river. The tones from the throats of the black workers touched each other, caressed each other. On the deck of the boat a red-faced mate stood swearing as though at the sky and the river.

The words coming from the throats of the black workers could not be understood by the boy, but were strong and lovely. Afterwards when he thought of that moment Bruce always remembered the singing voices of the Negro deck-hands as colors. Streaming reds, browns, golden yellows, coming out of black throats. He grew strangely excited inside himself, and his mother, sitting beside him, was also excited. 'Ah, my baby! Ah, my baby!' Sounds caught and held in black throats. Notes split into quarter-notes. The word, as meaning, of no importance. Perhaps words were always unimportant. There were strange words about a 'banjo dog.' What was a 'banjo dog'? 'Ah, my banjo dog! Oh, oh! Oh, oh! Ah, my banjo dog!'

Brown bodies trotting, black bodies trotting. The bodies of all the men running up and down the landing-stage were one body. One could not be distinguished from another. They were lost in each other.

Could the bodies of people be so lost in each other? Bruce's mother had taken the boy's hand and held it closely, warmly. Near-by stood the slender young man who had got on the boat in the morning. Did he know how the mother and the boy felt at that moment and did he want to be a part of them? There was no doubt that all day, as the boat labored up-river, there had been something between the woman and the man, something of which they had both been but semi-conscious. The school-teacher had not known, but the boy and the slender young man's companion had known. Long after that evening sometimes — thoughts coming into the head of a man who had once been a boy on a boat with his mother. All day as the man had gone about the boat he had talked to his companion, but there had been a call in him toward the woman with the child. Something within him went toward the woman as the sun went toward the western horizon.

Now the evening sun seemed to be about to drop into the river, far off to the west, and the sky was rosy-red.

The young man's hand rested on the shoulder of his companion, but his face was turned toward the woman and the child. The woman's face was red, like the evening sky. She did not look at the young man, but away from across the river, and the boy looked from the young man's face to his mother's face. His mother's hand gripped his hand tightly.

Bruce never had any brothers or sisters. Could it be that his mother had wanted more children? Long afterwards, sometimes — that time after he left Bernice, when he was floating down the Mississippi River in an open boat, before he lost his boat one night in a storm when he had gone ashore — odd things happened. He pulled the boat ashore under a tree somewhere and lay down on the grass on the river bank. An empty river filled with ghosts before his eyes. He was half asleep, half awake. Fancies flooded his mind. Before the storm came that blew his boat away, he lay for a long time in the darkness near the water's edge reliving another evening on a river. The strangeness and the wonder of things — in nature — he had known as a boy and that he had somehow later lost — the sense lost living in a city and being married to Bernice — could he get it back again? There was the strangeness and wonder of trees, skies, city streets, black men, white men — of buildings, words, sounds, thoughts, fancies. Perhaps white men's getting on so fast in life, having newspapers, advertising, great cities, smart clever minds, ruling the world, had cost them more than they had gained. They hadn't gained much.

That young man Bruce had once seen on an Ohio River boat when he was a boy taking the trip up-river with his father and mother — had he on that evening been something of what Bruce later became? It would be an odd turn of the mind if the young man had never existed — if a boy's mind had invented him. Suppose he had just invented him later — as something — to explain his mother to himself as a means for getting close to the woman, his mother. The man's memory of the woman, his mother, might also be an invention. A mind like Bruce's sought explanations for everything.

On the boat on the Ohio River, evening coming on fast. There was a town sitting high up on a bluff and three or four people had got off the boat. The niggers kept singing — singing and trotting — dancing up and down a landing-stage. A broken-down hack, to which two decrepit-looking horses were hitched, went away up along a street toward the town on the bluff. On the shore were two white men. One was small and alert and had an account book in his hand. He was checking off the grain bags as they were brought ashore. 'One-hundred-twenty-two, twenty-three, twenty-four.' 'Ah, my banjo dog! Oh, ho! Oh, ho!'

The second white man on the shore was tall and lean and there was something wild about his eyes. On the still evening air the voice of the captain of the boat, talking to Bruce's father up above in the pilot-house or on the deck above, could be distinctly heard. 'He's a crazy man.' The second white man ashore sat at the top of the levee with his knees drawn up between his arms. His body rocked slowly to and fro in the rhythm of the singing Negroes. The man had been in some kind of an accident. There was a cut on his long lean cheek and the blood had run down into his dirty beard and dried there. There was a tiny streak of red faintly seen like the streak of fiery red in the red sky of the west the boy could see when he looked away down-river toward the setting sun. The injured man was dressed in ragged clothes and his lips hung open, thick lips hanging open like niggers' lips when they sang. His body rocked. The body of the slender young man on the boat, trying to keep up a conversation with his companion, the broad-shouldered man, was rocking almost imperceptibly. The body of the woman who was Bruce's mother was rocking.

To the boy on the boat that evening the whole world, the sky, the boat, the shore running away into the gathering darkness, seemed rocking with the voices of the singing niggers.

Had the whole thing been but a fancy, a whim? Had he, as a boy, gone to sleep on a boat with his hand gripped in his mother's hand and dreamed it all? It had been hot all day on the narrow-decked river boat. The gray waters running along beside the boat made a boy sleepy.

What had happened between a small woman sitting silently on the deck of a boat and a young man with a tiny mustache who talked all day to his friend, never addressing a word to the woman? What could happen between people that no one knew anything about, and they themselves knew little about?

As Bruce walked beside Sponge Martin and passed a woman sitting in an automobile and something — a flashing kind of thing passed between them — what did it signify?

On the boat, that day on the river, Bruce's mother had turned her face toward the young man, even as the boy watched the two faces. It was as though she had suddenly consented to something — a kiss, perhaps.

No one had known but the boy and perhaps — as a wild fanciful notion — the crazy man sitting on the river levee and staring at the boat — his thick lips hanging open. 'He's three-quarters white and one-quarter nigger, and he's been crazy for ten years,' the voice of the captain explained to the school-teacher on the deck above.

The crazy man sat hunched up ashore, on the top of the levee, until the boat was pulling away from the landing, and then he got to his feet and shouted. Later the captain said he did it whenever a boat landed at the town. The man was harmless, the captain said. The crazy man with the streak of red blood on his cheek got to his feet and stood up very straight and tall. His body seemed like the trunk of a dead tree growing at the levee top. There might have been a dead tree there. The boy might have gone to sleep and dreamed it all. He had been strangely attracted to the slender young man. He might have wanted the young man near himself and had let his fancy draw him near through the body of a woman, his mother.

How ragged and dirty were the clothes of the crazy man! A kiss had passed between the young woman on deck and the slender young man. The crazy man shouted something. 'Keep afloat! Keep afloat!' he cried, and all the niggers down below on the lower deck of the boat were silent. The body of the young man with the mustache quivered. A woman's body quivered. A boy's body quivered.

'All right,' the captain's voice shouted. 'It's all right. We'll take care of ourselves.'

'He's just a harmless lunatic, comes down every time a boat comes in and always shouts something like that,' the captain explained to Bruce's father as the boat swung out into the stream.

'All right,' the captain's voice shouted. 'It's all right. We'll take care of ourselves.'

'He's just a harmless lunatic, comes down every time a boat comes in and always shouts something like that,' the captain explained to Bruce's father as the boat swung out into the swell.

IX. EDITORIAL

Smythe County News

A Beginning

EVERY WEEK the pages of the paper are to be filled. The new editor, who is also an author, knows but few people of the town. He has moments of dread. At times he says to himself, 'Why have I arranged to do this? Why have I let myself in for this?'

The town nestles among the hills. 'There are all these people walking up and down the street. Will they come to like me? Will I like them?'

It is going to be a peculiarly intimate relation. The small-town weekly is not a daily. It is not a question of gathering news.

He drives his car down to the town and parks it on Main Street. Since Sinclair Lewis wrote his book he has been hating the words, 'Main Street.' 'I will call it something else,' he says to himself. He hates all expressions that become, as is said, 'a part of the language.' He is to hate later the name 'Elmer Gantry,' as representing preachers and 'Babbitt,' as representing the business men of the American small town.

'The names are lies in themselves,' he is saying to himself. 'They are too easy. There is too much malice in them.'

And now he is walking along the street. Perhaps people are pointing him out. 'That is our new editor. He also writes books. What do you suppose he is like?'

Alas, some of them may have read some of the editor's books. The thought sends a little shiver down his back. 'They may have taken them literally,' he is saying to himself.

But are books not to be taken so? Certainly not. Books are books. They are to be taken as books.

But who will understand that?

Now be quiet. Quit being frightened.

An Editor's Thoughts

AN EDITOR'S THOUGHTS — not published. Terror. These people. Suppose they find me out!

Can I do this thing? What do I know of all these lives?

I have been out of a small town too long. How close it is here! I cannot breathe.

These people have known each other always. They must know everything about each other. I could not bear to have everything known about me.

I do not want to be intimate with people. Why did I come here to a small town?

I have lived too long in cities. In the city I could go around the first corner and be lost. I was one more figure moving through the city streets with many thousands of other figures.

I am known in a small literary and intellectual circle. How easy to avoid all such circles!

Here I can avoid no one. All will be found out about me.

The men in my shop — how nice they are! They are watching me. I am boss here. They are wondering what I will be like.

I have eminence of a sort in some places, but there is no eminence here. Here I must stand on my own feet. Will the men here in the shop like me? Already I like them.

They come to work in the morning. They laugh. They quarrel a little. I feel awkward with them.

Notes for Newspaper Readers

THERE IS A LITTLE ALLEYWAY back of the shop. From the window where I sit writing, I can, by turning my head slightly, see into the courthouse yard and to the post-office door.

The post-office is the town gathering place. The morning mail from the East comes in just after eight o'clock. Men begin to gather at about that hour. Back of the glass front of the post-office the clerks are at work distributing the mail.

I see the prominent men of the town gathered. There is the judge, three or four lawyers, the merchants, the bankers. This is a Virginia town. These people have not moved about much. Not many new people have come in. As yet, I feel a little strange here.

There is a poor, bedraggled woman in the alleyway. She has two small children with her. The children look half-starved. They are picking up bits of coal and wood and putting them in a basket. Presently she and her children will go home and build a fire. They will huddle about it. The morning is cold.

Thoughts drifting in a man's mind. Mountains rise up out of this valley in all directions. The valley is broad and rich. Ever since I have been in this valley, I have been reading every book I could find about the life here. Everyone knows that Virginia is one of our oldest states. In the early days, when all eastern and central Virginia had already been settled for a long time, this country remained untouched.

There was the country east of the mountains. The whites had that. Then came the Blue Ridge Range. Beyond that another range, the tail end of the Appalachians, trailing down across Virginia and into North Carolina.

A rich country of little upland valleys. There was a great salt lick at Roanoke and another near us, at Saltville. Game was abundant. In all of this country, blue grass grows naturally. It is wonderful for fattening stock. During the spring, summer, and fall months, thousands of fat cattle and sheep are driven down through our main street to the railroad yards.

Before the white men got over the mountains and into these valleys, all of this country was the happy hunting ground of the Indians. None of the tribes lived here, but the Shawnees, the Chickasaws, the Mingos, even the Indians from Ohio and New York State, came here to hunt.

Then the white hunters came, Daniel Boone and the others. They went back over the mountains telling great tales. Settlers came. Each settler picked out his own little valley and built his cabin.

Great land companies were formed to exploit the country. George Washington got in on that. The English governor owed him something for his services during the French and Indian War. George knew how to take care of himself in a financial way. The early settlers in the little valleys had to fight the Indians for their lives on the one hand, and fight it out with the great speculative land company for the very soil under their feet.

An independent people, full of personality. The town has not yet had the problem of assimilating foreign-born citizens.

Everyone knows everyone else. Their fathers were known and their grandfathers. A newcomer like myself — I have been in this country only three years — sees the change going on here that has gone on all over America.

Presently there will be more factories. Labor is plentiful and can yet be bought at a low price. That, in the end, will bring the factories.

The drama of a small town always unrolling before the eyes. Now a crier comes out and calls from the courthouse steps. Court is about to go into session.

It is a case involving mountain people. I go over there. Courts have always frightened me a little. Formerly, when I lived in Chicago, I knew a good many newspaper men. They went freely into the courts, even into the judge's chamber. They spoke freely to the judge, 'Hello, Jim,' they said.

And there was the sheriff. I have always been afraid of sheriffs. It may be that every writer is instinctively afraid of being arrested. I was arrested once. That was up in Ohio. A sheriff picked me up as a diamond thief. He took me off to a police court. Two or three men in uniform gathered about and began hurling questions at me. I stood trembling. What a queer feeling of guilt!

Now, I go into our courtroom freely. The sheriff and the judge smile at me. Behold, I am a power in the land. I own a newspaper. I even go into the sheriff's office. He and I have a cigarette together.

In the courtroom outside country people are gathered. They are afraid in the presence of the law, as I was once afraid. A court official is telling me about his daughter, who has got a prize in school. I know what he wants. He is proud of his daughter. He wants that put in the paper. It will go in.

In the courtroom I can go into the sacred precincts inside the bar. How brave I am! These days I feel as I did when I was a boy and got a job tending race-horses. What did I care about wages? I could consort shoulder to shoulder with the great, with horsemen.

I walked beside drivers of race-horses, touched their elbows.

The witness on the stand is lying. He is a small boy. His father and his uncle have had a fight. One has haled the other into court. The fight took place on a country road, just as evening was coming on. The men threw rocks at each other.

The boy has been told a story he must repeat in court. What a ridiculous story! He is swearing that his father stood just so, beside the road. The uncle came along the road, swearing. He threw rocks at the boy's father. The father stood like a statue beside the road. He did not throw any rocks until he had been hit twice. What an amazingly gentle, patient mountain man. Now the lawyers are asking the boy searching questions. He is confused. The color leaves his face. His hands grip the chair in which he sits. I know how the boy feels. He feels as I used to feel when I went into court — before I became an editor and, therefore, brave.

Frightened country people gathered in the courtroom. Presently their turn will come. What a terrible thing is the law!

I am glad I am not a lawyer. I am a newspaper man.

A brother newspaper man has come in. He runs another weekly newspaper in a neighboring town. I have become part of a vast brotherhood. We talk of the cost of getting out a newspaper; how to make the merchants advertise more than they do. Advertising is the breath of our nostrils.

The newspaper man has gone out. After all, running a country weekly is not running a newspaper. In our hearts, we country editors know that. We are not after news. If anyone wants news, let them take a daily. We are after the small events of small-town people's lives.

The country newspaper is the drug store: it is the space back of the stove in the hardware store: it is the farmhouse kitchen.

There was a man on a gray horse went along a mountain road one day last week. Farmer Cooper was in a distant field and could not make out the rider of the gray horse. He has been bothered ever since. 'Ma, who do you suppose it was?' Now he has his weekly copy of our paper. He is sitting in the kitchen, reading.

Aha, there it is. 'Ed Barrow, from up Sugar Grove way, rode his gray horse into town on Wednesday of last week. He reports a fine bunch of steers to sell.'

An old colonel with a gray beard comes into the office and takes a chair near my own. His hands tremble. In the Civil War he was a Reb. Once there was a raid of Union troops down into this country. There was a battle over near Saltville, just across Walker's Mountain from where we are sitting now.

The old man describes the battle, in which he took part as a young soldier. It was getting toward the end of the war. The Colonel was but a boy then. All of the men of this section had gone off to join Lee before Richmond. Grant was pounding away at Lee during those days. It was near the end of things.

And a battle here — in this quiet place. Old men and boys rushing to the Stars and Bars. Who knows, my own father may have been along on that raiding party. They were trying to get up to the Norfolk and Western Railroad, to tear it up. Stealing chickens on the way, too.

Old men and boys rushing through the hills, the Colonel among them. He describes the battle in the hills; the driving off of the Yanks. It takes an hour to tell. It is a good story. Well, no hurry. We country editors have no dead line. If we do not get to press today, we will go to press tomorrow. After the Colonel leaves, leaning heavily on his cane, a heavy-faced woman with a determined jaw comes in.

She wants a piece put in the paper. She had two sons. One of them was killed last year in a railroad accident. With several other boys he was in a Ford. There was moon whiskey in the Ford. The driver was reckless. He drove before an oncoming train at a grade crossing and two boys were killed.

The boy's mother has written a piece about the boy. She says he was a good boy and feared God. 'I hope,' she says in the piece, 'that what has happened to Harry will be a warning to his brother, Zeb.' Evidently Zeb is a bit out of hand, too.

'Will you print it?' she asks. Surely, we will.

She is followed by a shy, fair maiden in a blue dress.

The maiden also has something to put in the paper. She hands it to me and goes out. I look at the paper. 'Miss Ruby Small of Carrollville was in town Tuesday to get her teeth fixed.'

Well, well, Ruby, are you having trouble with your teeth, and you so young, too.

There is no question, the dentists of this town should do more advertising in our paper.

Night. Your country editor walks about his town. He belongs to the great brotherhood of the inkpots. He does not have to rush like the city newspaper man, nor does he need to be high-toned and literary, like your magazine editor.

Your country editor is thinking up schemes. He is trying to think how to make the merchants of his town advertise more. He thinks of that for a time, and then thinks of his town.

More and more he is growing familiar with it. The threads of its life run through his fingers. He knows, oh, what does he not know?

And the people of the town, knowing what he knows, a little afraid, keep passing and looking at him. He is just a little outside their lives. He is something special. He writes. That alone sets him apart.

Sleepless Nights

A DOG KEEPS BARKING. You get up and read a book. At night everything is distorted. There is someone else asleep in the next room. You want something in there. Really you do not want anything but sleep. There is a book in the room on a table by your friend's head. Why do you want just that book?

You do not want it at all. You want to make a noise and awaken your friend. You succeed.

He wakes up and stares at you with sleepy eyes. You begin to complain. 'I can't sleep,' you say. He pretends to be concerned. You begin talking hopefully, but now he has rolled over in his bed and is asleep again.

All the world is asleep. Your nerves are jumping. You try to lie quiet, but do not succeed. If you are a smoker you smoke many cigarettes. Your throat becomes hot and dry.

O Lord, help you. Now you have begun thinking about yourself. You begin thinking up impossibly shrewd things to say to people next day. Suppose you are a writer. You write in fancy with a new and striking eloquence. What marvelous sentences! You get up and put some of them down. You forget the anguish that prompted them the next morning and hate them.

I dare say you are not a writer. You are a banker, a manufacturer, a merchant, a workingman. You become so clever you amaze yourself. It may be you pile up money, you make a new invention.

There is a man with whom you have had a quarrel. In fancy you meet him on the street. He is a bit impertinent and you knock him down. How many men I have whipped in fancy on sleepless nights! What beautiful women have been in love with me!

After such a night you get up the next morning feeling seedy, of course. You go out into the street. All about are people who have just arisen from refreshing sleep. How old you feel! What a dead cold place the world is!

The Marion Band

WHAT DOES A BAND mean to a town? Better to ask what is a town without a band? Life in a town goes on, just so. You know how it is. Merchants selling goods, lawyers fighting their cases, farmers coming into town to buy goods. Spring, summer, fall, and winter. People in their houses, women cooking, making beds. Life is dull enough.

Days come. See, the men of the band have put on their uniforms and are coming up along the street. The big drum is booming, the horns going.

Just suppose now, in our town, we are visited by some great man. Hurrah now, let's give him a big day. It may be the governor of the state or some other dignitary. Our principal men are going to meet him down at the station. They have their best cars there, the biggest and best cars we have in town, all our leading citizens. And no band. Pshaw! What a frost!

And what about Armistice Day and the Fourth of July?

Or when the fair is on?

Older men, staid citizens of a town may be able to get along without a band, but what about the boys?

When I was a boy my one great yearning was to play the biggest horn in the town band. I never made it. There never was much music in me.

Still and all, I'm not a jealous man. What I can't have I don't want to take away from the other fellow.

I still like a band better than almost anything else in a town. Band music just suits me. There they come up the street. Lately I have only seen the Marion Band in action a few times and then they didn't have any drum major. I hope they get one again soon. I like to see the fellow in the big bearskin hat with his staff, stepping high and wide. I'd like to do it myself, but I haven't got the figure for it.

And how faithful and devoted the band members are! The men of our Marion Band, for example, go off to practice twice a week. Far from getting paid for their work, they do it without pay. The members even pay dues to keep the band going.

Recently, until these last few weeks our Marion Band has had a band leader who was paid a good salary because he was a good man. He was there to keep the boys up to snuff and would be there now, but that he is sick.

But the boys are at it just the same. They are keeping the band going.

There are men in the Marion Band who make a sacrifice every time they go out to play. Bear this in mind. When we want our band, most other towns, that haven't any band, would like one, too. Our band gets offers to go all over southwest Virginia. Such offers almost always come when we need them here and they stay at home. Instead of going out and raking in money, they stay here and give their services.

And there are individual members of the band who make a sacrifice every time they go out to play. Do they kick? Not they.

The boys of the band like their band, and so do we. Hurrah, here they come. Music floating on the breeze. Every heart jumping. Life. Music. Zipp!

We like that.

The people of Marion owe it to their band to give it the heartiest kind of support. Get back of them. When they need a little money to keep going, shell out.

A good band is the best investment a town can make. We, in Marion, have a corking good one. Let's stand by it.

Election Day Shooting

ELECTION DAY saw a bad case of shooting over in Grayson County. Paul Halsey, living on the Fairwood Road, shot a man named Young. As we got the story, there had been bad blood between the two men for some time. Their farms joined each other.

As the story is told in Grayson County, Young recently shot a horse belonging to Halsey. It seemed this man Young has been in such trouble before. On election day he went to Halsey's house. As Halsey tells the story, Young invited him out to the barn saying he was sorry he had shot the horse and wanted to settle.

A son accompanied Young on the visit to Halsey. They got Halsey into the barn and then closed the door. The elder Young pulled at a gun and told Halsey to make his peace with God as he was about to die.

The son was in the meantime standing outside the barn and firing shots into Halsey's house.

In the barn a very dramatic scene must have been taking place. Young put his pistol close to Halsey's face and was about to fire when, with a quick upward movement of his arm, Halsey knocked the gun up. The shot went through the roof of the barn.

Halsey then jumped to his feet and getting a pistol out of his pocket began to shoot. One of the shots lodged in the hip of the elder Young, another in his arm. All of this was on election day. Young with his son drove to Troutdale, where, in spite of his wounds, he stopped to vote. Then he drove to a doctor at Grant. The doctor being unable to get the bullet lodged in his hip, he was taken to the hospital, where, after the bullet had been removed, he escaped by crawling through a window. At the time of this writing his whereabouts is unknown.

Gil Stephenson

GIL IS AN OLD WORKMAN who has been all his life in this one Virginia town.

He worked in a factory when he was a small boy. That was just at the end of the Civil War.

They were getting barites out of the hills here then. There was a long dark building. A crusher crushed the ore. It rolled down a long chute. The boys picked out the stone and other impurities.

Afterward Gil began working at the printing trade. He has been at it forty years, has set enough type to go across the State.

He started a little paper of his own — *The Marion Democrat*. I publish it now.

In those days everything was done by hand. All the type was set by hand and the press was turned by hand.

Gil's wife helped with the paper. His children helped. There was never a man in this world who has more loyal children than Gil Stephenson. They have all been a help to him and he has been a help to them.

On press days they went out into the street and got a 'nigger' to come in and turn the press. He turned out an entire edition for fifty cents.

Mrs. Stephenson addressed the papers by hand.

Advertisers didn't pay much for space and subscribers often paid their subscriptions with potatoes, cabbages, loads of wood, corn for making corn meal.

Tramp printers floating in.

'Well, have you any work?' 'No.'

'Here's something for breakfast, though — and a cup of coffee.'

The printers shuffled out to a little restaurant.

Presently they came back and all began to set type. They set enough to pay for the firewood and the breakfast.

Some of them were fast as lightning too.

There were old fellows, worn-out, cast aside — old drunkards.

Then there were young fellows — going on their trade journey.

Sometimes — along in the morning — they caught a freight out of town.

'Well, good-bye — good luck.'

Gil still sets type at his case every day. He is a grandfather now. His body is as well and strong as that of a young man.

He likes his trade. 'You can't cheat or fake at it,' he says — 'every defect shows.'

Of course defects show everywhere, in all trades where workmen are slipshod, but people do not know the difference.

Sometimes, when the presses are going in our shop and Gil is feeding, we find a defect.

'Oh, let it go. Who cares?'

'Who cares? Who cares?'

'Railroad it.'

'We got to get this paper out.'

The press runs on. Suddenly it stops. Gil climbs down from his press-feeding platform.

'Oh, it will only take a minute,' he says.

Well, he had to stop — he couldn't go on.

'That's Gil all right,' the others in the shop say, and laugh.

When Knighthood Was in Flower

THAT WAS A LONG TIME AGO. It is said, however, that Walter Pierce, out on Walker's Creek, in the Hungry's Mother section, has a lot of the old flare in him.

A few days ago he was driving along the road with his uncle, J. A. Pierce. They came across the Evans boys beside the road. Some other fellows, among them Ed Smith, were with the Evans boys. For a long time there has been bad feeling between the Pierce and Evans factions out that way.

By the story brought out in Justice Dickinson's court, in the trial on Monday, words started between the two factions. Walter Pierce and his uncle got out of the car. It is said that Walter Pierce offered to let himself and any one of the Evans factions be searched for concealed weapons.

Then, when they were found all clean, they were to go into a field and fight it out.

That's the way they used to do things in the old days of Knights and Kings.

No one seemed to want to do it. The Pierces started to get back into the car.

The claim is that a young man named Ed Smith picked up a rock and tried to see if he was good enough to get into the big league. He probably is. Anyway, he clipped J. A. Pierce on the forehead with the rock and his doing so cost him twenty-five dollars in Justice Dickinson's court.

Today all is quiet on Hungry's Mother.

Human Misery

WHEN IT SINKS low enough and gets caught in the trap of life, human life can be both dangerous and terrible.

Thomas Patterson, who says he is from Martinville, West Virginia, drifted into town on Monday. The man is a dope. You know what that means. When he got to Marion he was desperate. He went first to the office of Mayor Dickinson and then to Doctor Weindell. The M.D. could not supply him with the drug he craved. He got desperate and ugly and attacked Doctor Weindell, striking him in the face and cutting his lip. Then he fled. It was a brutal and uncalled-for attack.

It would not do, of course, to let such a man run loose. Men and boys took up the chase. Highway Policeman Jack Williams, Rush Hayes, Sheriff Dillard, all got busy.

Patterson was cornered at the East End filling station and showed fight. He was, however, surrounded and without further injury to anyone was lodged in jail. Everyone breathed a bit easier.

It happens that this writer never sees a thing of this sort without an inward shudder. It was a gray dismal day. I cannot escape this trick of identifying myself with such a poor human. As he runs through the street, I imagine myself running. I imagine myself also the victim of some terrible habit, driven to desperation, brutalized.

In Washington

IN WASHINGTON, where I have been sent to interview the Secretary of Commerce, Mr. Hoover. I do not like the job much. Why did I take it?

I am always undertaking something the Lord never intended me to do.

I have arrived in the city in the early morning and am not to see the man until late afternoon. It is bitter cold. When I saw Washington last, some fifteen or twenty years ago, it was merely a great straggling town. Now it has become a modern city.

I have been at a big hotel and have left my bag. I begin wondering what I shall do with my day.

We who live in country towns miss certain things. The radio and the phonograph can bring us music by the best orchestras — if there are any bests — we can hear speakers talk, but there are things we cannot get.

We cannot see the best players on the stage and we cannot see paintings.

I decided to go to a museum.

There are days for everything. Was this a day to see paintings? I should, no doubt, have gone to talk to some politician, but I knew no politicians as politicians. No one ever talks politics to me. I went to the new Freer Gallery.

The Freer Gallery, named for its builder, was built by a rich man of Detroit and was intended primarily to house the paintings of the American painter Whistler. In it are housed, as well, many old and rare objects of Chinese and Japanese art.

I went to the gallery in the morning and it was quite empty but for the attendants. There was a hushed quiet over the place. The walls and the attendants seemed crying out at me, 'Be careful, walk quietly, this is a sacred place.'

Sacred, indeed. What a strange thing is the life of the artist!

Standing in the gallery and looking at these paintings, conscious all the time of the uniformed attendants watching me, afraid perhaps I might steal some of these sacred objects, an odd feeling of annoyance creeping over me.

Such a man as Whistler lives. His work is condemned or praised by the men of his own time. It has been the fate of some men, who have produced the greatest art, made the greatest discoveries in science, the greatest contributions to scholarship, to live and die unknown. They are perhaps the lucky men.

Such a man was Whistler, fighting for fame. He was always a great fighter. Once he wrote a book called *The Gentle Art of Making Enemies*. He knew how to do that all right.

Much of his energy must have been spent in fighting for fame. Well, he has won. He has fame. Fame, in the end, does not always mean worth. If you keep insisting that you are a great man, after a time people will believe. It doesn't necessarily mean you are great.

James McNeill Whistler was not one of the great painters of the world. His fighting and his personality got him somewhere. A rich patron of the arts, Mr. Freer, became devoted to him. He has spent hundreds of thousands of dollars, his time, his own energy, in making Mr. Whistler's fame secure. Mr. Freer, because of his devotion to another, may possibly be a finer and a greater man than Mr. Whistler.

As for myself, I could not get over the feeling that much of Mr. Whistler's work is vastly overestimated. Many of these paintings, carefully guarded by paid attendants, housed in this great stone building, are commonplace enough.

I went out of the famous Peacock Room and into the room where the older art treasures are housed. There were the old Chinese and Japanese things.

Objects of art come out of a day when there is no such thing as publicity — painting by reticent, devoted men. Whistler has been rather widely advertised as having brought over into his own day much of the fineness of these older painters. He has not brought over so much.

Such a short time ago, some fifty years, and Whistler's house in London was being sold over his head. Many of these paintings, so sumptuously housed now, were sold then for a few shillings. Have they increased in value so much?

The value of the older Chinese and Japanese things is fixed. Money cannot express it. There is 'The Waves at Matsushinea,' painted by some unknown man called 'Satatsu' in the seventeenth century. In another painting the Chinese Emperor Ming Huang is with his concubine Kuei-fei in a garden. What a charming lady! It is spring. She is singing to make the flowers bloom for her emperor.

And there is another painting. The Emperor Weu, of the Chow Dynasty, is meeting the sage, Chiang Tzu-ya. The two men are meeting on an island in a winding lake. All nature seems hushed and quiet. Clouds are standing still in the sky, as though intent on the scene below. There is a sense in the painting of infinite time, space, distance.

Mr. Hoover and I did not meet on an island in a winding lake.

There were no fleecy clouds floating in the sky; no sense of infinite time, space, distance.

It may be that Mr. Hoover has in him the making of an emperor, but I am no sage.

If I had been a sage I would not have been where I was.

I was in a great office building in the modern city of Washington. Before me sat a well-dressed man of perhaps fifty. Like myself, he was a bit too fat. He had leaned too long over a desk, over figures and plans, and I had leaned too long over a typewriter. Besides that Mr. Hoover had just been to a dentist.

And he did not want to be interviewed.

'Are you an interviewer?' he asked.

'Yes,' I said doubtfully.

I had never been such a thing before. I am a writer of books, sometimes a teller of tales. I run a country weekly. Country weeklies are not newspapers. We do not interview people. I am not a politically-minded man. Always I am asking myself the question, 'Why does any man want to be President? Why does any man want power?'

By my philosophy power is the forerunner of corruption.

To be a bright, intelligent newspaper interviewer, I should have asked Mr. Hoover some embarrassing questions. He was a member of the cabinet of Mr. Harding, sat cheek by jowl with Mr. Fall and Mr. Daugherty. A stench arose from that sitting. What about it?

The question trembled on my lips.

Other questions crowding into my mind. 'What of the League of Nations, our attitude toward the small republics of Central America?'

Better that I should not ask such questions. The man would twist me about his little finger. 'It is just possible he knows something about leagues of nations and all such things, but what do you know?' I was now asking myself.

A fragment of song floated up into my mind, even then, at that unfortunate moment. The song was like the clouds floating above that island when the Emperor Weu went to meet Chiang Tzu-ya.

> 'My freedom sleeps in a mulberry bush.
> My country is in the shivering legs of a little lost dog.'

'I am not going to be interviewed,' Mr. Hoover said again.

'I don't care,' I said.

As a matter of fact, I did not care two straws. I had made a futile trip to Washington. Well, it was not futile. I had seen the Emperor Ming Huang with his concubine Kuei-fei walking in a garden.

The Emperor Ming Huang had walked in his garden with Kuei-fei in another age than my own. There were no factories in that age. Men did not rush through the streets in automobiles. There were no radios, no airplanes.

Just the same, men fought wars, men were cruel and greedy, as in my own age.

My mind full of things far removed from Mr. Hoover and his age, I was going out the door, having got nothing from him, having failed as a modern newspaper correspondent — a task that no such man as myself should have undertaken — when Mr. Hoover called me back.

'I will not be interviewed, but we can talk,' he said. Mr. Hoover was being kind. He must have felt my incompetence. I understood what he meant. He meant only that things were to be in his own hands. We were to speak only of those things that Mr. Hoover cared to discuss.

He began to talk now, first of the Mississippi problem. It was a huge problem, he said, but it could be met. There was a way out.

There was the river cutting down through the heart of the country, twisting and winding. Had I not spent days and weeks on the great river? I told him I had. 'It is uncontrollable,' I said. 'The Mississippi is a thing in nature. It is nature.' But did not Joshua make the sun stand still? I remembered a summer when I took the Mississippi as a god, became a river worshiper.

I was in a boat fishing on the Mississippi when a flood came. I felt its power, it put the fear of God into my heart.

But Mr. Hoover had been down there and was not afraid. He spoke of spillways. There was to be a new river bed creeping down westward of the Mississippi — all through the lower country.

Then, when great floods came rampaging and tearing down and Mother Mississippi was on a spree, she was to be split in two. Two Mother Mississippis, gentled now, going down to the sea.

'What a man!' I said to myself.

And could he also handle like that the industrial age?

There was the question. That also had become to me like a thing in nature.

I had, after all, got down to the heart of what I wanted to ask Mr. Hoover.

The industrial age has been sweeping forward ever since I was a boy. I have seen the river of it swell and swell. It has swept over the entire land. The industrialists may not be Ming Huangs, but they are in power.

They have raised this Mr. Hoover up out of the ranks of men as perhaps the finest Republican example of manhood and ability in present-day American political and industrial life. He is, apparently, a man very sure of himself. His career has been a notable one. From a small beginning he has risen steadily in power. There has never been any check. I felt, looking at him, that he has never known failure.

It is too bad never to have known that. Never to have known miserable nights of remorse, feeling the world too big and strange and difficult for you.

Well, power also, when it is sure of itself, can gentle a man. Mr. Hoover has nice eyes, a clear, cool voice. He gave me long rows of figures showing how the industrialists have improved things for the common man. We spoke of Mr. Ford and he was high in his praise of the man. 'When I go to ride in an automobile,' he said, 'it does not matter to me that there are a million automobiles on the road just like mine. I am going somewhere and want to get there in what comfort I can and at the lowest cost.'

That, it seemed to me, summed up Mr. Hoover's philosophy of life.

When you have a man's philosophy of life, why stay about? Why bother the man?

Mr. Hoover spoke of the farmers. It is quite true that, in the distribution of the good things the industrial age has brought, the industrialists and the financiers have got rather the best of it. Labor has been able to take good care of itself, Mr. Hoover thinks. The farmer is another problem. Here is one place where the modern system has not quite worked.

It is a matter, he said, of too much waste between the farmer and the consumer. I gathered that the whole system of merchandising would have to be brought up into the new age.

'Something like the systems of chain stores,' I suggested. He fended me off there. I presume any man in political life has to be cautious.

The merchant class is a large class. There are votes there. My mind flopped back to my own town. Voters gathered in the evening at the back of the drug store, the hardware store, the grocery store. The small, individual merchant, who is, I gather, at the bottom of the farmer's troubles, has power, too — in his own store.

There had been something hanging in my mind for a long time. I thought I would at least take a shot at it. All of this industrialism and standardization growing up in my day. I had seen it grow and grow. A whole nation riding in the same kind of cars, smoking the same kind of cigars, wearing the same kind of clothes, thinking the same thoughts.

Individualism, among the masses of the people, gradually dying.

You get a few men, drawn up and become powerful because they control the mass needs and the mass thought. No questions asked any more. All doubting men thrown aside.

Young men, buried yet down in the mass, squirming about. They not liking too well the harness of industrialism and standardization. Men coming into power, not as Lincoln came, nor yet as Napoleon came.

At the bottom of it all, a growing number of the younger men feeling hopeless boredom.

Is the heavy boredom of a standardized civilization true for Mr. Hoover as it is sometimes true for me? I asked Mr. Hoover that question and for the first time during our talk he did not seem comfortable.

But power is power. He fended off again. After all, the age and the system of the age that may destroy one man may make another. Mr. Hoover has been made by his age. Apparently, he is satisfied with it.

I got out of Mr. Hoover's presence feeling we had got nowhere. Surely it wasn't his fault. I went walking for a long time in the streets of Washington. The more I walked, the more sure I was that Mr. Hoover is the ideal among Republican men to be the present-day President of the United States — if he can make them see it.

Other men feel that. I asked several men I had never seen before.

I asked a man who drove a streetcar, one who opened oysters, another who scrubbed the floor in the lobby of a hotel.

'He is the ideal man,' they all said. They were afraid the politicians would not give him a chance. The reason given was that he has too much brains.

But these men's opinions have also been made by the standardized newspaper opinion of the age in which they live. Their expression of doubt was merely resentment. Mr. Hoover is the blameless man. In Mr. Hoover's head has developed the ideal brain for his time. Are the other leaders of his party afraid of him? Surely theirs are not the nameless fears of such men as myself.

It would be a little odd if, the age having produced a perfect thing, a man who does so very well and with such fine spirit just what every one apparently believes they want done — should be thrown aside, being too perfect.

There is no doubt in my own mind. I am convinced Mr. Hoover would make the ideal Republican President.

No one will ever sing songs about Mr. Hoover after he is President — if they decide to give him the chance. There will be no paintings made of him walking at evening in a garden while a lovely lady sings to make the flowers bloom.

But it is not an age of painting, not an age of song.

And so there was I walking in the streets of Washington, having made a failure of my day. I had tried to be smart and had not been smart. I had got myself into a false position. What happens to the age in which a man lives is like the Mississippi, a thing in nature. It is no good quarreling with the age in which you live.

I had come to Washington, I think, wanting to like Mr. Hoover, and had ended by admiring him. He had not warmed me. I went over past the White House and tried to think of Lincoln living there. Then I went back to the Freer Gallery for another look at Ming Huang walking in his garden and listening to the voice of Kuei-fei — but it was closed for the night.

Winter Day in Town

SNOW on the sidewalks, in the streets. The time of cold rains, cold winds. How nice the houses are now. The editor of this paper likes to walk in the streets alone at night. He goes down one street, crosses over, and goes along another. The houses are all lighted. There are fires burning.

People sitting in the houses, men, women, and children. Houses are like people. I beg you all when you walk thus, when your minds are not occupied with your own affairs, to begin thinking of houses.

The houses have faces. The windows are eyes. Some houses smile at you, others frown.

There are some houses that are always dark. People in them crawl off early to bed. You hear no laughter from such houses, no one sings.

Other houses are proud. They are well kept. As you pass they seem to look at you with a sort of 'keep off the grass' expression. You hurry past such houses.

I know houses that always seem to be whispering to me. There are secrets hidden in such houses. They plead with you not to disturb them. Alas, I am an inveterate hunter of tales. Odd things happen to people behind the walls of houses. Many people are one thing inside their houses and another on the street. Sometimes the secrets, hidden away behind the walls of houses, are merely sad, but sometimes they are exciting too.

There are evenings when I walk thus and see houses that they all seem to be talking to me. They are trying to tell me what I cannot understand.

I go past a dozen houses, two dozen. There are the glad houses, the gay ones, the one where all the doors seem ready to burst open. Some houses shout at me. 'Come in,' they cry.

The man who loves life and people shows it in the way he walks along the street. His house would tell us his secret if we could only understand.

Tom Greer

A SLOW-SPEAKING, sensible man, with a thousand friends. He loves wit and has a keen sense of humor. Men respect him for his solidity. When he tells you something, you believe it.

His business is one of the most interesting in town.

As a business man 'Tom' Greer, Riley Thomas Greer — to be exact — reminds you more of a European business man than an American.

The modern American idea of 'bigness' at any cost has not caught him. He is in business now with the same associates who have been with him almost from the beginning. The business is not a corporation but a partnership, and associated with Mr. Greer is his cousin, George W. Greer, who conducts a branch of the business at Pikesville, Kentucky, and Mr. C. C. Stafford of Kentucky.

To a writing man there is a touch of romance to the business of dealing in roots, herbs, and barks. Walking through Mr. Greer's big warehouses, where there are bales of goods on all sides and here and there, spread out on the floor to dry, fragrant roots, barks and herbs, there floats through the mind visions of high mountain valleys, lonely spots along mountain streams, dense mountain forests.

Mr. Greer is a dealer in roots, herbs, and barks, the largest dealer, perhaps, in the country. Products from his warehouse go to cities all over the world.

Here are some of them:

Virginia Snake Root, Stillingia Root, Senega Snake Root, Slippery Elm Bark, well rossed, Shonny Haw Bark.

One hundred and fifty such items on Mr. Greer's price lists. Who would not be a Stillingia if they could, and well rossed, too?

Or a Shonny Haw.

Well do we remember the last time we were well rossed. What a headache we had! But that is neither here nor anywhere else.

Would you know any of these things if you saw them in the forest? Would you know a Pipsissewa? How about a Bugleweed Herb?

People do know them, mountain people, women and boys.

Tom Greer was a boy over in Watauga County, North Carolina. His parents did not have any more money than we have now. As a boy he used to go around gathering Shonny Haw and Pipsissewa. He sold it to a little country store six miles away.

In that country, at that time, they had school only three months a year and then the schoolhouse burned down. Tom Greer missed most of the disadvantages of modern education.

No one ever told him that he was anything special or that Italy lay over the Alps and so he grew up to be the nice quiet man we all know.

It was, from all accounts, a rather hard growing up. There he was, with Marion, Virginia, the nearest railroad station, sixty-five miles north. He went to work in a country store. Already he knew the practical side of gathering roots and herbs and now he learned something about the commercial side. He had got together two or three hundred dollars. You know how that boy had to work and save and go without to get that.

He had, however, got something else too. There was a little company formed, Tom Greer, his cousin George, and two or three others, all mountain men. He had got the confidence of his neighbors.

They sent Tom and his cousin George out to scout the land. Tom landed in Marion and his cousin George in Pikesville, Kentucky. They were both the same kind of men. When they had made up their minds, they had made up their minds.

And so they went back and got their families and came out to the railroad in covered wagons, Tom to Marion and his cousin on to Pikesville.

Tom Greer began business here in a small way — very, very small in fact. He had to teach the mountain people in the hills about Marion the medicinal roots and herbs. Many of them he gathered himself. There was little or no money. Mrs. Greer helped. In fact, Mrs. Greer has become an expert in certain branches of the business now.

Besides roots, herbs, and barks, pollen is now used in some of the modern treatments of diseases such as hay fever and asthma.

Pollen is gathered from the blossoms of all sorts of weeds, flowers and grasses. It is delicate, particular business and must be done by an expert. This has become Mrs. Greer's line.

And in the meantime, all over the hills, people, largely women, go out into the woods to gather the medicinal herbs and barks that are sent into the Greer warehouse and prepared for shipment. The growth of the business has been slow but sure. From a few thousand dollars a year it has grown so that there is now annually shipped from a quarter to a half-million dollars' worth of goods.

The business is run as it was first started. When it was new and at a period of financial stress, Mr. Charles C. Stafford, a well-to-do farmer from near Pikesville, Kentucky, put into the business some six thousand additional working capital and did it against the advice of his banker and merely because he liked the looks of Tom Greer and his cousin George.

For that little act of generosity and keen judgment of human nature, Mr. Stafford has been getting back each year about the full amount he put in and has been getting it for many years. There have been years when he got two or three times that much.

As I said at the beginning, Mr. Tom Greer is like a good many European business men. Many temptations have come to him to spread out, to spread-eagle, to plunge into this or that. However, they have really not been temptations at all.

He has always been interested in his own business. He likes it, never loses interest. Today he is the same quiet unassuming man he was when he came to Marion — some say, laughingly — barefooted out of the hills. He is a man going about his affairs quietly and efficiently, rolling a bit of wit under his tongue, enjoying his town, his neighbors and the business in which he has been so successful.

Snowy Nights

I DON'T SO OFTEN WISH I were rich, but sometimes I do. I am always seeing things I want — a fast red automobile, a grand house to live in. I would like a string of running horses. Also I would keep a few fast trotters and pacers.

I would like to wear silks. Once I had a grand idea. You know how the performers dress at the Grand Opera in the cities. Kingly robes. I thought I would go and get me a lot of second-hand kingly robes and wear them about. Wouldn't I look grand going down Marion's Main Stret in a kingly robe?

If I could only have remained always about thirty-three or thirty-four! A lot of people talk of being tired of life. I am not tired of it. It makes me sick to think I can't go banging about for the next three hundred years.

Watching the show — watching the wheels go round.

You know that Negro song, 'There is a wheel, within a wheel, away up yonder in the sky.'

I like to walk around trying to think why people do as they do, why some are what is called, 'good' and others what is called, 'bad.'

On Sunday night, the seventeenth of March, year of our Lord,

1928. The town was very quiet and still. It had been snowing all day and all the night before.

The snow began with a rain, wetting everything thoroughly, so that the snow, when it came, all stuck.

It was still snowing when I set out from my house. The world was white.

In my mind a line, just snatched out of a book of poems I had been reading. The book by Miss Marjorie Meeker of Columbus, Ohio.

> 'This wary winter that was white so long.'

Winter of life, eh.

> 'This wary winter that was white so long.'

I kept saying the words over to myself as I walked, loving them.

Loving, too, the memory I had of the woman who wrote the lines. I saw her once sitting in her big fine house.

Everyone who lives here knows how white and beautiful that Sunday night was in Marion, Virginia.

I walked out Main Street to where the houses end to the east and then back again, through town to where they end at the west.

It may have been rather late. There was no one abroad. When I had got out west of town, I climbed over a fence into a field.

A few people driving closed cars on the highway. The lights of the cars were nice, playing over the fields and among the branches of trees.

Every limb and twig of the trees outlined in white.

I wishing suddenly and crazily for a horse to ride, a white clean-limbed galloping horse. Thinking of that old painter Rider's galloping horse in the mysterious night. Have you ever seen that painting?

> 'This wary winter that was white so long.'

A white horse, galloping across fields, in and out of white forests.

Or a sleigh with a fine team of trotters or pacers hitched to it, eh? Such a team as I once drove but never owned. Fiery boys they were.

I was working for their owner then — a mere groom — not a proud editor as I am now. Alas, you see, there is no aristocratic blood in me.

Once, on just such another wonder night as that of last Sunday, the owner of that team was away from home. In the barn there was a sleigh with white swans' heads thrust out in front.

I was in love with a little country girl just at that time.

And so, on that night, I stole the team and the sleigh out of the barn, not putting on the sleighbells, not wanting anyone to hear and tell my boss.

Fiery blacks, the team were. The owner was a grand man, such a man as I would like some day to be, but can't quite cut it.

I had managed to slip the team out of town and presently there I was, in the country before a farmhouse, the house in which that girl lived. I hallooed to her. She came out to my call, but her father came too. He said she couldn't go.

The whole world was white that night. There must have been something white and swift and nice in me, in the team and in the girl. There were warm robes in the sleigh.

So the girl stood in tears on the porch of the house. Growling, her father went inside. I said nothing and the girl said nothing.

Suddenly she made a little run down to me and climbed into the sleigh. Her face was white like the night. 'Quick!' she said and we drove off.

That was a ride. Once the black horses ran away. We were crossing a bridge. The sound of their own hoofs on the floor of the bridge frightened them. I let them run until they were tired of it, but did manage to keep them in the road and the sleigh right side up.

And so my country girl and I rode in the white night like a prince and a princess — in the grand manner. What the father said to her when I took her home, I don't know. You may be sure I avoided him. I got one cold quick kiss in the darkness before the house and lit out.

And the man who owned the fine horses never knew. It was a lucky night for me.

'This wary winter that was white so long.'

Wanting my youth back, of course. Walking in the white night in that field that Sunday night, every little bush and weed stood up straight and white. The sky was bluish-black overhead.

Thinking of youth, wanting my own youth to go on and on a long long time, I began thinking how our town might be more gay.

It was then I wanted to be rich. 'If I were only rich!' I cried. Plans began to form in my mind. I would buy me a huge old house with a garden here in Marion.

The house would have big rooms, all with big open fires for cold nights, and there would be a swimming pool in the garden back of the house.

I would publish my two Marion papers in rooms at the front of the house.

And I would have a library with many books and a place to dance and the Marion Band would come and play for the dances on a Saturday night.

And there would be quiet nooks in the house and in the garden for old people to sit and for lovers.

And it would all be free.

And country people would come into town for the fun, and city people would come here to see us. I could think of many people I would like to have come.

Now and then perhaps a poet or a singer or a painter to spend a few days.

And I would walk around like a lord, and edit my papers and dance with the pretty girls and wear the loudest clothes I could buy and stay young forever.

If I were only rich now!

All of this in my head as I walked in that field and in the white road and no one abroad but myself and saying over and over to myself those words of the poet . . .

'This wary winter that was white so long.'

Among the Drifters

THE WORKMEN used to come into my room and talk and lie. It was a large, barn-like room on V—— Street, on the West Side in Chicago. There were a lot of factories out that way and a railroad ran along under my window.

Often enough in that house our talks were interrupted by freight engines shuffling cars up and down outside. The bell rang and sometimes the whistle screamed. Two freight cars went together with a bang.

The room in which we sat was on the second floor of an old frame house. Although the house was not ten years old, the floors already sagged. When a heavy freight train went by outside, the walls trembled.

During the evening a half-dozen pails of beer were brought in from a neighboring saloon. We drank the beer, smoked our pipes, and talked.

We had our philosopher, our mystic, our politician, and there was a man who recited Bobby Burns. He was a Scotchman, of course, an engineer.

The men loved lying to me, they would have liked to have me believe they were all dangerous men.

They were talking one time about death and murder. What do you feel at the moment of death?

How does it feel to kill someone? Suppose you get away with it. How do you feel the rest of your life?

A man used to come in from the next room down the hall, a tall countrified fellow. He was habitually silent. We were always sending him out for beer. You know how young fellows are — 'I'll pay for it, who'll go for it?' The tall fellow — his name was Jake — was always willing. He bought his own share, too, but never drank much.

He never talked much either.

We had been talking of death and killings and all the others had gone out — to their own rooms.

It was a black rainy night and I was sitting by the open window watching the switchmen down below on the railroad tracks. I could see their lanterns in the darkness, the headlights of the engines, the way the rain cut through the streaks of light.

Something queer happened. A shiver ran down my back. When I turned, Jake was standing and looking at me.

His face was a little drawn. There was something queer about his eyes. He had come into the room without making any sound.

When I looked at him, he went and sat in a chair. He was making queer nervous movements with his fingers, opening and closing his fists.

He began to tell me something. Whether it was the truth or not, I do not know. Anyway, he talked.

'They were speaking of killing in here,' he said. 'I killed my wife.'

'I didn't intend to do it,' he said quickly. He had an odd little falsetto note in his voice.

'If I did not intend to kill, you ask me why did I have a gun in my hand?'

I had asked him nothing of the sort, had said nothing about a gun. If he had killed his wife and wanted to tell me about it, it was all right with me.

'It was very simple,' he went on. You meet all sorts when you are an itinerant laborer as I was then. At one time I had been a hobo. You meet queer ones that way, too. They get up all sorts of desperate lies.

'I was in a field above the house,' Jake said. 'I was a farmer then.' If he was trying to tell me a story of himself, he was taking a lot for granted. He was taking it for granted I wanted to hear the story, that I knew something about him. To tell the truth, I wished he would go.

He had, however, got a start on the story and was bound to tell it. I listened, of course.

'I was in the field above the house,' he said again. 'It was depressing weather. I was husking corn and it began to rain.

'When I had got through work, it was almost dark and I started home. I was coming down a muddy lane beside a wood.

'The leaves had all fallen off the trees in the wood.' When he told me that simple fact, he smiled a sickly smile. What he thought was funny about it I don't know.

The leaves had fallen off the trees and there were wet leaves clinging to his shoes.

He said there had been dogs prowling about his farm at night. He had thought he saw one that night going down the hill. He said he was thinking of sheep killing dogs. He mentioned also that during the previous summer there had been tall flowering weeds growing beside the lane in the shadow of the woods.

He seemed to be telling me these details, wanting to get at something, and yet hesitating. Was he fending off telling what he wanted to tell or was he just working me up?

'My farming had gone to pieces,' he said suddenly. 'It was because I had married wrong.' He said he had married a woman he despised. He began to tell me about her.

'I married her because I thought I had to do it,' he said. 'It was what we called in our country, "a shotgun marriage."'

And now he was telling me about his courtship and his marriage. As looking directly at him seemed to make him uncomfortable, I turned my eyes away.

He said he was little more than a boy when he got mixed up with the woman he married and that his father and mother were both dead.

He and his sister were living together on what had been his father's farm. His sister was older than himself. She was engaged to be married, to a school-teacher, he said.

One evening he had gone to a near-by town. He drove there in a buggy. There was a dance in the town, a public dance, but he did not go. He got in with some young men in town and had a few drinks. He thought he might have got a little drunk.

'I started home,' he said. 'It was about eleven o'clock. On the road, just after I got out of town, I met a woman walking and she was crying.

'Her name was Elsie Hardy.'

My visitor explained that the woman he had met in the road belonged to a tough family.

She had ridden into town with her brother — a young fellow Jake knew, a notorious young rough — and when they got to town he found out there was a dance and told his sister to go on home.

She told Jake she had stayed about town hoping to find some one going out her way. She was afraid alone, she said.

Jake had got the woman Elsie into his buggy and he said they were both somewhat shy. The Hardys, he said, lived in a poor mean house over a hill, about a half-mile back from the road and beyond where he lived. There was a short cut over the hill and through a wood. He said he felt a little queer being with her, as the Hardys had all been a rough lot and his own people had been all right.

He walked with Elsie over the hill and through the woods, and as he had described how the wet dead leaves clung to his shoes on another evening, so now he described the pattern of the moonlight on the path in the wood.

'I went crazy,' he said, 'and took the woman. She resisted a little, not much.

'Afterward, and while I was lying with her, her brother came up through the woods.'

He explained that Elsie's brother had two young town men with him and that they had tied their horses in the road near Jake's horse. They were going over the hill to the Hardys' house to get whiskey. They were already drunk.

Of course they had seen Jake's buggy in the road and when they got to the Hardy house, Elsie was not there.

She was in the woods with Jake, behind some bushes. 'I lit out as soon as I could,' he said, 'but what good did that do?'

What he half-expected to happen, he said, did happen. He was working in the field one afternoon, a few months later, and looked up to see Elsie coming across the field. Her brother and father were down below in the wood and had guns slung over their arms. Jake's sister was away from home.

Elsie, he said, came to him and told him her brother and father had said that he, Jake, would have to marry her. 'I'm that way,' she said.

'All right,' he told her.

He spoke of how thin she was. He said her neck was scrawny and thin. 'Her hair was thin, too,' he said.

And so Jake had gone down to his barn, passing Elsie's father and brother in the road without speaking to them and, getting out his buggy, drove Elsie some eighteen miles to the county seat where he got a license and they got married.

When he got home, his sister had heard of what was up and had packed her things and left. He said his sister made a pretty good marriage. She married, he said, a school-teacher.

And so, I gathered, there was Jake, on his father's farm with his wife and she had had a child and it died and he was discouraged and blue. He said the farm belonged half to his sister.

'I hoped to get away,' he said.

He spoke again of the evening — after his marriage — when he had been husking corn. It was night, and rainy and dark.

He said there was a loaded gun in a granary near the barn. You will remember he had already spoken of having thought he had seen dogs when he was in the lane above.

The dogs, he said, were the Hardy dogs. They had already killed some of the neighbors' sheep. He thought they were hanging about his place because Elsie was there.

He took the gun in his hands and went silently around the house and into a neighboring field, wanting to kill one of the dogs. He ached to kill something belonging to the Hardys, he said. He only owned eight sheep and there they were. They were huddled against the fence at the edge of the field. There wasn't a dog in sight.

With the gun in his hand, Jake went from the field around the house to the kitchen door. The kitchen door was standing open. It must have been a warm night. His wife Elsie was cooking something in a pan on the stove. She was preparing his supper.

She was standing beside the stove and had a coal-oil lamp in her hand. She was leaning over the stove and holding the lamp above her head. He put his gun to his shoulder.

What was in his mind he said he did not know. He declared that, except for the one evening when he was with her in the woods on the moonlight night and before her brother came, he had always hated her.

He hated being married to her. 'She had such a scrawny neck,' he said. He was a great fellow for details.

He said he stood looking at her and that he pointed the gun at her head. His hand trembled. It is certain his hands and his voice trembled when he was telling me the tale. If he was a liar he was a good one all right.

He could not bear shooting his wife, so he raised the gun a trifle and shot the lamp out of her hand. The contents of the lamp ran down over the stove.

'Then,' he said, 'there was a blinding flash.' It almost knocked him down. He recovered and stepping forward closed the door.

'I became foxy,' he said. 'What I did was the most natural thing in the world.'

He had closed the kitchen door and had run back up the hill through the darkness to where he had been husking corn. He hid the gun in a corn shock.

As it turned out, no one had heard the shot and now his house was afire. In a short time someone saw the fire from the road, or they saw the reflection against the sky, and came running.

He waited, he said, until they got there before he ran down the hill. Both his house and his barn burned to the ground.

No one ever suspected him, he said. I remember that when he said it he got up off the chair and stood before me.

He declared again that no one had ever suspected him of killing his wife and said that, in fact, he did not kill her. I shot the lamp out of her hand,' he said, and smiled. Then he went out of the room.

It might not have been true. At that time in my life I associated with a lot of mighty queer men. Some of them would have been entirely capable of inventing the tale Jake had told.

They would tell you tales like that and then, if you believed, they laughed.

Whether or not this one was a liar I never found out. As I have said, we were all itinerant workers. He did not come to my room for the next three or four evenings and when I inquired about him of the woman who kept the house she said he was gone.

Most of the men in that house were such abominable liars. He may just have been a liar or he may have been an itinerant workman, drifting about with that on his mind.

Conversing with Authors

FOR A LONG TIME NOW I have been thinking that something should be written giving some rather formal rules for conversations between authors and common people. As the matter stands, both authors and people suffer a good deal through lack of understanding of each other. There are, I am told, some thirty thousand clubs in America that hire authors to come and lecture to them. Authors go to these places when in need of funds and must be met at trains and, as you can see for yourself, the field is pretty rich. Even at a dollar a club, thirty thousand clubs should bring in thirty thousand dollars — a lot of money to an author. I myself have a plan I would like to propose to a few of these clubs. I will lecture in any town on the following understanding, that is to say, twenty-five cents to hear me lecture — a dollar for the privilege of not hearing me.

But we were speaking of the matter of conversations. Authors, as everyone knows, naturally pine for solitude, but they do go about a good deal. I was in Kalamazoo, Michigan, one day, and met ten in the hotel lobby during the afternoon. Authors are becoming so large a part of our population that we should all try to understand them better. On shipboard they usually manage to conceal themselves in some obscure place, say at the captain's table, but ashore they are more in evidence.

They are, of course, very sensitive people. I, myself, have noticed that — when I have lectured somewhere — people, after the lecture, realizing my sensitive nature, are very reluctant about giving me money. As I stay on and on, they grow more reluctant. When the matter becomes pressing, they do not walk up boldly and give me the money, but put it in an envelope. They act as though I were a preacher and had just married someone — or had done something else of which I was ashamed.

It is because they think I am sensitive on the subject of money — and, of course, I am.

But, as I just said, an author, pining for solitude in a strange town, at once goes and tells someone he is there and that he is an author. 'I am the man who wrote *Buckets of Blood*,' he says to the taxi-driver who takes him to the hotel. 'Do not let anyone know. I am very sensitive and love solitude.' He says something of the same sort to the hotel clerk.

At once people, feeling how deeply he loves solitude, come to see him. There is need of a technique. Even among ourselves we authors hardly ever know what to say to each other.

In the first place, I think it would be better if the subject of money were not mentioned. Those of us who make very little money are sensitive on the subject and those who make a good deal are ashamed. The subject had better be left alone. The main thing to bear in mind is our extreme sensitivity.

Also, if he happens to be an American author, I would not ask him who he thinks is the greatest American author. That is also a subject that causes extreme embarrassment. How many times I myself have been asked that question and how it does upset me! I swallow hard, grow a little red in the face, and do not know what to say. Some time ago an editor had the bright idea of having an American poet pick, each month, the man or woman he thought had written the best poem. I was in Chicago at the time and I remember that

Mr. Carl Sandburg, when it came his turn, picked a man whose poem had appeared in a newspaper in a small town, of interior Arkansas, if I remember correctly. No one could get the paper to read. I thought it very clever of Mr. Sandburg. Since that time I work something of the same kind when people ask me about short-story writers or novelists.

Authors are very, very sensitive. You would never believe how sensitive they are. They may not be quite as sensitive as actors, but they run them a close second.

In general it is a bad thing to speak at any great length of an author's work unless you have read a little of it. He will almost always catch you. Critics often do it very well, but they have had a lot of experience. If you haven't much time, quotations may usually be had out of newspapers. In passing an opinion do not use the critic's exact words. Give them a turn of your own.

There is one thing you may always do with safety. This may be worked successfully, even if you have never read a word your author has written. First of all suggest that the mind of the author is too deep for you. Say something like this — 'Your mind is too deep for me, but I always carry away with me a feeling of power and beauty. It is because your sentences are filled with haunting beauty. You do write such beautiful sentences.'

If you will but say something like that, I am sure it will be enough. Bear in mind that no author ever thought himself capable of writing a bad sentence. If you want to win his entire gratitude, not to say fervent devotion, and have an opportunity to look into one of his books, you might commit one sentence to memory. The happiness you will bring to your author will repay you for your trouble. It does not matter what sentence you choose. Choose any sentence. Surely, that will not be very much trouble.

I am only making a point of this because authors are becoming so large a part of our population. We might get into another war. We need to stand together. We should constantly be saying to ourselves — 'See America first.'

But I was speaking of conversations. Or was I telling you how sensitive authors are? They are really very sensitive people.

In going into a room where there are several authors, do not try to please them all. It would be better to pick out one author and devote yourself to him — or her. The others may be left for another time. If you try to speak kindly to two authors on the same occasion and they catch you at it, you will only cause hard feelings. If you can praise the one author at the expense of another, you will bring home to him in the most forceful way the fact of your own discernment. That is because he is so sensitive. For all you know, he may make you the hero of his next book.

It is very nice to ask an author whether or not he takes his characters out of real life. He enjoys that.

It is very unfortunate to approach an author and say to him that you cannot get his books out of the library, that they are always out. This brings home to him the matter of money, it touches, that is to say, upon the question of his income. But it has been agreed that the money question is to be altogether avoided.

If I had more time I would say something about the sensitivity of authors, but you may have noticed that yourself. O, the sensitivity of authors — particularly in the matter of money!

Authors in general do a great deal of swearing under their breaths. That is other people's fault. It is because they are compelled by circumstances to associate so much with people not as sensitive as themselves.

When it comes to the morals of authors . . . Well, after all, this is a matter that, like money, had perhaps better be left alone. It is a delicate subject. It is so easy to make a mistake. Too many people are likely to go up to an author and suggest that, although many other authors may be immoral, they are sure he is not, that he is, in fact, a good man. Something of that sort, carelessly said, may make an author unhappy for months.

I have seen old friendships destroyed by such carelessness as that. An author I knew very well committed suicide after hearing something like that. Whatever you do never question the immorality of your author.

Do not go to an author and tell him that you are too busy to read very much. When you decide to quit drinking, you do not call up your bootlegger to give him the glad news. But this brings up again the question of income and we had already decided to let that subject alone.

It is always very nice, when you are in the midst of a conversation with an author, to suggest to him that his work reminds you strongly of the work of some other man. It makes him very happy. Say to him that, when you read his books, you always begin thinking of Mr. George Moore. Then tell him how much you admire Mr. Moore. Watch the glad, sweet light come into his eyes.

By all means, when you are where authors have congregated, do not speak of anything but books. To speak of the weather, things to eat, horse-races, or any topic other than authors and their work is very rude. Who wants to be rude to an author? It is the one thing we are all trying to avoid.

You are in a room with an author and there he is. Look how handsome he is. As likely as not, if you speak of ordinary things, you will disturb his thoughts. He is sure to be thinking. You may be quite certain that, as you go about your ordinary affairs, he has been consorting with the gods. When you have been in bed and sleeping, he has been among the stars. Authors hardly ever sleep.

The main thing to bear in mind in carrying on conversations with authors is that they are no ordinary beings and do not think ordinary thoughts. If your author is a good author, and I take it for granted you would not associate with him at all if he were not great, the whole purpose of his life is to live quite separated from ordinary people.

He loves the heights and, therefore, wants to be constantly thinking of books. O, how he loves conversing of books, thinking of books! And how, in particular, he loves thinking of and conversing of other men's books! Do not ever let this thought go out of your mind.

Authors really want so little and there are so many of them. They are very, very humble, and as I suggested but a moment ago, O, how sensitive they are! All we need to do to get along better with them is to be a little more thoughtful. I am quite sure that, on account of the growing number of our magazines and the eagerness for intellectual stimulation, so characteristic of Americans in general, the race of authors will grow. That is why the subject is so important. For a long time I myself had the notion that like the Negro race the race of authors would tend to breed out, that they would in short become whiter, but I am losing hope of that.

Authors become thicker and thicker. Hardly anyone can tell when he may be put into position of having to hold a conversation with one of them. We should all try to learn how to do it. I have tried to make some suggestions that may be of help. Perhaps you can think up some for yourself.

The main thing is to be prepared. As I have said, we Americans should stand closer together. Perhaps someone will shortly write a book on this subject. I hope they will. We need more books. That is one of the crying needs of our life.

Some lecture manager or someone who has worked a good deal in a publishing office or has had a good deal of experience at an editor's desk might by a little effort do something on this subject that would be really good. A book might me compiled telling how to converse with each particular author.

We might begin with visiting authors.

However, I dare say it would take too many volumes. It would cost too much. There I go — speaking of money again. You can readily see that I, who am an author myself, do not know how to handle this matter.

Really I would suggest letting authors alone but that I am very fond of some of them. I do not want to see them commit suicide. And then, besides, we are in such crying need of books.

Something will have to be done. Someone with more keenness will have to teach us all how to converse and live with our authors.

Segregation might be a way out of the problem.

one of them. We should all try to learn how to do it. I have tried to make some suggestions that may be of help. Perhaps you can think up some for yourself.

The main thing is to be prepared. As I have said, we Americans should spend close together. Perhaps someone will shortly write a book on this subject. I hope they will. We need more books. That is one of the crying needs of our life.

Some Identified managers or someone who has worked a good deal in a publishing office or has had a good deal of experience as an editor ... might by a little effort do something on this subject that would be really good. A book might me compiled telling how to converse with each particular author.

We might begin with visiting authors.

However I ... say it would take too many volumes. It would cost too much. There I go—speaking of money again. You can readily see that I, who am an author myself, do not know how to handle this matter.

Really I would suggest leaving authors alone but that I am very fond of some of them. I do not want to see them commit suicide. And then, besides, we are in such crying need of books.

Something will have to be done. Someone with more keenness will have to teach us all how to converse and live with our authors. Segregation might be a way out of the problem.

X. THE HERO

Father Abraham: A Lincoln Fragment

Father Abraham: A Lincoln Fragment

No, he is not weak, Sir; but he is eminently a man of the
atmosphere which surrounds him. He has not yet got out
of Springfield, Illinois, Sir. . . . He does not know that
he is President-elect of the United States, Sir, he does not see
that that shadow he casts is any bigger now than it was last
year. It will not take him long to find it out when he has
got established in the White House, Sir.

JUDGE STEPHEN A. DOUGLAS

T HE WRITERS on Lincoln followed Lincoln — and what a lot of
them there have been! They traveled up and down his tracks in slow-
going day trains, rode in buggies and later in automobiles. They thoroughly went over the ground. What a lot of them! Every year more
and more Lincoln books. Historical facts brought forward, challenged
and denied.

'Lincoln told off-color stories. He knew the story of the miner and
the mule, told it with a peculiar gusto, in a high, rather shrill voice
that once heard never could be forgotten.'

'He broke into peals of laughter after telling one of his own stories.'

'Lincoln never told an off-color story in his life. Under his admit-
tedly crude exterior, he was very refined.'

'He never was an agnostic. He was a true Christian.'

There was one man in a long coat who had been a preacher in a city
suburban church, who was intent upon proving that Abraham never
did tell a vulgar story. He may have been right, but surely not in just
the way he meant. He wrote a book about what he found out —
two or three books, in fact — and later he gave up preaching and went
about delivering lectures.

Billy Herndon wrote a book, too. He always did have it in for Mary Todd Lincoln and Mary had it in for him, but Billy got the best of her in the end. While Lincoln was alive and long before anyone ever thought of writing a book or delivering a lecture about him, Mary used to jump on Abraham once a month about poor Billy. Billy had been drunk again and raising hell, as usual, like as not. He just did escape jail once or twice. Then something went wrong at the house. There never was such a house for things to go wrong in. That was the main reason why Abraham, for so many years, stayed away from it so much. Let's say the girl had quit again or the neighbors' chickens had got over the fence and dropped their droppings on the steps by the kitchen door and Mary had got her shoes mussed.

Wow! That was the time for Billy Herndon to get what-for. Mary wanted Abraham to throw Billy out of the law partnership, thought it wasn't respectable, being tied up with him.

And she could talk a blue streak. Did you ever see a nice furry rabbit after it has been skinned? Such a sweet little thing that rabbit, fur so soft and downy! Just the thing to picture on Easter postcards and all that sort of thing.

Then you take the same rabbit skinned, ready for the pot. Better put it in the pot quick. It looks like a dead cat.

That's what Mary could do to Billy Herndon and Billy knew it.

And so, after Abraham was dead and Mary was dead, Billy had his inning. He told, right out in print, that story about how Abraham didn't really want to marry Mary at all and how he went back on her in the face of the whole town on their wedding night. Billy didn't get the shades of that story very well, but never mind that. He never exactly got the shades of anything, really, that Billy.

He became one of the writers, like the preacher in the long coat, like young John Hay, Nicolay, and several very earnest women too — with things of their own to prove — an English lord, and how many others — college professors, historians, almost everyone who had known Abraham, or had thought they knew him. Never such a maker of scribblers as Father Abraham in the end! Even Hill Lamon, Uncle Jesse Dubois, David Davis, Leonard Swett — men like that turned into inkslingers too. Steve Douglas also might have written a book about him had he lived a little longer.

A maker of scribblers! And pictures of his neck-yokes have been reproduced, and pictures of houses in which he lived, of chairs in which he sat. Pictures of Lincoln, a rather ridiculous-looking man, visiting General McClellan after the Battle of Antietam. General Mc-Clellan looking rather like a self-satisfied drygoods clerk — But these all were writers and not the story-tellers. Had they been story-tellers, they would have perceived that Abraham was himself the story-teller, from the beginning.

None of them understood that and perhaps Father Abraham did not understand, but, anyway, it began when he was a young lad and never stopped. Even at the end and after the great struggle, even at Gettysburg and on that dramatic day of the first inauguration, when Steve Douglas did that nice little bit about holding Abraham's hat, even then and always it was story-telling.

I mean that he had a certain gift not clearly understood by many people. When it appears, people tend to call it selflessness, but that is not exactly what it is. It is a certain ability to separate something deeply yourself from the rest of you, put something deeply yourself out before you. You see yourself in a mental image. Seeing yourself in a certain situation makes you understand the motives and actions of people in that situation. You look at this idea, this part of yourself; as Carl Sandburg would say, 'Take a good look at yourself.' You walk about it, think about it. The point is, it is no longer yours. It has rights of its own, laws of its own. Perhaps it is in a piece of your work. There is a block of stone, say, or a block of wood. It may be carved now only in such or such a fashion. Or a canvas. Paint may be spread on it, but only in such or such a way. They talk about the plastic arts, the absolute art of sculpture. As if all arts were not absolute in this way.

This faculty for placing a part of oneself outside of oneself definitely developed itself in Lincoln. What separated itself from him became like an object.

Since he had this faculty, surely he belongs to me, an American story-teller, as I to him.

This is certain, that since I was a boy, I have been deeply feeling the personality of the man, Lincoln. As is the case with so many other Americans, he is the figure closest to my heart. When I was a boy, the shadow of Abraham Lincoln was still heavy over my land. The Civil War was not so far away. On all sides one found men who had taken part in it. Something of the flavor of life in all of our town in Civil War days, in the days before the Civil War in fact, clung to the life I saw and led. There were no electric lights in the small Middle-Western town in which I lived. The streets were not paved. In winter mud lay deep in them. There was but one telephone in the town.

Women had large families, led hard laborious lives. The community was closely drawn together. There were no movies, no phonographs. Radios were undreamt of. In such a community, while there was a passion for education, the idea of education was an intellectual one. It meant the gathering of facts, storing them away in the mind. There was no thought of educating the senses. The very notion of any education that might come to mean complete sensual pleasure in life would have seemed shocking.

Politics was the most vital issue in men's lives. When there was an election, our men went in procession through the street. They carried kerosene torches. Everyone was deeply excited. Men still believed that the tone of their lives might be noticeably changed by the defeat or success of a political party.

There were fights in the saloons. Men standing about chewing tobacco, telling off-color stories.

'Have you heard the one of the mule and the miner?'

Some of the stories had what was called a 'nub.' That meant that there was a point made. Something ridiculous or pretentious in what William Dean Howells was later fond of calling 'our common lives' was shown up. And there would be my father in the saloons with the men, telling his stories. He was locally quite famous. And Lincoln used to figure in many of my father's stories.

The figure of the man Lincoln took root in my boyhood mind. When I became a man, I constantly read books about him, about the background whence he came. Then, after I became an author, the figure of a man I called Lincoln has kept in my imagination. I shall try to make a picture of that figure. Nor am I going to rake over the Lincoln field, to take trips to New Salem in Illinois, to Springfield, Illinois, to read old newspapers. My excuse is the scene of Lincoln's death, the pronouncement from some member of his cabinet, 'Now he belongs to the ages.' It is the penalty of great men, artists, and others, not only to be misunderstood, but to belong to the ages, and surely if America has produced a great man, Lincoln is he. And the ages, too, have always belonged to the tellers of stories.

How about a look, then, at my Father Abraham?

I

Nothing could have been more astonishing than that he was to be President. But it was not altogether astonishing when it came. There had been a hint of it in Abraham's mind for a long time. The man had always been, from the first, both proud and humble. Sometimes thoughts within him made him sink into depths, feel himself lower in the mire than the pigs that used to lie in the mud in the streets of Elizabethtown, Kentucky, where he was a child.

At the same time there was something in him that held him erect. He was like a tree, having its roots in black mire, its upper branches reaching toward the sky.

Sometimes he tried to figure out his own purpose. He had been doing that since he was a boy. It seemed to him he had no purpose. He did not feel himself a leader. He was a questioner, a groper. In those moods, it would have been utterly incredible to him that he was, in fact, to become the hero of his country, the one man of all the men America has produced who was to stay in people's minds as representing something finer in themselves.

It was not that Abraham did not think there was fineness in himself. He was an odd contradiction, knew himself as an odd contradiction.

In the first place, there was no question but that he was coarse. He was the son of a man named Thomas Lincoln, a no-account, a weak, vacillating man. There was nothing in his inheritance to make him feel rich, self-assured, firm on his feet. Perhaps the men with whom he associated, had always associated, had also helped to make him coarse. He was peculiarly subject, in outward things, to the influence of others.

A man with a coarse homely body, legs too long, skin yellow and dry-looking, hair coarse, face too long. It was hard to think he could ever be attractive to women.

A man needs women. He needs to feel that a few women, at least, have found him physically attractive. Such an experience makes a man walk about more firmly. Abraham had thought about women a great deal, more than anyone ever guessed. Before he went up to Springfield to become a lawyer, when he was in the country store at New Salem and later when he was postmaster there, he used to think of women a great deal.

The country and small-town girls of Abe's day were shy and awkward in the presence of young men. Abraham was shy and awkward in their presence.

When he was a storekeeper in Offut's store and later when that fellow Berry ran the store and when a girl came in and after making her purchase went out, he felt intensely relieved. 'My God!' he said to himself. Young men who could go freely about with girls, who could laugh and talk with them, aroused in him an intense jealousy. He wanted to hate such young men and, at the same time, he wanted, with all his soul, to be such as they.

There were not many young women about. Well, he was a young man. Since he had been a child, he had always liked being where older women were at work. He liked sitting unnoticed in a room with them. They were sewing or cooking. His stepmother, Sally Lincoln, was cutting bread.

Another woman standing at the door of the Lincoln house, a neighbor woman.

Quiet voices, a sense of well-being in a boy's heart.

When you are older, you begin having another feeling. There is a vague, shadowy hope.

Men were always hanging about the store. They liked Abraham. You know how men are, at least that kind. They were country yokels, hired men working on farms, farmers' sons.

In Abraham's town, no one had any money, no one wore good clothes.

During the evenings, especially on Saturday nights, crowds gathered around the store. The men all chewed tobacco and drank whiskey.

In the winter time their boots and clothes were covered with mud. The main street of New Salem was deep in mud.

Frozen mud in the streets in the winter time. Abraham's feet were always cold. His hands were cold. Both his arms and legs were too long. The blood, perhaps, could not get down there.

The store at New Salem was in a cheap frame building and in winter days and nights the cold winds crept in. Men came tramping in out of the deep snow. Hard balls of snow had formed on their boots.

They stood in the store and stamped like horses. They sat on boxes and put their feet against the stove. Steam arose. There was the rank smell of stables and of clothes worn a long time without washing. The stove sat in a box of sawdust. The men spat tobacco juice into the sawdust.

When the men stamped on the floor, everything in the store shook. There were cups for the whiskey-drinkers on a shelf at the back. They clinked together. The whiskey was in barrels. Abraham was the only man in town who could lift a barrel of whiskey in his two hands and drink from the bunghole.

Wood was cheap. Abraham or some other hanger-on put great chunks of it in the fire. The stove grew red-hot.

The men standing or sitting about chewed tobacco, drank whiskey, and talked. Abraham neither chewed nor drank. There might have been something deep down inside him offended by the sight of the men chewing. The taste of whiskey rather sickened him. He often talked more than any of the others. At other times he was strangely silent.

No one knew it, but once he had been drunk. It wasn't while he was running a store, but afterward, after he had been to the state legislature and to the Black Hawk War. A lot of young men were in the store drinking one night.

They stayed until quite late. It was one of Abraham's quiet times. Usually he was in the forefront of everything, talking politics, telling stories, wrestling with some strong young fellow, taking part in the horse-play that sometimes went on. But that evening he was in another mood.

When he grew silent, you could almost feel his silence.

Sometimes it was a kind of deep discouragement with everything about his life. He became morose. It was as though his own mind plunged deep down into his own long body.

He thought he saw himself as he was.

He was more ambitious than any man in town. There was something in him wanted to rise in the world.

Rising in the world might mean, for one thing, getting rid of the stigma of his family. His father was no good. Abraham had tried to do his duty by his father, he had stayed with him, worked for him without pay longer than most sons, but how glad he had been to get away.

The man, Thomas Lincoln, Abraham's father, was ignorant and shiftless. Even in a poor community he was always the poorest man.

It was all a matter of mismanagement. His father was a visionary, a poor, feeble visionary.

Abraham knew he also was a visionary. The thought frightened him. The world was the world. You had to study the world. Most of all you had to study men. You found out what men were like. Then you managed them. Abraham already knew he could do that. He had got elected to the state legislature. That meant getting men's confidence, getting them to vote for him.

You don't toady to men to do that, not if you are Abe's kind. You say to them, 'Go and vote for me.'

No, you don't do it that way either. You make them go and do it without saying anything directly. They are with you, they see you, hear you speak. To themselves they say, 'Here is a strong honest man.' Say it yourself and they may believe you for a time, but not for long. You have to make them say it, make their hearts say it.

It means not putting yourself up too high or down too low. You have to be patient, have understanding. Understanding comes very, very slowly.

Abraham's mother was what she was, too. There were stories about her. She was said to have been an illegitimate — a bastard.

That meant a lot in the community in which Abraham lived.

He got to thinking about his family sometimes and that led to thoughts of himself. He was so awkward, so ungainly. He would be going along all right, would be quite cheerful in fact, and then some little thing would happen.

It was always connected with people, sometimes with men, more often with women.

A young girl had come into the store that afternoon. She wanted something — a pound of coffee. Abraham gave it to her. They were alone together. He tried to say something. If he could only, for example, make a pretty speech. He tried.

The girl went out laughing. What a come-down. It sent him off into a long period of gloom.

He was in such a period of gloom that night. No one knew. He was alone in the store. There had been a lot of young fellows in that evening and he had been silent and gloomy while they talked.

While they had been talking, he had been sprawling on the counter, his long legs on the floor, his head in his hands. No one had paid much attention to him. Even when he was a young man, he was called 'Old Abe.'

'Old Abe is in one of his spells, let him alone.'

It was a good thing he was physically strong. If he had been a weak man physically, one always having imaginary or real illnesses, like his father . . .

In that community he would have had no chance. New Salem was full of ignorant young men. Ignorant men are likely to be cruel. He already knew that.

Plenty of bullies about. A bully is a cruel man. He likes to see other people suffer.

Perhaps a bully is a weak man. He is ashamed of his own weaknesses. If I can make some other man seem weaker than I am!

The young man had gone out of the store. Sometimes, when men get together like that in a frontier store, things go pretty well. They get to telling stories. Abe was good at that. He could take an old story that had been told over and over and give it a little twist of his own.

He made up stories, too. Sometimes his stories were a little daring. There was a story around town that he, Abe Lincoln, did not believe in God.

What had he to do with God, one way or the other? At that time he neither believed nor disbelieved. He tried to keep out of religious discussions.

The stories about his being an unbeliever had sprung out of his talent for story-telling. Sometimes he just made his stories up. Something happened. A little series of things happened.

There were creeks running down through that part of Illinois to the Sangamon River. In the spring, when the heavy rains came, the creeks were flooded.

A man got two calves drowned.

Abe told the story. He had made it up. He said the man, whose name was Hank Bardshore, stood on the bank of the creek looking at the two drowned calves. They had been washed up against a pile of driftwood. When he told the story, Abe got a little carried away. He said the man, Henry Bardshore, stood on the banks of the creek and saw the two dead calves. There was a neighbor with him.

'Take him up one side and down the other and God Almighty does about as much harm as he does good,' Abe said Hank Bardshore had said. He imitated Hank's voice saying it.

Hank hadn't said anything of the kind. It was sacrilegious. When Hank Bardshore heard about it, he was half-mad, half-pleased.

It was funny all right. Everyone laughed when they heard the story. Hank Bardshore got credit for wit he did not have.

Abe, who told it, who really made it up, got credit for being too free with God. He hadn't been thinking about God at all.

There was a man over in the next county, really a sacrilegious man, who spoke of God as 'John R. God.' Abe heard him do it when he was over there. The man was a natural kind of showman as Abe was himself. He was entertaining some men in a tavern.

He spoke of God that way and it pleased Abe. Afterward in the store he got it off himself. He spoke of God as 'John R. God' two or three times, and then afterward spoke of him as old 'J. R.' A man came and said something about snow. 'Do you think it will snow?' 'I don't know,' Abe said. 'It's up to J. R.'

That sort of thing is all right and gets a laugh, but in a community such as Abe lived in, it gets you in bad repute.

People begin to say you don't believe in God. The story that you are an agnostic or an atheist or something of that sort gets around.

There were such stories around about Abe. They came back to him.

The stories made him sad. He wanted to be liked, to be popular, had an intense desire to be popular.

Sometimes he got to thinking. Something happened like the girl laughing at him trying to make a pretty speech.

Or one of the men hanging about the store said something. He made some reference to Abe's long legs, or to the fact that he, Abe, did not believe in God.

The other men paid no attention. The remark was forgotten.

Abe was, however, more sensitive than the man knew. He went into a period of deep gloom. 'You could cut it with a knife, like cheese,' someone said.

Abe did not hear. He was half-lying with his head in his hands as he was that night when he got drunk.

Suppose you think yourself utterly worthless, low. You come of low people. There is in you an intense desire to rise. You know you can't.

You are too ignorant, too low-down.

You get to thinking about it and fall into a gloom that makes your heart ache.

He was thinking about it that night in the store, at New Salem, when he was postmaster there.

There were some young fellows in the store drinking, chewing tobacco, telling stories, and talking politics and religion.

It got late and they all went home. 'Good night, Abe,' they said. He did not answer.

They laughed at him and went out.

There was no one in the store but Abe and the storekeeper. He was a small fat man with several days' growth of beard on his face. He started putting out the lights.

Then, when there was but one light left burning, he stood and looked at Abe. Abe did not move. The storekeeper took a key out of his pocket and put it on the counter near him. He might have sensed something of Abe's deep gloom. It was like a disease that numbs all the senses. Nothing touches other men like the sadness of a strong man.

The storekeeper felt something stir within himself. His voice grew gentle, 'You lock up, Abe,' he said. He went along the street in the darkness to his house feeling oddly tender. 'Abe's all right,' he said to himself.

Abraham did not know how long he stayed there that night, like that, sunk in gloom.

Later, he aroused himself. He never had drunk whiskey before that night. Whiskey was five cents a drink. He put twenty-five cents on the counter where the storekeeper would find it in the morning. He took one drink and then another and another. When he had taken five drinks, he managed to put out the lights and close the store.

It was snowing outside. The streets were silent and empty. He was drunk.

He was staying, boarding, at a tavern. There was a girl there named Rutledge. Her father owned a mill. They were solid, nice people. The girl, whose name was Ann, had taken his fancy. He thought if he could get her, if she would marry him, it would be like beginning to live. At night he dreamed of it. The girl had never seemed to him to be laughing at his tall awkward body. He was in love with her, but had not told anyone.

He never thought he could get her, that he could get any such woman. He thought Ann was beautiful. What would she be wanting of a man like him?

That night, when he got drunk, the time no one knew about, he got sick. He had walked out of town, not daring to go home in the condition he was in, wading in deep snow. He had stopped by a rail fence.

He was terribly sick, had to hold on to the fence to keep from falling.

He realized that he was near a house out that way. A dog came from the house. Evidently the dog knew him. He came up quite close, smelled of Abe's long, floppy legs — they were surely floppy that night — then went silently away.

Abe thought the dog had contempt for him. He did not blame the dog.

But even when he was drunk, Abe kept his sense of humor. He never quite lost that. He thought sometimes, if he ever did lose it, he would go insane.

He thought it very silly and foolish for a man, built as he was, with such long ridiculous legs, to get drunk.

There were some men who could do it, while others couldn't. Doing it might be a great relief if it did not make a man sick. It might give a man boldness.

Well, it made Abe sick. It made him more ridiculous than he was when sober.

It was like getting women. Some men can do it, others can't.

Abe could not drink, he could not get any pleasure out of drinking. He found it out that night.

It was a good thing, he thought, that no one knew. He never tried it again.

II

It was late that night when Abe reached the tavern. The cold had sobered him, but his hands and feet were icy cold. The front door of the tavern was not locked.

Abe went in and upstairs to his room. It was a bare little room. He undressed and got into bed.

It was freezing cold in bed too. The night was very silent now. It had quit snowing and the moon had come out. There was one small window in his room. It was covered with frost.

He did not mind the cold too much. If you cover up and are patient, warmth gradually comes. He remembered plenty of other cold nights, heavy snow on the ground, trees in the forest cracking with cold. It was that way when he was a child in Kentucky and later at Pigeon Creek. Pigeon Creek, the Lincolns lived all winter in a cabin that had only three sides.

Abe had got a sense of something strange and in some way lovely out of many such cold, lonely nights. When he was a small lad at Pigeon Creek, his father went off to Kentucky in the winter, hoping to get him a new wife.

That was shortly after Abe's mother died. The Lincoln children were left alone. When he was a mere child in Kentucky, a neighbor woman had taught him not to be afraid at night in the dark. He and the woman were in a room and the woman hung an old dark dress over a window. 'Night is like that,' she had said to the child. 'Everything is the same as in the day. The whole world is just an enormous room with something hung over the window.'

The figure had caught the boy's fancy. It had made him unafraid in the dark. It had made him able to walk in the forest at night, hearing strange sounds unafraid.

The world was an enormous room, but it was too empty. That was why he wanted someone in the room with him.

He wanted someone to lie close beside him at night, feeling the warmth of that other person.

He was cold, cold. It wasn't just physical cold.

He lay in the room in the tavern thinking. After he had been in one of his depressed times, his head was particularly clear. The drinking he had done that night had also done something to him.

It had made him desperately sick, but after such a sickness sometimes an odd clearness comes. The mind is like a cool running stream.

He was in the room in the tavern, the cold moonlight coming in, and his mind was like the moonlight. He was too much alone, had always been too much alone. He was too cold.

The men, the young men about the store and on the streets of New Salem, warmed something in him sometimes, but they froze it too.

The young men were like himself. Most of them constantly got drunk. Abe had tried that, had tried it that very night.

With the young men he talked, wrestled, and told stories. Sometimes when he was with them a sudden warmth of companionship seemed to well up out of them and out of himself.

They all became a little excited. Stories were told. Abe could outdo them all in story-telling.

Everything seemed to get warmer and warmer. There was a kind of mutual excitement. Abe broadened his stories. He had made the others laugh. He would make them laugh harder.

All the others felt what Abe felt.

There was something fine going on. There was something coarse and ugly going on.

It was inside Abe. It was inside all the others.

It was like a white boy running a race with a beast.

You get odd notions in your head, living a long winter alone in a lonely cabin, with other children. Sometimes at night you lie awake. You can't get warm enough to sleep. You get odd notions later when you are a young man and in particular if you are a young man different physically from all the others about.

You have longer legs, longer arms, you are stronger. Without your exactly intending it, things center about yourself. It is like being the tallest tree in a forest. Thousands of other trees standing there. Everyone looks at the tall tree.

You have to be careful not to be self-conscious, not to be always showing off.

You have constantly, every minute of the day, to fight something in yourself.

It was the race between the white boy and the beast, between what is fine and what is ugly, pretentious, evasive.

Profanity in the air.

Abe told stories. He had pride in his story-telling — to make every story have a nub.

Sometimes he got too eager, wanting perhaps to be liked, to keep everyone laughing.

His stories grew coarser. He told stories without point — just to be telling them.

There was a word on his lips, on the lips of the others.

A moment of abandon. Some grip Abe was always trying to keep on himself was gone.

He was a horse that had run away, a strong horse. His laughter became horse laughter — his words horse words.

He who loved to give a story a certain delicate twist of his own had lost his power.

He became ashamed, deeply ashamed. Where there had been a warmth of companionship, there was now but coldness. It was a familiar coldness to Abraham.

Voices of other men drifting away from him. He got sometimes in the midst of other men feeling as alone as though he were in a vast desert or at the North Pole.

Or in the forest.

The race with the beast.

Others perhaps feeling the same thing. That might be why so many young men in New Salem got drunk. They lived as Abe did, in ugly rooms in ugly little houses. They were poor as he was. Drinking carried them off into a world of illusion. They became in fancy mighty men.

The man who was naturally weak and afraid became strong. Then he lied and boasted. Fights started among the young men. Sometimes they cut each other with knives.

Blood on the floor of one of the stores, or the tavern floor, in the dirt of the road before some store.

But no, loneliness in the forest was somewhat different. Something besides yourself was living there. Trees that stand up above other trees as you, physically, stood up among men.

He remembered once, when he was in the war — the Black Hawk War that wasn't a war — he left the men of his company and went into the dense forest.

He went to a tall tree, taller than any other tree in sight. There was no one there. He patted the rough bark of the tree as though it had been a friend.

'You are all right,' he said to the tree.

It was a childish thing to do. He laughed to himself.

In the bed that night, after he had been drunk, he was not laughing.

He was in love, had been dreaming dreams. If he could marry Ann Rutledge, if she would have him, he would have all his life a companionship that would destroy his inner loneliness.

He would have someone warm and close to himself, a part of himself and yet not himself.

Ann Rutledge was gentle, she was quiet.

He was terribly afraid she would not have him. He had been afraid that evening in the store, had been seized with fear, while the others were talking.

The fear had grown stronger and stronger. It had become a kind of ecstasy of fear. If he could not get Ann Rutledge, he would be alone always. In the end, the coarser side of his own nature would come more and more to the surface. He would sink to the level of the men about him. Perhaps he had already done that.

Abe Lincoln was a man of his generation. There was a sensual side to his nature, but he was afraid of it. Sometimes he thought of Ann in a very intimate way. His imagination ran away with him. In fancy he saw her beside him in bed. She was naked. His hands touched her body.

He was greedy. It was the same feeling he had when, with men, he was too greedy to make them laugh, to make himself the central figure.

Greediness leading to what he felt was vileness, emphasizing the wrong thing.

It was because he was at bottom vile.

He sank into one of his periods of deep gloom. Perhaps his drinking alone that night had come about because he hoped, through drinking, to surrender to his own greediness.

He might even have thought that, through drink, he would find courage to creep into Ann Rutledge's room. If she would not have him as a husband, he would take her, anyway. He was physically strong, could do what he pleased. After he had taken her, she would have to marry him.

'Do I want her for just that purpose, to satisfy the greedy, lustful side of myself?'

Abe Lincoln asked himself that question that night in the room in the tavern. It was almost morning. His body had grown almost warm.

He got out of bed and stood on the floor in the little room. Ann Rutledge was asleep in another room upstairs in the tavern.

He knew where her room was. He went out into a little hallway. The floors were very cold. When he had gone to bed, he was still weak from the illness brought on by his drinking. He had merely taken off his long trousers and his huge socks.

He had got into bed in his shirt. Now he made a ridiculous figure in the moonlight, with his long bare legs, his head almost touching the ceiling.

When he went outside the room into the hallway, he had to stoop. He went to Ann's door, stood by her door, he wanted to be closer to her.

His legs and feet were freezing. He began to shiver. His teeth chattered.

What would happen if Ann came out at the door? He had a moment of fancying he might have courage to take her into his arms. She might be clad in her nightgown.

Her warm body, fresh from sleep against his cold body. Something flamed up in him — desire, blind greedy desire, he thought it.

Once he even raised his right hand to knock on her door, perhaps to knock the door down. He was strong enough. Well, he knew himself better than that. There never was a chance he could do it.

In the forest that time, in the presence of the tallest tree in the forest, he had patted the tree with his hand.

'You are all right,' he had said to the tree.

'Abe Lincoln, you are a fool, you are an old fool,' he said to himself that night in the tavern.

He said the words to himself softly as he went back into his own room and got again into his bed.

He was icy cold again and would have to wait a long time to get warm.

Well, he had been cold before. He knew how to wait. He was conscientious, some men thought childishly conscientious. The store-keeper had left the key to the store in his possession; had asked Abe to lock the store.

He began wondering if he had locked it. Getting up again, he put on his clothes and went through the icy streets to the store door.

It was locked all right. He would have to get up early to return the key. It was already so late that there was no use going to bed again.

There was a stove downstairs in the cabin. He lighted a fire. When at last he grew warmer, he slept a little, sitting upright in the chair with his mouth open.

He was dreaming of Ann. It was a good thing for his suit she did not see him then. When he had been ill he had made a mess on the front of his coat. It had frozen there.

III

It was the spring of 1837 when Abraham Lincoln moved to Springfield, Illinois. Birds were singing in the town, farmers were planting crops. In new cleared land, the logs and bushes cleared during the winter were being piled in great piles and fired. The smoke curled up through the low branches of trees. On some of the trees the green had begun to show. Lincoln rode to Springfield on a borrowed horse. It wasn't a very good one. The better horses were all at work in the fields.

Lincoln had been studying law. When he and Berry had the store at New Salem, he had, by a lucky accident, got hold of a copy of Blackstone. He had read it as though it were the most absorbing book in the world.

It was not that he was a student or had the student's type of mind.

He had just passed through a dark time, one of the darkest times of his life. Studying had been an intense relief. He had been at it hard all that winter. He thought it had helped to keep him from going insane.

After all his doubts of his own courage, he had, during the summer before, asked Ann Rutledge, of New Salem, to marry him and she had said she would.

Almost immediately after she became ill. She died. Her death came in the late fall, just as the leaves were dying on the trees.

There had been an hour that to Abe Lincoln was the blackest of his life. Ann Rutledge was dying and he was sent for. He went into the room where she lay.

She was too ill for much talk. In such times of serious or dangerous illness in a frontier community, neighbor women came in. There were several such women in the house. Abe always remembered sharply one of the women. She was an extraordinarily tall woman with a peculiar mouth. The mouth was like the mouth of a squirrel. The teeth, not white like a squirrel's, little but long and discolored, protruded over her lower lip. The teeth were wide apart. She might have been a woman of thirty-five or even forty. No doubt she was the wife of some man of the town.

She was in the room where Ann lay when Abe went in. Everyone in town knew that Ann and Abe were engaged. The woman was standing near Ann's bed. She was like Abe in that she was so tall; her head almost reached to the low ceiling. There was a strand of yellow hair hanging down over her face. Her hands were large, like Abe's hands.

Perhaps he had noticed her particularly because he had been told that Ann was dying. He looked at the strange woman because he did not dare look at Ann.

The woman had passed silently out of the room. As she went out, she laid one of her large hands on Abe's shoulder.

It might have been the touch of the strange woman's hand that had saved him from insanity.

Abe's despair that day did not come from the belief that the woman he was losing was the most lovely of women. Since he had loved Ann, he had never compared her with other women.

She was his woman. To him she had become a thing of utter loveliness, of infinite sweetness.

Whether or not she was all he then thought her, Abe later did
not know. She was that to him. She and Abe had talked but little.
During the summer they had walked out together a few times. When
they came together they were often silent — two dumb young things
under the summer trees, under the summer moons.

To Abe, her interest in him, her consenting to be his wife, had been
enough. One evening he had been with her and suddenly had got
courage to ask the question.

Perhaps she was somewhat like himself. There was something
reticent in her nature. She had not answered for what had seemed a
long time and then had said simply that she would marry him.

He hadn't even kissed her. It was Sunday evening and she had
been to church. Abe hadn't been. He had met her at the church door
and had asked if he could walk home with her.

They had gone directly home, walking very slowly. He had asked
her and had been answered.

Afterward he had to ask her people. That wasn't so hard.

It had been for him a joyous quiet time. After he knew he was to
have her, a passionate longing to hurry up the day of their marriage
crept over him. He held it down, said nothing. He would let her fix
the time. His reticence was due to the feeling that had come to him
that night in the winter as he lay in the cold bed.

He wanted possession of her body and was afraid of the feeling.
He was afraid because he wanted something else now. There was a
dreadful responsibility in marriage. What was it? He could not give
it a name.

It was a possibility of long, quiet possession. He had kept pushing
his passions back and back. Ann Rutledge might have been doing
that with herself. She might have loved him, wanted him, as he did
her.

He was sure of one thing. If he were loved as he wanted to be, the
realization of it would have to come slowly.

More and more, as the time for marrying her drew nearer, he had
held something within himself back and back. No other woman in
his life ever aroused his passions as Ann Rutledge had. Indeed, there
was no other woman he could not have lived without. Later, he knew

that, had he never got another woman afterward, his life, the tone of his life, would not have been much changed. But, had Ann lived and had he not gotten her, he would have gone to pieces. He knew that.

It was because his passions were so thoroughly aroused at the time that he wanted to hold them down. On some nights he could not sleep for wanting her. He got out of bed and read law, made himself read law.

When he had been with her, usually on Sunday evenings, and there were others about, other young men and women, he stayed with the young men, talking with them. He had been ashamed that anyone should see how much he cared for Ann, ashamed even that she should see.

And now she would never see.

When he went into the room where she lay dying, it was late in the afternoon.

He knew she was going to die as soon as the other woman, the tall one with the squirrel-like mouth, had gone away.

Ann must have known, too. He sat in a chair beside her bed. They did not talk. She might have been too ill for words. Perhaps she did not know him.

He took her hand. They were alone. He wanted to crush the hand — it was a small plump hand — in his own big one, but didn't. He held it lightly.

Ann moaned a little, said a few incoherent words. Time passed. To Abe it seemed he might have been sitting like that for days. As a matter of fact, he was in the room with Ann but twenty minutes.

Then the doctor came for his visit. He was a heavy-looking short man with gray whiskers growing on each side of his face. He wore a fancy vest. There were stains on his vest. No doubt he was a tobacco-chewer, a slovenly man. Two women came into the room with him.

Abe got up out of his chair. It was the most painful thing he ever did. When he raised a leg to walk, it was as though the doctor standing there were cutting the leg from his body.

On such occasions everyone is polite, everyone is kind.

Abe knew, a long time afterward, that, had Ann Rutledge lived, had he married her, the marriage might well have been like any other marriage. Life with her might have killed the ambition in him that later made him rise in the world.

Although he was then but young, he had always been a shrewd observer of people. He knew how marriages usually turn out.

In every marriage there is, however, a chance. Men like Abe Lincoln are after something in marriage. It is a plunge into the dark, deliberately taken on the chance of coming out into the light.

Something Abe wanted, that he always wanted and never got.

He went out of Ann Rutledge's living presence and into the streets. It was late summer. Already the days were growing short. Abe walked down through the little main street of New Salem and into the country.

He did not stay in the road, but climbed a fence and crossed a field. He thought of suicide. He went into a wood and stood with his back to a tree.

The black hour had come. Ann was dying in the room in the house in town. She might already have died. A man with a mind like that of Abraham Lincoln's must sometimes let it have play. He can hold on to himself most of the time, but sometimes he lets go.

He began thinking about himself and his chances in life. If he had got Ann, he might have settled down in New Salem. The town was small, a mere backwoods settlement. However, life could be lived there as it could in any other place.

You live your life in your own house, in a few people about you. A man who is really married lives in his wife. She lives in him.

Before marriage he has seen life through his own eyes. Afterward he must see it through two people's eyes. He is no longer a solitary thing walking around. He is two people.

Thinking Ann Rutledge beautiful and having always, since he had grown up out of boyhood, having thought of himself as physically ugly, he was to have shared in Ann's beauty.

It would have become his beauty, a part of himself.

What he was losing in her death was an abstract thing.

Losing her would be like losing the sense of truth, of God. He put it to himself that way.

It seemed to him that without her, he would always be a crippled man. He grew desperate. 'I can't! I can't!' he cried aloud.

His shrill voice rang out in the silent wood. There was no one else there. He had walked a long way from the road. It was the same shrill voice that was always making men laugh in the town and in the store.

The forest in which he stood was not empty. There was a waiting kind of silence down within himself that was unfathomable. There was a stillness, an emptiness that hurt. His long body ached with it. Had he had a knife with him or a gun, he might have shot or stabbed himself. The physical pain of a knife or a gun wound would have been a relief. Once he even felt in his pocket, hoping to find a pocket knife.

'If I had one, I would open a vein in my arm. I could die quietly here, bothering no one. The blood would come slowly out of my body.'

There were noises outside himself, the little noises of nature. A man on horseback passed on the distant road. He heard the clatter of the horse's hooves on the hard road.

He heard a little wild animal run through the forest.

It was quite dark outside Abe and within. He did not know how long he stayed in the wood that night.

There was a man named Bowlin Green who lived on a farm near New Salem with his wife. It was a house he had often visited. The Bowlin Greens were gentle people, friends of Ann Rutledge. They were simple good people who had come out into the new country and settled on a little farm near Clary's Grove. They hadn't fitted in there, being unable to swear, drink whiskey, take part in the rough-and-tumble political meetings with which the community entertained itself. They had settled down on their small farm and planted flowers all about the house, and Ann had found out about them. She had taken Abe there two or three times.

He went that night to Bowlin Green's house, stayed there all that fall and a part of the winter. They were glad to have him. Bowlin Green would not take any money for his board.

It was Bowlin Green's wife who had told him when Ann died. He had not shed any tears. When she told him, his body did not even tremble.

He had renounced something, the hope of Ann's living, that night in the wood, and with it something else.

He had renounced the hope of the life of direct personal love. Abe did not put that thought into words then or later. He was to marry and have children.

It did not matter. He was to live his life without direct personal love. The woman he might have loved was dead. Abe knew it that night in the woods. He knew it when he went from the woods to Bowlin Green's house. To keep the thought from growing too strong in him, he spent all that winter studying.

IV

Not to be too eager, too ambitious, but not to stand aside and lose all. Yet if you are poor, an unsightly man, without social graces, there are many delicate things in life you will never get.

The dream Abe Lincoln had of a life led with Ann Rutledge might have been just a dream. He had to give it up, but in giving it up did not give up all.

Bowlin Green and his wife at New Salem had got something in life. The man did not come to hang about the store with other men at night. Both he and his wife worked hard. There was little money to be spent. They made every cent count for something.

On a frontier farm things are usually done in a large, rather slovenly manner. Life is in that style. The house in which people live and the stores in the town are thrown together hurriedly. There is always the feeling of impermanency. New people were always coming into town. Every town dreamed of becoming a city. There was a great restlessness all through the great central portion of America in the heart of which Abraham Lincoln lived.

His own father had drifted into Indiana from Kentucky. He drifted from Kentucky to Illinois. When he went from Kentucky to Indiana, he went following a dream. In Indiana he built a house and there his wife died. He went back to Kentucky, to the town where he had formerly lived and got him a new wife.

He was lucky. The new wife was better fixed than he was. The second marriage seemed a step up. He got with her a whole wagon-load of new furniture. However, when he got, with his new wife, to Indiana, the house he had built was a sight to see. It was just a shelter. The house had no doors, it had no windows or floors. There was just one large bare room with a fireplace at one end, and the rain, the wind, and the snow blowing through.

Bowlin Green on the little farm near New Salem would not have wintered his animals in such a place. Thomas Lincoln had wintered his children there. He could see nothing particularly wrong with the house.

The new wife had made Thomas fix the place up. Fixing it up was a matter of labor. It was a matter of having eyes to see what is wrong.

A house is something, a farm something. In New Salem people let their domestic animals pick up a living as best they could. The horse was an important part of every man's life, but men paid little or no attention to their horses. Bony, wind-broken horses in the streets of New Salem. Horse-trading was a favorite diversion. There was little or no connection between a man and his horse. A man had one horse today, tomorrow he traded it and got another. If he had got the best of the trade, he felt victorious.

The horse he had traded was wind-broken. The other man hadn't been sharp enough to notice. Ha! Joy in one man's heart, gloom in another's.

However, the wind-broken horse remained on the streets of the town, was still a part of the town's life. There was only another man out of luck.

A sense in everyone of the importance of the individual, and a life without privacy. A young democracy. Everyone building for the future, believing in the future, letting the present go. This is to be the greatest country on earth. The country as a whole had become, to the man in the street, what the church had been to men of the Middle Ages in Europe. It was the center of a new mysticism. For the present, for the things immediately about, no thought. The men who had built the cathedrals in Europe lived in dirty hovels. Men in America were to build a great free republic living in similar hovels.

But on Bowlin Green's little farm all of the stock was fat. The fences in the fields were well built. There was grass growing by the front door, beds of flowers along the walk leading from the road. Even the farmyard was clean, the litter from the animals piled in neat piles.

Inside the house little pots of flowers growing even in the winter.

Bowlin Green and his wife stayed on their own farm, in their own house. They liked it there.

On most of the other farms about, mud, by the front door and by the kitchen door. The wood gathered for the winter's burning was not neatly piled. It was thrown helter-skelter into the mud.

Hogs wallowing in mud in a dirty pen near the kitchen door. The farmyards seas of mud. Stench arising from the pig pens and from the barns. In town, also, nearly every house had its barns and its pigpens in the same condition. They were closer together than on the farms. The stench was greater. Mingled with the stench of animals a human stench. Bathing was difficult and impractical. The towns had no sewers. There was a little privy built of boards in every back yard. Often they were not cleaned until filled to the top of the ground. On winter days women seen dodging out of the kitchen doors of houses, dodging into the little house in the yard. A whole school of broad jokes and stories built upon such scenes in the privies. At the taverns and back of the stores — and back of the schoolhouses — writing on the walls, pictures drawn.

Abe Lincoln had in his repertoire stories built broadly on the necessary functions of the body. There was a kind of satisfaction in making others physically ridiculous by a well-turned tale.

Abe had fled to the Bowlin Green farm when he lost his Ann. Life was ordered there. It was tightened up. He thought Ann would have been just such another woman as Mrs. Green. She, Ann, had always been neat about her person, she was gentle and quiet.

With Ann, had she lived, he might have had some such another life as the life led in the Bowlin Green house.

Would it have turned out that way? In the following spring, as he went on the borrowed horse from New Salem to Springfield, he was asking himself that question.

The horse he had borrowed for the ride down was a bony, ill-conditioned one. He was to leave it at a certain place in Springfield. He had his few law books in his saddle-bags, very little money in his pocket.

He was trying to think out the difference between himself and the man Bowlin Green. There was a difference.

Everything about Bowlin Green was tight and neat. He had sharp eyes and saw everything before him very clearly.

The man and his wife had lived together a long time. They had achieved together something Abe had dreamed vaguely he might achieve with Ann. A kind of strong gentleness in living. It might be true aristocracy.

Ann had wanted just such a life for herself and Abe when they got married. It may have been that Bowlin Green had shrewdly guessed that, had Ann lived, had the marriage come off, Ann would have been a disappointed, perhaps an unhappy woman. But she had not lived.

She had died, and it was evident that the tall young man she was to have married, the man who had failed as storekeeper and who mixed in politics and hung about the taverns and stores swapping stories with other men, was not what she had thought him.

Bowlin Green and his wife may have doubted whether Ann could ever have made of Abe the sort of man she could have understood.

However, it did not matter. Ann was dead.

They had wanted him to stay with them. There was something very fine about Abe. Both Bowlin Green and his wife had felt that. He hadn't any money. He was postmaster at New Salem, but the office paid little or nothing. He did a little surveying. He had been in politics, had been to the state legislature. After the failure of Berry and Lincoln, storekeepers, he was heavily in debt.

In order to have the feeling of paying his way, Abe had worked about the farm with Bowlin Green. In the winter, when there were no crops to plant or to be tended, most of the neighboring farmers did nothing.

They did their chores in the morning and at night. During the day they went to town. Crowds of loafers gathered at the tavern and in the stores.

They swapped horses, told yarns, told lies, quarreled sometimes.

All that winter Abe had stayed away from them. He stayed on the Bowlin Green farm, split fence rails and firewood to pay his way, helped clear some new land.

In the evening he studied. Study was not easy for him. He had got a few books, Shakespeare, the Bible, a book of poetry by Byron. He read slowly, laboriously. All winter he had been fighting something in himself. The woman, Ann Rutledge, had aroused his passions. Most men, when their passions have been aroused by one woman and they cannot get her, will take another.

Abe might have done that if it hadn't been for Bowlin Green and his wife and for the persistent studying.

He tried to make his mind fit itself into a definite groove. That was a task. It was difficult, but the very difficulty was a satisfaction. He noticed how sharply both Bowlin Green and his wife took things into account.

Abe, who was large and vague, fought to have his mind become definite — a working mind that would fit into the scheme of life about him. The thought of becoming like his father, another Thomas Lincoln, sickened him. He could not, like Bowlin Green, a man he admired intensely, narrow his life down to a small circle. One or two friends, a little farm, a wife. The minor details of running a farm perfectly, of running a house.

There are men like that, worthy men. They may be the most worthy men. I am, however, not made that way. I have to take myself as I am, try to do something with myself as I am.

It was a young man's struggle being fought out that winter in the farmhouse. All young men will understand it. Abe Lincoln is what he is in American life because his struggle was so typical.

All of Abe's life had been a semi-public life. In most of the houses there was little or no privacy. Large families were raised in a house with but one room. In such a life, if you are to have privacy, you must create it within yourself.

During that last winter in New Salem sometimes Abe was silent for days. He arose in the morning and ate his breakfast in silence. Often he went with Bowlin Green to split rails. Bowlin Green talked and Abe listened.

Sometimes he fell into a deep abstract mood. He was thinking of Ann, wanting her. When it snowed, he thought of the snow falling on her grave. It was as though she were lying naked somewhere in the cold. The flakes of snow falling on his own face seemed to hurt him. He had difficulty to keep from crying out.

He went back with Bowlin Green to his house. The Bowlin Greens slept in a room off the larger living room where Abe had a cot. He lay on the cot with a candle at his head and tried to study.

He committed some line of Shakespeare to memory. To do it he had to say the line over and over a hundred times.

Sometimes he got up and went outdoors. Once he went to Ann's grave, but never did it but the one time.

There was insanity out-of-doors for him just then. He felt it. The nights had become too vast, too terrible for him.

He went back into the house and studied again.

He had stayed away from people all that winter, but could not do that when he got to Springfield.

In going there, he was plunging into the world. He had sought refuge from the world in Ann, in Bowlin Green and his wife, in his studies.

There was no use his going to Springfield and setting up as a lawyer if he intended to withdraw from life.

Already, during the years of his life in New Salem, before he fell in love with Ann, Abe had been in politics. He had been in the state legislature and had been largely instrumental in having the state capital moved to Springfield.

He would be known there. Springfield was a growing, a coming town.

Going to Springfield, to set up as a lawyer there, would mean a new step for him. With all his heart he dreaded it. As he rode along the country road that day, it seemed to him the ghost of Thomas Lincoln, his father, was lurking somewhere back of him.

If he could only have been the Bowlin Green kind of a man, a man leading a narrow good life in a good way. He couldn't. To try, to stay in New Salem, was to become a nobody, a slovenly, dreaming, ineffectual nobody.

To go forward was to arouse himself. It would be like trying to lift himself by his own bootstraps. He was pretty sure he would fail. He felt he had to try.

Abe rode near the town of Springfield that day and then turned back. The horse on which he rode was old. Old horses learn to hate leaving the place to which they are accustomed. You have to whip and urge them along the road away from home, but turn them back, toward their own farm, and they seem to become young again.

Abe Lincoln and the horse he rode were much alike that day going from New Salem to Springfield. When he turned back, the old horse went eagerly forward. He rode back along the road for nearly a mile before he got up courage to turn again. He had met two other men in the road and was ashamed in their presence.

He did not know them. They were countrymen. 'Which is the road to Springfield?' he asked. He knew well enough.

The men laughed and rode on. 'You are going the wrong way,' they said. They were laughing at the tall sad-looking young man and the equally tall sad-looking horse he rode.

The horse looked even more sad and hopeless when Abe forced his head around.

He rode into Springfield keeping the two countrymen in sight. He was afraid he would lose his courage again if he were left alone.

V

There he is, walking along a street in the town of Springfield, Illinois, in the heart of the Mid-American empire in the eighteen-fifties. A time is coming in which that same Mid-American empire is to be the world's bread-basket, the great feeding trough of millions. But in Father Abraham's time, the feeding trough was just being built.

How many millions of bushels of wheat to be raised?

How many millions of feet of lumber to be cut?

How many millions of bushels of yellow ears of corn, lying in golden heaps on black ground, in falls?

Corn shocks standing, armies of corn standing at attention when winter snows spread white over the land.

Herds of cattle walking over white snow-covered ground in the winter, walking and nibbling away at the corn stalks.

Cattle making a rustling sound in the winter corn.

The black rich lands of Illinois, Indiana, Ohio, Wisconsin, Nebraska, Kansas, Iowa.

What a land of gold, of spaces, towns, well-fed peoples, horses marching before plows, their great breasts opening for prairie winds to blow in, ingenious men with dry cold New England blood in them making tractors to replace the horses, grim-walled factories coming into the towns.

Land of plenty, great feeding trough, Father Abraham's land.

Slowly, with the slowness of long shambling legs, he goes along a street. The knees shaking a little. The legs not very good. Abraham never got his feet warm, never got his big hands warm. Too far for the blood to travel away down there from the heart and then to be pumped back to the heart again. A narrow head, like the head of a thoroughbred horse, a head full of thoughts, dreams, memories coming and going, a strange mystic kind of glow sometimes, an inner feeling of shame and fear mixed with self-confidence, ambition.

The town through which he goes is ugly in a way undreamed of by modern American men, who, for all their hurry, are beginning to make towns, streets of towns, houses — in which they can live.

In the eighteen-fifties, streets of the towns wandered away aimlessly to the beginning of great uncultivated open spaces covered with bushes.

In the forests quiet, too much quiet. There is mystery, strangeness. Huge strange shapes invade the fancies of men and children. The absence of forests had left something unvoiced in the men who had come through forests to the open land where trees grew mainly in the creek and river bottoms — to the land of open spaces, that become golden in the spring, fire-red in the fall.

But for men of the forests, the wide-open prairies, winds, the stars at night, will not answer. We are of the pack and with the pack we must run.

How mussy the scattered pack in the new land!

Springfield, in which Father Abraham walked, was a new town and already fixed in the gray of premature old age. Warped boards on the sides of houses, warped boards for sidewalks beside roads deep in mud all winter, deep with gray dust all summer. Never a spot of color, never a house built for the line of a house against trees, against the side of a hill, against the line of a far prairie horizon. Hogs living in pens by kitchen doors — the pens not often cleaned.

There are places in the world, periods in the development of places when one cannot invite to oneself, because of some inner shame of self and place, the caresses of others, the caresses of the thoughts of others, the caresses of the hands and the bodies of others. Today, even in America, even in cities like Detroit and Chicago, now, there are times and places where men fit into their environments, wear their city and town streets, wear their farms and houses as a beautiful woman wears a gown. But in the eighteen-fifties in Mid-America there were no such places.

In the little country courthouses, into which Father Abraham went day after day and in the country taverns into which he went at night, there was dirt on the floor. Into the common rooms of the tavern, where the big stove was and where men gathered in the evening, there came the smell of the stables near-by. Men drank strong whiskey, smoked, chewed tobacco and spat on the floor. Life was horsey. In spite of inner sensibilities, one accepted horseyness, made it a part of life and of story-telling, which was life getting itself expressed. Smells!

The toilet arrangements for people, also in little pens often not far from kitchen doors. They used to have a saying in Father Abraham's time in Mid-America, 'It loomed like a backhouse in a storm,' they said, describing something from which there was no escape.

A town, half a hog-wallow then, and in the midst of it the man, tall, old before his time, falling to pieces like a cheaply built frame house after twenty unpainted years, going to pieces with long, hard years, yet to be lived in it by the man inside, by Father Abraham himself.

In Springfield, the long gaunt tired man, who was at heart a story-teller, had plunged into a new life. The town of New Salem from which he had just come was already a defeated town. Springfield was on the boom. The state capital had recently been moved there. Abe, during his time in the state legislature, had been the leader of the movement that had brought that about.

He had very little money; but that first day in Springfield went at once to a cabinet-maker and arranged to have a single bed made. Both his body and mind were still sore. People who never pass through periods of deep depression will never quite understand the depth to which such a man can go.

Having ordered a bed made for himself, Abe went to the store of a man named Speed. He had intended buying fittings for his bed.

Then he would find a room somewhere and put the bed in the room.

He would hang out his shingle and begin the practice of law if he could get clients.

The fittings for the bed came to seventeen dollars. When the man, Speed, told him, there was a sinking of his heart.

It was more money than he had, more money than he was likely to have for a long time.

He stood before the counter in the store with his saddle-bags hung on his long arms. His law books were in the saddle-bags with two or three extra shirts. What clothes he had were on his back. They weren't much. He was, at the moment, the only customer in the store.

The man named Speed looked at him. He looked at the man named Speed.

Not very often such customers came into a store. On Abe's face there was a look so woe-begone, so hopeless, that the man named Speed felt like laughing and at the same time like crying.

'What's the matter?' he asked. Abe told him. It was more money than he had, more than he was likely to have for a long time.

Joshua Speed was a single man. He lived in a room upstairs over the store. There was a double bed in the room.

The man standing before him that day, with the utterly hopeless look on his long face, was a man, but at the same time he was something else.

In all of the Lincoln portraits there is something striking. Abe's face is the face of a man and is at the same time the face of an old woman. From the time he was a young man, he had that kind of a face.

There was on his face at the moment a look no man can resist. To Speed it was like driving in a country road and meeting a tired old woman. Abe might have been Joshua Speed's mother. He might be a friend. There is a kind of world-old weariness, an acceptance of life in his face. All the great poets of the world have had such faces.

It made an irresistible appeal to Joshua Speed. He mentioned the room and the double bed upstairs over the store. 'You can stay with me, can sleep up there with me if you want to,' he said.

Abe tramped silently up the stairs. He dropped the saddle-bags, containing the law books on the floor, and came down again.

'Speed, I've moved in,' he said.

With his young old woman's face and the tall gaunt form clad in poor shabby clothes, he had gone out of the store into the street.

He went to the taverns of the town, to the markets where men were selling products from the surrounding farms. Springfield was the center of a rich farming country. He passed tall, lean men with unshaven faces. A drove of sheep went through the street kicking up dust. Horse-traders moved from group to group. There was a man with a flattened nose and a lean bay horse. 'He looks like the devil, but you watch.' The horse dashed down the street going at a tremendous trot, wheeled at the end of the street and came wheeling back. 'You see,' cried the flatnosed man addressing a group of young farmers, 'his wind is sound. He can keep it up all day. There isn't another horse like him in Sangamon County.'

One of the young farmers came forward and began examining the horse's legs. Hog-buyers with whips in their hands moved about.

On the sidewalks young lawyers, everyone of them also a politician, went about among the farmers. They shook hands, asked about the corn-planting, spoke of the weather. Steve Douglas, with whom Abe was to have a bitter fight and whom he was to conquer, was there, small and alert. Beside Abe he seemed a pigmy. Abe met him that day.

He met many men he knew. The terrible depression that had gripped him that morning when he rode into the town had passed. He was in his world. Ann Rutledge and the life in the Bowlin Greens' house was after all a little strange to him. Nothing about this scene was strange.

From the beginning and until the end, Abraham Lincoln was a man's man. He was that from the moment he walked out of the room in New Salem, Illinois, where Ann Rutledge lay dying.

Abe Lincoln, the inner Lincoln, most people do not understand and yet do understand, was that kind of a man from the beginning. Becoming exalted, he singled out men. Between him and even the crudest of men, there was a bond. It was a time in American life when the word democracy still meant something.

A few Eastern men had found their way into Springfield, young lawyers, doctors, and merchants had come West to make their way, but most of the men present were products of the farms of the near-by country. Most of them had lived the same kind of poor meager lives Abe had. Many of these had heard of him, others knew him. A group of men gathered about him that first day. When he told them he had come to Springfield to set up as a lawyer, they began to laugh. He would have to meet some slick ones in the new town.

They began laughing about the town he had come from. A contest of wits started. A man from the hill country, a hog-buyer from down Alton way, said that if Abe came to his town and started a law practice there, he would soon wear off his long legs climbing up and down hills. He was a short, fat man with short, stumpy legs. He declared that once, before he went to live in the hill country, he had legs as long as Abe's.

A laugh arose. Everyone went to a near-by tavern. Abe told a story of a visit he once made into the hills. He described the life in the hills. He said he was in one place where they had to rough-lock the rabbits to get them up and down hill.

He told a story of a man going out of his hillside house to attend to his morning necessities. The man had stopped beneath some bushes at the edge of a ravine. Abe stooped down on the tavern floor to show the man's position. It was, he said, early morning and the grass was wet with dew.

The man's foot slipped and he fell into the ravine. He went crashing down through bushes. As it turned out, he broke his leg, but he was a man very loyal to his own country. He hadn't had to —— The bushes had obliged as he went crashing down into the ravine.

It was the kind of story Abe knew how to tell. He acted it all out, sitting on his haunches and groaning, then going through the motions of falling. To make it more realistic, he even let down his suspenders.

Almost at once he had put out his lawyer's shingle and begun to get clients. He was liked by men. They felt his honesty, liked to be with him.

In public, he was a raconteur, the best in town. There was nothing highfaluting about Abe. If you told him a broad story, he matched it with another. In private, he was shrewd. In a law case, he had a gift for getting down to the common sense of the matter. Many cases he settled out of court. When he did that, he charged nothing. He seemed to be one lawyer not after money.

There was a fund of human sympathy in him. He understood the lives of the men about him. When, in Springfield, he began to rise, when his law practice grew and in politics he ran for and was elected to Congress, they felt that it was one of themselves running.

He remained old Abe, the farmer boy, the story-teller. All of his stories had a peculiar twist. He could take an old story told by some traveler in the tavern at night and localize it. Many of his tales had a breadth and bigness like himself. They were broad, but there was a definite huge picture left in the mind.

The man falling into the deep ravine, crashing through bushes, his trousers down, his legs tangled in his trousers. Getting himself cleaned as he fell. It was something to chuckle over afterward.

As the months passed, Abe got more and more law cases. He was always in court, whenever court was being held, fighting some case.

With a jury, Abe had a peculiar talent. The juries in most cases were made up of farmers, countrymen, such as he had been. Most young lawyers, when they had been admitted to the bar, forgot the class to which they had belonged.

They had moved up into a new class, were educated men. They confused the juries' minds with legal phraseology, technicalities. Abe tried to keep everything as simple as he could. He talked to the jurors as another farmer, as a man like themselves. Many of the jurors were uneducated men. They spoke the lingo of the period, of the frontiers, and so did Abe.

He was taken into partnership with a well-known lawyer of Springfield, one whose reputation was already made. Abe Lincoln became the law partner of Stephen T. Logan.

The offer came as a surprise to him. It came after his own fortunes had begun to pick up and after his marriage to Mary Todd.

Stephen T. Logan was neat and precise. He had what was known as a lawyer's mind. His office was well-kept, everything in order. At that time Abe, as though to accentuate his own tallness, wore a tall plug hat. When he was postmaster at New Salem, he used to conduct the post-office in his hat. Letters that could not be delivered were carried around in his hatband until they became worn and greasy.

It was so also with his law papers. Young lawyers, wanting to confuse him, hid his hat. Abe searching for it in the courtroom was a ridiculous figure. His long face became troubled. More than likely he turned the incident to his client's advantage. He had been trying to get a continuance. His case was not ready. He got it that way. Often he was suspected of having put up some fellow to hide the hat. He was capable of such shrewd tomfoolery. Something to get the jury laughing, to get them in the right frame of mind toward himself and his client. From the very first he had refused cases that hung on technicalities. It was partly that he was helpless in such cases and partly that he did not like them.

A case that hung on a technicality was likely to be a crooked case, he said. Once he deserted a client in open court. It was a case concerning the settlement of a debt. The man had told Abe one story and in court another story came out.

The debt had really been paid. Abe's client was a liar. Abe walked out of the courtroom and to a near-by tavern. When he was sent for, he told the court attaché to tell the judge to do as he pleased with his client. There was a washbasin in the tavern. Abe poured water out of a pitcher and began washing his hands. 'You tell the judge I'm dirty, that I'm washing myself,' he said.

The court attaché went back and delivered Abe's message in the open court. The courts were the theaters of the frontier. Whenever court was sitting, crowds of men gathered. Such stories got around. The man who had heard such a story today was, as likely as not, serving as a juror tomorrow. In every jury, all over that section of Illinois, Abe soon had his followers. His taking a case half-won it. The juror who believed in Abe's honesty as he believed in God whispered to the other jurors.

'Abe wouldn't have taken the fellow's case if it wasn't straight,' he said.

VI

An honesty that is half earnest, half policy. Abe became the center of frontier discussion. His honesty was called into question. A slick lawyer, after all. It was a time when the country was filled with amateur philosophers. Often at one of the taverns at night, the men did not drink or tell stories. They fell into long discussions.

Some of the lawyers said that Abe was honest as a matter of policy merely. His very honesty was twisted to become a point against him. He was ostensibly honest to establish a reputation for honesty. Such a man was at bottom dishonest.

By such a method of reasoning you could, as Abe pointed out, prove anything.

As Abe, like most frontier lawyers, was also interested in politics, his political opponents entered the field against him.

The people who had settled the Middle West were almost without exception Protestants. It is the nature of Protestantism to break up into sects. Dozens of sects in Springfield in Abe Lincoln's day. Some fine question of theology always being discussed.

To Abe, the technical points of theology were like the technical points of the law. He tried to avoid all such discussions. Others of the frontier lawyers set up as thinkers. The materialistic philosophy of life, afterward so attractive to Mark Twain, Robert Ingersoll, and other Americans, blossomed in the taverns.

Knowing the Protestant religious tendency of the frontier people, they tried to make him out an atheist.

An atheist is a man who does not believe in the existence of God.

Abe neither believed nor disbelieved. He had been brought up as a boy in the heavily forested regions of Kentucky and southern Indiana. All forest people are mystics.

Abe's mysticism could not, however, find expression in words. It had something to do with the sun going down at night over the flat stretches of prairie lands. It had something to do with being alone in the forest on still summer afternoons.

Long before Abe Lincoln's time, forest people of another and older country had found in the forest the impulse for building cathedrals to God. Gothic architecture was a forest-inspired art.

Tall trees forming aisles in the forest. The trees arching high overhead. Single trees reaching up and up. The slender topmost branches of tall forest trees swaying in a summer wind.

The topmost branch of a tall forest tree was very like the finger of God. It was like the cross atop a cathedral. When he was a boy, Abe had spent long days, weeks, and months alone in the forests. At Pigeon Creek he went into the forest to cut firewood.

After his father took up land at New Salem, where his own youth was spent, he stayed about for two or three years, cutting fence rails, helping to fence the new farm.

Yet at times he used the figure of God in his tales.

The men with whom Abe associated about the taverns and in the courtroom were always telling stories about the relationships between the sexes. Abe often did it himself.

It was a subject easily made ridiculous. Rabelais had done that, and Balzac, Fielding, Molière, and Shakespeare; Falstaff in bed with Doll Tearsheet. The position of people in love-making. The man making love to a woman had become an animal. So easily to debase, to make funny the man in that position. The woman too.

If they were real lovers, there was a thing going on inside that saved them. Their physical ecstasy was but the outer expression of an inner ecstasy.

In tale-telling, when you wanted to get a laugh, you left the inner thing out. It was a thing you couldn't express. People who tried to talk of love seriously ended by getting mushy. Love was an indefinite thing like Abe's notions of God. And just as in talking about love, people left out the inner thing, so in talking of God he left it out there too. And when he spoke of God in a half-laughing way, seemed too familiar with the figure of God, people misunderstood. It was that sort of thing had built up the notion that he was an atheist.

It was a notion used against him when he ran for Congress.

He ran against a man named Peter Cartwright, a half-illiterate preacher. The preacher was a narrow, bigoted man. He brought up things against Abe. Many of the things he said were true.

Abe had to rest back on men's regard for him.

After all, most men were like himself. They were a compound of good and bad. In the matter of his election to Congress, he has to rest upon a general recognition of that fact. That he was not pretentious, that he was, at bottom, sound.

See him now, entering the office of Lincoln and Herndon.

After he had become a lawyer in Springfield, Abe had not long remained a partner of the meticulously exact and careful Logan. The two men got on each other's nerves. In all outward things, Abe appeared slovenly and careless. His clothes were not the clothes of a prosperous and rising young lawyer. He would not enter things carefully in the firm's books. Law papers were misplaced.

Though for years he practiced law in Springfield, and in county seats all over the new state of Illinois, he never knew much law. When another lawyer would have been secluded in a room, looking up the law in a particular case, Abe was in some tavern swapping stories with court hangers-on or with some other lawyer. In the courtroom he tried always to disregard the finer points of the law and to make his appeal direct to the jury. He became what was called a great jury lawyer.

Abe had left the law partnership with the man Logan because he knew Logan was hurt and offended by his carelessness, by something in his own nature he could not cure, did not, perhaps, want to cure. He had gone into partnership with a young, eager man. Logan had been older than Abe, while Herndon was younger.

Herndon was a hard worker, a devoted slave to Abe, a talker. Abe thought him rather rattle-headed, always going too fast. He liked him.

The firm had their office in a big room upstairs over a store. There was an old couch by the door.

Abe would come into the office from court or from talking with other men in a tavern or in the street. He had been telling stories, making others laugh, laughing with them. His laughter was like the neighing of a horse. It could be heard for blocks.

Having been with men, Abe wanted to be alone. Abe always had a hunger for spending long hours alone. A boy at home in his father's house, Abe had had a hunger for reading. There weren't many books about, but he managed to get a few. When he was reading, he became lost to all the life about him. His father or his stepmother, Sally Lincoln, when they wanted him to do something, some needed chores about the house, shouted at him. Shouting did no good. His stepmother or his father had to come and forcibly take the book out of his hands. When it was taken from him, he, for a moment, sat perfectly still, in a daze. His stepmother was made to feel he was far away somewhere into some strange place with the writer of the book.

He had been far away somewhere and came back slowly. He was like one coming out of a trance. His stepmother, who had already told him several times what she wanted done, had to tell him again. He went and did what he was told to do and then at the first opportunity came back again to the book and into the imaginary world out of which he had come.

The Lincoln who could not remember where he had put a law paper could spend long, solitary hours on the trail of some dream.

Abe came into the office of Lincoln and Herndon and threw himself on a couch. People said he was lazy. His long body was always tired. Sometimes he told people, 'I was born tired, I'm bone tired.'

He lay on the couch and forgot his body. His huge feet stuck out beyond the end of the couch. They were grotesque feet, attached to grotesquely long legs. He had a thin long neck. His chest was narrow, his hair uncombed.

When he was at home, he lay thus sometimes on the floor in the hall near the front door. His great feet could be seen by neighbors passing up and down the street. The neighbors laughed. Abe's wife, Mary Todd Lincoln, was offended.

Abe Lincoln had married. He had become the father of children. His wife was a proud, arrogant little woman. She was a shrew, a woman with a notoriously bad temper. In Springfield, everyone laughed because of her outbursts of temper.

When Abe realized what he had been doing, he was sorry.

His wife's name was Mary Todd Lincoln. The Todds had been somebody in the State of Kentucky. They were a proud, slave-holding family. The family had produced men of note. Abe had heard all about the Todds, had heard about them a thousand times.

He was sorry for his wife, from the day he married her he was sorry for her.

However, he could not help being what he was. He had been that way always. Perhaps, had Ann Rutledge lived, had he married her, it would have been as bad for her.

At any rate, Ann would not have scolded. She was a neat soul, Ann was, like Mrs. Bowlin Green of New Salem. She would have tried and tried to keep Abe's house clean and neat, and all her efforts would have been abortive.

Might he not have destroyed her peace of mind as he had destroyed the peace of mind of his law partner, Logan?

His wife, Mary, would never be such a woman. She was a fighter, Mary was.

His young law partner, Herndon, was a fighter. He was always coming into the office filled with excitement. He talked and talked and Abe did not hear. Dust lay deep on the floor in the office. There was dust on the flat-topped desks. Abe's old tall hat was on a chair by the couch. He had taken off his shoes. Often there were holes in his stockings. His great toes stuck out.

Young Herndon talked and talked. He might have been telling Abe the details of some case that was to come up for trial the next day. Early in their partnership, Herndon had become an abolitionist. He talked often of the evils of slavery.

At such times, Lincoln heard nothing. He was reliving scenes of his own life. There was a deep, creative thing going on down within him. He was again a boy in the forest. He was alone in the deep woods, on a summer day or at night was walking over hills. He was with men in a tavern hearing stories. It was at such times that, lost in dreams, he built the tales that had already made him famous.

Well, something had happened. Two men, farmhands, were in a tavern drinking beer. They were half-drunk. One of the men put salt in his beer.

Abe, lying there, imagined a conversation between the two.

One of the drunken farmhands protested the putting of the salt in the beer. He was, evidently, a devout man. He said that if God had intended there should be salt in beer, he would have put it in himself. Abe thought he would tell the story of the conversation between the farmhands in a tavern. He would give it a local twist, make it sound real. He saw in fancy the faces of the two farmhands talking of God and beer. He would get a laugh out of that.

Sometimes he merely reconstructed old stories, got out of books. He had read Shakespeare and Balzac. Balzac had written a book called *Droll Stories*. They were mostly about monks and feudal nobles. Abe retold them in fancy, gave them a turn of his own.

Sometimes, as he lay there, a smile crept over his features. At other times he grew sad. Everyone, afterward, remembered how woe-begone his long features sometimes grew.

He was again with the young woman, Ann Rutledge, his sweetheart, walking under the trees on a summer night. The two had been spending the evening at the home of Bowlin Green. As they walked home, they stopped by a bridge. Abe took Ann into his arms, kissed her. To an engaged couple that was permitted. Abe felt again the soft touch of her lips. Her young breasts were firm and round. He was to have had her for his own. It might not have turned out. He might, in the end, have made her unhappy.

However, there would have been delicious full moments.

Sometimes in Abe's dream-times, when he became for a long period totally oblivious of the life about him, his thoughts were entirely sad.

Again he was in the room with Ann Rutledge, and she was dying. She was dead and buried.

The dead body of Ann Rutledge was in the cold ground.

Again he was with Ann when she was alive, when he had kissed her, when he had held her body against his body.

Something palpitating with life.

Sometimes he could feel again the swelling of Ann's young breasts. There was a quivering of her young flanks. An answering quiver in his body.

Then death — snow falling on Ann's grave. What was warm became cold. He felt the cold in his own body. Even on hot summer days he was sometimes cold.

Abe's one chance of getting something he wanted and needed in his life was gone. Ann was dead and in her grave. There was snow falling on her grave. The flakes of snow came like living fire falling on his own flesh.

A double marriage had become part of his life, confusing him, filling his life with phantoms.

Mary was a Kentuckian, one of the Todds of Kentucky, and the whole affair had about it some of the air of a Kentucky gentleman going to the horse-races at Louisville, at Churchill Downs, and picking out the horse he thought could win the Derby.

The Derby, you see, is a long race, and it is for colts and is run in the spring. About seven out of ten times — when the race is run — it has been raining and the track is as heavy as lead.

Well then, if you are a good Kentuckian, as Mary was, and you go out there to look them over and you are shrewd and capable about horses, you don't pick out a winner because he is handsome and a show horse and all that.

What you do is to walk around all the horses and look and look. And you take account of the shape of the head and how the eyes are set in the head and what your horse's breasts are like and how about his withers and legs and all that.

You want a stayer for the Derby. It is no place for a flash.

She had picked Abe Lincoln out as one might go to the race-track where a dozen colts are lined up before the judges' stand, and then, after looking over the colts, had pointed one out, saying, 'This colt will run. It is to be a long race and this ugly duckling of a colt, that looks so like the very devil, has got the stuff in him. He'll wear all the others out. I'll bet on him. He's got the stuff in him.'

She had arranged everything, and Abe had fallen in with her plans. 'You see, it's like this — I've got good blood in me and know about the world of successful men and women, how to move about in it, what clothes to wear, what you say when you go into a room where ladies and gentlemen are sitting, how you act, and all that. You yourself are an ugly, ungainly man, but you have ability. You are shrewd and you know how to get and keep men's confidence. With a little management you can go far, be a big man. We won't have much foolishness about it, none of the sentiment stuff you had in your mind when you thought you were going to marry that vulgar little country girl, Ann, but we'll make a combination that will succeed if you'll let me manage things.'

Mary hadn't ever said anything like that, right out, but that was about what she had in her mind when she began to take up with Abe. She was one of the Todds of Kentucky! She was somebody, and she thought he was a nobody who had something in him. When they were together, they seldom spoke of his people, but there was a good deal of talk of her own people, of the Todds of Kentucky.

At first, he was pleased and flattered by it, and tickled that a Todd of Kentucky would waste her time with him. There was flattery, surprise, amazement, that she had wanted him at all. It had stirred him deeply, made him glad down inside himself.

When he had first begun to know Mary, he had himself become a lawyer, and been to the state legislature, had pulled the wires that had got the state capital moved from Vandalia to Springfield, had made himself felt among the younger men of Springfield so that a successful lawyer like Judge Logan was willing and was glad to take him in as a law partner.

He had become something his mother, Nancy Hanks, Thomas Lincoln, his father, the two Hanks boys, something no one of his blood had ever dreamed one of their blood could become.

He had become that, but did that put him on a par with such a one as Mary Todd? Hardly.

What he was, what he was becoming through his own impulses, would have satisfied Ann. Was he long, gaunt, and awkward? Was the voice coming out of his long neck a little strange and squeaky, the movements of his arms and legs almost grotesque? Not to Ann surely. To her he was fulfillment, the fountain at which she drank, food for her own body's need in long nights. Beauty there to Ann.

Could he be that to Mary Todd? Abe had run away from her, had rebelled at the thought of living always close to someone who did not want him as he was, but wanted him always as becoming something she herself had planned.

How unlike Ann she was! One could say to oneself that Ann loved. Had she lived, and had Abe married her, she would have spent little enough time thinking of what she wanted Abe to be.

A marriage in the world of fancy with Ann! On the first night when Abe married Mary at last and they had gone to the Globe Hotel in Springfield and night had come . . .

When all the sounds were stilled, when the last drinker had left the tavern bar — a middle-aged and unsteady-legged drinker stumbling along a plank sidewalk — when a door shutting in some house far down a village street had seemed to shut the town up for the night, leaving only Abe and his bride awake.

Then, when they, too, had dropped from each other after the embrace.

Then there was something.

A scene in a forest, in the very place to which Abe had run that night when Ann died.

It was the very spot, but now it was day rather than night, and he was not lying on the ground, but standing beside a tree. Before him a path led away through the trees, a winding path lined with bushes, the leaves of which were all turning to gold in the light of an afternoon sun that sifted down through the trees.

It was gold, tawny, yellow gold, touched with living red. And in the path, not coming toward him, not going away from him, just standing . . .

Waiting as she must always wait now . . .

There had stood Ann — his other bride.

VII

Breasts like fragrant ripe apples,
Shy words whispered in the night,
The still night there, waiting, where a long arm can reach out through a
    window, thrusting into it,
New corn growing suddenly, madly, like fire dancing,
Legs like soft pillars, tapering upward, drawing upward,
The warm return to the seat of life,
Renewal, the bath of renewal.

Two marriages, then, to live in Abe's inner consciousness of himself, to vulgarize him, to ennoble him.

The marriage with Ann that didn't come off remained more real than the one with Mary that was such an undeniable fact. Abe could lie beside Mary, be for hours in a room with her, hear her voice, see her little plump, nervous figure hurrying from room to room, scolding, fussing, getting furiously angry about nothing, know her as his wife who would live with him until he died, and all the time she had no reality for him at all.

He tried to give her reality and hadn't succeeded.

On that first night, after the young Illinois lawyer had finally married his Mary, it was the dead Ann who came to lie with him.

That was unfair to Mary, as he knew — unfair to make love to his memories of Ann and to her body through Mary's body.

He had felt that from the first, and that was the reason the first attempt at marriage had gone wrong. A woman like Mary Todd, intense, sure of herself, arrogant, such a woman could be easily hurt.

Now, indeed, it was worth while having the gift of story-telling. Every evening, while the legislature was in session, he could get a group about him, in his room at the hotel or in the lobby over at the State House, and already he had found out that his brain had two separate and distinct sections that could both work at one time. His brain was like a house with two rooms, perhaps three or four, a dozen rooms. The story-telling induced men's minds to come within the circle of his mind as they came in their physical beings to the tavern, the office, or to his room. The story-teller met them at the door and took them into a large room where there was a fire, drinks, and tobacco. Lordy God, what stories a man might make up to tell if he didn't have to think about his audience, didn't have to think about making them laugh, didn't have to accomplish any purpose except the telling of the story itself! As he talked, making them laugh, keeping their minds off their own schemes, his small gray eyes watched and watched. Here was something to make him forget Ann for a time, forget the nights he was to have had in the warmth of Ann's presence. One by one he could take the men his gift as a story-teller had brought to him into other rooms of his mind.

Other men had things they wanted done in the legislature. He could trade with them, make combinations, appeal to prejudices, feel little growing ambitions.

There was this game, then, at which his mind could play. It did not have to concern itself alone with the rearrangements of stories he had heard other men tell badly, finding new words, new turns or combinations of words that would get the laugh, would drive the point home. Any way to keep your mind occupied. The more ways you find to keep it occupied, the better. Leave no room in the house of the mind unoccupied. Do not leave empty places for the ghost of Ann Rutledge to wander in.

Yet again and again it wandered in.

Or he would dream of something else. Something concerning himself. A boy who grows up as Abe had grown, becoming taller and taller, his body unlike the bodies of other young men about him, rearing itself up like a tall tree, has impossible dreams.

His body becomes in dreams something light and graceful. He was a white young boy running through the world, beloved by all people because of his beauty.

There is an unattainable thing always being reached for.

You cannot achieve it, you can't, you can't.

'The world is out of joint.'

There was the young king's son Shakespeare wrote about — Hamlet. Abe Lincoln had entered into the figure and the soul of Hamlet.

Abe had always been a reader. He knew his Old Testament, his Shakespeare. Solomon building his temple. The figures of Shakespeare's plays. Gold and silver vessels. Workmen brought from afar to turn cunningly gold and silver vessels for Solomon's temples.

Shakespeare's figures of youth. Kingly, princely figures. Golden robes. The splendor of courts. In the long, quiet summer afternoons, when he was not out on circuit, Father Abraham stayed away from his own house, stayed away from all women as much as he could. In an age of breaking new ground in a new land, women easily slip into the background. They become ineffectually angry, like Father Abraham's Mary, or silent like the new land itself, silent things into which seed is put that more and more men may come into the land. Lying on the long couch, or on his back on the floor, with his big feet sticking up, often he would have a book in his big cold hands. He read the book aloud, read the Bible, read Will Shakespeare, ferreted out and stuck to the books all true word-fellows have always loved, the books in which the word is the law, the books that are made out of the sense that words are like jewels made to lie close together, in clusters.

And when you are sunk in dreams, when your own life not seeming livable, you try to enter into other lives, suddenly it may be you enter into a life outside yours, deeply penetrate into the feelings of others. You become other people. Dreams can be balanced things.

On an evening of late fall, six or eight men had gathered in one of the little hotel offices and more were coming in. Soon all the chairs were occupied and men stood along the wall or leaned against the counter. Leonard Swett was there and David Davis.

Also Hill Lamon. Lamon was a big man physically, like Father Abraham himself, but unlike Abraham he was handsome, a great fellow, six feet two, with broad shoulders and a splendid lithe, graceful body. Hill had soft eyes, like the eyes of a child, and nothing ever seemed to hurt him. What a soft smooth skin! Abraham used to sit looking at him and wondering why every woman who saw him did not fall instantly in love with him. What would he himself not give for such an easy, graceful manner, such a bland assurance about life!

When he and Hill slept in the same room, upstairs in one of the taverns, Hill always went instantly to sleep. He lay with an arm under one of the soft smooth cheeks and was like a sleeping child, as innocent as that, as assured, unquestioning. In his presence, Abraham, lying awake and thinking, turning things slowly over and over in his mind — well, he felt old and strong like a father. One thing he knew — Hill Lamon would never be troubled by the things that troubled him. Perhaps Judge Davis, Swett, and the others were not so troubled either, but of Lamon, he was sure. Hill could laugh, take a woman, drink with men, try a farmhand for murder, take either the one side or the other in a case in the courtroom, a case that perhaps spelled ruin for some poor farmer, and nothing touched him. It must be good to be like that. If Abraham had been like that, he might have succeeded when he had his chance, when he went to Congress; might have succeeded with women too.

Now he, the older man, was thinking again. Men were crowding into the room, storekeepers, country doctors, local lawyers, loafers. The air was heavy with tobacco smoke. Men passed in and out at the door of the near-by barroom where they had been having after-supper drinks of whiskey.

Sitting there, Abraham kept thinking of a rape case they had been trying over at the courthouse that afternoon. The man, a stupid-looking young German farmer, very strong and big and with a blood-red face, had no children of his own and he and his wife had taken a young girl to raise. She had been bound out to him. Abraham hadn't happened to be in the case himself, but Hill Lamon had appeared for the State and had got the German convicted — had got him sent to the penitentiary for ten years, and the other lawyers had crowded up to congratulate him. Then the young German, with a frightened look on his beefy face, had been led away, followed by his equally beefy-looking wife — now also white and frightened — and the lawyers, the judge, and the courthouse hangers-on had all come over to the tavern to have a drink before going in to supper.

Lamon had forgotten the whole matter; perhaps the others had forgotten. Now they were all thinking of something else, talking of something else. Only Abraham sat in silence, his long legs drawn up, his head thrust forward, in his pale gray eyes that lost, absorbed look that always puzzled his friends.

Something raw and tender, far down inside himself, was being whipped by little thoughts. Why were none of the others so whipped? He was being the brutal German farmer who had hurt the back of a young girl of fourteen, alone with him in a farmhouse when his wife had gone to town for supplies, who had so injured the back of a young girl that she might never walk again. He was being the brutal German farmer, and the young girl, frightened and hurt, and then the wife of the German farmer, who had tried so hard to give the child a bad character in the courtroom in order that her husband be not sent away to prison and her own and her husband's plans for getting rich as farmers and cattle-raisers be not disturbed.

Thoughts like little whips stinging and hurting a raw place far down inside.

The criminal law, then, was a matter of revenge. A brutal man did a brutal thing and the State became brutal in turn. Lawyers, like himself, Hill Lamon and the others, became instruments for the law's revenge. They became little whips with which to beat the raw, tender place far down inside the young German. Did such a young fellow have such a raw, tender place down inside himself? Was that strange, wavering look Abraham had seen in his eyes, and in his wife's eyes when he was led away to prison, the effort to look defiant, to smile when it hurt the lips to smile, did all that come because the prisoner was being whipped by little stinging thoughts. One might think of him, with his big lustful body, as a boy confused by the lusts of a man, as a boy who has accidentally broken something delicate.

A floating out upon a sea of thoughts, memories, becoming nothing in oneself, living in the moods of others, the thoughts and impulses of others. Being just the story-teller studying his materials, accepting all life as materials. Now Abraham had slipped far away from all the others in the room with him. The remembered figure of the young farmer going away to prison had called up other figures. He thought of a group of Negroes he had once seen chained to the deck of an Ohio River steamer when he had been down to Louisville to visit his friend Joshua Speed; thought of Speed himself as another questioner, a man like himself, unsure of himself. He and Speed had talked. Speed was one of the few men with whom he had really talked. To the others he had told stories.

The Negroes lying in filthy rags on the deck of the steamer with the heavy chains on them, within sight of all the passengers, were like children. They laughed, sang songs. When one of them moved the chains rattled, but the sound did not interrupt the laughter and the singing.

Down at Springfield there was an absurd man named Jim Shields. What a silly, pompous little fool! When he was a young fellow, Abraham had managed to make a public fool of Shields by writing some absurd letters to a newspaper, letters from an imaginary place called 'the lost country,' and everyone had applauded. The letters had helped make Abraham popular, had even brought Mary back to him after the horror of that first attempt at marriage, and yet what a cruel affair that must have been for Jim Shields! Perhaps Abraham had himself done to the absurd little politician something of the same sort of thing the young farmer had done to a frightened girl in a barn on a lonely farm.

And now Abraham, a grown man, who had been to Congress, who was presumed to lead the thoughts of other men, was being something other than himself in so vital a sense that it hurt almost unbearably. He was being something that all the others in the crowded little tavern office with him could never have understood.

For one thing, he was being the man who had gone to prison, was knowing to the roots of himself that what the man had done he himself might have done.

He was being the male, full of lust, determined, blind with determination, and the man's thrifty, scheming wife, while at the same time he was being a frightened little girl threatened and overpowered by a man, who was himself too.

Could anyone in the room with the long, gaunt man, who could tell such funny Rabelaisian stories, who could be quite as vulgar as the most vulgar, who could at times outdo them all in stinging wit and in cruelty, too, could anyone in the room understand that he could also be a frightened, overworked little bound girl on a farm, a child whose father was a drunken farmhand and whose mother was dead, a child who had been overworked always, who had been raised half in a large barn with cattle, pigs, and horses, and half in a crowded badly aired farm kitchen, who had never known anything of desires except the simple, direct desires of animals, the desires of cows and sows for the male and motherhood, the trumpeted desire of the stallion for the mare, the desire of all animals for food and more food to keep strong and lustful the desiring animal in themselves?

The little farm girl Abraham was being had just come to her fourteenth year and something was happening to her. Could Abraham really be such a one?

Long afterward, and after he had become famous, one or two discerning ones noted that, although his body was like the body of an old tree and his face like the side of a hill washed by many rains, his skin was delicate and fine like the skin of a young girl.

VIII

The young girl — Abraham was now being — was standing in a barn built of logs on a day in July. Abraham's own mother, Nancy Hanks, might have been, at fourteen, just such another.

The girl in the barn had a slender, boyish body and her thin cheeks were flushed. Something was happening to her. For weeks, ever since the coming of spring that year, something had been happening.

For one thing, her breasts were no longer formless things. The breasts that had been like the breasts of a boy were now pushing out, taking form. One could think of seeds planted in warm soil. The ground heaves up. Little round hard mounds are formed. One is sometimes feverishly active and sometimes strangely listless. Tears come unexpectedly, and at night there are dreams that frighten, that make one cry out — huge shapes forming out of darkness, the stump of a tree, that had stood near where the barn now stood, suddenly pushing up out of the ground, becoming taller than the barn, going on and on, up into the sky, and then weaving back and forth as though about to fall.

One ran madly across fields among bushes, but the gigantic stump kept falling and falling. The bushes in the field tore one's clothes. Now there was just a naked child running, and there were long streaks of blood on the child's legs. That was where they had been scratched by the bushes.

The thing was to escape the falling tree, to escape from the strange, terrifying shapes in the sky, in the darkness of the loft of a farmhouse at night.

The child had come from the house to bring a heavy pail of swill to some pigs in a pen near the barn and then to feed the horses her employer had just driven in from the fields, and now the horses were thrusting their heads through an opening at the front of their stalls and were making soft, suggestive little noises. 'Feed me. Feed me,' they were saying.

In the house the young farmer, whose wife had gone off to town for supplies, was also being fed. The child in the barn had prepared meat and potatoes for the man and had put them steaming hot upon a table in the kitchen. Then she had run off to the barn to feed the horses and the pigs.

She threw long ears of yellow corn into the feed boxes before the horses and the soft, pleading sounds they had been making were quieted. How cool and firm and hard and round the ears of corn felt in the hand! Even their roughness felt good against the hot skin on the inside of her hands. She held one of the ears against her hot flushed cheeks and then went to rub her hand over the soft nose of one of the horses.

She went slowly, hesitatingly, toward the house. In the kitchen all was silent. Her employer had eaten his meat and potatoes hastily and had gone upstairs into a bedroom. He was a proud and prosperous young man, one of the few in the new country whose house had a second story. Why had he and his wife, both such strong people, had no children?

And why was the young girl, standing in the silent farm kitchen, so terrified?

Since early spring of that year something new and strange had come into her relations with the other two people in the house. Before that spring she had existed for them but as one of the horses in the barn or one of the pigs in the pen by the barn. For them she had a certain value and for that reason must be kept alive, fed, clothed — after a fashion.

Well, she did certain work, worked all of the time, in fact. For the most part, she fed the animal life of the place, fed the animal life in the owners in their house and in the four-legged creatures in their barn. She fed the horses and cows, swept the house, helped milk the cows, carried swill to the pigs, churned the cream into butter, threw feed in to the horses. Often the woman of the house, who was as strong as a man, went off to the fields to work like a man, and then the child did all of the heavy work of the house and barn.

Thin legs always hurrying, always running here and there. All about, a sea of animal life through which the thin legs beat constantly. A child with thin legs trying to swim through life into life. On some nights, at the busy times on the farm and after she had got into her own loft — a tiny hole without windows over the hot kitchen — her legs ached from so much running and she could not sleep.

All day the legs had been flying, carrying her from one open mouth to another. Flocks of chickens ran after her as she scurried from the kitchen door to the barn, two dogs the farmer owned wagged their tails and whined pleadingly, ducks opened their flat bills and made a hungry quacking sound, pigs grunted, four calves that were being taught to drink milk from a pail bawled, horses whinnied.

There was a long field in which the cows were pastured that came down to the log barn, and near at hand the entrance to a lane in which elder bushes grew beside a rail fence.

It was in the lane that ran beside the pasture in the early spring, when tender new leaves were just beginning to show in the bushes and when there was a soft, suggestive haze hanging like a cloud among the branches of the trees in a wood that grew beside a distant creek, that the change in the attitude of the man of the house toward the girl child had begun.

It was in the middle of the warm spring afternoon when everything began. The farmer and his wife had been planting corn in a distant newly plowed field and the man had come back to the barn for a fresh bag of seed. All day both the man and his wife had been working barefooted, two strongly built, habitually silent people walking with bare broad feet across black newly turned prairie land. The wife dropped the kernels of corn, four or five at a time, into the depression made where the man had run a marker across the field, and the man followed and covered the seed with a hoe.

Now he had come to the barn for more seed, had come striding barefooted up along the green lane beside the elder bushes toward the barn. Corn to be mated with the black prairie land, birds mating in the distant wood, bees and insects hovering above the bushes that grew along the lane.

What had drawn the child, so suddenly developing into womanhood, out of the barn and into the lane at just that moment? She should have been at work. There were things aplenty to do. When there was no other work, one could clean out the stalls back of where the animals stood at night. A small girl could not carry a great fork-ful of manure and pitch it through a barn door onto the manure pile, but she could manage small forkfuls. A feverish kind of quickness often made up for the lack of strength.

She had just wandered aimlessly out at the barn door and into the lane. Her thin cheeks were flushed and something hurt inside her body, for days something had been hurting inside her body.

Was something hurting inside all of the animals in the barn and in the near-by pens and fields that spring? Two or three among the herd of cows in the field near at hand were acting strangely. They tried awkwardly to climb upon each other, pushed violently against each other, hitting each other with their great shoulder bones. A small hickory tree stood among the stumps in the pasture and one of the cows went and leaned heavily against it. She seemed intent upon pushing it out of the ground. The tree bent dangerously as she threw her heavy body against it.

The girl was watching the cows, fascinated. Their actions seemed to be expressing something she herself felt. She also wanted to push with her body against something. Near where she stood one or two rails had fallen from the fence so that the top rail was low. It just came to her breasts and she went to lean against it and, closing her eyes, pushed against the hard rough wood, hard and hard. It hurt, but there was something delicious in the feeling of being hurt by some-thing pressing thus against her body, steadily, persistently. Pushing harder and harder against the rail, she succeeded in moving it out of the supports that held it at the ends so that it fell into the field.

It was thus, standing by the fence thus, with perplexed eyes and flushed cheeks, that something began between herself and the man on the farm. He had come up along the lane from the distant field with an empty grain bag slung across his shoulders. His shirt was open at the neck and heavy black hair grew on his chest. His bare feet in the grassy lane had made no sound. They were broad strong feet and when he had left the field were black with hard gritty soil, but the young grass in the lane had brushed much of the black soil away. Patches of white showed here and there.

As for the girl, she was terribly afraid. Was it because the man had found her idle? Usually when she met him, about the barn or in the barnyard, he gave some order. 'Get some more hay down out of the loft. Take water in to the horses.' His voice was gruff, abrupt. Well, he was himself never idle. But ten years before, his father, a well-to-do German farmer, had started him off to America, giving him money to buy a farm, and already he had ten times as many acres as his father had ever owned, and it had all come about because of hard and constant work. The wife, who had come out to him from Germany, also worked, constantly, persistently, as he did. They had taken the child of the drunken farmhand whose wife was dead, because they had no children of their own and because they could get her for nothing. They agreed to send her to school a certain number of weeks each year, and to give her a fixed sum of money when she was eighteen, but no one bothered to inquire too closely into the execution of such agreements.

The man jerked the empty grain bag from his shoulder and with it gripped tightly in his hand stood staring at the girl. She seemed unable to move, but stood with one hand clutching a rail of the fence and staring back at him. What a strange look in her eyes! She was frightened — yes — but there was something else in the eyes, too, something she could not control, something of which she was unaware. It caught and held him.

His mind moved slowly. Well, his own wife had had no children. She was a little old for a wife, seven years older than himself. On spring days like this everything in nature — cattle, horses, trees, bushes, the grass under the bare feet — everything was soft and weak and at the same time strong.

He walked past the girl, whose eyes followed him, and took a few steps toward the barn where he was to get a fresh bag of seed, and then stopped again. There was something about the dumb, frightened girl that made her seem different from anything she had ever been before. She was coming alive. Young calves did that at the end of the first year; colts took a year or two longer. A man who had led all of his life among animals knew certain things about which he did not need to have thoughts. The breasts of the young girl had suddenly begun forming.

He went into the barn, threw the empty grain bag into a corner and prepared to lift to his shoulder a filled bag, but before doing so he went out again into the barnyard. The girl had run away, into the house.

'I'll have to go a little easy here,' he thought. About the farm girl he did not think very much. She was a young female thing, just coming into life, and he was the only male about the place, was the only male who came near her, was likely to come near her. Life had taught him that all young female things were afraid, but their fears did not mean anything specially. The mares were often afraid of the stallion, the young cows of the bulls, but what did that mean? — just nothing — and it meant little enough, too, in the peasant girls, among whom he had been raised as a lad.

There was, however, the wife — that was a little different. Even though the wife bore him no kids, she worked well and was all right. She was still his wife. No need taking any chances of trouble. 'Wait,' something down inside himself said softly. A shrewd look came into his little eyes, and when he had gone halfway across the farmyard toward the kitchen door, he stopped and after standing and for some minutes looking steadily at the kitchen door, he turned and returning to the barn threw the two-bushel bag of shelled corn over his shoulder and went away down the lane without looking back. He walked easily — not jauntily, but steadily and strongly as a farm horse hitched to an empty wagon might have walked.

Days and weeks passed. The wheat ripened and was cut and threshed. On the black prairie land where the farmer and his wife had labored on the spring day, the corn stood shoulder-high. At the threshing time a young man who had come to work by the day in the threshing was taken by the girl at work in the kitchen and tried to make up to her, but when, some two or three weeks later, he came to the house on a Sunday evening and wanted to take her riding, he was met in the road before the house and ordered away. While the wife kept the girl busy in the house, the German went into the road and told the young man to go away and not to come back. The younger man was in a buggy and had a long whip in his hand and the German stood in the road. For a moment it seemed there was about to be a fight. The younger man took the whip from the socket and the German doubled his fists.

In the end, however, the horse and not the man in the road received the blow from the whip. The young man had evidently not been deeply enough touched by the farm girl to fight for her. He drove away, and the German went back into his house smiling triumphantly.

He was still waiting, and now there would surely be no one to interfere with him. Well, the girl belonged to him. Would the wife attempt to interfere? Well, she had better not. Such men as himself were slow, but they were determined. When, later, his wife began to show a sudden and unusual severity in her treatment of the bound girl, he remonstrated. 'You shut up,' he said, looking steadily at his wife. 'You let her alone. Quit scolding.' There was a heavy finality about his words uttered in the girl's presence. To his wife he was saying, in order that there be no misunderstanding, 'She belongs to me now, not to us. I want her for my own purpose, but you do not need to see what goes on. You can shut your eyes, can't you? I'll take her when you aren't around. Now that I have driven that young fellow away, I can take her at my own time. No hurry.'

During the long hot days of the summer the girl avoided looking directly at her employer when they were alone together and he said little to her. Outwardly things went on as before, but now more than ever her nights were troubled and more than ever she emerged out of childhood into womanhood. Form grew out of formlessness, and at moments the man was almost tender, giving the same abrupt orders as he had always given, but in a new tone. 'Throw feed in to the horses. Give the calves a pail of skim milk,' he said, keeping a steady hand on the farmwork, seeing that everything was done at its proper time, but now there was a new quality in the sounds that came from between his lips. Had he but known of her helplessness, of the confused little desires whispering within her, of her going toward him and fleeing from him, he might now have been a father, a brother, even a lover, but he knew nothing. 'I must not scare her too much before the time,' was the only definite thought he had.

And on the day when his wife drove off to the town, fifteen miles away, he was confident.

The wife did not want to go, had been putting off going for a week. So she knew, then, had guessed what he was up to? Well, it was all right. Let her do all the guessing she pleased. When I get the girl — that way — she'll be mine for keeps then. I'll have two women here working for me as long as I want them. She won't be trotting off with some young squirt and marrying him. There won't any young squirt want her. If she has a kid, the wife will be sore, but what of it? She hasn't had any kids for me, has she? Well, I'll keep both women and the kid, too. There won't anyone say very much about it to a rich man like me.

In the wife's mind, as she drove away, quite different thoughts. 'Might as well get it over with if it's got to happen. A man always gets crazy about a young thing like that, but they get over it pretty fast, too. Anyway, there ain't any danger of his forgetting I'm his wife and can do more work than she can ever do. He'll be my man in the end because we're both Germans and both workers and we understand each other. When he gets sick of her, then my turn will come. I'll make it so hot for her around here that she'll be glad enough to run away and then we won't have to give her that money when her time as a bound girl is over.'

A tall, troubled-looking man with legs drawn up almost to his chin sitting in a chair by a stove in a central Illinois tavern on an evening of the eighteen-fifties. About him the rough life of the new country getting itself expressed. Politics, whiskey-drinking, story-telling. In the new country everything young. The land itself young, gray haired men calling themselves boys, seeing life as boys, living lives filled with the thoughtless cruelty of boys. Only the silent absorbed man in the chair old.

'Old Abe — yes — sure. He was born old, was old at twenty, at fifteen, at thirty. Remember that letter he wrote Billy Herndon from Congress when he was down there. Had heard a speech by Alexander Stevens and had written to Billy, saying, "my old eyes are wet with tears." An old man, eh — and he was only thirty-nine then.'

A tall, troubled-looking man sitting in a tavern office, lost in his own thoughts, and the other men sitting and standing about, waiting for him to come out of it. Hill Lamon is talking to Leonard Swett. 'It was an easy thing, convicting that young German. After the doctor's wife testified, I wouldn't have needed to call another witness, wouldn't have needed to spend three minutes summing up. That jury would have settled the matter without getting up out of their chairs. I only wish it had been possible to get him hung, that's all I wish.'

Talk, laughter. Men waiting for old Abe to come back out of his lost place and tell a few hot ones. 'Did you ever hear him tell that one about the drunken man, the hired girl, and the tub of salt pork? Get him to tell you the one about the town girl milking the cow.'

A tall, troubled man who found relief for his own intense inner thoughts and feelings by telling stories. Suppose some of them knew what he had really been feeling that afternoon over at the courthouse when the German was being tried? Better not let people know how he saw himself in the brutal young German as well as in the frightened girl the man had injured by his brutality.

Better come to people on their own terms, on terms they could understand. Even women would never understand how he sometimes felt, at least no woman he had ever known. It was sure the woman he had married, his Mary, wouldn't understand.

Well, he would begin telling them stories in a minute, but now he couldn't come out of the mood he was in for any of them. He was still being the young farm girl. He was still being the dumb, determined young farmer waiting for his chance at the girl. He was being the farmer's wife, driving off to town, angry and determined, but shrewd. He, Father Abraham, knew how to be shrewd, too. A slight flush had come upon the worn shapeless face of the man in the chair.

The farmer had worked all morning in his fields, and then, at the noon hour, had driven his horses to the barn. He went into the kitchen and sitting down at a table began eating his meat and potatoes. A clock on a shelf back of his head was ticking loudly. The room was hot. Flies flew in swarms about the table.

The girl stood near the kitchen stove, not looking at him. Her face was flushed and her hands hot and trembling. She had burned a finger and was holding the burned spot between her lips. What soft firm little things, her lips. The man's heavy legs twitched.

Now was the time!

Wait a little — no hurry!

The girl ran off to the barn, making the excuse that there was a pail of swill to be taken to the pigs. She threw ears of corn in to the horses, gripping each long rough ear tightly before letting it go. The rough ears felt so good in the hands and against the hot cheeks.

The farmer, having finished his midday meal, went heavily up a flight of stairs, the boards making a creaking sound underfoot. At the head of the stairs was a room with a bed made of corn husks, in which he and his wife slept, and another room in which, during the wet, cold winter months he kept his seed corn, bags filled with wheat and oats for seed and seed corn drying in husks. Upstairs there they kept dry and in fine shape for the spring planting.

He sat on the edge of the bed, waiting. The girl had gone off to the barn, but presently she would be coming back into the kitchen below.

She was afraid of him — yes, she was afraid — but habit was a strong thing. It was time now to wash the dishes. She was afraid, but she would be more afraid not to do her work. In a dumb kind of way he wished he knew how to make her less afraid. It would be so much better if she could just come to him, softly and tenderly, if she could creep up the stairs to him like a kitten. Afterward perhaps she might do that. On other days he would send his wife off to town, would make up excuses for sending her off to town, and then how softly and nicely the little girl downstairs would come creeping to him. 'My wife ain't much good. She's too heavy and big and she ain't had no kids either,' he thought. His slow, heavy mind went groping down through the kitchen and out to the barn where now the young female thing must be standing and trembling. 'It won't hurt her none,' he thought.

Time passed. How many minutes? Ten minutes, fifteen, twenty. Then he heard a slight sound from the kitchen below and smiled. She had thought she could creep into the kitchen and wash the dishes without making a sound, had she? A dish had struck softly against another dish, making a sharp little tinkling sound.

'Come here,' he called, his voice sounding loud and strange to himself. His voice was harsh and abrupt as when he told her to do something about the barn, feed the horses or carry skim milk to the calves, but he did not intend it that way, did not feel that way now.

He had gone to stand in the doorway at the head of the stairs and there he waited for her.

She came so slowly, with such a frightened look in her eyes. Well, he would like to take that look away, if he only knew how. He did not know how to speak, except roughly. Better keep still, better not say anything more at all.

Would she be able to get up the stairs to him, to where he could

get his strong hands on her? Her knees seemed to tremble and her
face was white. She looked sick. What was the matter with her?

She came toward him another step or two, and then something
broke. Well, that was really better. Now he knew what to do. Something always broke like that when the young frightened female went
toward the male. It was unbearable standing still like that and letting the pale-looking girl just come to him. Better to run after her.
When the male was pursuing the female, the male did not have to
think.

She stood for a second, halfway up the stairs, a foot upraised, and
then she turned and ran like a little rabbit, ran through the kitchen,
across the barnyard and into the barn. There was a little shed-like
place, where hay was thrown down from the loft above and into
which he backed his wagon when he brought corn to the barn in the
fall. In the side walls of the shed were openings through which one
could see the heads of the horses, now eating the corn she had thrown
in to them. She had thrown herself face downward upon a little pile
of straw and again there was difficulty.

She lay very still. Why had she not kept on running? It would be
easier to pounce upon her when she was running. The whole matter
had turned out to be more difficult than he had expected, and still
one had to go through with it. He was a male, wasn't he? She had
got to the time when a girl like her ought to be having a man. He
did not touch her and even stepped a little back. One of the horses
put a head through the opening before his stall and he put out his
hand and caressed the horse's nose as she had done but a short time
before. Why couldn't she understand that what was going to happen
wouldn't do her any real harm, that it was just what such female
things as herself were intended for from the beginning of time? He
felt very tender again.

Now that was better. She had got quickly to her feet again and was
trying to climb a ladder, attached to the side of the barn wall. Always
afterward, during his trial for attempted rape, he kept thinking how
much better it would have been had he just let her climb up the ladder to the hayloft. Then he could have gone up there to her and all
would have turned out all right.

What he did was to spring quickly across the intervening space and
grasp her leg. He laughed, a harsh-sounding laugh, but it wasn't in-

tended to be harsh. Also he said something, made a threat, pretended to be angry, but that was only to make her behave herself.

He hadn't expected she would just let go and fall, and anyway he meant to catch her if she did fall. When he got hold of her, his hand gave a little jerk and down she came and fell across the tongue of a wagon. He hadn't even noticed that the wagon was there, had been so intent upon her. Maybe he did say what she afterward remembered and what that meddling doctor's wife got out of her, but what of it? It was an accident, wasn't it? His own wife understood that, and if she didn't make a fuss about it, why should the others be so set on sending him to prison? When he was a lad, at home in Germany, things often happened such as he had intended should happen when he had caught the girl. Lots of things of that sort happened, in Germany, in the fields and in the barns. No one ever made much fuss about it.

When he tore her dress, he didn't know she was hurt. What kind of a man did they think he was? Well, if that neighbor hadn't come along just then, and hadn't ridden his horse right to the barn door, he might have got her into the house and got a doctor and stayed in the room while the doctor was there, so she couldn't blab to others about things that didn't concern them.

IX

Memories, fragments of stories floated in his mind. Scenes came and went. Meanings sometimes grew clearer. That young German farmer in the barn with the frightened girl, Ann Rutledge lying dead in the house at Clary's Grove, mornings when Abe was a boy and was walking alone along a country road, a little puff of dust rising from another road far away across the prairies, a bird, with vivid blue plumage, suddenly flying across the road, whispering sounds in the tops of trees, the strangeness of distant places, of death and life. At times whole lives lived in miniature, lives lived in the house of the mind, vivid ghosts fleeing past. Sometimes one knew oneself and everything in the world worth knowing. Sometimes also one knew nothing, was dense, baffled, confused. If one could only understand people, why men were sometimes lying, scheming, ugly things, and then suddenly became almost noble so that they aroused a strange, tender feeling within! Even men like that brutal young German had moments when he aroused tenderness. It was all right, sending him off to prison, no doubt, but in the moment when he was led away with that odd baffled hurt look in his eyes, Abe had wanted to go pat him on the shoulder as one might caress a horse that had been hurt by a falling tree and stood trembling with fright. Abe had felt that he might have said to the man, quite honestly, 'Never mind. It happened. Well, it might have happened to me, to any of us, to Lamon, the judge, any man in this room. We might, any of us, have been brutal like that.' Confusion and more confusion. If one could begin to understand the matter in others, then perhaps one could begin to understand onself.

Was there any sense in sending that German to prison? How could a man like that understand what he had done? There should be someone to understand, help a little.

Smart men, such as Abe had seen when he was in Congress, knew all about right and wrong, and other quite innocent nice men, who never did much thinking, fellows like Hill Lamon, also seemed to feel they knew such things, but how could a man like Abe ever know?

The men of the East, fellows who had advantages, who knew books, who had traveled, who were smart, keen, alert — all such fellows had evidently come to a decision about the Westerners long ago. One felt in their presence always a vein of contempt. 'You are all right for cutting down trees, breaking prairie land, all that sort of thing, but when it comes to more important matters, things of the mind, you'd better leave such things to us,' the Easterners always seemed to be saying.

As for Southerners, sometimes one hated them. A Southerner could creep off to a brown girl, his slave, lie with her, and the next day talk big about the Southern gentleman — believing his own words, too.

Why had such men the power to make an awkward man feel more awkward? What happened was that one became in their presence unnecessarily vulgar, rubbed it in, as it were. That sort of thing was always happening when Western men met men of the East and South.

Did such men go through life never having doubts such as those which occasionally shook to the core men such as Father Abraham?

When a man rose up in the world, did he need to become cocksure, smarty?

Better not think too much of such things. Take yourself as you are. You are a backwoodsman, come of nameless people, poor whites, crude whiskey-drinking lumberjacks. In Kentucky, when she was a young girl there, when she was like that other little farm girl the German hurt in the barn, ignorant, emotional, with her breasts just beginning to form, full of strange wild hunger, she, Nancy Hanks, Abe's mother, took it out in going to religious meeting and howling. That's what they did when they got worked up, Abe's people, they howled. They howled like animals in the little towns at the edges of the forests, and then, in the end, when they couldn't stand it any longer, the males and the females took each other like beasts of the forests and sons were born.

Could the smart, quick fellows understand? Better not think about it, better tell stories, crack jokes. If you can't find anyone to be close to who understands the hidden, unexpressed parts of yourself, better get what you can out of the people you are with.

How many stories that could never be told! When you are a back-woods lawyer telling stories in a country tavern to a backwoods audience, better make your stories broad. Make 'em laugh. Draw it broad. Give 'em that one about the thistle that grew by the path to the back-house and the girl whose feller came into the house howling with pain, that's the kind.

You stay around a little while and then you die. That's the whole of it, anyway. There are some men who are never young. Into a long head, shaped like the head of a thoroughbred horse, what thoughts, memories, hidden impulses, may be tucked away out of sight without anyone ever knowing, without anyone ever suspecting!

Not much chance anyone ever knowing. Not much chance ever doing anything that would let them know. Maybe no one cares.

Lord, what a lot of years. Let 'em march, gray years, all alike. Clary's Grove and Ann Rutledge, law — easy enough to get started at that in Illinois in the eighteen-fifties — riding circuit, the attempt to get the mind tuned to a finer pitch, for words, for thoughts. Months and months of a kind of feverish inner activity followed by long months and years of slothfulness. Might as well be slothful, lie on the floor on your back and tell yarns to make men laugh, make your own awkwardness more awkward, your own grotesqueness more grotesque. Once Abe had spent weeks and weeks, working like an insane man, trying to do a thing called squaring the circle. He had to give it up. It couldn't be done. All his life had been like that. You can't do what can't be done. You can't make a silk purse out of a swine's ear.

If Mary had only understood, that first time when their marriage didn't come off, or that other fall night in forty-two when it did come off.

In Congress at thirty-nine. Abe remembered that journey down to Washington, the dreams and hopes. It had all turned out blah! — like marriage, like everything else.

Then back again to the little ugly towns, fighting little unimportant law cases most of the time, sitting night after night in country taverns, telling stories, entertaining other men like himself, getting through the years until death came.

'Oh, why should the spirit of mortal be proud?'

That had been a hot still summer night when Ann Rutledge lay dead in the little house at Clary's Grove, and he himself, then a young man, had gone for a walk alone, to fight things out with himself. He had gone from the house of Ann's parents, the little frame backwoods tavern, out along a road to Bowlin Green's place. What a night! Abe had never before or since sunk quite as deep down into the sea of despair as he did during the walk along the dark country road to the farmhouse. He remembered they had told him about Ann's death when he was eating supper and he had gone right on eating, saying nothing. Would he go look at her, lying dead in the parlor of the tavern? There would be a woman or two there and they would be doing what they called 'laying Ann out.'

Better to wait a little, walk a little. Abe had walked from seven until nine, when he went to the tavern and into the room. All the little fussy things women at such times do to the bodies of the dead had been done. Ann's hair had been combed and she had been dressed in her best dress, the very one she had on when she and Abe had first come to understand each other.

Of what had that understanding consisted? Mary Todd was smart and a lot of the men Abe knew then and later were smart, but none of them had ever quite understood as Ann had.

She had understood his shy gentleness so often covered up with vulgarity, had understood the raw, tender place buried deep down within him, the place that was always being hurt by the coarseness in himself and others. She had loved him, Ann.

How many times later had he not lived over every thought and impulse of that night. He had been like a hurt animal, and that was something a singing, shouting nigger might understand. Later he tried, tried all his life in fact, to be something other than animal, but the memory of that first night of dumb animal sorrow stayed. It never got wiped out.

Abe remembered that when he got into the room where Ann lay, he had stepped close to her and looked down. Two candles had been so arranged that they had thrown their light down upon her face. It was the dead face of the only woman he was ever to love, who ever loved him. The skin was chalky-white and the lips that had been so full of blood, so red with warm blood, were white too. Under the eyes the white was turning black.

Words, even at that moment. Abe was always a man of words. A jumble of words in the mind, something about death and worms. Shakespeare, Shakespeare made the dead so terribly dead by his words.

Abe had gone out of Ann's presence and along the dark street of the town to the town's edge, counting his steps. That was a queer little trick he had. When something within him was about to break, when some tiny cord that held his whole life together was so stretched that it was ready to snap and leave him a helpless, chattering thing, he always did little mathematical tricks. He did over problems in his mind, looked ahead toward a distant tree and guessed how many steps would get him there. He counted, 'twenty-two, twenty-three, twenty-four, twenty-five.'

What had Ann meant to him? Better not try to think about it. 'Twenty-six, twenty-seven, twenty-eight.'

Ann had had gentleness. He saw her going out to him simply as a child might have gone. It had all begun at a backwoods party and later, at the tavern, where Abe was boarding and where Ann waited on table. Men, horse-traders, and others were always about, fellows who would have tried to get gay with Ann if Abe hadn't been there.

Everyone knew Abe could fight and that he would fight. They had let Ann alone when Abe was around, all of them. He could give her what a man should give a woman, protection, tenderness. He had needed her and she needed him. Nothing much said about it. The whole just making a place for Abe inside Ann and a place for Ann inside Abe.

In what? In what had been growing up between them.

What unvoiced things in young Abe when he had known and loved Ann and knew that she knew and loved him! He had known. There had been mighty little said, but he had known.

Had known dimly of a life in which one is loved by a strong, good, and gentle woman. There had been a kind of vision. On a certain day he was going to marry Ann and what was already known to them would be known to all. Something would have happened that would have connected him with all of the strong gentle people in the world, people like Bowlin Green and his wife, with all the gentle older people who had come with the harsh rough people into the new country.

There would have been a marriage, and the two people, the man and woman, would have gone together into a room. Night and darkness, darkness in a room of a small board or log house in central Illinois in eighteen-thirty-five.

On such a night, in such a place, for two people, like Ann and Abe together, both shy, each understanding the shyness of the other, what things might have happened!

Their life together, their love, that was to seal them together, make their love a lifelong thing, might have grown like a seed planted in warm ground.

In such a room, on such a night, sounds, smells, warmth. The laughing, drinking people all gone away. Abe did not drink, not that he thought it wrong, but drink made him ill, poisoned him, made him feel like a sick cat.

Two people like himself and Ann close together in a warm room in the darkness. Everything about Ann warm. Her warm graceful young body finding warmth and grace in his body. They lying still beside each other, holding each other closely and lying still.

How close they were now to everything that meant anything to them, to the things of the new country that no one ever said anything about, but that meant the most to everyone! When they were still like that, all the senses were strangely alive. Even a long gaunt man whose blood traveled slowly so that his feet and hands seldom got warm, even such a man was in a warm glow. All the senses alive, strangely alive.

How close to the ground they were lying! In the silent night, outside the window, the stealthy night life of animals. In a barn, somewhere off in the distance, the heavy gentle movements of cows and horses. Away off in the forest somewhere, a wild animal screamed. Was it a scream of pain or ecstasy?

Yes, he had walked for hours that night of Ann's death, striving to hold fast to something that was slipping away. The whole experience with Ann had been like that, as though with his big hands he were trying to grip a thin rag of white smoke blown away from him by a strong wind. Twice he had gone past Bowlin Green's house before he had courage to go in.

There was a creek crossed by a log bridge in the road just beyond the Bowlin Green place, and when Abe had crossed it for the second time that night, the queer thing happened. He remembered it. There had been very distinctly a notion about Ann's being something like a small white cloud floating along in the road just ahead of him. By the time he reached the bridge, he had broken into a run. It may have been that what he had in his mind at the moment was not unlike the desire toward suicide, a determination to go with Ann, wherever she was going. The white thing danced in the darkness of the road ahead and he had kept running and calling. There was no one about. In the new country you could sometimes go on for miles along a road without coming to a house. The Bowlin Green place he had passed awhile before stood on a little knoll and there had been a light in the farmhouse kitchen. That would have been Bowlin Green himself sitting up and reading. He often did that, half through the night. Like Abe himself, the gentle little old farmer loved books, words, ideas worked out into words.

The solitary light had kept appearing and disappearing. Along the creek the road he had followed grew clumps of tall trees, and then came open spaces, long stretches of prairie land with bushes growing often enough waist-high — hazelnuts, elders, sumac, ivy, berry-vines.

Now and then the trees grew out from the creek and there was a forest covering fifteen or twenty acres.

There it had happened. Yes, he had plunged into the darkness of one of these places, and it was in there, under the trees, in the intense black silence that he had fought things out with himself. It was a plain question of taking hold on to something, knowing deep down in the roots of him whether or not he wanted to take hold.

It became a long fight, lasting two or three hours, and he got through it because many little things helped that he had never thought of before. Perhaps his own mother, Nancy Hanks, getting religion and howling among the poor whites of the Kentucky hills in her girl-hood, might have understood what happened to her son that night as no one else could have understood. There had been the same sense of something big, terrible, and mysterious outside herself in the lonely woman at the forest's edge. The mother had called the thing God, had cried out to it. 'Take me to your arms, Jesus,' she had cried over and over, in a kind of wild ecstasy of longing.

Her son also had cried out, but not to God or the Son of God. To something in himself. It was a question now of whether or not he wanted life alone, with himself, with Abe Lincoln. That he had had to decide. There was something determined in him. 'She's gone. She's dead,' he told himself, over and over. The notion that Ann was a white puff of smoke blown along in the darkness just ahead of him in the road, among the trees in the dark woods, had had to be put away. No good just running and knocking his head and shoulders against trees. He had tried that for a time and torn his coat and made his shoulder bleed. Then he had stopped.

He had got down on the ground at the foot of a large tree and for a long time lain still. The road he had been following took a long turn following the winding creek, and the Bowlin Green house could now be seen across the open prairie. The light was still there in the kitchen, where old Bowlin Green himself sat reading.

That was a human thing he had had to contemplate — the quiet man, long past middle age, thrown into a rough community, but keeping his gentleness and goodness in spite of everything, making flowers grow in his dooryard instead of planting a pigpen there, being just plain good without any pretense about it, getting all he could out of life through books, the skies at night, flowers growing.

The light from the farmhouse had burned steadily, like a larger star shining just below all the other stars in the cold, deep blue night sky above. In the trees the wind had made sounds.

The sky and the stars were far away, like Ann Rutledge, now. The winds in the trees above came from nowhere and were going nowhere.

There was something to be understood that had had to be understood then and there, by him lying on the ground at the foot of the tree in the darkness — that had to be understood deep down within himself. When it had been grasped, he would be able to go toward the light in the farmhouse, go and let Bowlin Green and his wife give him human comfort —— The thing to be understood had to do with something outside himself, with the ground on which he was lying, with the roots of the tree near which he was lying, with the roots that went far down into the ground rather than with its branches that reached up to the stars and were caressed by the vagrant winds that had come from nowhere and that were going nowhere.

So he had lain for two hours that night on the ground at the foot of the tree, trying to press his body down into the ground where Ann's body would be put on the next day, listening as he had never listened before.

Yes, that man had passed on horseback on a distant road. The little wild animal had run through the forest.

For what had he been listening? He had had to get God, that was it, and for him there was necessary a God other than the one to which his mother, Nancy Hanks, had called so madly at the edge of another forest. Something within him had been reaching and reaching, not for the thin, vanishing wreath of white smoke that had danced before his eyes as he ran madly along the road, but for the God that was in the roots of trees, that was in corn growing, that was earth itself and all that walketh and liveth on the earth — that was in himself.

Trees grew slowly, taking a long time to get up to the sky and to fruit-bearing. If one could think of it so, it might be that every stalk of corn that grew in a long black Illinois field suffered through some hour as then he had suffered. There was always the question of life and death, 'to be or not to be.' He, Abe Lincoln, by getting to his feet and running his head against a tree, by putting all of the driving force of his long powerful body back of one rush, could have crushed life out of himself in a moment.

A moment's madness, a midsummer night's madness, a powerful long gaunt man who had loosed his grotesqueness running madly after a white puff of smoke in darkness trying to grasp it, a defiance of God, of death — then a death for himself, too. A man not made to be beautiful might thus for a moment have become beautiful and then passed away. Many men before Father Abraham's time had decided to defy God and had died doing so. They made themes for poets — such men.

As for himself, he had lain still on the ground for an hour, two hours, and then gotten to his feet. Had he gotten something out before himself and into himself? Was it the patience of trees? Had he really gotten the lesson of life out of the earth beneath his body as he lay suffering on the ground in the darkness?

Yes, he had gotten the seeds of his patience. That was it. It had been a patient, sad man, still confused, still having within him the seeds also of madness, who had climbed fences, waded across creeks, and gone slowly across open spaces toward the house of Bowlin Green, toward the house where love, the thing he had hoped to find with Ann Rutledge, was a living fact, existing, not for himself, but for other men.

Reader, now and then, in the world of men, there is a man born free, a man come out of nowhere, going nowhere, a man into whom all things of his day flow freely, out of whom all things of his day flow freely. Such a one does not feel himself as important. Nothing seems important, and still he feels the life about him as important, feels young girls creeping into barns with farmhands on warm spring afternoons, feels wild geese flying northward far up in the sky, trees coming into green, dead leaves of trees scurrying before a wind in the fall, young green shoots of corn coming up out of black ground in new cleared land, feels the desire of birds to sing at the mating time, feels inner laughter as precise shivering old maids hurry along paths toward backhouses on winter afternoons, feels just the impulse of a law partner, a Billy Herndon, when he has got drunk again and has talked too much — feels all there is in the life about, accepts all there is. Such men do not make life, but they color it. Life, as it lies before their eyes, as it expresses itself in the speech and action of the people directly about them, is their material. It is to them what the stone is to the sculptor, what sounds are to the makers of song.

Father Abraham in all likelihood always was a poet. It is strange to think so. Few republics ever have had poets as presidents. In the world's history there have been poet kings, but not many. Strange that a poet should have become President of the United States!

Yet it is not to be wondered at. He could penetrate deeply the feelings of others. From the very first he expressed something inexpressible in the lives of the men about him. He was strong as they were strong. Their weakness was his weakness. He was always a defeated man in quest of the impossible. He was the man who could not make his inner life quite find satisfaction in the scene of his outer one. It was only in the form of a symbol that he, like all artists, could fit it in. Finally he did fit that inner life into the outer one . . .

1930.

XI. TOWARD DEMOCRACY

Machine Song

Song written at Columbus, Georgia, in a moment of ecstasy
born of a visit to a cotton mill. . . .

IT HAS BEEN GOING ON now for thiry, forty, fifty, sixty years. I
mean the machine song. It began away back of that. I am speaking of
the great chorus, the grand song.

I am speaking of machinery in America, the song of it, the clatter of
it, the whurrrr, the screech, the hummmm, the murmur, the shout of it.

It was there before the World War, before the Civil War.

The machines talk like blackbirds in a meadow at the edge of a
cornfield; the machines shout, they dance on their iron legs.

The machines have a thousand, a million little steel fingers. They
grasp things. Their fingers grasp steel. They grasp the most delicate
cotton and silk fibers. There are great hands of steel, giant hands.

They are picking up and are handling iron pillars, great steel beams.
The hands are themselves machines. They grasp huge beams of steel,
swing them high up.

Steel hands are tearing up the earth. The fingers reach down
through stone, through clay and muck.

They swing great handfuls of earth and stone aloft. They carry steel
beams weighing tons, running with them madly across a room.

They make bridges. They make great dams. They feed upon the
power in rivers. They eat white coal.

Wheels are groaning, wheels are screeching.

It is good to get these sounds into the ears. It is good to see these
sights with the eyes. See the smoke rolling up, the black smoke. See
the fire belching from the great retorts. The machines are cruel as
men are cruel. The little flesh and blood fingers of men's hands drive,
direct, control the machines.

604

The machines wear out as men do. Machines are scrapped, thrown on the scrap heap.

At the edges of American cities you will see fields and gullies filled with iron and steel scraps.

There, in that gully, beneath bushes, overgrown by weeds, is an automobile that, but a year or two ago, slid smoothly over roads at forty, fifty, sixty, eighty miles an hour.

How smoothly it ran, how surely! It carried me from Chicago to Miami.

I was in Chicago, and it was bleak and cold there. I wanted the sun. Cold winds blew in from the lake. My bones ached. I wanted the sun. I am no longer young. I wanted the sun.

I got into the machine. It was gaily painted. I tell you there will no man live in my day who does not accept the machine.

I myself rejected it. I scorned it. I swore at it. It is destroying my life and the lives of all the men of my time, I said.

The machine gave its life to me, into my keeping. My hands guided it. With one turn of my wrists I could have destroyed the machine and myself.

There were crowds of people in the streets of some of the towns and cities through which I passed. I could have destroyed fifty people and myself in destroying the machine.

I passed through Illinois, through Kentucky, Tennessee, North Carolina, and went on into Florida. I saw rains, I saw mountains, I saw rivers.

I had a thousand sensations. At night I slept in hotels. I sat in hotel lobbies and talked to men.

Today I made two hundred and fifty-eight miles.

Today I made three hundred and ten miles.

Today I made four hundred miles.

We were stupid, sitting thus, telling each other these bare facts. We told each other nothing of what we meant. We could not tell each other.

There were fat men and lean men, old men and young men. In each man a thousand sensations not told. We were trying to express something we could not express.

I am sick of my old self that protested against the machine. I am sick of that self in me, that self in me, that self in me, that would not live in my own age.

That self in me.

That self in me.

That self in me.

I was a fool. How did I know it would serve me like this?

I went to lie by the river banks. I walked in fields where there were no machines.

Is the machine more cruel than the rain?

Is the machine more cruel than distance?

Is the machine more cruel than snow?

Is the machine more cruel than the sun?

Now the machine in which I rode so gaily from Chicago to Miami, the long, graceful machine, painted a bright scarlet — now it is on a scrap heap. It is in a gully under weeds. In a few years I shall be underground. I shall be on a scrap heap.

What is worth saving of the machine, in which I rode from Chicago to Miami, passing rivers, passing towns, passing cities, passing fields and forests — what is worth saving of the machine will go into the great retorts. It will be melted into new machines. It will sing and fly and work again. What is worth while in me will go into a stalk of corn, into a tree.

I went in the machine from Chicago to Miami. Bitter winds and snow blew about me. My hands that guided the machine were cold.

It ran gaily. There was a soft, murmuring sound. Something within the machine sang and something within me sang. Something within me beat with the steady, rhythmic beating of the machine.

In my own age.

In my own age.

In my own age.

Individuality gone.

Let it go.

Who am I that I should survive?

Let it go.
Let it go.

Steady with the hand. Give thyself, man.

I sing now of the glories of a ride in a machine, from Chicago to Miami.

Miles have become minutes. If I had music in me, I would orchestrate this. There would no longer be one field, one clump of trees making a wood, one town, one river, one bridge over a river.

An automobile, going at forty, at fifty, at sixty miles an hour, passing over a bridge, strikes a certain key. There is a little note struck.

Whurrrr.

It vibrates through the nerves of the body. The ears receive sound. The nerves of the body absorb the sound.

The nerves of the body receive flying things through the ears and the eyes. They absorb fields, rivers, bridges.

Towns, cities, clumps of trees that come down to the road.

A clump of trees comes down to the road just so in Illinois.
A clump of trees comes down to the road just so in Tennessee.
Again in Kentucky, Virginia, North Carolina.
There is a man walking in the road in Kentucky.
There is a man walking in the road in Georgia.
The car passes over a viaduct. It makes a sound.
Whurrrr.

There are faces seen, a thousand faces. A thousand, a hundred thousand pairs of hands are grasping the steering wheels of automobiles.

I have lost myself in a hundred thousand men, in a hundred thousand women. It is good to be so lost.

Cattle, standing in fields, beside barns, in Illinois, Kentucky, Georgia, Kansas.

Bridges, rivers beneath bridges, dead trees standing solitary in fields, clumps of trees coming down to the road.

New movement.

New music, not heard, felt in the nerves. Come on here, orchestrate
this.

Touch this key— a field.

That key — a sloping field.

A creek covered with ice.

A snow-covered field.

Curves in the road.

More curves.

It rains now. The rain beats against the nose of the car.

Who will sing the song of the machine, of the automobile, of the
airplane?

Who will sing the song of the factories?

We are in the new age. Welcome, men, women, and children into
the new age.

Will you accept it?

Will you go into the factories to work?

Will you quit having contempt for those who work in the factories?

You singers, will you go in?

You painters, will you go in?

Will you take the new life? Will you take the factories, the inside
and the outside of the factories, as once you took rivers, fields, grassy
slopes of fields?

Will you take the blue lights inside of factories at night as once
you took sunlight and moonlight?

Will you take a new age? Will you give yourself to a new age?

Will you love factory girls as you love automobiles?

Will you give up individuality?

Will you live, or die?

Will you accept the new age?

Will you give yourself to the new age?

Loom Dance

THEY HAD BROUGHT a 'minute-man' into one of the Southern cotton-mill towns. A doctor told me this story. The minute-men come from the North. They are efficiency experts. The North, as everyone knows, is the old home of efficiency. The minute-man comes into a mill with a watch in his hand. He stands about. He is one of the fathers of the 'stretch-out' system. The idea is like this:

There is a woman here who works at the looms. She is a weaver. She is taking care, let us say, of thirty looms. The question is — Is she doing all she can?

It is put up to her. 'If you can take care of more looms, you can make more money.' The workers are all paid by the piece-work system.

'I will stand here with this watch in my hand. You go ahead and work. Be natural. Work as you always did.

'I will watch every movement you make. I will co-ordinate your movements.

'Now, you see, you have stopped to gossip with another woman, another weaver.

'That time you talked for four minutes.

'Time is money, my dear.

'And you have gone to the toilet. You stayed in there seven minutes. Was that necessary? Could not you have done everything necessary in three minutes?

'Three minutes here, four minutes there. Minutes, you see, make hours and hours make cloth.'

I said it was put up to her, the weaver. Well, you know how such things are put up to employees in any factory. 'I am going to try this,' says the boss. 'Do you approve?'

'Sure.'

What else is to be said?

There are plenty of people out of work, God knows.

You don't want to lose your job, do you?

(The boss speaking.)

'Well, I asked them about it. They all approved.

'Why, I had several of them into my office. "Is everything all right?" I asked. "Are you perfectly satisfied about everything?"

' "Sure," they all said.'

It should be understood, if you do not understand, that the weaver in the modern cotton mill does not run his loom. He does not pull levers. The loom runs on and on. It is so arranged that if one of the threads among many thousand threads breaks, the loom automatically stops.

It is the weaver's job to spring forward. The broken thread must be found. Down inside the loom there are little steel fingers that grasp the threads. The ends of the broken thread must be found and passed through the finger that is to hold just that thread. The weaver's knot must be tied. It is a swiftly made, hard little knot. It will not show in the finished cloth. The loom may run for a long time and no thread break, and then, in a minute, threads may break in several looms.

The looms in the weaving-rooms are arranged in long rows. The weaver passes up and down. Nowadays, in modern mills, she does not have to change the bobbins. The bobbins are automatically fed into the loom. When a bobbin has become empty, it falls out and a new one takes its place. A full cylinder of bobbins is up there, atop the loom. The full bobbins fall into their places as loaded cartridges fall into place when a revolver is fired.

So there is the weaver. All she, or he, has to do is to walk up and down. Let us say that twenty or thirty looms are to be watched. The looms are of about the breadth of an ordinary writing desk or the chest of drawers standing in your bedroom.

You walk past twenty or thirty of them, keeping your eyes open. They are all in rapid motion, dancing. You must be on the alert. You are like a school-teacher watching a group of children.

But these looms, these children of the weaver, do not stand still. They dance in their places. There is a play of light from the factory windows and from the white cloth against the dark frames of the looms.

Belts are flying. Wheels are turning.

The threads — often hundreds to the inch — lie closely in the loom, a little steel finger holding each thread. The bobbin flies across, putting in the cross-threads. It flies so rapidly the eye cannot see it.

That is a dance, too.

The loom itself seems to jump off the floor. There is a quick, jerky movement, a clatter. The loom is setting each cross-thread firmly in place, making firm, smooth cloth.

The dance of the looms is a crazy dance. It is jerky, abrupt, mechanical. It would be interesting to see some dancer do a loom dance on the stage. A new kind of music would have to be found for it.

There are fifteen looms dancing, twenty, thirty, forty. Lights are dancing over the looms. There is always, day in, day out, this strange, jerky movement, infinitely complex. The noise in the room is terrific.

The job of the minute-man is to watch the operator. This woman makes too many false movements. 'Do it like this.'

The thing is to study the movements, not only of the weavers, but of the machines. The thing is to more perfectly co-ordinate the two.

It is called by the weavers the 'stretch-out.'

It is possible by careful study, by watching an operator (a weaver) hour after hour, standing with watch in hand, following the weaver up and down, to increase the efficiency by as much as one hundred per cent. It has been done.

Instead of thirty-six looms, let us say seventy-two. Something gained, eh? Every other operator replaced.

Let us say a woman weaver makes twelve dollars a week. Let her make sixteen. That will be better for her.

You still have eight dollars gained.

What about the operator replaced? What of her?

But you cannot think too much of that if you are to follow modern industry. To every factory new machines are coming. They all throw workmen out of work. That is the whole point. The best brains in America are engaged in that. They are making more and more complex, strange, and wonderful machines that throw people out of work.

They don't do it for that reason. The mill-owner doesn't buy for that reason. To think of mill-owners as brutes is just nonsense. They have about as much chance to stop what is going on as you have.

What is going on is the most exciting thing in modern life. Modern industry is a river in flood, it is a flow of refined power.

It is a dance.

The minute-man the doctor told me about made a mistake. He was holding his watch on the wrong woman.

She had been compelled to go to the toilet and he followed her to the door and stood there, watch in hand.

It happened that the woman had a husband, also a weaver, working in the same room.

He stood watching the man who was holding the watch on his wife in there. His looms were dancing — the loom dance.

And then suddenly he began to dance. He hopped up and down in an absurd, jerky way. Cries, queer and seemingly meaningless cries, came from his throat.

He danced for a moment like that, and then he sprang forward. He knocked the minute-man down. Other weavers, men and women, came running. Now they were all dancing up and down. Cries were coming from many throats.

The weaver who was the husband of the woman back of the door had knocked the minute-man down, and now was dancing upon his body. He kept making queer sounds. He may have been trying to make the music for the new loom dance.

The minute-man from the North was not a large man. He was slender and had blue eyes and light, curly hair and wore glasses.

The glasses had fallen on the floor.

His watch had fallen on the floor.

All the looms in the room kept running.

Lights danced in the room.

The looms kept dancing.

A weaver was dancing on a minute-man's watch.

A weaver was dancing on a minute-man's glasses.

Other weavers kept coming.

They came running. Men and women came from the spinning-room.

There were more cries.

There was music in the mill.

And really you must get into your picture the woman — in there.

We can't leave her out.

She would be trying, nervously, to arrange her clothes. She would have heard her husband's cries.

She, too, would be dancing, grotesquely, in a confined place.

In all the mills the women and girls hate more than anything else being watched when they go to the toilet.

They speak of that among themselves. They hate it more than they hate long hours and low wages.

There is a kind of deep human humiliation in that.

There is this secret part of me, this secret function, the waste of my body being eliminated. We do not speak of that. It is done secretly.

We must all do it and all know we must all do it. Rightly seen, it is but a part of our relations with nature.

But we civilized people are no longer a part of nature. We live in houses. We go into factories.

These may be a part of nature, too. We are trying to adjust ourselves. Give us time.

You — do not stand outside of this door to this little room, holding a watch in your hand, when I go in here.

There are some things in this world, even in our modern mass-production world, not permitted.

There are things that will make a weaver dance the crazy dance of the looms.

There was a minute-man who wanted to co-ordinate the movements of weavers to the movements of machines.

He did it.

The legs of weavers became hard and stiff like legs of looms. There was an intense up-and-down movement. Cries arose from many throats. They blended strangely with the clatter of looms.

As for the minute-man, some other men, foremen, superintendents, and the like, got him out of there. They dragged him out at a side door and into a mill yard. The yard became filled with dancing, shouting men, women and girls. They got him into another machine, an automobile, and hurried him away. They patched him up. The doctor who patched him up told me the story.

He had some ribs broken and was badly bruised, but he lived all right. He did not go back into the mill.

The 'stretch-out' system was dropped in that mill in the South. The loom dance of the weavers stopped it that time.

Mill Girls

Doris Hoffman, who worked in the spinning-room at the Langdon Cotton Mill, Langdon, Georgia, had a dim but ever-present consciousness of a world outside the cotton mill where she worked and the cotton-mill village where she lived with her husband, Ed Hoffman. She was conscious of automobiles, of passenger trains seen now and then through windows as they went whirling past the mill (don't be wasting time now at windows, time-wasters get fired in these times), of movies in movie theaters, of swell clothes a woman might own, of voices coming over radios. There wasn't any radio in their house. They hadn't got one. She was very conscious of people. In the mill sometimes she felt like playing the devil. She would have liked playing with the other girls in the spinning-room, dancing with them, singing with them. Come on, now, let's sing. Let's dance. She was young. She made up songs sometimes. She was a smart, fast workwoman. She liked men. Her husband, Ed Hoffman, wasn't a very strong man. She would have liked a strong young man. There was such a strong young man working in the mill one summer before she married. She thought about him often after her marriage.

Just the same, she wouldn't have gone back on Ed Hoffman, not she. She knew that and Ed knew it.

On some days you couldn't touch Doris. Ed couldn't have touched her. She was closed up, quiet and warm. She was like a tree or like a hill lying still in warm sunlight. She worked quite automatically in the big, light spinning-room of the Langdon Cotton Mill, the room with the lights, the flying machines, the subtile, changing flying forms — you couldn't touch her on such days, but she did her work all right. She could always do more than her share of work.

615

One Saturday, in the fall, there was a fair in Langdon. It wasn't right by the cotton mill nor in the town. It was in an empty field by the river, out beyond the cotton mill and the cotton-mill town. People from Langdon, if they went out there, went mostly in cars. The fair was there all week and a good many people from Langdon went out. They had the field lighted with electric lights so they could have shows at night.

It wasn't a horse fair. It was a fair of shows. There was a Ferris wheel and a merry-go-round and stands for selling things and places to ring canes and a free show on a platform. There were places for dancing, one for whites and one for Negroes. Saturday, the last day of the fair, was a day for mill hands and for poor-white farmers and for Negroes mostly. Hardly any of the town people went on that day. There were hardly any fights or drunks or anything. To get the mill people it was arranged that the mill baseball team should play a game with a mill team from Wilford, Georgia. The mill at Wilford was a small one, just a little yarn mill. It was pretty sure that the Langdon mill team would have it easy. They would be almost dead sure to win.

Doris Hoffman had consciousness of the fair all week. All the girls in her room at the mill had consciousness of it. The mill at Langdon ran night and day. You put in five ten-hour shifts and one five-hour shift. You had it off from Saturday noon till Sunday night at twelve, when the night shift started the new week.

Doris was strong. She could go places and do things her husband, Ed, couldn't go and do. He was always feeling done up and had to lie down. She went to the fair with three mill girls named Grace and Nell and Fanny. It would have been easier and a shorter way around to go by the railroad track, but Nell, who was also a strong girl like Doris, said, 'Let's go through town,' so they all did. It wasn't so nice for Grace, who was weak, going the long way, but she never said a thing. They came back the short way, by the railroad tracks that followed the winding of the river. They went to Langdon Main Street and turned to the right. Then they went through nice streets. Then it was a long way on a dirt road. It was pretty dusty.

The river that went below the mill and the railroad tracks wound around. You could go to Main Street, in Langdon, and turn to the right and get into a road that went on out to the fair. You walked through a street of nice houses, not all alike, as in a mill village, but each one different, with yards and grass and flowers and girls sitting on the porch, no older than Doris herself, but not married, not with a man and kid and a sick mother-in-law, and you got to a flat place by the same river that went past the mill.

Grace would eat her supper quickly after her day in the mill and she would clean up quickly. You get to eating quickly when you eat alone. You don't care what you eat. She would clean up and do the dishes quickly. She was tired. She hurried. Then she went out on the porch and took off her shoes. She liked to lie on her back.

There wasn't any street lamp along there. That was a good thing. It took Doris longer to clean up, and then, besides, she had to nurse her baby and get it to sleep. It was lucky it was a healthy kid and slept well. It was like Doris. It was naturally strong. Doris spoke to Grace about her mother-in-law. She always called her 'Mrs. Hoffman.' She said, 'Mrs. Hoffman's worse today' or 'She's better.'

'She bled a little.' She didn't like to put her baby in the front room of the four-room house, where all four of the Hoffmans ate and sat on Sundays and where Mrs. Hoffman lay when she lay down, but she didn't want Mrs. Hoffman to know that she didn't want that. It would hurt her feelings. Ed had built his mother a kind of low couch to lie on. He was handy. She could lie down easily and get up easily. Doris didn't like to put her baby in there. She was afraid the baby would get it. She told Grace that 'I'm afraid all the time he'll get it.' She put her baby, after it was nursed and ready to go to sleep, in the bed where she and Ed slept in another room. Ed had been sleeping, during the day, in the same bed, but when he got up in the afternoon, he made the bed up fresh for Doris. Ed was that way. He was nice that way.

Ed was almost like a girl in some things.

Doris had big breasts, but Grace hadn't hardly any at all. That might have been because Doris had had a kid. No, it wasn't. She had big breasts before that, before she ever even got married.

Doris went out to Grace at night. In the mill she and Grace worked in the same big light long spinning-room between the rows of bobbins. They ran up and down or walked up and down or stopped a minute to talk. When you work with someone that way all day every day, you can't help getting to like them. You get to love them. It's like being married almost. You know when they are tired because you are tired. If your feet ache you know theirs do. You can't tell just walking through a place and seeing people working. You don't know. You don't feel it.

There was a man came through the spinning-room in the middle of 'the morning and in the middle of the afternoon selling things. They let him. He sold a big chunk of soft candy called 'Milky Way,' and he sold Coca-Cola. They let him. You blew in ten cents. It hurt to blow it in, but you did. You got the habit and you did. It braced you. Grace could hardly wait when she was working. She was laid off by the time she and Doris and Fanny and Nell went to the fair. There was hard times. A lot were laid off.

They always took the weaker ones, of course. They knew all right. They didn't say to a girl, 'Do you need it?' They said, 'We won't need you now for a while.' Grace needed it, but not so badly as some. She had Tom Musgrave and her mother working.

So they had laid her off. It was tight times, not flush times. It was harder work. They made Doris's side longer. They'd be laying off Ed next. It was hard enough without that.

Sometimes, when Doris was in a bitter mood, she would have liked to go on a strike. She had never been on a strike. There had never been one at the Langdon mills, but she knew about strikes. Ed had told her.

Anyway, if you won or lost, it was a try. It was fighting. It was trying to get your rights. 'I'll bet it would be swell,' she thought sometimes.

They had cut Ed's pay and Tom Musgrave's and his mother's pay. They charged just as much for house rent and everything. You had to pay just about as much for things. They said you didn't, but you did. There was a little flame of anger always in Doris at about the time she went to the fair with Grace and Fanny and Nell. She went most of all because she wanted Grace to go and have some fun and forget and get it off her mind. Grace wouldn't have gone if Doris hadn't gone. She would go anywhere Doris did. They hadn't laid Nell and Fanny off yet.

When Doris went out to Grace, when they were both working yet, before the tight times came so bad, before they made Doris's side so much longer and gave Ed and Tom and Ma Musgrave so many more looms . . . Ed said it kept him on the jump now so he couldn't think . . . he said it tired him out worse than ever keeping up, and he looked it. . . . Doris herself kept up by working, she said, almost twice as fast . . . before all that happened, in the good times yet, she used to go out like that to Grace at night.

Grace was so tired, lying on the porch. Particularly on hot nights she was so tired. There would maybe be some people in the mill-village street, but not many. There wasn't any street lamp right near the Musgrave-Hoffman house.

They could lie in darkness beside each other. Grace was like Ed, Doris's husband. She hardly ever spoke in the daytime, but at night, when it was all dark and hot, she would talk. Ed was that way. Grace wasn't like Doris, raised in a mill town. She and her brother Tom and her Pa and Ma had been raised on a farm in the North Georgia hills. It wasn't much of a farm, Grace said. You could hardly raise a thing, but it was nice. She said they would have stayed there maybe, only her father died. They owed some money and the farm had to be sold and Tom couldn't get work, so they came to Langdon.

There was a kind of waterfall near their farm when they had a farm. It wasn't exactly a waterfall, Grace said. This would be at night, before Grace got laid off, when she was so tired at night and was lying on the porch. Doris would come to her and would sit down by her or lie down and would not talk loud but whisper.

Grace would have her shoes off. She would have her dress open wide all down the neck. 'Take your stockings off, Grace,' Doris would whisper.

There was a fair in Langdon. . . . It was in October, 1929. . . . The mill closed at noon. Doris's husband was lying down at home. She had left her baby with her mother-in-law. She saw things, aplenty. There were the Ferris wheel and a long street-like place with banners up and pictures on . . . a fat woman and a woman with snakes around her neck and a two-headed man and a woman in a tree with fuzzy hair and, Nell said, 'God knows what else,' and a man on a box talking about it all. There were some girls in tights not very clean. They and the men all yelled together, 'Yea, yea, yea,' to get the people to come.

There were niggers there aplenty, it seemed, town niggers and country niggers, thousands of them, it seemed.

There were country people aplenty, white people. They had come mostly in rickety wagons drawn by mules. The fair had been going on all week, but Saturday was the big day. In the big field, where the fair was held, the grass was mostly worn away. All that part of Georgia, when there wasn't any grass, was red. It was as red as blood.

The ground was rich. Weeds and grass grew tall and thick there. Whoever owned the ground had rented it to the fair people. They came in trucks to bring the fair there. There was a night show and a day show.

You didn't pay anything to get in. There was a free baseball game on the day when Doris went to the fair with Nell and Grace and Fanny, and there was a free show by performers, to be on a platform in the middle of the fair. Doris felt a little guilty going when her husband Ed couldn't go, didn't feel like it, but he had kept on saying, 'Go on, Doris. Go with the girls.'

'Go on with the girls.'

Fanny and Nell kept saying, 'Ah, come on.' Grace didn't say anything. She never did.

Doris felt motherly toward Grace. Grace was always so tired after a day in the mill. After a day in the mill, when night came, Grace said, 'I'm so tired.' She had dark circles under her eyes. Doris's husband, Ed Hoffman, worked in the mill nights. He was a loom-fixer . . . a pretty smart man, but not strong.

So when . . . on ordinary nights, when Doris came home from the mill and when her husband Ed had gone to work . . . he worked nights and she worked days, so they were only together on Saturday afternoons and nights and Sunday and Sunday night until twelve . . . they usually went to church on Sunday nights, taking Ed's mother with them . . . she'd go to church when she couldn't get up strength to go anywhere else. . . .

On just ordinary nights, when the long day in the mill was at an end, when Doris had done what housework at home there was left to do and had nursed the baby and it had gone to sleep and her mother-in-law was lying down, she went outside. The mother-in-law got the supper for Ed and then he left and Doris came and ate and there were the dishes to do. 'You're tired,' the mother-in-law said, 'I'll do them.' 'No, you won't,' Doris said. She had a way of saying things so people minded what she said. They did what she told them to do.

There would be Grace waiting for Doris outside. She would be lying on the porch if it was a hot night.

The Hoffman house wasn't really the Hoffman house at all. It was a mill-village house. It was a double house. There were forty houses just like it in that street. Doris and Ed and Ed's mother, Ma Hoffman, who had tuberculosis and couldn't work any more, lived on one side and Grace Musgrave and her brother Tom and their mother, Ma Musgrave, lived on the other. Tom wasn't married. There was just a thin wall between them. There were two front doors, but there was just one porch, a narrow one running clear across the front of the house. Tom Musgrave and Ma Musgrave, like Ed, worked nights. Grace was alone in her side of the house at night. She wasn't afraid. She said to Doris, 'I'm not afraid.' 'You're so near,' she said. Ma Musgrave got the supper in that house and then she and Tom Musgrave went. They left enough for Grace. She washed the dishes, like Doris did. They left at the same time Ed Hoffman did.

You had to go in time to check in and get ready. When you worked days, you had to stay right on the job till quitting time and then clean up. Doris and Grace both worked in the spinning-room at the mill and Ed and Tom Musgrave were loom-fixers. Ma Musgrave was a weaver.

At night, when Doris had got her work done and nursed her kid and it had gone to sleep and Grace had her work done, Doris went out to Grace. Grace was one of the kind that will work and work and won't give up, and so was Doris.

Only Grace wasn't strong like Doris. She was frail and had black hair and dark brown eyes that looked unnaturally big in her thin small face and she had a small mouth. Doris had a big mouth and a big head. Her body was long, but her legs were short. They were strong. Grace's legs were round and nice. They were like a man likes a girl's legs to be and she had pretty small feet, but they weren't strong. They couldn't stand the racket. 'I don't wonder,' Doris said, 'they's so little and so pretty.' After a day in the mill . . . on your feet all day, running up and down, a body's feet hurt. Doris's smarted, but not like Grace's. 'They hurt so,' Grace said. She always meant her feet when she said that. 'Take off your stockings.'

'No, you wait. I'll take them off for you.'

Doris took them off for Grace.

'Now you lie still.'

She'd feel Grace all over. She didn't exactly feel her. She rubbed her. Everyone said that knew that Doris had good rubbing hands. She had strong quick hands. They were alive hands. What she did to Grace she did also to Ed, her husband, when he was off on Saturday night and they slept together. He needed it all right. She rubbed Grace's feet and her legs and her shoulders and her neck and everywhere. She began at the top and then began at the bottom. 'Now turn over,' she said. She rubbed her back a long time. She did that to Ed too.

She rubbed her awhile and then she talked. She began talking. Ed always began talking when Doris rubbed him that way. They didn't talk about the same things. Ed was a man of ideas. He could read and write and Doris and Grace couldn't. When he had time to read, he read both newspapers and books. Grace couldn't read or write any more than Doris could. They hadn't been brought up to it. Ed had wanted to be a preacher, but he hadn't made it. He'd have made it if he hadn't been so shy; he couldn't stand up before people and talk.

If his father had lived, he might have got up nerve and made it. His father, when he was alive, wanted him to. He saved and sent him to school. Doris could write her name and could spell out a few words if she tried, but Grace couldn't do even that much. When Doris rubbed Ed with her strong hands, that never did seem to get tired, he talked of ideas. He had got it into his head he would like to be a man to get up a union.

He had got it into his head mill people might get up a union and strike. He talked about it. Sometimes, when Doris had been rubbing him a long time, he got to laughing and laughed at himself.

He said, 'I talk about myself getting up a union.' Once, before Doris knew him, he had worked at a mill in another town where they had a union. They had a strike, too, and got licked. Ed said he didn't care. He said it was good times. He was just a young kid then. That was before Doris met and married him, before he came to Langdon. His father was alive then. He laughed and said: 'I got ideas but no nerve. I'd like to get up a union here and I ain't got the nerve.' He laughed at himself that way.

There was a young man from town who worked in the mill that Ed said was a spy. Doris didn't think he was, but didn't say so. She didn't want to quarrel with Ed. She liked the young man from town, liked to think about him. She thought about him at night sometimes when Ed was off at work at the mill.

Grace, when Doris rubbed her, at night when Grace was so tired, never did talk about ideas.

She liked to describe places. There was a little waterfall, in a little creek, with some bushes, near the farm where she lived before her father died and she and her brother Tom and her mother moved to Langdon and got to be mill people. There wasn't just one waterfall, a big one. There was one over rocks and then another and another and another. There was coolness, a shady place with rocks and bushes. There was water, Grace said, acting as though it was alive. It seemed to whisper and then it talked, she said. If you went a little way it was like horses trotting. There was a little pool beneath each fall.

She used to go there when she was a child. There were fish in the pools, but if you kept still, after a while they paid no attention. Grace's father died when she and her brother Tom were children yet, but they didn't have to sell the farm right away, not for a year or two, so they went there all the time.

It was near their house.

It was wonderful to hear Grace talk of it. Doris thought that on a hot night, when she was tired herself and her own feet smarted, it was the nicest thing she ever knew. In the hot cotton-mill town, in Georgia, where the nights are so still and hot, when Doris had got her baby to sleep at last and had rubbed Grace and had rubbed her until Grace said the tiredness had all gone out of her feet and her arms and her legs and the smarting and the tenseness and all . . .

You'd have thought that Grace's brother Tom Musgrave, who was such a homely tall-like man and had never married and whose teeth were all so black and who had such a big Adam's apple . . . you'd never have thought a man like that, when he was a small boy, would have been so nice to his little sister.

Taking her to pools and waterfalls and fishing.

He was so homely you'd never have thought he could be Grace's brother at all.

You'd have never thought a girl like Grace, who was always getting tired so easily and who was ordinarily so silent and who was always looking, when she had her job in the mill yet, as though she was going to faint or something . . . you'd have never thought, when you rubbed her and rubbed her as Doris did, so patiently and nice, liking to, you'd never have thought she could talk as she did about places and things.

II

The fair at Langdon, Georgia, fed Doris Hoffman's consciousness of worlds outside her own mill-bound world. That was a world of Grace and Ed and Mrs. Hoffman and Nell and thread being made and flying machinery and wages and talk of the new stretch-out system that had been put in at the mill and always wages and hours and things like that. It wasn't varied enough. It was too much always the same. Doris couldn't read. The fair was something to tell Ed about afterward at night in bed. It was nice also for Grace to go. She didn't seem to get so tired.

The shows and the merry-go-round and the Ferris wheel came from some far outside world. There were show people shouting in front of tents and girls in tights who maybe never had been in any mill but had traveled everywhere. There were men selling jewelry, sharp-eyed men who had the nerve to say anything to a body. Perhaps they and the shows had been up North and out West, where the cowboys were, and on Broadway in New York and everywhere. Doris knew about all of these things because she had been to the movies quite a lot.

Being just a mill hand, born one, was like being always a prisoner. You couldn't get out of knowing that. You were housed in, shut up. People, outside people, not mill hands, thought you were different. They looked down on you. They couldn't help it. They couldn't know how you got sometimes, wanting to explode, hating everyone and everything. When you got that way, you had to hold on tight and shut up. It was the best way.

The show people went places. They were in Langdon, Georgia, for a week and then they disappeared. Nell and Fanny and Doris all thought the same thing that day when they first got to the fair and began to look around, but they didn't talk about it. Maybe Grace didn't feel what the rest felt. She was gentler and tireder. She would have been a home body if some man had married her. Doris didn't understand why some man hadn't. It might be that the show girls, at the hula-hula tent, weren't so nice, in their tights and showing their legs, but they weren't mill hands anyway. Nell in particular was in rebellion. She almost always was. Nell could swear like a man. She didn't give a damn. 'God, I'd like to try it myself,' she was thinking that day when the four first got to the fair.

Before she had her kid, Doris and Ed, her husband, used to go to the movies a lot. It was fun, something to talk about; she liked it, particularly Charley Chaplin and Westerns. She liked about crooks and people getting in tight places and fighting and shooting. It made her nerves tingle. There were pictures about rich people, how they lived, etc. They wore wonderful dresses.

They went to parties and dances. There were young girls and they were ruined. You saw a scene, in the movies, in a garden. There was a high stone fence with vines on it. There was a moon.

There were nice grass and flower beds and little houses with vines and with seats inside.

A young girl came out of a house, out at a side door, with a man, older than she was, a lot. She was beautifully dressed. She had on a low-neck dress. That was what you wore at parties among swells. He talked to her. He took her into his arms and kissed her. He had a gray mustache. He led her away to a seat in a little open house in the yard.

There was a poor young man who wanted to marry her. He didn't have any money. The rich man got her. He betrayed her. He ruined her. Such plays, in the movies, gave Doris a queer feeling inside. She walked home with Ed to the mill house in the mill village where they lived and they didn't talk. It would be funny if Ed wished, just for a while, that he was rich and could live in a house like that and ruin such a young girl. If he did, he didn't say so. Doris was wishing something. After seeing such a show sometimes, she wished some rich wicked man would come and ruin her just once, not for keeps but just once, in such a garden, back of such a house . . . so quiet and the moonlight shining . . . you knowing you didn't have to get up and get breakfast and hurry off to the mill at half-past five, rain or snow, winter and summer . . . if you had swell underwear and were beautiful.

Westerns were nice. There were men always riding horses and they had guns and shot each other. They were always fighting about some woman. 'Not my kind,' Doris thought. Even a cowboy wouldn't be such a fool about a mill girl. Doris was curious, rather philosophical, alert. 'Even if I had the money and the clothes and the underwear and the silk stockings to wear every day, I guess I wouldn't be any swell,' she thought. She was short of body and firm-breasted. Her head was big and so was her mouth. She had strong white teeth. Most of the mill girls had bad teeth. If there was always a lurking sense of beauty, following her sturdy little figure like a shadow, going every day to the mill with her, coming home, going with her when she went somewhere with other mill girls, it wasn't very obvious. Not many people saw it.

Things got suddenly ridiculous and funny to her. It might happen any time. She wanted to scream and dance. She had to hang on to herself. If you got too gay in the mill, out you went. Then where were you?

There was Tom Shaw, who was the president of the Langdon mill, the big gun there. He didn't come into the mill often . . . he stayed in the office . . . but now and then he did come. He walked through looking, or he brought some visitors through. He was such a funny, self-important little man that Doris wanted to laugh at him, but she didn't. When he came past her side, or walked through, or the foreman or the superintendent came, before Grace got laid off, she was always scared. Mostly about Grace. Grace hardly ever had her side up.

If you didn't keep your side right up, if someone came along and too many of your bobbins were stopped . . .

Thread was wound on bobbins in the spinning-room of a mill. A side was one side of a long narrow hallway between rows of flying bobbins. Thousands of separate threads came down from up above somewhere to be wound, each thread on its own bobbin, and if it broke the bobbin stopped. You could tell how many had stopped at one time by just looking. The bobbin stood still. It was waiting for you to come quickly and tie the broken thread in again. There might be four bobbins stopped at one end of your side and at the same time, at the other end, a long walk, there might be three more stopped. The thread, coming to feed the bobbins, so they could go to the loom-room, kept coming and coming. 'If it would only stop, just for an hour!' Doris thought sometimes, not often. If a girl only didn't have to see it coming and coming all day long or, if she was on the night shift, all night long! It kept coming all day long, all night long. It was wound onto bobbins that were to go into the loom-room where Ed and Tom Musgrave and Ma Musgrave worked. When the bobbins on your side were full, a man, who was called 'a doffer,' came and took the full bobbins away. He took out the full bobbins and put in empty ones. He pushed a little cart along before him and it was taken away filled with the loaded bobbins.

There were millions and millions of bobbins to be filled. They never ran out of empty bobbins. It seemed there must be hundreds of millions of them, like stars, or like drops of water in a river or grains of sand in a field. Getting out now and then to a place like that fair, where there were shows and people you had never seen and people talking and niggers laughing and hundreds of other mill hands like herself and Grace and Nell and Fanny, not in the mill now but outside, was a great relief. Thread and bobbins got out of your head for a while, anyway.

They didn't go on so much in Doris's head when she was not in the mill at work. They did in Grace's head. Doris didn't know so well how it was with Fanny and Nell.

At the fair there was a man performed free on the trapeze. He was funny. Even Grace laughed at him. Nell and Fanny laughed hard and so did Doris. Nell, since Grace had been laid off, had taken Grace's place in the mill next to Doris. She hadn't taken Grace's place purposely. She couldn't help it. She was a tall girl with yellow hair and long legs. Men fell for her. She could put the bee on men. She was on the square just the same.

Men liked her. The foreman in the spinning-room, a young man but with a bald head and married, would have liked to get Nell. He wasn't the only one. Even at the fair the show men and others, who

didn't know the four girls, looked at her most. They made cracks at
her. They got too smart. Nell could swear like a man. She went to
church, but she swore. She didn't care what she said. When Grace
got laid off, when the tight times came, Nell, who was put on her side
with Doris, said, 'The dirty skunks, they laid Grace off,' she said. She
came in there where Doris was, at work, with her head up. She always carried it up. . . . 'It's damn lucky she's got Tom and her mother
working,' she said to Doris. 'Maybe she can make it go with Tom and
her mother working, if they don't get laid off,' she said. 'She oughtn't
to be to work in here nohow. Don't you think so?'

Doris did think so. She liked and admired Nell, but not as she did
Grace. She liked the to-hell-with-everything about Nell. 'I wish I had
it,' she thought sometimes. If there ever was a strike in the Langdon
mills, if they got up a union, as they talked about doing sometimes,
not openly but secretly, in whispers, Nell would be in it strong. Nell
would goddamn the foreman and the sup when they weren't around,
but when they came around . . . Of course she wasn't a fool. She gave
them the eye. They liked it. Her eyes seemed to be saying, 'Ain't you
splendid?' She didn't mean it. Her eyes always seemed to be saying
something to men. 'All right. Get me if you can,' they said. 'I'm
getable,' they said. 'If you're man enough.'

Nell wasn't married, but there were a dozen men in the mill, married and unmarried, who had tried to make her. The young unmarried ones meant marriage. Nell said: 'You got to work 'em. You got
to keep them guessing, but don't give in to them unless they make
you.' 'Make them think you think they're swell,' she said.

'Goddam their souls,' she said sometimes.

The young man, unmarried, who was doffer on their side, the side
Grace and Doris had been on and then Nell and Doris, after Grace
got laid off, used not to say much when he came around when Grace
was there. He was sorry for Grace. Grace never could quite keep up
her side. Doris was always having to leave her side and work Grace's
side so she wouldn't be shown up. He knew it. He used to whisper
sometimes to Doris. 'The poor kid,' he said. 'If Jim Lewis gets on to
her she gets laid off.' Jim Lewis was the room foreman. He was the
one who was hot on Nell. He was a bald man, about thirty, with a

wife and two kids. When Nell took Grace's side the young fellow who was doffer there changed.

He was always kidding with Nell, trying to date her up. He called her 'legs.' 'Hello, legs,' he said. 'What about it? What about a date? What about the movies tonight?'

'Come on,' he said, 'I'll take you.'

'Not tonight,' she said. 'We'll think it over,' she said.

She kept giving him the eye, keeping him on it.

'Not tonight. I'm busy tonight.' You'd have thought she had a man dated up for almost every night in the week. She didn't. She never went out alone with men, didn't walk with them or talk with them outside the mill. She stuck to the other girls. 'I like them better,' she told Doris. 'Some of them, a lot of them, are cats, but they got more spunk in them than the men.' She talked rough enough about the young doffer when he had to leave their side and go to the next side. 'The damn little skate,' she said. 'He thinks he can date me up.' She laughed, but it wasn't a very pleasant laugh.

At the fair there was an open space, right in the center of the field, where all the ten-cent side shows were and there was a free show. There were a man and woman who danced on roller skates and did tricks and a little girl in tights who danced and two men who tumbled over each other and over chairs and tables and everything. There was a man kept coming out on the platform. He had a megaphone. 'Professor Mathews. Where's Professor Mathews?' he kept calling through the megaphone.

'Professor Mathews. Professor Mathews.'

Professor Mathews was to be the trapeze performer. He was to be the best thing in the show. The handbills they had put out said so.

There was a long wait. It was Saturday and there weren't many town people from Langdon at the fair, hardly any, maybe none. . . . Doris didn't think she saw any that looked like that. If they had been there, they had come earlier in the week. It was nigger's day. It was a day for mill hands and for a lot of poor farmers with mules and their families.

The niggers kept pretty much off to themselves. They generally did. There were separate stands for them to eat at. You could hear them laughing and talking everywhere. There were fat old Negro women with their Negro men and young Negro girls in bright-colored dresses and the young bucks after them.

It was a hot day in the fall. There was a jam of people. The four girls kept off by themselves. It was a hot day.

The field had been all overgrown with weeds and with tall grass, but now it was mostly all tramped down. There was hardly any. There were mostly dust and bare places coming and it was all red. Doris had got into one of her moods. She was in a 'don't-touch-me' mood. She had got silent.

Grace clung to her. She stayed right close. She didn't much like Nell's and Fanny's being there. Fanny was short and fat and had little short fat fingers.

Nell said of her . . . not at the fair but before that, in the mill, she said: 'Fanny's lucky. She's got a man and no kids.' Doris didn't know exactly how she did feel about her own kid. It was at home with her mother-in-law, Ed's mother.

Ed was lying up. He would lie up the whole afternoon. 'You go on,' he had said to Doris when the girls came for her. He would get a newspaper or a book and lie up all afternoon on the bed. He would take his shirt and shoes off. The Hoffmans didn't have any books except a Bible and some children's books Ed had left over from his boyhood, but he could get books from the library. There was a branch of the Langdon town library in the mill village.

There was a man called 'a well-fare worker,' employed by the Langdon mills. He had a house on the best street of houses in the village, the street in which the day superintendent and some of the other higher-ups lived. Some of the foremen lived over there. The foreman of the spinning-room did.

The well-fare worker's name was Mr. Smith. The front room of his house had been made into a branch library. His wife kept it. Ed would put on his good clothes, after Doris left, and go get a book. He would take back the book he got the week before and get another. The well-fare worker's wife would be nice to him. She'd think: 'He's nice. He cares for higher things.' He liked stories about men, men who had actually lived and had been big men. He had read about big men like Napoleon Bonepart and General Lee and Lord Wellington and Disralie. He read in the books in the afternoon all week, after he woke up.

After Doris got in the don't-touch-me mood that day at the fair and was that way a little while, the others noticed how she was. Grace noticed first, but didn't say anything. 'What the hell's the matter?' Nell said. 'I got the woozies,' Doris said. She didn't have any woozies at all. She didn't have the blues. It wasn't that.

Sometimes with a person it's this way . . . the place you are in is there but it isn't there. If you are at a fair it's that way. If you are at work in a mill it's that way.

You hear things. You touch things. You don't.

You do and you don't. You can't explain. Doris might even be in bed with Ed. They liked to lie awake a long time on Saturday night. It was the only night they had. They could sleep in the morning. You were there and you weren't there. You might, as Doris did sometimes, if you were a woman and married to a good man like Ed, be thinking about some man, not your husband. You might be wishing for him and not wishing, not going back on your own man but wishing just the same. Another man, like that young town man with red hair Doris saw sometimes in the mill, the one they said was a spy. Doris could smile, a far-off smile, at herself mostly. She wasn't the only one who was that way sometimes. Ed was sometimes. You spoke to him and he answered, but he was away off somewhere. It might have been the books with Ed. He might be somewhere with Napoleon Bonepart or with Lord Wellington or some one like that. He might be a big-bug himself instead of just a mill hand. You couldn't tell what he was being.

You could smell it, you could taste it, you could see it. It didn't touch you.

There was a Ferris wheel at the fair . . . ten cents. There was a merry-go-round . . . ten cents. Stands were selling hot dogs and Coca-Cola and lemonade and Milky Ways at the fair.

There were little wheels you could gamble on. A mill hand from the Langdon mill, that day Doris went with Grace and Nell and Fanny, lost twenty-seven dollars. He had saved it up. The girls didn't hear about it until Monday at the mill. 'The damn fool,' Nell said to

Doris. 'Don't the damn fool know you can't beat them at their own game?' 'If they weren't out to get you, what would they be there for?' she asked. There was a little bright shining wheel with an arrow that went around. It stopped on numbers. The mill hand lost a dollar and then another. He got excited. He plunked down ten dollars. He thought, 'I'll keep up till I get even.' 'The damn fool,' Nell said to Doris.

Nell felt about a game like that, she felt: 'You can't beat it.' She felt about men: 'You can't beat it.' Doris liked Nell. She thought about her. 'If she ever gives up, she'll give up hard,' she thought. It wouldn't be exactly like herself and her husband Ed, she thought, Ed asking her. Her thinking, 'I might as well, I guess. A woman might as well have herself a man.' If Nell ever gave in to a man, it would be a cave-in.

'Professor Mathews. Professor Mathews. Professor Mathews.'

Professor Mathews was the man who was on the bills to perform on the trapeze at the fair. He wasn't there. They couldn't find him. It was Saturday. Perhaps he had got drunk. 'I'll bet he's off somewhere drunk,' Fanny said to Nell. Fanny was standing beside Nell. Grace stayed right close to Doris all that day. Not saying a word hardly. She was little and pale. As Nell and Fanny walked toward the place where the free show was to be, a man laughed at them. He laughed at Nell and Fanny walking together. He was a showman. 'Hello,' he said to another man, 'there's the long and short of it.' The other man laughed. 'Go to hell,' Nell said. The four girls stood close together to watch the trapeze performance. 'They advertise a trapeze performance free and then they don't have it,' Nell said. 'He's off drunk,' Fanny said. There was a man who was tanked up. He came forward out of the crowd. He was a man who looked like a farmer. He had red hair and no hat. He came forward out of the crowd. He reeled. He could hardly stand up. He had on blue overalls. He had a big Adam's apple. 'Ain't your Professor Mathews here?' he managed to ask the man on the platform, the one who had the megaphone. 'I'm a trapeze performer,' he said. The man who was on the platform laughed. He put the megaphone under his arm.

The sky above the fairground at Langdon, Georgia, that day was blue. It was a clear light blue. It was hot. All the girls in Doris's gang had on thin dresses. Doris had on blue. The sky that day was the bluest she had ever seen, Doris thought.

The drunken man said, 'If you can't find your Professor Mathews I can do it.'

'You can?' (The eyes of the man on the platform registered surprise, amusement, doubt.)

'You damn right I can. I'm a Yank, I am.'

The man had to hold on to the edge of the platform. He almost fell. He fell back and fell forward. He could just stand.

'You can?'

'Yes, I can.'

'Where'd you learn?'

'I learned up North. I'm a Yank. I learned on an apple-tree limb up North.'

'Yankee Doodle,' the man shouted. He opened his mouth wide and shouted, 'Yankee Doodle.'

So that was what a Yank was like. Doris had never seen a Yank before, not to know he was a Yank. Nell and Fanny laughed.

Crowds of niggers laughed. Crowds of mill hands standing and looking laughed. The man on the platform had to fairly lift the drunken man up. He got him almost up once and then let him fall, just to make a fool of him. The next try he got him up. 'Like a fool. Just like a fool man,' Nell said.

The man performed good, after all. He didn't at first. He fell and fell. He'd get up on the trapeze and then he'd fall on the platform. He fell on his face, on his neck, on his head, on his back.

The people laughed and laughed. Afterward Nell said, 'I cracked my damn sides laughing at the damn fool.' Fanny laughed hard, too. Even Grace laughed a little. Doris didn't. It wasn't her laughing day. She felt all right, but it wasn't her laughing day. The man on the trapeze fell and fell and then he seemed to get sober. He performed all right. He performed good.

The girls had a Coca-Cola. They had a Milky Way. They had a ride on the Ferris wheel. There were little seats so you could sit two by two, so Grace sat with Doris, Nell with Fanny. Nell would have rather been with Doris. She let Grace be. Grace didn't set 'em up like the others did, one a Coca-Cola, one a Milky Way and one a Ferris-wheel ride. She couldn't. She was broke. She was laid off.

There are days when nothing can touch you. If you are just a mill girl in a Southern cotton mill, it doesn't matter. Something lives inside you that looks and sees. What does anything matter to you? It is queer about such days. The machinery in the mill gets on your nerves terribly some days, but on such days it doesn't. On such days you are far away from people, but, it's odd, sometimes then you are most attractive to them. They all want to crowd up close. 'Give. Give me. Give me.'

'Give what?'

You haven't got a thing. You are just that way. 'Here I am. You can't touch me.'

Doris was in the Ferris wheel with Grace. Grace was scared. She hadn't wanted to go up in it, but when she saw Doris was going she got in. She clung to Doris.

The wheel went up and up and then down and down . . . a great circle. There was a town, a great circle. Doris could see the town of Langdon, the courthouse and some office-buildings and the Presbyterian church. She could see, around a shoulder of hill, the smoke-stack of the mill. She couldn't see the mill village.

She could see trees where the town was, a lot of trees. They were shade trees before houses in town, before the houses of people who didn't work in any mill, but in stores or offices; or who were doctors or lawyers or maybe judges — not having any use for mill people. She could see the river stretching away in a great bend around the town of Langdon. The river was always yellow. It never seemed to get clear. It was golden yellow. It was golden yellow against a blue sky. It was against trees and bushes. It was a sluggish river.

Doris would have liked to see the streets of her mill village from up there. She couldn't. A shoulder of land made it impossible. The Ferris wheel went down. She thought, 'I'd like to see where I live, from high up there.'

You couldn't rightly say that people like Doris, Nell, Grace, and Fanny lived in their houses. They lived in the mill. All week nearly all of their waking hours were in there.

In the winter they went when it was dark. They came away at night when it was dark. Their lives were walled in, shut in. How could anyone ever know who hadn't done it from childhood, through young girlhood and on into womanhood? It was the same with the mill men. They were a special people.

Their lives were in rooms. The life of Nell and Doris in the spinning-room of the Langdon mill was in a room. It was a big light room.

It wasn't ugly. It was big and light. It was wonderful.

Their life was in a little narrow hallway inside a big room. The walls of the hallway were machines. Light came from above. A fine soft spray of water, really mist, came from above. That was to keep the flying thread soft and flexible for the machines.

Flying machines. Singing machines. Machines making walls to a little alive hallway in a big room.

The hallway was narrow. Doris hadn't ever measured how wide it was.

You began as a child. You stayed until you were old or worn out. The machines went up and up. Thread came down and down. It fluttered. You had to keep it damp. It fluttered. If you didn't keep it damp it would be always breaking. In the hot summer the dampness made you sweat more and more. It made you sweat worse. It kept you wringing wet with sweat.

Nell said, 'Who gives a damn for us? We're only machines ourselves. Who gives a damn for us?' On some days Nell growled. She swore. She said, 'We're making cloth. Who gives a damn? Some whore maybe'll get her a new dress out of some rich man.' Nell talked plain. She swore. She hated.

'What difference does it make who gives a damn? Who wants them to give a damn?'

There was lint in the air, fine floating lint. It was what gave some people tuberculosis, some said. It might have given it to Ed's mother, Ma Hoffman. Lying on her couch Ed had made, and coughing. She coughed when Doris was there at night, when Ed was there in the daytime, in the afternoon when he was lying in his bed, when he was reading about General Lee or General Grant or Napoleon Bonepart. Doris hoped her kid wouldn't get it.

Nell said: 'We work from cantsee to cantsee. They got us. They got the bee on us. They know it. They got us hog-tied. We work from cantsee to cantsee.' Nell was tall, swaggering, profane. Her breasts weren't big, like Doris's . . . almost too big . . . or like Fanny's or too little, just nothing, a flat place, like a man, like Grace's. They were just right, not too big or not too little.

If a man ever got Nell, he'd get her hard. Doris knew that. She felt it. She didn't know how she knew, but she knew. Nell would fight and swear and fight. 'No, you don't. Damn you. I ain't that kind.' 'You go to hell.'

When she gave up, she'd cry like a child.

If a man got her, he'd have her. She'd be his. She wouldn't talk about it much, but, if a man got her, she'd be his. Doris almost wished she were a man, to try, thinking of Nell.

A girl thought of such things. She had to be thinking about something. All day, every day, thread, thread, thread. It flying, breaking, flying, breaking. Sometimes Doris wished she could swear like Nell. She wished sometimes she were Nell's kind, not her own kind. Grace said, when she was working in the mill on the side where Nell now worked, once at night, after she had come home . . . a hot night . . . she said . . .

Doris was rubbing Grace with her hands, softly, strongly, the way she could rub, not too hard, not too soft. She rubbed her all over. Grace liked it so. She was so tired. She could hardly do her dishes that night. She said: 'I got thread in my brain. Rub it there. I got thread in my brain.' She kept thanking Doris for rubbing her. 'Thank you. O, thank you, Doris,' she said.

In the Ferris wheel Grace was scared when it went up. She clung to Doris and shut her eyes. Doris kept hers wide open. She didn't want to miss a thing.

Nell would have looked Jesus Christ in the eyes. She would have looked Napoleon Bonepart in the eyes or Robert E. Lee. Doris's husband thought Doris was that way, too, but she wasn't just the way her husband thought she was. She knew that. Once Ed talked to his mother about Doris. Doris didn't hear it. It was in the afternoon when Ed had woke up and when Doris was at work. He said: 'If she had a thought against me, she'd tell it. If she had even a thought about another man, she'd tell me.' It wasn't true. If Doris had heard it, she would have laughed. 'He's got me wrong,' she would have said. He couldn't have known about the thoughts she sometimes had about other men, like that young red-haired man in the mill, the one they all thought was maybe a spy. What would have been the use telling him that?

You could be in a room with Doris and she'd be there and not there. She'd never get on your nerves. Nell said that once to Fanny and it was true.

She didn't say: 'Look. Here I am. I'm Doris. Pay attention to me.' She didn't care whether you paid attention or not.

Her husband Ed could be in a room. He could be reading there on a Sunday. Doris would be lying down, too, on the same bed, beside Ed. Ed's mother could be lying on the front porch on the couch Ed had made for her. Ed would have put it out there for her. Ed would have put it out there for her so she could get the air.

It would be hot summer.

The baby could be out there playing on the porch. He could be crawling around. Ed had made a little fence so he couldn't crawl off the porch. Ed's mother could watch him. Her cough kept her awake.

Ed could be on the bed beside Doris. He could be thinking about the people in the book he was reading. If he had been a writer, he could have been on the bed beside Doris writing his books. Nothing in her said: 'Look at me. Pay attention to me.' It never did.

Nell said: 'She goes toward you. She's warm toward you.' If Nell had been a man, she'd have been after Doris. She said to Fanny once: 'I'd be after her. I'd want her.'

Doris never hated anyone. She never hated anything.

Doris could rub warmth into people. She could rub relaxation into people, with her hands. Sometimes when she was in the spinning-room at the mill, keeping up her side, her breasts hurt. After she got Ed and her baby, she nursed her baby early when she woke up. Her baby woke her up early. She gave him a little warm drink again before she went off to work.

She went home and nursed her baby again at noon. In the night she nursed him. On Saturday nights the baby slept with her and Ed.

Ed had nice feelings. Before she married him, when they were going together . . . they both worked in the mill then, too . . . Ed had a day job then . . . Ed used to walk with her. He used to sit in Doris's mother's and father's house with her at night in the dark.

Doris had been in the mill, in the spinning-room, since she was twelve. So had Ed been. He had been in the loom room since he was fifteen.

On the day when Doris was in the Ferris wheel with Grace . . . Grace clinging to her . . . Grace with her eyes shut because she was afraid . . . Fan and Nell in the next seat below . . . Fan whooping with laughter . . . Nell yelled.

Doris kept seeing things.

She saw two fat Negro women, far off, fishing in the river.

She saw cotton fields, far off.

There was a man driving an automobile in a road between cotton fields. He made a red dust.

She saw some of the buildings of the town of Langdon and the smokestack at the cotton mill where she worked.

There was a man selling patent medicine in a field near the one where the fair was being held. Doris saw him. He had only Negroes gathered about him. He was on the back of a truck. He was selling patent medicine to niggers.

She saw a crowd, a surging crowd on the fairgrounds, Negroes and whites, lint-heads (cotton-mill workers) and niggers. Most of the mill girls hated Negroes. Doris didn't.

She saw a young man she knew. He was the strong-looking red-headed young town man who had got a job in the mill.

He had been there working twice. He came one summer and then the next summer he didn't come. Now he was back again. He was a sweeper. The girls in the mill said: 'I'll bet he's a spy. What else is he? If he isn't a spy, why would he be here?'

He worked in the mill the first time. Doris wasn't married then. Then he went away and someone said he went to college. Doris got married to Ed the next summer.

Then he came back. It was tight times with people being laid off, but he got a job back. They had put in the stretch-out and they were laying people off and there was talk of a union. 'Let's have a union.'

'Mr. Shaw won't stand for it. The sup won't stand for it.'

'I don't care. Let's have a union.'

Doris didn't get laid off. She had to work a longer side. Ed had to do more. He could hardly do what he did do before. When that young fellow with the red hair ... they called him 'Red' ... when he came back they all said he must be a spy.

There was a woman, a strange woman, came to town and got hold of Nell and told her who to write to about a union and Nell came at night, on a Saturday night, to the Hoffman house and said to Doris, 'Can I speak to Ed, Doris?' and Doris said, 'Yes.' She wanted Ed to write to some people to get a union, to send someone. 'A communist one I hope,' she said. She had heard that was the worst kind. She wanted the worst. Ed was afraid. He wouldn't at first. 'It's hard times,' he said, 'it's Hoover times.' He said he wouldn't at first.

'It's no time,' he said. He was scared. 'I'll get fired or laid off,' he said, but Doris said, 'Ah, go ahead,' and Nell said, 'Ah, go ahead,' and he did.

Nell said: 'Don't tell a soul. Don't tell a damn soul.' It was exciting.

The red-haired young man had come back to work in the mill. His poppy had been a doctor in Langdon and he used to doctor sick mill people, but he had died. He was on the square ...

His son was just a sweeper in the mill. He played ball on the mill ball team and was a crack player. That day, when Doris was at the fair, in the Ferris wheel, she saw him. The mill ball team usually played ball on the ball field the mill owned, right by the mill, but that day they were playing right near the fair. It was a big day for mill people.

There was to be a dance that night at the fair on a big platform — ten cents. There were two platforms, one for niggers, one for whites, not very near. Grace and Nell and Doris didn't intend to stay. Doris couldn't. Fanny stayed. Her husband came and she stayed.

There was to be a greased pig caught after the baseball game. They didn't stay for that. They went on home after the Ferris-wheel ride.

Nell said, speaking of that young red-haired man from town who played on the mill ball team, 'I'll bet he's a spy,' she said. 'The damn rat,' she said, 'the skunk. I'll bet he's a spy.'

They were having the union formed. Ed got letters. He was afraid they'd get onto him every time he got a letter. 'What's in it?' Doris asked. It was exciting. He got cards to be signed up to join the union. There was a man coming. There was to be a big open union meeting to come out in the open as soon as they had enough signed up. It wasn't communist. Nell had been wrong about that. It was just a union, not the worse kind. Nell said to Ed, 'They can't fire you for that.'

'Yes, they can. The hell they can't!' He was scared. Nell said she bet young Red Oliver was a damn spy. Ed said, 'I'll bet he is.'

Doris knew he wasn't. She said he wasn't.

'How do you know?'

'I just know.'

When she was in the spinning-room of the mill at work, she could just see in the daytime, down the long passageway, lined with the flying bobbins on both sides, a little piece of sky. There was a little piece of tree, the limb of a tree, somewhere far off, over by the river maybe . . . you couldn't see it always, only when a wind blew. A wind blew and swayed it, and then, if you looked up just then, you saw it. She had been seeing it since she was twelve. Lots of times she had thought, 'When I get outside sometime, I'm going to look and see where that tree is,' but when she got outside, she couldn't tell. She had been seeing it since she was twelve. She was eighteen now. There weren't any threads in her head. There weren't any threads in her legs from standing so long where thread was made.

That young man, that red-haired young man, used to give her the eye. Grace, when he was there first, didn't know and Nell didn't know. She wasn't married to Ed the first time. Ed didn't know.

He got around that way when he could. He came and looked at her. She looked at him, like that.

Doris's breasts hurt in the late afternoon when she was in the mill. They began hurting steadily before quitting time, when she had her baby and hadn't weaned him yet. She was weaning him but hadn't got him weaned. When she was in the mill, before she married Ed and when that red-haired young man came around and looked at her, she felt funny. That day, when she was in the Ferris wheel and saw Red Oliver playing baseball with the mill team and was looking at him he was at bat and he hit a ball hard and ran.

It was nice to see him run. He was young and strong. He didn't see her of course. Her breasts began to hurt a little. It made her think of her kid. When the Ferris-wheel ride was over and they came down and had got out she told the rest she guessed she'd have to be getting along back home. 'I got to go home,' she said. 'I got to nurse my kid.'

Nell and Grace went with her. They came home by the railroad tracks. It was a shorter way. Fanny started with them, but she met her husband and he said, 'Let's stay,' and so she stayed.

The TVA

There is the Tennessee River. It starts up in the Blue Ridge country. Little rivers come racing down, the Clinch, the Holston, and others. The Tennessee is a hill-country river, working its way down valleys, under big hills, little hills, now creeping west, now south, now north — Virginia, West Virginia, Kentucky, Tennessee, down into northern Alabama. The hill country of northern Georgia is in the TVA sphere of influence. That is what this TVA thing is, 'a sphere of influence.'

It is something to dream and hope for, this land drained by the Tennessee. There are a few rich valleys, growing blue grass. There are mountain ranges. Once all these mountains and hills were covered with magnificent forests. It was one of the two Morgans who are in charge of this vast enterprise with David Lilienthal, H. A. Morgan, the land man, the folk man of the project, who talked to me of that. He was president of the University of Tennessee before he got into this thing and he is a land man.

He talked for an hour and I got a sharp sense of the land-loving man. There was the story of how the hill lands had been robbed. No use blaming anyone. The big timber men came to denude the hills. Then the little ones with the 'peckerwood' mills came to clean up.

The farmers were left on the hills. Traditions grew up about these people. John Fox wrote of them in *The Trail of the Lonesome Pine*. Not so good. Jeeter, of Erskine Caldwell's *Tobacco Road*, is nearer the real thing. They were of the feud country, a pretty romantic lot, in books and stories. In real life they were something else — in real life it was a pitiful rather than a romantic story.

It was the story of a people clinging, year after year, to little hillside

642

farms. Every year they got poorer and poorer. Some of these men went out of their hills to the coal mines and later to the factory towns that had come into the hills, but many came back. There is the love of his own country in the hill man. He does not want to leave the hills.

The depression brought the hill men back faster. I went into little upland valleys where a farm of thirty or forty acres might once have sustained one family. (It would have been poor enough fare — hard enough living for the one family.)

But now, often, on such a farm I found three or four families. Sons had come back to their mountain fathers, bringing wives, bringing children. They had built little huts — often without windows.

'At least here, on my father's land, a little corn can be raised. There will be a cabin floor to sleep on at night. It is less terrible than walking among the out-of-works, in some industrial town.'

There is a story of an Englishman coming into the hill country, going among the hill men. The Englishman was stunned.

'These hill men are English,' he said. 'I don't like it.'

'You don't like what?'

'I don't like their failing; I don't like to think of Englishmen as failures in a new land.'

It is a land of tall, straight men — the kind of stock out of which came Daniel Boone, Andrew Jackson, Andrew Johnson. They have fine-looking children, these men. The children fade young. The women fade young.

There is bad diet. No money. The soil gets thinner and thinner with every passing year. Most of this hill land should go back into forest. Every rain that washes down the hillsides takes more of the soil away.

Suppose you put the hills back into forest, what are you to do with these people? Are you to herd them down into industrial cities, where there are already too many men out of work, living on charity?

You have to think of the fact that what we call the modern world has pretty much gone on past these people, as it has gone completely past the tenant farmers, farther south. There are these mountaineers, millions of them scattered over a vast territory, touching several states. These are not the foriegners of whom we Americans can say so glibly — 'If they do not like it here, let them go back where they came from.'

These men are from the oldest American stock we have. It is the kind of stock out of which came Abraham Lincoln. Thomas Lincoln, his father, and Nancy Hanks, his mother, were poor whites of the hills.

And there is all this other stuff about us of which we Americans are so proud, our well-equipped houses, motor cars, bathrooms, warm clothes — what we call our American standard of living. All these things not touching these mountain people.

They are clinging to their hills in one of the most beautiful lands in the world.

'Can we take what they and their hills already have — adding nothing — find the riches in their hills — and give these men modern life? If this modern mechanical life is any good, it should be good for these people.'

There is wealth in the land on which these people have tried to live. It is a new kind of wealth, the wealth of the modern man, of the modern world. It is wealth in the form of energy.

Power — the coinage of the modern world!

There is plenty of power — the private companies have only got a little of it so far — flowing silently away, along the Tennessee, along the rivers that come down out of the hills to make the Tennessee.

Long ago, I'm told, army engineers went through these hills. They drew up a kind of plan, having in mind the use of all this wasted power in case of war, power to be harnessed, to make munitions, to kill men.

There came the World War and the building of the Wilson Dam at Muscle Shoals. That is where the Tennessee, in its wanderings, dips down into northern Alabama, thrusts down into the land of cotton. It is something to be seen. All good Americans should go and see it. If the Russians had it there would be parades, special editions of illustrated magazines got out and distributed by the Government.

There it is, however, completely magnificent. You go down, by elevator, some ten stories, under the earth, under the roaring river, and walk out into great light clean rooms. There is a song, the song of the great motors. You are stirred. Something in you — the mechanically minded American in you — begins to sing. Everything is so huge, so suggestive of power, and at the same time so delicate. You walk about muttering.

'No wonder the Russians wanted our engineers,' you say to yourself.

The great motors sing on, each motor as large as a city room. There is a proud kind of rebirth of Americanism in you.

'Some of our boys did this,' you say to yourself, throwing out your chest.

The Wilson Dam never was made to impound much water. The idea was to take the power directly out of the swirl of water rushing down over the shoals.

But sometimes it doesn't rush. Dry seasons come, far up-river and in the little rivers. The forest-denuded hills do not hold back the water after rains. Every time you build another dam up-river, you get power out of the new dam and you increase the power at Muscle Shoals. They are building two dams now, each to make a great lake, the Joe Wheeler, some twenty-five miles above the Wilson, and the Norris, far up-river, a day's drive, near Knoxville. They will both make great lakes, the shore line of the Norris to be some nine hundred miles, it to be at places two hundred feet deep.

Power stored to make a steady stream of power — power from the Wilson being used to build the Joe Wheeler and the Norris — the river being made to harness itself. There is a new kind of poetry in that thought.

These, the first of perhaps a dozen dams to be built along one river — power aplenty for great stretches of country far outside the sphere of influence of the present TVA.

The power to be used, to give an opportunity to small industries, reduce the power costs in towns over a wide country, make electrical power available in homes where it cannot now be used — the money coming in to go back into the country out of which the power came —

Denuded hills to be reforested, soil-washing stopped.

This soil-washing, going on in every denuded hill country, filling your lakes with mud after you build your dams, utterly destroying, making a barren waste of wide stretches of country. It's hard to dramatize the slow, steady year-after-year eating away of soil richness. Whole lands have been destroyed by it, made into deserts. The Government foresters, working with the CCC boys, are like wronged children in their eagerness to make their work understood. 'Tell them about it. Please tell them,' they keep saying. They follow you around eagerly. 'You are a writer. Can't you tell them? Can't you make them understand that we are builders? These CCC camps. We are taking these city kids and making builders of them. The boys in the camps begin to understand. Please make everyone understand.'

Engineers and foresters going at night, after the day's work, to country towns in the district, to country schoolhouses, lecturing, explaining. I found in these men working on the TVA something I have been hungry to find, men working at work they love, not thinking of money or promotion, happy men, laughing men. They think they are saving something. They think they are making something.

I went into the TVA accompanied by a friend, a business man who lives in Chicago. Formerly he was a college professor. Once he wrote a beautiful novel that got little or no attention. He was poor and went into business. He succeeded.

But like a good many American business men, he wasn't very happy in his success. When the New Deal was announced, he went in for it, head over heels.

He was strong for the NRA, but recently he has been skeptical. I had written him, telling him that I was going to look at the TVA, and he wanted to go along. We met in Knoxville and spent most of the first night in a hotel room, talking.

He was discouraged.

'It isn't going to work,' he said. He was speaking of the NRA. 'They are trying to fix prices now. The small man is doomed.' He is himself not one of the small men. 'You can't stop the chiselers. You can't. You can't.'

We went to look at the TVA. We did look. We listened. We went down among the workers on the dams. We went into power houses, visited men in their offices. Sometimes we were accompanied by enthusiasts, engineers, foresters, and others, and often we were alone. We had our own car.

We kept talking. We kept looking. A change came over my friend.

'So this is the South,' he said.

He had the Northern man's point of view. To the Southerner the South is the Deep South. He began talking of the TVA as the South's opportunity. In spite of the fact that my friend was once a college professor, he is an educated man. He knows his American history.

'Look what we Northerners did to the South,' he kept saying as his enthusiasm grew. 'And now this.'

We took our look at the TVA, the immediate sphere of influence, and pushed on down into the Deep South. We got into the back country, going by back roads.

Men were plowing in the Southern fields. There was the thing, always a new wonder to the city man, the patience of men with the earth, the way they cling to it. We were in a poor district. They are not hard to find in the back country of the Deep South. There were these miles of back roads, deeply rutted, even dangerous, bridges fallen into decay.

'It is a kind of inferno,' my friend kept saying. We had just left the land of new hope, men busy, the strikingly charming Government-built town of Norris, at Norris Dam, going up, men laughing at their work——

Memory in us both of a lunch had with a dozen foresters in a town in the heart of the TVA — the town sitting on land that would presently be a lake bottom — the laughter in the room, the anxiety of the men that their story be told straight——

'Don't talk too big. Don't promise too much. We may be stopped.'

That against the land of desolation, of no hope — the poor farmers, getting poorer every year. The cotton allotment in the South wasn't going to be of much help to the people along the road we had got into. It would go to the landowners, and not one out of ten of the little farmers, white or black, along the road we traveled would own the land he was plowing——

Poor little unpainted cabins half fallen down. Pale women with tired eyes. Undernourished children playing in bare yards before the cabins.

'There are too many of these.'

We had got into an argument. My friend had lived his boyhood on an Iowa farm.

'You have places as bad as this in your Chicago,' I said, not wanting him to think all American misery was in the South.

'I know, but not on the land! In the end, everything comes back to the land.

'The people who cannot love the land on which they live are a lost people.

'It is right that all America should try this experiment in the South,' he said.

There were the one-mule farmers patiently plowing the land beside the road.

'It is wonderful the way man goes on. In spite of defeat, he goes on,' my friend said.

Two old men came out of a strip of pine woods. They were toothless, bent old men, Southerners, poor whites, going along the road in silence. We passed them.

My friend leaned out of the car. He was excited.

'Hey!' he called.

The two old men stopped and stared at us. I stopped the car. My friend hesitated.

'Drive on,' he said. He turned to me and laughed. 'I wanted to tell them something. I can't,' he said. 'It would sound too silly.'

'What?' I said.

'Something new in American life is begun back there, and it mustn't be stopped,' he said.

I thought it was the feeling, alive in him, as it is still curiously alive in so many Americans, alive in spite of greed, chiseling, desire for fake money, bigness. The feeling of men for men — desire to some day work for others. The TVA may be a beginning.

Tough Babes in the Woods

T HEY HAVE MADE a little town under the hill — between two hills — in a narrow valley down which flows a mountain stream. This is one of a dozen such little towns I have been in during the last week, and they are all pretty much alike. There is an army man and a forester or two in each camp. The army men have charge of the camp. They differ. Some add little homelike touches, others do not. There may be twenty or thirty or fifty houses in such a camp town, and it may have one street or two or three. They are laying down sidewalks in the one I have just been in. This is the time of mud in the valleys and in the hills. Soon the spring rains will be coming here.

The boys in this camp town, at the edge of which I am sitting — I am sitting with my notebook on a flat stone under a rhododendron bush — the boys go up the hills and bring down flat stones. They are laying sidewalks along the street down which I look, making their town neat against the muddy time to come. A man goes about among them directing the work, a tall, lean, intelligent man of thirty. He is the forester of this camp — a soft-speaking Southerner — and this is Saturday, so the boys do not go to work in the woods. It is a clear, quiet day and rather warm. Spring will be coming soon in this southern Appalachian country. I hear a little animal moving back of me in the woods. A hawk floats in the clear blue sky above the valley.

When I drove over to this mountain camp this morning, I saw a man plowing a hillside above the next valley to the south. He was a lean, ragged, hard-bitten mountain man, and he lived in a one-room cabin at the end of the field he was plowing. I have seen as many as nineteen children in one family in such a cabin. I have seen poverty that has made me halt. I have seen a thousand such cabins perched on hills in southwestern Virginia, Pennsylvania, West Virginia, Tennessee, northern Georgia, Kentucky, and westward, across the Mississippi, in the Ozark Mountains of Missouri, and only two weeks ago, in the city of New York, I saw just such a cabin on the stage, in a play called *Tobacco Road*.

Tobacco road, indeed! It is a road to ruin — this poor-white hillside farming going on year after year, over millions of acres of the American hill country. As for the poor-white Georgia cracker man of the Georgia plains, tied to his cotton and tobacco farming on poor, exhausted soil, his story is a different one. We are in the hills now. This is the story of the hill man. The story here also one of wasted fine material. I know the mountain men, and when I am at home I live among them. The story of the lives they live, how they got like that, the death of the children of this fine stock by undernourishment — this is another tragic American story. How I have hated the romanticists who have thrown the cloud of romance about such lives!

But I am trying to tell now the story of the camp towns, of the CCC coming to these hills. They are scattered out over the country, hundreds, even thousands of such little temporary towns — the Government putting them up. The houses of the towns are long one-story affairs built of thick building paper. They stand up high and dry above the valley bottoms on stone foundations.

There is a commissary building, a mess hall, a post-office, a library, a temporary hospital. They are all temporary houses.

Suppose they shouldn't be temporary. Suppose what is going on here is but a beginning. It is an interesting idea that this thing that has now begun in America — Government having a thought of the land, men in Washington, in Government, daring to say — 'We'll begin trying it.'

Trying what?

Suppose it should come down to this, that there is a plot on foot in America — men actually serious about it — a plot, let's say, to save America from the Americans.

Actually they are serious about the plot, some of them. I have been in Washington — talked to men there, men who struck me as first-rate, serious-minded men — not at all romantic. I do not mean bankers or industrialists. I mean men of another type — scientific men,

Government engineers, foresters, hard-working men, most of whom have been employed for years in the Interior and the Agricultural Departments.

Much of what these men told me is, as they say in Washington now, 'off the record.' It is still, it seems, somewhat irregular, even a little dangerous, to have dreams of a greater America, an America really used. You can't call names.

'What, you dream of a physical America controlled, plowing of the land controlled — this or that section of America to be permanently in forest — river-flow control, floods controlled at the flood source?

'You say that one great flood — let us say of Mother Mississippi — may cost more than ten years' constructive work back in the hills, in denuded forests where floods begin?

'This, off the record. Someone may think I am a Socialist or a Bolshevik.'

Men's minds pushing, somewhat timidly, into a new social view of physical America. How are they to tell the story to that lean mountain man? Let us say that he owns his few poor hillside acres. Who is to tell him, 'Thou shalt not'? The right to go on plowing, where plowing is sheer land destruction — the traditional right of the American individualist, big or little.

'It's mine.'

'It's mine.'

Who is to say to me, a free American, 'Thou shalt not'?

Into this camp have come boys, the greater number of them from American cities. They are young boys, most of them about high-school age. But for this depression, in the natural flow of an older American life — it seems suddenly old now — as things have been running in America for the last two, three, or four generations, these boys, being for the most part city and town boys, would have come out of school and would have become clerks or factory hands.

Or — and this would go for a lot of them — they would have become tough city guys — the kind that make bright young gangsters — the kind you see leaning against walls near gang hangouts in cities.

'How much to kill a man?'

'How much?'

But, you see, even the rackets have become a bit thin now, clerkships have fallen away, prohibition has gone, the factories are not exactly howling for men.

So these CCC camps have gathered them in, all kinds of men.

That forester down there, directing the boys as they lay sidewalks in their new woods town, was in Montana last year. He had under him out there some two or three hundred boys, mostly from the East Side of New York — tough birds — most of them, he says. He speaks of them with an affectionate grin. 'Boy, what we had to do to them — what they did to us!' They have been jerked up out of that environment, hauled in fast trains across two-thirds of the United States and thrown into a forest camp some seven thousand feet up in the magnificent hills. They had to build the camps, keep themselves clean, keep their bedding and their quarters clean, learn to swing an axe — 'We had to watch them like babes that they did not kill each other with the axes.' The boys learned to make beds, learned the necessary sanitary laws that must govern men living in camps, the give-and-take of man to man, so essential to life where men live, sleep, talk, dream, in one great room — rows of cots all in the open — the door at the end of the room open — sight of the wooded hills when you go to sleep at night, when you wake in the morning ——

These men, the greater majority of them out of the crowded factory towns.

'It's the beginning of some kind of revolution in life — for them at least.'

'Sure.'

Not every man can swing an axe. Some men, born in the forests, never get the knack. There are Babe Ruths among axemen too.

It is a kind of revolution in many lives that goes both backward and forward. Forward, let's say, to a possible conception of an America that shall belong essentially to all Americans — as one thoughtful, serious-minded man, who felt he owed something to the ground under his feet, might feel toward one farm — such a man as might say to himself — 'I want to leave this piece of ground, on which I have lived my life and made my living, a better piece of ground than it was when I came upon it.' You get the idea — at least a dream of all American farmers saying 'We'll live to build, not destroy.'

Something of that sort.

Let's say, a new comprehensive forward look and then also, in this CCC thing something else — a kind of movement backward to an earlier American tone of life, when life did center about the forests and the land, when men went out and fought it out with Nature and got something men can get in no other way — a kind of man-making process that factory work and clerkships haven't as yet been able to bring into men's lives.

To use the land also to make men.

To use men also to make the land.

Who in America doesn't know what, over great stretches of country, we Americans have done to the land? Soil erosion going on that is costing us each year more than the entire cost of our military and naval establishments, and all of this due to the old belief that if I own a piece of land I have the right to do as I please with it. I can tear off the forest.

'It's mine, isn't it?'

The valley down which I look as I sit writing is one of a thousand such valleys in the range of mountains that stretches across our country from East to West, separating the North from the South. It is a stream-source country. This country with the great stretches of cut-over lands in northern Michigan, Wisconsin, and Minnesota is the stream source from which comes much of the water of the Mississippi. The valley down which I look is watered by one of the little rivers that come down from the hills. There might be fifty such streams in one county in this country. The natives tell me that all were formerly good trout and bass streams. They went softly along through the deep woods. They were icy cold even in summer. They were steady year-round streams, fed by mountain springs. The valley is broken by many little side valleys. It is like an old saw with many teeth broken out. In each little side valley may be found a few underfed mountain families, persistently plowing hillside lands that will not and cannot make them a living.

These CCC camps are a beginning. If you look at the map you will see them scattered most thickly along the Pacific Coast, north at the headwaters of the Mississippi and in these border mountains between the North and South, and on the southern side of these hills where the streams go down to the Atlantic. There are camps now everywhere in these hills along the southern Appalachian, the Cumberland, the Blue Ridge, and westward to the Mississippi and the Ozarks. They extend eastward to where, at Lynchburg, Virginia, the big hills end and the little ones step softly down to the Tidewater country.

It may well be that all of this land, except only the valley bottoms, should be wiped out as farming lands. Let the trees again have the hills. There should be better use for the life of these hill men, starving and destroying in these hills.

The hand of Government is reaching out and out. The Government is acquiring all the time more and more thousands of acres of these hill lands.

They are having classes in the camps. They are teaching geography and history. As the boys work in the forests, a forester goes with them. They are learning to tell the ash from the maple and the spruce from the oak. It is a tremendous educational experiment.

The greater number of the boys are city-bred. They are from the families of the poor. They are young American-born — Poles, Italians, Jews, Lithuanians, and Germans — the first generation away from the old country. They are short squat figures of American men in the making, with the twang of the city speech on their lips. Nearly all of the boys in this camp town are out of the back streets of Newark, Hoboken, Jersey City, and New York.

'Where are you from, buddy?' I say to one of them.

'Oh, take a look. What do you t'ink?'

'I'm from Avenue A.'

The mountain men who come into the camp, to work, or just to look, stand staring at the city boys. They laugh softly. Such awkward axe-swinging. Some of these mountain men have been axe-swingers since they were babes. Some of them, the older ones, worked in the lumber camps in these hills when the first forests, the great forests, were cut away. They tell you about it. First the great companies with the big band mills came, taking the best, and these were followed by the little peckerwood mills — often a model T Ford engine and a saw, cleaning up what the big ones left.

There was destruction and waste aplenty. Who cared? Individualism. The old America. 'You should have seen it before they came,' an old mountain man said. A kind of awe creeps into his voice. 'The forest was like a great church. Oh, the great trees! You sank to your knees in the moss underfoot.'

I myself remember an old man who came to my father's house when I was a boy. He was an old, old man from an Ohio River town where my own father once lived, and he talked to my father of the river. 'I remember when I was a boy,' he said, 'I swam with other boys in the Ohio. It was a clear stream then. We used to swim way out and look down. The water was so clear we could see the bottom.'

There is something still to be seen in this CCC movement. It isn't just an idea of giving a certain number of men work, helping them over the depression.

The leaves of the forest trees, even the young new trees, now growing, fall and lie on the ground. Next year more leaves fall. There is a soft porous bottom made. Moss begins to grow. It is a great blotter. Pinchot of Pennsylvania, when he was making his first fight against forest destruction, used to go before control committees with a wide board in his hand. He set the board on a table at an angle of forty-five degrees and poured a glass of water down it.

Then he took the same board and tacked blotting paper on it. Again he poured water down the board, but this time it did not rush off. That told the story. It is a thing the Government can do and that the individual cannot do. There are these millions of acres of watershed land, none of it any good for farming. It should go back into forests, making future wealth.

Rains come and wash the plowed lands away and every rain takes its toll of richness. You go through these hill lands in the spring and summer, seeing the hill men at the plow, often on lands so steep you wonder that the man and bony horse do not both roll to the bottom — men slowly and painfully plowing, planting, and hoeing — then the rains — there the fields go.

It would not have mattered so much if it were only one field, a few fields plowed and lost, great gashes in the hillsides, water rushing down pellmell, floods in the low lands, towns destroyed. There are still millions of such fields being plowed. The whole country pays.

Multiply it. Multiply it.

The forester comes up to me along the street of the camp. He sees me sitting and writing under the rhododendron bush and hesitates. 'Hello,' I say.

'I do not want to disturb you.'

We grin at each other.

'Come on,' he says.

Putting my notebook into my pocket, I go and get into his truck and we begin climbing up a mountain road. It's risky going. This is one of the new roads the city boys have made. It rained last night and the car slithers about. Up and up we go, far up into the hills and the car stops. We go on afoot. We go into the brush. Climbing over fallen logs, up and up. 'I wanted to show you a tree they didn't get,' he says, referring to the early lumber men. We stop before a great spruce far up in the hills. 'They had to leave it,' he says. 'They couldn't get to it.'

We are sitting now on a rocky promontory and looking way over the hills. From up here the smaller hills are like the waves of the sea in a storm. The man I am with is one of the believers. He talks and talks. He is sore at the lumber man who beat him into these forests.

'The Government should never have let them do it,' he keeps saying. 'We should have had a chance. Our men should have been here.' He declares that under the foresters the lumber companies might have taken as much lumber without denuding the hills. 'They could have taken out all the good timber and left the half-grown trees that in another generation would have made a second great cutting.'

Now it will take us fifty years to get back what was wantonly destroyed. He stands beside me on the mountain-top swearing, but it is already an old story to me, this cry of the forester. Now they are in the woods again. They are directing the work of these boys in the CCC camps.

The depression has given them their chance. 'Hurrah for the depression,' one of them said to me. They are making a new kind of American man out of the city boy in the woods, and they are planning at least to begin to make a new land with the help of such boys.

'Please Let Me Explain'

ON THE ROAD I saw many people trying to catch a ride. There were old men and young men, some of them quite respectably dressed, and others in rags. I saw two different families, father, mother, and children, with little packs on their backs tramping the roads. I had goods in the back of my car and had room but for one passenger at a time. I picked up two men, carrying one of them a part of the way, dropping him at his destination, then picking up another. The first was an old man, respectably dressed, like a well-to-do workingman of ten years ago and with a little gray mustache. He told me that five years ago he was a big wheat farmer in the West. He had a good deal of land, but wanted more, and so he went into debt at the bank and bought more land. He owed money at the bank and could not pay. The price of wheat fell and fell. The bank examiner came to his town and told the bank they had to get rid of their frozen assets. The man was sold out. 'In my section,' he said, 'at least seventy-five per cent of the farmers will be sold out unless things change and change quickly.' The man never had any children, but he and his wife had adopted children. His wife is dead. He has had to throw his children back upon their own people, who are, he told me, very poor. 'I have become a common workman,' he said, 'but who wants me?' The man was strong and alert at sixty-five, but who nowadays wants a workman of sixty-five?

Every man and in particular every American is anxious to tell you his life history. He wants to explain himself.

In America every man who is broke, down on his luck, is half-ashamed of the fact. Everywhere now you see people who are not yet broke. They have possessions. They have not lost their farms or their

657

stores or their houses. In spite of the depression they may still have some money left. Perhaps they are ashamed, too. It may be that nowadays all of us who are not entirely broke and see people everywhere in destitution are a little ashamed of our own safety. We have an inclination to say — 'The fellow could get a job if he wanted to work.' It makes us feel better. Or we say — 'Look at these fellows. Nearly all of them own automobiles.'

We forget how it was here in America a few years ago, in times of prosperity. Then every man who had a job and any kind of an income and who didn't own an automobile was driven almost crazy by high-pressure salesmen. Radio salesmen were after him, automobile salesmen, refrigerator salesmen. He was made to feel that he wasn't any man at all unless he went in debt for a car or for a radio. All the big men in American life cried out constantly — 'Spend. Spend.' Well, the poor fellow did it. Now he has the car and owes money for it. He can't run it and he can't sell it. The position of the American in times like these is somewhat different from the position of any other man in the world. That should be borne in mind.

For example, let us compare him with the European man. In Europe the common man does not expect ever to rise in the world. The man is born into a certain position in life and in ninety-five cases out of a hundred he stays there. Let us say the man's father owns a little wineshop or a grocery store or is a small farmer, a landowner. The son expects to follow in his father's footsteps. He doesn't expect to rise in the world and others do not expect him to rise. To be sure, there are exceptions. Men of extraordinary energy or genius do arise and push themselves forward. But such men are rare. The man whose father owns a little wineshop inherits the wineshop when his father dies, but he doesn't begin thinking — 'How can I make my wineshop bigger?' He doesn't begin scheming to own a dozen wineshops. His father lived in a certain way, and he in turn fully expects to live in the same way, is quite content usually to live that way. For example, I have been going to Europe every five or six years now for perhaps twenty-five years. I always go to Paris. In the Rue Jacob in Paris there is a certain little wineshop. There are rows of winebottles upon shelves running from the floor to the ceiling. The man now running that shop is about my own age. His father ran it and his grandfather. It was never smaller than it is now and perhaps never will become any larger. The man knows personally every customer who comes into his shop. He even remembers me. If, after five years, I go into his shop again, as I always do when I go to Paris, he looks up and smiles. 'Hello,' he says. 'You are back here. You are looking very well. You haven't been here for a long time.'

He has a son who will in turn some day run the shop, but no one is telling the son that when his time comes he should hustle to make the shop bigger, that he should live in a larger house than the one his father lived in, or that he should be in any way anything bigger and grander than his father and his grandfather. You can see, of course, that this fact gives the son a certain solid feeling about life. He is a man who has his roots in the place where he was born. The fact gives him a kind of strength that is good to see. The man will not always have to be explaining himself to everyone. 'I am the keeper of a wineshop,' he says, or, 'I drive this dust cart.' I have seen men going along the road in European countries driving carts that it was good to see. There the man went along the road. He had his whip under his arm. His hat was cocked on the side of his head. There was even a strut. 'Well, look at me if you want to. I am here driving this cart. I am a cart driver. What of it?' Even the very beggars in some of the European countries have this air.

On the other hand, there is the American. He can't, of course, be like that. It is a very queer thing, but the truth is that we Americans, who talk so proudly of our individuality and of our independence, are always going about explaining ourselves. It is easy to see how it came about.

We Americans have all been taught, from childhood, that it is a sort of moral obligation for each of us to rise, to get up in the world. I am sure there must be thousands, perhaps millions, of Americans whose experience in this respect has been like my own. Progress. Progress. That was the cry.

We were all taught that there is a certain kind of disgrace in being poor. How sharply I remember how the men of my own town spoke to me when I was a lad! The mayor of the town did it, the merchants did it, the judge spoke to me, a preacher spoke to me. I was a rather energetic, hustling boy. I was strong, cheerful, and willing. I wasn't afraid of work. I have bcome lazier since.

'Good boy. Be a hustler. Go after it. That's right. Make money. Money makes the mare go,' they said.

There it was, right from the beginning. You had to have money to rise in the world, to be a bigger, showier man than others in order to respect yourself. Of course, every man wants to respect himself. Money was the outward sign of inner merit. Men are still judged in that way in America. I must suppose that some of the men that spoke to me thus at that time — for example, the preacher, the judge, and others — did not exactly mean what they were saying. It was easier, more simple, to put it in that way, and then I must suppose, too, that in an earlier day in America, when the country was being built up, there was a kind of merit in being always active, always on the go, a hustler. If you had got money, men could judge you easier. 'He has accumulated money. He must be all right.' It was the easier way of passing judgment.

It is always, of course, easiest to judge the merits of any man's work by physical facts. Here is a man who has built the highest building in the world, made the most automobiles, has driven an airplane or an automobile faster than any other man, is the richest man in the world. By the American standard that man is, almost automatically, a man of merit. It is obvious.

But now we Americans have been caught up with. The newspapers, the politicians who want to get into office, and others are telling us that the depression we are now in is only a temporary thing. The chances are, however, that it is something more than temporary, that it may become permanent. There are a good many signs nowadays that we are at the end of one stage of civilization and must pass into another. A good many men think that what must pass is the age of capitalism, that some of these days soon now all of the great trusts, the chain stores, the big mills, and factories, and even the land, must be taken over by the State. The age of individual opportunity to accumulate may be passing, and if this is true, it is going to be hard for the American to adjust himself.

If you do not think this is true, the next time you are on the road pick up one of the Americans now down and out. Talk to him in a friendly way. See how quickly he begins to explain himself, to apologize. It may be that he has nothing to do with the circumstances that have put him where he is, but just the same he feels guilty. He does not blame his civilization. He feels that in some way he is not a good American because he has not risen above his fellows.

There is the wheat farmer who for a few years was a prosperous farmer. Now he is down and out. He is old and knows he cannot get work. He was going to live with some of his dead wife's relatives and was ashamed. He needed little encouragement from me to begin explaining himself. Although he had worked hard all his life, raising food for people to eat, he was in no way indignant about what his civilization had done to him. He should have been smarter, shrewder, should have taken more advantage of other men. 'It's my own fault,' he said; 'I was not smart enough.' It is the average American's point of view yet and it is a little hard to contemplate. You would think in times like these men would be actively thinking and planning for the future. If it is true, as some of us now think, that we are coming to the end of one age, and going into another, you would think that everyone here would be planning for the future — that our big men would be submitting plans — that we would all be thinking and working to make all life here better for all of us, but, as a matter of fact, nothing of the sort is being done yet by Americans. Only a few people — and they are not called good Americans — seem to be making any plans at all for the future. Most of them are as yet considered crazy and dangerous people.

However, yesterday, when I was driving on the road after I had picked up my first man and taken him to his destination, I picked up a second man who did have a plan. It wasn't his own plan. It was a thing he thought would happen. He was a young man and looked as though he had been ill. He was rather shabbily dressed. I picked him up at the edge of a town and he told me that he had been going through the town trying to sell to some one for twenty-five cents a pocket knife he still had in his possession. He wanted to get the money to buy himself something to eat, and I tried to talk to him to see if he had any plan for the future in America.

He said he had been thinking it over. He said he thought that the rich in America and the well-to-do people here would presently pass a law. He said he expected it would be done, that he looked forward to seeing it done. He said he thought that the poor and the unemployed in America would have to be killed. It was, he thought, the only way out. He said he had thought about it a good deal. He was a rather sensitive-looking man.

'But you would be one of the first to be killed,' I said.

'I know, but,' he said, 'you see I haven't succeeded. I don't believe I ever will succeed,' he said. 'I might as well be put out of the way.'

It is, as yet, I suspect, about the average American point of view. It is simple. It would no doubt be easier than tackling the terrific problem of what we are to do with America and Americans in the new age that is apparently coming.

Bud (*As Kit Saw Him*)

A YOUNG MAN from back in the hills came to visit the consumptive young man. His name, Kit said, was Bud, and the sick young man's name was Frank. Bud was Frank's cousin. Kit laughed, speaking of Bud. He was a strong young fellow, very dark and with a small bullet-like head, covered with coarse black hair.

The young consumptive, Frank, had arranged for an evening. 'We're going to do something,' he said. He got Kit and Agnes, the red-haired one. 'She was fierce,' Kit said. Frank went and brought a large bottle of moon whiskey. It was the only time Kit had ever known him to drink.

They set out, again to the fields, the four of them, in the moonlight on a summer night. 'We went out of the mill village, but not to the town. We went around it.' They kept circling the town, going through fields, avoiding farmhouses. 'We would stop and sit down. We'd drink. The stuff burned my throat.'

Kit had got a little wild. 'I had been ashamed to go near anyone, but I wasn't any more.' They were going up a little hill and she ran to the young man Bud and threw her arms about his neck. She kissed him, and Agnes and Frank both laughed. 'Frank didn't get a bit tired that night,' she said.

There were some brushpiles on top of a low hill, where some farmer had been at work, clearing land overgrown by brush, and she got some matches from Bud and ran to light them.

'Then we all ran, laughing, not to be caught by some farmer when the flames leaped up through the brushpiles. Frank also ran. Kit said he seemed to forget about being ill, although it was but a few weeks before he died.

They got over on another hill, to another farm, and lying on the ground watched, the four of them, their bodies close together. Kit said it was fine, watching the fires on the hill. They kept drinking out of the bottle. A farmer, with his wife and three children, came from a farmhouse and stood by the fires. He kept staring about. He had two dogs and they barked. Frank's cousin, Bud, his shyness also swept away by the drink, got to his feet. 'Howdee! Howdee!' he shouted at the top of his voice.

They got up and ran farther away. She said that Agnes, who was so fierce — 'She was loud-mouthed,' Kit said — got very gentle.

Bud, the cousin from the hills, had a stunt he did. He was a young fellow who had a passion for horses, and as his people were very poor, he could not own a horse. 'At least,' Frank told Kit, walking with her that night, 'he couldn't own one he wanted.' Frank had been drinking steadily. He was such a talker. 'He got gabby,' Kit said. He wanted to explain his cousin.

The cousin had gone one time on a trip with a truck. Frank told Kit that Bud lived near a town called Brevard, in North Carolina, and that there was a big tannery in a near-by town.

They had begun to take truckloads of leather through the hills and up through the Shenandoah Valley of Virginia to the Eastern cities and Bud knew a fellow who drove one of the trucks.

'I bet you don't know how big the world is,' Frank said to Kit. The sick young man was very gay. He seemed strong. His cousin had told him the story of his trip out into the big world and it was as though it had been an experience of his own. 'He was that kind,' Kit said. 'He could imagine things.'

They all sat down on the grass in a field and Frank kept talking. Agnes and Bud sat some distance away. They began playing. First they wrestled and then they chased each other about the field. Frank was proud of his cousin. 'He's smart. He's seen a lot,' he said.

'I'll bet you don't know how big the world is.' In their wanderings that night the four people had got back to where they could see, in the distance, the lights of their mill town. Frank pointed toward it.

'There must be a thousand, a million towns, bigger'n that,' he said. He pointed to the sky. 'There's as many towns as the stars up there,' he said.

'And people too.' He tried to tell Kit of the people Bud had seen in city streets, of the crowds of people, well-dressed people, he said. He thought it must have been wonderful for Bud, seeing all that and, getting suddenly sad, said he'd give anything, even one of his arms or a leg, have them sawed off, just to be well himself and go out like that to see so much.

Frank's sadness didn't last long that night. The fellow Bud was with, an older man of the mountain town, had got the job as truck-driver after working in a garage. He had been on the trips to Eastern cities several times. He had planned to go to Philadelphia, but he went the long way, to show Bud Baltimore and Washington.

And somewhere in Pennsylvania, or Frank said it might have been in Virginia, there was a big horse farm where fine saddle horses were trained and, knowing how Bud felt about horses, the man had stopped the truck.

'There were people, beautifully dressed, and horses, more beautiful than the people.' Frank spoke as though he had seen everything himself. Kit said he was like a fellow reading something out of a book. There were the people in a field, walking around . . . there were white fences like a house — painted . . .well-dressed men and beautiful women. 'The grass was just like on a lawn,' Bud had said. 'There were shining thin dresses with flowers on them.'

'They didn't charge anything to get in.' If it hadn't been for the truck, Bud and the man could have gone in. He didn't want to leave his truck.

'So they stopped the truck in the road and Bud crawled up and sat on top of it.'

There were barns as big as a factory. There was an old man, with a white beard and with a young woman on his arm. They were walking in the field, but came down near the fence by the road where the truck was. They passed so close to the fence that the young woman's gown touched it. 'She smelled like a flower or like a Balm of Gilead tree when it is in bloom, or like sassafras,' Bud had said.

They were bringing horses into the field and they were being put through their gaits, shown off. They trotted, freely, fiercely. They racked. They single-footed and galloped. Some of the riders shouted as though with delight at being on such beautiful beasts, and all the people standing and watching clapped their hands. There was one rider, all in black, with a shiny black hat and a white stiff-looking shirt. The shirt was very white, and he had a long whip. 'Hi-hi,' he called to his horse in a shrill voice. 'He had the best horse of them all, the most beautiful one.'

Frank thought that very likely the man with the best horse owned the place where the horses were being shown.

He explained that Bud, having had always a passionate interest in horses, had remembered about the exhibition in the field more than all the rest seen during the trip. He couldn't own such a horse, couldn't get one, and so, Frank said, he became a horse, and when Kit laughed, thinking perhaps he had again gone a little out of his head, like that other time when he cursed so, he called to Bud.

'Come here, Bud, and you, Agnes,' Frank called, and the couple came across the field. 'Now, Bud, you be a horse,' he said, and Kit and Agnes both laughed. 'We howled,' Kit said. 'It was such a crazy idea.'

But she said Bud did it. There was a grassy bare place before them and Bud took something from his pocket. It was, she said, a pair of hoofs. 'They were made of leather and Bud could strap them on his hands.' The cousin strapped the hoofs on his hands and got down on all fours.

'He was a horse,' she said.

'He was a bear.'

She had never seen a bear. 'I know, anyway, that's the way a bear looks.'

'The cousin was small and big, too. He was black almost,' Kit said. He could shamble. He could walk like a bear.

He could walk like a dog.

He could prance like a horse. 'You take a horse, a stallion, when he's excited. He could go like that.' She got excited, speaking of it, saying it was so strange to see, so uncanny.

He could walk on eggs and not break the shells.

'It may be all men would rather be horses,' Kit said, telling of the odd experience that night in the field. As she told of it, she kept laughing, a high shrill laugh, unlike herself.

There was white moonlight on a little sloping field, with a flat place below, where she, Frank, and Agnes sat, Kit said.

'Does a sheep ever want to be a man?' she said.

'Does a cow ever want to be a man?'

The little dark, squat man from the mountains had a shambling gait, going across an open moonlit place, on green cropped grass — sight of a Southern mill town in the distance . . . electric lights showing down there. He could prance, trot, single-foot, pace. He could do the slow gallop and the fast gallop.

The town in the distance, the lights of it were against a night sky. 'We've got industries, we've got progress,' I kept thinking, irrelevantly enough, as Kit told of her extraordinary evening.

The man Bud, young yet, a mountain boy, was short, dark, and squat.

'We've got big factories, in North Carolina, owned by the Dukes. There is a Miss Duke who has more millions of dollars than any young woman who ever lived in the world.

'We've got cigarette factories, we've got cotton and silk and rayon mills,' I thought.

There was a man, in a field, in the moonlight, being a horse. He had caught just the horse rhythm. He could rack fast, across the green earth, in the moonlight, throwing his horse legs out . . . his arms, strong, young, and muscular, that had become legs. They were very strong, his muscular brown, swarthy arms that had become horses' legs, with hoofs.

Kit said he could prance. 'He could trot, rack, single-foot,' she kept saying, a kind of wonder in her voice.

'He was beautiful. He frightened you,' she said. 'He was so in earnest about it.' He was determined, absorbed in being a horse — not a common horse, but a highly trained, highly bred, aristocrat among horses.

'Look, I'm doing it. I am being a horse, I am a horse.'

The pale tall cousin, Frank, the consumptive one, got terribly excited and, for some reason, so also did Kit and Agnes. The man, who was a horse, was in the green flat place where the moonlight was. There was a fence beyond the flat place, and he went, with the bright, sharp trot of a horse, toward it. He leaped on all fours. The consumptive, Frank, got to his feet. Kit thought he might have been a little drunk. He was very proud of his cousin. Agnes held the bottle. She stood up and waved it above her head.

There was another flat meadow beyond the one where the horseman had trotted, single-footed, pranced, and again he trotted back toward them. Again he leaped on all fours and again he cleared the fence. 'A high one,' Kit said.

Frank was standing. He was trembling. He might have been drunk. He was weaving back and forth. 'See!' he shouted. 'He can do it! He can be it!'

Kit was terribly afraid that Frank would suddenly become ill, and so she began to protest. 'Don't. Quit it now!' she cried. She ran and put her arms about Frank's shoulders. 'I knew he wanted so to be strong, to be a horse like that,' she explained. She stood holding the young man Frank, and the big red-haired woman Agnes ran down a little slope to where Bud, absorbed, was still prancing, on all fours, in the moonlight . . . he was preparing to leap the fence again and Agnes swore as she ran.

'Now quit it!' she called; 'goddam you, you quit it!' She was terribly in earnest, although she laughed. There had been enough of it.

'Why, you little black sonofabitch,' she said, when she had caught Bud and had made him quit it. She was standing near him and he was unstrapping the hoofs from his hands and stowing them away in his pockets. Kit said that Agnes kept swearing at him. She wasn't really angry. She liked him a lot. Agnes kept laughing and swearing while Bud put the hoofs away in his pockets and they both came back up the slope.

'We sat on the ground and finished the bottle,' Kit said, 'but Frank and I didn't talk any more about Bud.'

It was Agnes who talked. 'She wasn't going to miss that chance,' Kit said.

Agnes was a big vital woman — woman enough, Kit afterward thought, but not the kind most men would fall for. She was too big, too strong and vital. She thought too much. When Kit had left the mill, when she had been through many adventures, was a bit older,

and in her own way sophisticated, Kit spent a good deal of time thinking of Agnes.

She always spoke of her, however, with a smile. It was an affectionate smile. What were such women as Agnes to do? Most of the
men, the workmen, young and old, in the cotton mill . . . so many
of them like the consumptive Frank . . . if they were not tubercular
they were at least stoop-shouldered men, many with narrow chests . . .
they had spent too much of their young lives eating cotton lint, breathing it into their lungs.

It might be that Agnes needed and even wanted gentling by life, by
intimacy with some man, but where among the mill men was she to
find one to do it to her? If she had been married to a farmer, say,
somewhere out on the Western plains, heavy hard work to do, shoulder to shoulder with a man, her partner and lover . . .

Unlike the others in the field that night she had read books, she had
been to meetings. Although she was still young, she had worked in
several mills, had been in strikes and at strike meetings. There had
been socialist agitators in the mill towns and the Communists had
come in. Later, after Kit left the mill, Agnes was a figure in the
communist strike at Gastonia in North Carolina.

She had been playing with Bud, the horse-man, in the field as Frank
had talked to Kit, but had overheard some of the talk. Once or twice
she had left Bud. They had been wrestling, laughing and pushing
each other about, but suddenly stopped. She gave Bud a push that
sent him sprawling. 'Now quit. Let me alone. I don't want to,' she
said, and there was something in her voice that commanded. It was
always there when she wanted to use it.

She left Bud standing, or sprawled thus . . . he was laughing. The
play between them had been like two puppies at play. She walked
away from him.

She came to stand near where Kit and Frank were sitting. Frank
was telling of Bud's trip into the East, of the things he had seen, of the
men and women of the saddle-horse farm, and Bud's excitement, lying on top of the truck parked in the road. She had stood near them
for a moment, listening intently, saying nothing, and then, with a
shrug of her shoulders, had walked away. She began again the play
with Bud.

The four people were seated on the grass on the little hill and had finished the bottle. Agnes looked at Bud, who had stowed away his leather hoofs. 'Why, you little black bastard . . . that you should have learned to do that,' she said, and, having said it, laughed. She was wanting to tell Kit and the two men something of what she thought the significance of what Bud had seen on his trip into the East — down out of the hill country and into the low country — and hesitated because she was trying to find words for what was in her mind. She was an odd and a striking figure sitting thus. Her legs, like strong pillars, were spread apart and she had big shoulders and a strong neck.

Her neck was like the necks of men Kit saw later, when she married and went with her husband to professional wrestling matches, and, although her head looked small, it was covered with a mass of thick yellow hair that had become disarranged during her wrestling bouts with Bud and now hung in a thick mass over her shoulders.

'It is just so, everywhere,' she said suddenly. She had lighted a cigarette — she was the only one of the little party that smoked — and when she talked, her arms moved about, as though she were addressing an audience, making gestures, like one of the professional speakers, the agitators she had heard. The lighted end of the cigarette kept making little bright arches before the eyes of the others.

They had all become silent, and she told them of her thoughts. There was, she said, something rotten in the fact that Bud, with his love of fine horses and wanting one, had to come down to being a horse. 'What the hell — I'll bet you he works harder than any of the guys who own the horses,' she said, and, reaching over to where Bud sat, grasped his arms. She gave him a little push so that he fell over and lay on his side and then began again to attempt to put her thoughts into words.

Agnes was excited and, although the others did not understand some of the words and thoughts that came pouring out of her, they also got excited. She talked a little incoherently and brokenly. She was young and strong. Perhaps she felt within herself the conviction growing that in the life of the factory there was no chance for something within herself to grow, that it was choked there; the conviction that is in so many younger Americans now, that the day of opportunity is gone here, an old myth that in America anyone may rise to dizzy heights of splendor quite exploded. She tried passionately to express the thing most wanted, by all men and women, not only in America but over the entire earth. She thought it was some basis of self-respect. The performance of Bud in the field, his becoming for the time a horse, not a man, had in some odd way hurt her. 'It isn't that we want — to give up manhood.' She could not put her thoughts into such straight words, but Kit and perhaps Frank, for all his pride in his cousin's performance, had been shocked as well as amused. 'The thing we want — the thing we want —— ' Agnes was struggling for words. In spite of the jumble of words that came from her she did in some way get her thoughts into the others.

The thing most essentially wanted by all men and women, always, everywhere. 'Give me some basis of self-respect. Let me stand on my own feet.'

The thing felt sometimes by even the poorest little mountain farmer, working as young Bud did his tiny bit of poor mountain land.

'See! Look! I did it!' In the factories, Agnes said, growing coherent and for a moment talking coherently, a man or woman got too much lost, was made to feel too small. She was remembering her experience in union struggles in factories, the right of the workers to organize, to feel themselves as having even a small part in the running of the factories and the conditions under which they labored, this right always being denied and ridiculed. Kit thought Agnes was thinking of the moment, not of Bud and his performance, but of the tubercular Frank. In the factory she said great care was taken to keep the dust from accumulating on the machines. Hoods came down over the machines to suck the dust from them while the workers were left to breathe it into their lungs.

The farmer . . . 'See! Look! I did it!

'I have made the corn stand upon this poor little piece of land. I have worked here and something has resulted.

'I went, in the winter, up into the woods. I brought down leaf mold. I gathered together brush and burned it. I had no money to buy fertilizer. I put the leaf mold from the woods and the ashes from the fires on the land and plowed them in. I made something grow. Look! It is the best stand of corn in all of this neighborhood.'

Pride in work, in something done. Kit thought later that Agnes had been hurt by Bud's performance, by something not very healthy she had felt in it. It might have been too much humility. She did not understand what it was that night in the field. The night was, however, educational to her.

Man wanting so little really. See the farmer, even on poor land, who has raised a small patch of good corn. He can walk a little more proudly. Something grows in man through work. It can be killed when his work is degraded.

Workers in factories also wanting — Agnes was terribly in earnest. 'She was more educated than the rest of us,' Kit said. The thing most wanted is so little, so seldom, understood. 'They think we want revolution, to kill someone,' Agnes said. 'It is all nonsense,' she declared. She had begun talking over the heads of the others, but, in a dim way, they did all understand. Kit, when she told of Agnes's talk, had been through a lot. She was older and shrewder than the hill girls in the field.

'Why, even — it is seldom anyone speaks of it — we want love, understanding, respect. Do not do that to man which takes from him his self-respect.

'Do not do it.

'Do not do it.'

In the woman worker Agnes, in the field with the others, there was something perhaps half man.

And also, Kit knew, something that could be made tender.

Kit remembered an incident in the factory. There was a young girl with her hand hurt in one of the machines and the profane strong Agnes had been deeply touched by the suffering of another. Afterward Agnes had gone up and down on her 'side,' doing her work, but there were tears in her eyes and she cursed as she worked. The girl who had been hurt was very pretty and she would lose two or three fingers.

'She'll be maimed. It will spoil her chance of getting what she wants.'

Kit had understood that. She herself was attractive to men.

Something, more deeply felt, Agnes was trying to put into words. She didn't succeed very well. She had heard speakers talk. She had read books. The factory workers in America were, after all, not as yet too far away from their fathers and grandfathers. Agnes called them 'our old people.' She also had come to the factories out of a mountain home. For the most part the people of the mountains had been in America for many generations. They were not too far away from something else, something once very much alive . . . individuality . . . the day of America's greater richness . . .

Day of the farmers on their own land . . . plenty of free land to be had for the taking . . .

Day of the craftsman too . . .

'There is that wagon, carriage, suit of clothes . . . worn by that dude you see going along the street there . . . the pair of shoes . . . that chair, bed . . . this table at which we sit eating the food grown on our own land here . . .

'The cotton from our fields, flax and the wool from our sheep. In the log cabin that was my father's house there stood an old spinning wheel. It still stands there, in a corner, forgotten. Let it stand. I do not want it back . . .

'It is, however, a symbol . . . day of our participation . . . of our own hands doing completely. They could give us the feeling back, in the factories, if they would. They won't. They are stupid. They don't want to understand.

'The big factories, so huge, so magnificent. Who are they making cloth for?'

Agnes turned fiercely upon Kit. 'Say, you swell kid, you want silk stockings to wear, now, don't you?' She awoke, made real a hunger that was in Kit. It was a hunger that influenced all her later life . . .

The big factories, so huge, so magnificent, the thousands of fast beautiful machines . . .

'They have a way of making us feel, too much, just a part of the machines. Why do they want to do it? It hurts. It eats in.

'The continual strutting of those up above . . . they think, they believe, they are above us . . . the way their women do it . . . why do they do it, the fools?

'They want us to be humble. Are they humble?

'We come out of the factory after one of the long days or a longer night. Do they think we are blind? Can't we see? We see so much blossoming in America, fine roads being built, the automobiles, always getting faster, more beautiful. We see rich women, richly gowned. We see beautiful houses built for those who never made anything with their hands.'

Agnes spoke fiercely of Bud's experience, of his seeing the rich men in the field showing off the beautiful saddle horses. Who were they? Had they a right to such creatures? Bud became uncomfortable. He sat with head down muttering words the others could not hear.

'Fools, why don't they give us a chance?' Agnes spoke of labor leaders who had come to factories where she had been employed. Why didn't they get more down to the guts of things, why didn't they? They were always talking about wages and hours. 'I don't care about that, not first of all,' Agnes said. She jumped to her feet and stood over the others. Her cigarette had been thrown aside. 'I want . . . I want . . . Oh, hell!' she said. There was a moment of silence and then she looked down at the others and laughed. 'Well, come on. Let's get out of here. I've blown off steam long enough. Time to go home,' she said, and the others got to their feet and followed her, across the field and over a fence into the road.

They walked down along the road, the four of them, an oddly mixed lot. It was a dirt road, gravelled and smooth, and presently they came to a place of houses. It was quite near the town, some two or three miles outside the town limits, their own mill village, as were other mill villages, quite separated from the real town . . .

Place of others, their lives, of the lawyers, doctors, individual workmen . . . what was left of these in such towns . . . shoe-repair men, house painters, clerks in stores, men who delivered milk and eggs to houses, truck-drivers, carpenters, plumbers . . .

The mill workers, in their own company-owned place, always so oddly separated from all of these.

They were in a place of estates, off a main road, all the land for a mile up and down the road having been bought up by a few families . . . big houses with plenty of land, little clumps of forest. Their own mill village would have been off to the right. As they were on high ground, they could see its lights in the distance.

They had come to this place of big estates, and Kit thought that Agnes, although by lecturing the others she had got something off her chest, was still a little high. She went striding ahead of the others and there was something fierce and determined in her figure. She did not speak to the others. They had come to one of the big houses, built in that separated place, and there was a dance going on inside. There were others, besides themselves, out for a night of it.

Agnes stopped in the road and they all stopped. She was the dominant one. They passed the entrance to a particular estate, the house a huge one, brightly lighted . . . sounds of music coming from the house . . . shining automobiles parked along a driveway . . . wide green lawn with occasional trees . . .

There was a hedge built around the estate and Agnes stopped in the road.

There was excitement in her voice, in her manner. 'Come on, all of you,' she said, and bolted through the hedge. The others followed. They were puzzled.

They had got into a place near some stables where, no doubt, fine saddle horses were also kept. Kit thought she heard the sound of horses moving restlessly in stalls in the stables. There was a new building, being constructed of brick. Piles of brick were lying about. For a moment they stood in silence near the stables, and then Agnes, making a motion to the others, went on toward the house, the others following.

They went along a green lawn. Kit said there were flowering bushes. They were now all excited and followed Agnes with thumping hearts. What an adventure, to be in such a place! What was Agnes up to?

She led them along, their figures stooping, running forward, keeping behind the bushes, until they had got near the house. There was a little open place, with more flowering bushes, and they could look directly in.

Inside there was a dance going on. They were all young people in there, Kit explained. No doubt they were the sons and daughters of the rich and the well-to-do, of the 'nice' people of the Southern towns, sons and daughters of the millowners, of holders of stocks in the mills. There were a half-dozen mill villages near that particular Southern town . . .

The young people were reveling in the big country house, the sons and daughters of the owners of mill villages and mills, sons of corporation lawyers, young college men and women, home for the summer, sons and daughters of bankers. There were beautiful young women and tall young men in evening clothes. Whoever was giving the party — and, for all Kit knew, it might have been the wife of the president of the mill for which the three mill workers in the party outside labored — had got in an orchestra.

Kit herself did not know how long she stood there, in the open place by the bushes, so near the house. She said that Agnes had disappeared and that presently all became conscious of her absence. They were puzzled. They were frightened. They stood looking at each other, wanting to escape, to run for it, realizing all of them, the enormity of the fact of being there. In another moment they would all have bolted, but Agnes suddenly and silently reappeared. She had crept back to where the building was being erected and had a brick in her hand. If she had been excited, a little high, earlier, she was more so now. 'Wait,' she said, commanding the others.

She was high. She was on edge, and suddenly, inside the house, the dance came to an end. She had taken a stand a little in front of the others.

There was a moment of waiting, an intense moment to all of the little party outside. The dance had ended, and the orchestra, brought in for the occasion . . . they had been half-concealed behind palms and great bouquets of flowers in a corner of the big room . . . the men of the orchestra, also in evening clothes, stood up and stretched. The people of the party outside could hear the sound of the voices inside. Young women laughed, they chattered. There was the sound of the voices of young men.

'It is a swell party.'

'How about coming with me for a little walk outside?'

'It is a swell night.'

Oh, fortunate ones!

And now the people were moving out of the big room. In a moment more couples would be coming out to walk on the lawn. There would be flirtations, young men and women walking across a well-kept lawn in the soft darkness. It was evident that Agnes was very high. What was she up to? She was dancing about in a kind of ecstacy. There was a large plate-glass window that separated those outside from the revelers. Agnes swung wide one of her great arms and the brick went smashing through the window. There was an intense moment. Kit and her friends could see the startled faces of a group of people near an outer door, and then they all ran. They were led by Agnes, who kept exclaiming, 'Hot dog! Hot dog!' as she ran. 'Did you see their faces? Did you see their faces?'

They got to the hedge and through it to the road. It was dark out there. They could see over the hedge. On the opposite side of the road — a low fence to be got over — there was an open field, and just beyond a small clump of trees. There were other fields beyond the trees. They stood in the road waiting, all but Agnes wanting to continue the flight at once. She, however, still dominated them. 'No. Wait,' she said, and they all stood looking toward the house.

There was furor at the house. Men were running about. They ran to the parked cars and got flashlights. They called back and forth. The excitement in the house and on the green lawn and under the trees before the house went on and on. All in the party, except Agnes, were nervous and jumpy, and then, to increase their alarm, two young men with flashlights in their hands came through the hedge and stood in the road. They were some two hundred yards away and Frank was sick with nervousness. He began pleading in a whisper. 'Come. Come. We'll be caught. We'll be arrested. They'll send us to prison,' he pleaded.

The men in the road were coming toward them. They were throwing the light from the flashlights along the road and into the hedge. They were young men in evening clothes. They might have been young college men, home for the summer, young football players. Agnes leaned over and began whispering rapidly to Bud. 'We'll be over there. We'll wait over there.' She was pointing to the trees, just seen, across the fields. They all knew there were fields beyond. They had come that way.

The young mountain man, Bud, did not have time to strap on his leather hoofs. He went down on all fours. The young men in the road were advancing. They came in silence.

And now Bud was rushing down upon them. He was on all fours. He shambled along. He also had an idea. There was a low, growling, guttural sound coming from his lips. It was very uncanny to hear, there in the darkness.

It was something terrible, Kit said. There was a spot of light from one of the flashlights in the road and he scrambled across it. There was a cry from the lips of the young men. They bolted and he followed. When they crashed through the hedge, he leaped over, still on all fours.

He was down thus on all fours.

He went with amazing rapidity.

He was a huge dog.

He was a bear.

He was a horse.

He went shamble, shamble, growling as he went.

And now the others of the party ran. They got over a low fence and ran quickly across the field to the trees. They waited there and, Kit said, Agnes was nervous. She walked up and down before the others. 'He's all right. He'll take care of himself,' she muttered.

They stayed in the little grove until, at last, Bud came back to them and went directly to Agnes. Agnes threw her arms about his neck and embraced him. She held him in her arms and danced in the darkness. 'Oh, Bud! Bud!' she cried; 'oh, my darling!'

'Oh, you darling little sonofabitch!' she cried.

They went on, but the adventures of the night were not over. They had crossed several fields, working their way around toward their own village, but sat down by a creek. Frank had become ill. For a time he couldn't go on; and they stayed there, Frank lying on the grass at the creek's edge. He had whispered to Kit, asking her to hold his head. There were several outbreaks of coughing. They came, he became quieter, and then they came again. None of the others knew afterward how long they stayed in the field, but at last there was a hemorrhage. Kit was holding Frank's head and the moon had come up. He was at the creek's edge and asked Kit to hold his head over the creek. The moon was shining on the waters of the little creek, and Kit, so close to him, could see his blood gushing from between his lips and coloring the water of the stream.

Brown Bomber

It wasn't one of the Bomber's big fights, one of the million or half-million-dollar gates. There was no big gate, no National nor American League baseball park, big build-up, to get the big gate. The fellow he was to fight, neither Fred nor myself had ever heard of. His name was Jorge Brescia, and he was described, in the city newspapers . . . they took little or no account of the fight until the day before . . . as another possible 'Wild Bull of the Pampas.' The fight took place in a theater, a big one. They said it would seat seven thousand.

In the late afternoon we went, Fred and myself, to the theater, and got an official program. 'Look . . . eleven bones for a ring-side seat. Not for me.' We took the program with us into a bar. 'At that, I'd like to see him in action,' said Fred. Fred makes little, very human drawings for some of the bigger magazines. There were some men standing at the bar and Fred punched me. One of the men was talking, a big fellow with a cauliflower, almost a calabash, ear. He pounded on the bar with a big fist.

'Yeah,' he said, 'I tell you I know. I was up to his camp. They wanted me for one of his punching-bags. The sucker. Say, if I was five years younger, I'd take him on myself. I tell you this Argentine boy's liable to take him. You listen to me. That smoke's a sucker for a right.'

Fred and I had our drink. The papers said it was five to one on the Bomber, even money he'll take the Argentine in five rounds. I was looking through the program, 'Look, Fred.' I held it up. There was a piece about the Argentine fighter. I read aloud. 'There is Nordic blood in his veins, his grandfather being a native of Alsace-Lorraine, which accounts for his calmness under fire and his methodical way of fighting. He worked as a clerk for the Argentine Government while he was doing his amateur fighting.' I paused. I am quite sure my voice trembled a little.

'What's the matter?' Fred said.

I read on.

'And is one of the best-versed boys in literature in the fighting game.'

'Do you suppose he has read me?' I said.

'I don't suppose he's that bad,' said Fred.

We went far up, to the top gallery, top row. Three-fifty for a seat up there, and we must have got the last two. You couldn't sit any farther from the ring. We were tops. Back of us there was an open space where men could stand. We had got in pretty early and only the standing-room space was filled.

It was filled with Negro men, and already they were excited. You could feel the excitement in the air, a kind of quiet tenseness. 'Say, it means a lot to them, doesn't it?' Fred whispered.

Although the upper gallery was, as yet, but half-filled, we had some trouble getting our seats. There was a kind-hearted usher and he had picked two cripples out of the standing-room crowd and had put them into our places. They were a white man and a Negro, both crippled, both one-legged, both on crutches, and they were both pretty well spiffed. The usher stood looking at our ticket stubs. He scratched his head, looked again. He had a resigned air . . . 'Well, it has to be done. Hey, soldiers, you two guys got to get out of there.'

We were in a bad fix, and for a moment I thought Fred was going to weaken and surrender the seats. 'They're one-legged. They're on crutches,' he whispered. All the others up there, whites and blacks, had turned and were staring at us. The cripples had on the kind of caps the American Legion boys wear when they go to their annual conventions. The convention had just been held. I figured they had got their bonus and were on a bust.

They stood up, and for a moment I thought the white one was going to pitch forward, down over the heads of the people in the rows of seats below. A big Negro man reached over the little wooden fence back of our top row of seats and steadied him and the Negro soldier saved the situation. He grinned.

'Come on. Take your seats. You paid for them. Anyway, we're too drunk to see anything down there,' he said, pointing.

Another Negro man had reached over the fence to steady him. They made their way painfully out. The white man had bottles sticking out of a half-dozen of his pockets. His crutches knocked one of the bottles out of a side pocket and it rolled down the steps into one of the aisles. A Negro man brought it back to him. 'Come on, buddy,' said the white soldier to his Negro companion. 'You quit worrying now. The Bomber'll get him all right. Let's get out of here and be on our way,' he said.

It was time for the preliminary bouts and they weren't so good. The spot lights had come on, flooding the ring, far down there, making all clear, and the man who sat at my left, a little wizened white man, began a conversation. He whispered.

'You see,' he said, 'you can see more from up here than from a ring-side seat. I usually get a ring-side, but I wanted to try it up here,' he said. He seemed to want to apologize for not having spent more money. 'I'm a dentist,' he said. 'I can blow myself for a ring-side seat if I want.'

They were announcing the first preliminary bout and there was a small figure of a man, who spoke into a loud-speaker. He had on a dinner jacket. It seemed the bouts were put on by a man named Mike Jacobs, a very, very handsome man, if you judged by the big photograph of him that filled a whole page in the fight program. For some reason Mike was in bad with the crowd. At the mention of his name, loud groans arose all over the theater. There were the usual introductions, of men more or less famous in the fighting game. The names were all strange to me. As each man was introduced, he did a little half dance, ran to the center of the ring, put both hands above his head, whirled like a chicken when you cut its head off. He seemed to be shaking hands with himself, up there, above his head. It was a ceremony, something you do, no matter whether or not the cash customers applaud. The first two preliminary boys introduced to the crowd were sitting in their corners, each celebrity having done his dance, and the man in the dinner jacket ran from one to the other and seemed to whisper something into his ears. 'Do you suppose he tells them both he hopes they win?' Fred asked. He said he liked these little ceremonies of the ring. It made him think of the way big-league ball-players sent the ball flying gaily from man to man about the diamond when they have retired a batter.

As for the preliminary bouts, they weren't much. We were all waiting for the Bomber. There were boys from Texas, Pennsylvania, Long Island, Detroit, and one, named Eduardo Primo, from the Argentine. He got his all right. If the man who was to fight the Bomber was a Wild Bull of the Pampas, Fred said this one was a steer. He stood with his legs spread far apart while a Negro boy, a dancing, swift-moving one, kept lashing out at him. Round after round he stood, seeming never to move, taking it and taking it. He achieved something. His face was cut and his eyes swollen, but to the end he stood firmly upright on his legs.

We, up there in our top gallery, weren't caring. Our top gallery was full, packed, while, down below, the aristocrats of sport were sitting — millionaires, Fred said — in the ring-side seats, then the seven-fifty ones — fellows probably who owned stores or small factories — then the five-fifties. 'We might have been that good if you had loosened up,' Fred complained.

He was really glad to be where he was. I knew that. We were near the Negro men . . . big ones, small ones, young ones, old ones . . . these evidently Negro workmen, some in overalls, jammed in there behind the little fence at our backs. In the twenty or thirty rows of seats below us, more Negroes who had brought their women . . . these a little more 'upper class,' Fred thought . . . some of the women handsomely gowned . . . a few white men and white women. There was a middle-aged white woman who sat in the row just below us, and she was, as we were, nervous as she waited. She was a fat woman of forty-eight, with the hands of a working woman. She kept rubbing them together. She would be such a woman as might keep a rooming house for young unmarried clerks, somewhere on a side street in the city, in a section that had once been fashionable but now had gone down . . . her man perhaps gone off with a younger woman. Fred said afterward that he didn't think it was that. 'What you trying to do, work the poor woman for one of your sad short stories?' he said. 'Her old man's dead,' he said. 'They lived together a long and faithful life. He was true to her to the end,' he said.

She was nervous, as we were. She said she had heart disease. She kept turning to whisper to us, like the rest of us giving little or no attention to the preliminary bouts.

Men were standing up in the ring and whaling away. Black eyes,

swollen lips, and ugly cauliflower ears were being acquired, we looking occasionally, not caring. They would be men hoping to rise in the
pugilistic world, hoping to suddenly attract attention, get into the big
money.

'I got heart disease and I climbed the five flights of stairs to get up
here. I ain't caring about this man he's fighting tonight, but I want
him to have another chance at that Schmeling,' she said. She was
voicing something we all felt. It was the thing that had made us all,
whites and blacks, that night, so tense, so nervous. 'I don't want anyone else to get him until he gets in there again with that Schmeling.'

She had put her finger on it, touched the spot. The Schmeling had
got our Joe, the Brown Bomber, with a right, and all the newspapers
had been saying that the Argentine fighter, Brescia, had a powerful
right. There had been the whole romance of the Alabama Negro
Boy . . . the young Negro lad just a workman in a Ford plant at Fond
Du Lac, in Michigan . . . Joe Louis Barrow . . . the Barrow might have
been got from some Southern white family who had owned, say, his
grandfather . . . it had been dropped . . . But better even than Joe
Louis was the other name, probably given him by some newspaper
man — 'The Brown Bomber.'

And then, suddenly up and up. Riches flooding into him, perhaps.
It wasn't that we cared about. He was one of ours. He was a fellow
who could do a thing superbly.

And then that Schmeling had got him, with a right. Why, it must
have been an accident, the one blow stunning him like that. The fellow in the bar had said that the Bomber was a sucker for a right.
When Fred and I were sitting in the bar, I had taken a clipping out
of my pocket. It was from a German Nazi magazine, *Der Weltkampf*.
'Max Schmeling's victory over Joe Louis is a "Cultural Achievement"
for the white race,' it said. 'It clearly demonstrates the superiority of
the white intelligence.' It was that way of putting it, taking it, that
had touched us on the raw. It had got us all, white men and Negro
men. There had been, Fred had said, something mighty nice about
the way the American Negroes had taken the rise of the Bomber.
There had been in them no such nonsense about 'culture' . . . 'Superior intelligence.' It was a man doing brilliantly, superbly, the thing
he could do, was born to do. We all wanted something set right.

He came into the ring, and if we had been tense before, we grew more so. We leaned forward, silently waiting. He, the Bomber, seemed small. Fred spoke of it. It must have been because the Argentine was tall. By the program he was only three-quarters of an inch taller than Joe.

Or it might have been because he stood up straight, boxed from that position, while the Bomber was in a half crouch. The Bomber is yellow, a quite light and quite shiny silky lemon yellow. They wore some kind of a white thing in their mouths, I presume, to protect the teeth. It seems to be a part of a fighter's manager's job to put it in.

How quickly the round passed, the first one, not many blows struck. Fred thought they must be doing what he spoke of as 'feeling each other out.' The Argentine seemed to get increasingly tall and strong-looking. He kept retreating and the Bomber kept after him, crouching forward, very swift-seeming and cat-like. He was all grace. There were, to be sure, a few blows struck, or attempted, the Bomber getting in two or three and getting a hard one back. He kept after his man.

Round two . . . I can't remember. Among us, in our gallery, there was the same steady tenseness. It made your legs ache, under the knees. Fred was biting his nails. 'Quit it,' I said, but he didn't hear me. It all happened in the third, a sudden swift right, from the Argentine. It might be like the one Schmeling had landed, thus accomplishing the 'cultural achievement.'

The sudden swift flying of fists, so swift that I, at least, couldn't follow. The white man had been retreating and retreating, but suddenly he had pounced.

He had got the Bomber with that right, and for just a moment, our Bomber seemed as he must have seemed that night in the ring with Schmeling.

They were standing close now, whaling away at each other, and in that awful moment the Bomber did seem gone. We had all got to our feet, but up in our gallery there was no sound, while down there, close to the ring, the ring-side seat fellows were madly dancing and shouting. Their words flew up to us . . .

'The right! The right!'

'He's got him with the right!'

There was the sick feeling that mankind, the human race, had turned out to be what the pessimists are always saying it is — 'But what about the old stars and stripes?' I found myself asking. I went

Bolshevik and so did Fred. He was dancing nervously and making punches at the air with his fists. I was afraid he would soak in the neck the woman who had the heart disease. He didn't.

And then, swiftly ... hurrah ... Oh, such a deep sigh of relief! The Bomber had got clear. He wasn't hurt, not too badly. He had got clear, but at once, with a quick, graceful leap, came in again. There were two blows struck, a right and a left. I read about it later in a newspaper. I don't believe I saw them. To me it was like when you put a charge of dynamite under a rock and touch it off. The white man straightened. He stood stiffly, and then he went down, and presently ... I never saw the referee counting ... time just passed, and there was the Bomber, so strangely gentle and boyish-seeming, helping to carry the Argentine to his corner.

In our gallery, joy. There was dancing, laughing, shouting. 'My Country, 'Tis of Thee.' I'll never know how Fred and I got out of the jam, away from the happy, dancing whites and Negroes. The woman who had heart disease just sat silently in her seat, such a placid, satisfied look on her face.

When we were in the street, Fred said he was tired. 'Let's have us each a couple of sidecars.' He said he would pay for them. 'Look, isn't the country saved?' He was having himself a good time. 'This Argentine,' he added ... this when we had got into a bar ... he quoted ... 'This Argentine ... "He's one of the best-versed men in literature, in the fighting game!" I reckon you, being a literary man, that you're mighty sorry for him,' Fred said, grinning at me.

XII. SUMMARIES AND HARMONIES

Dedication of the Memoirs

I DO NOT BELIEVE I can write of my own marriages, being fair to both myself and the women involved. Once I was speaking of them to a friend.

'What is the matter with me, Frank?'

'Such fellows as you are often strong-headed,' he said. 'The demands you make of life are, you know, rather terrific. Most men finally accept the harness that life puts on them. You fellows cannot. You would die if you did.

'I'll say this for you,' he added. 'You do take life seriously. You believe in it. Many men come to the place where they take women purely as physical facts. Intimate contact with them is a physical necessity, but it is that and nothing more.

'Fellows like yourself demand more. You keep demanding this strange thing we call love. When it dies out, you go. You spend your life searching for it.'

My first three marriages each lasted exactly five years. I have always been sure that none of the women were to blame when our marriage failed. Any practitioner of the arts is a trial to live with.

We are never there. We go away, often for months at a time.

Well, we are there physically. We are in a house, or in a street, but we are at the same time far away.

One of us is, for example, writing a novel. For months he will be off away from the people immediately about. Inside himself he is living another life, often having nothing to do with the people with whom he is living his own physical life. Speak to him and he will answer you, but he does not really hear. You make an engagement with him. You are to meet him on a certain day, at a certain hour, in a restaurant or at a theater. Do you think he will keep it? Very likely he will not. When you made the engagement with him, your words did not register on his mind. He heard but did not hear.

It was because he was not there. When you spoke to him, he seemed to be sitting at his desk in a room in the house where you lived with him, but in reality he was in the captain's cabin of a ship, far out in the Pacific.

There was something tense going on in the cabin of the boat. There were two men and a woman in the little room. There had been a storm, and the ship, a small one, had been disabled. It was drifting.

The captain of the ship, an old man, had a young wife and the mate wanted her, and she had fallen in love with the mate. It was the ancient story.

The two men and the woman are having it out, there in the cabin. You see, the ship is leaking and will soon go down. It is a question of taking to boats, the boats perhaps drifting far apart.

Is the woman to go in the boat commanded by the captain or in that commanded by the mate, the man she loves? The whole matter is to be settled now in a few minutes. It may well be that, before they leave the cabin where they now sit facing each other, one of the two men will have been killed.

See how the woman standing there by the door trembles, how white she is.

So . . . as the writer is watching all this, a fourth unseen figure in the little ship's cabin, his own wife, comes to him. She wants to make an engagement. There is something she wants him to do for her.

'Sure. All right. Certainly I will.'

Why, he did not hear her at all. Her words were blown away by a wind. They did not register on his mind.

Who was that who came into this room? My wife? What is a wife? I have no wife. Did I marry someone? Where? When?

It is dreadful to live with such a man. It is only possible . . . Only a saint could do it.

There are months and months when you are merely dust under his feet. For him you have no existence. As well, during such times, be married to one of the dummies in a store window.

Almost all of my own friends, men of the theater, painters, musicians, have, in this matter of marriage, had the same experience I had had.

They have tried and failed, tried and failed. Some of them, upon the break-up of a marriage, have grown bitter. They write novels making the woman the central character. They grow bitter and ugly about it all.

How absurd! When one of us makes a failure of marriage, it is, almost inevitably, his own fault. He is what he is. He should not blame the woman.

The modern woman will not be kicked aside so. She wants children, she wants a certain security, for herself and for her children, but we fellows do not understand the impulse toward security. When we are secure, we are dead. There is nothing secure in our world out there, and, as for the matter of children, we are always having children of our own.

For example, someone is always asking me which one of my own stories I like best, which of all the characters I have put into books and stories I like best, and I have a pat answer for them.

'Go ask some mother who has had several children which one of them she likes best,' I answer.

It is a changing, shifting world, this world of the imagination in which we who work in any of the arts must live so much of our lives. We have it, and then we have it not. Oh, the blank days, the black despair that sometimes descends upon us!

We grow irritable. Speak to one of us at such a time and you will probably get a sharp, nasty answer. Trust us and we may betray your trust.

No. Do not ask me to write of the women with whom I have lived in marriage. I respect them too much to do it. That I have found a woman who, after ten years with me, can still laugh at me, who understands my wrinkles, who is there beside me, smilingly willing to forgive my idiosyncrasies, who after seeing through the years we have lived together my worst and my best — that, is my good fortune.

I am one of the lucky ones. Good luck has always been with me.

I dedicate this autobiography to my wife, Eleanor.

Introduction to the Memoirs

WHEN I READ of the lives of genuinely great men, how they have struggled and suffered; of Keats and Chekhov in their losing fight against disease, de Maupassant and Van Gogh struggling against insanity, Herbert Spencer fighting against poverty; of Charles Darwin and his trip to the tropics in the *Beagle* and his long months of horrible illness, his determination and perseverance; John Brown in his mad stroke for justice to the American Negroes, Abraham Lincoln in the White House during the four terrible years of our Civil War, Dostoievsky in the hour in which he faced a firing squad and in the years in a Siberian prison camp; when I read about these men and many others in the long, often tragic story of man's passionate devotion to some art, some science or idea of justice, and then look back on my own career as an American story-teller, I have to consider my life a most fortunate one.

Fortunate despite the fact that I cannot rank myself among the heroes. There has been something of struggle but little enough of the heroic in my life. For all my egotism, I know I am but a minor figure. Yet I had something of those men's devotion in my frame, and now, when I come to the point of summing up, of looking not forward but backward on events and people that have affected my life, I am compelled to exclaim —

'Oh thou fortunate one!' Lucky to have been born an American in what well may turn out to have been America's happiest period, to have been born poor and in a small town where community life was intimate and close, to have had to work as a laborer both in factories and on farms, thus to have known whence came the food that nourished my body and what toil went into its production, to have had the

691

mother and the invariably picturesque father I had; lucky in my brothers; on the whole, in my loves of women, in having been born with a talent; lucky in all my circumstances, in the friends I have made, even in my enemies——

But wait — where are my enemies Have I indeed any?

If I am hated anywhere, perhaps I am too great an egotist to know of it. Perhaps my entire feeling about myself flows from this egotism.

Once, when we were both young men in Chicago, Ben Hecht and I spoke of this possibility over a glass of beer. 'Yes, you are lucky and will always feel yourself lucky,' he said. If I were to fall into a river, he suggested, I wouldn't get wet.

'Man, it's because of your profound egotism. It is colossal. When you are snubbed, you do not know it. When someone condemns your work, you simply put him down as a fool. Some of us have to go through terrible times of doubt of our talents, but you never have to. You will sail blithely through life, often doing terrible things to others without at all knowing what you are doing. Friends will stand by you. When you are pressed, someone will always come to your rescue. You will always be loved more than you deserve. Your egotism . . . Why, man, it is so colossal that you will always be going about wearing an air of modesty and even of humility. You will even believe that you actually are humble. Lord God, man, but you are a lucky one!'

No doubt I am not quoting Ben exactly. He always was a very flowery talker. That, however, is the substance of what he said in the Chicago restaurant, and I have often since wondered if it were the truth.

Yet — what's wrong with this egotism? If a man doesn't delight in himself and the force in him and feel that he and it are wonders, how is all life to become important to him? The interest in the lives of others, the high evaluation of these lives, what are they but the overflow of the interest he finds in himself, the value he attributes to his own being?

But of this fortune — There was a secretary I once had, who worked with me for several years. She was about to get married. She came to say good-bye. A little smile played about the corner of her mouth. She stood hesitatingly at the door of the room in which we worked together. It was while I was still half a man of business.

'Mr. Anderson —'

'Yes?'

'There is something I have long been wanting to say, but I hardly know how.'

'What is coming?' I had begun asking myself. 'Why, go ahead, go ahead, child. Don't be afraid,' I said.

The glance of her eyes had become wicked.

'You will remember, Mr. Anderson, that you employed me out of a business office. You call me a child, but I am past thirty. We were both employed in that same business office. I happen to know what you did there.'

'Well?'

'I just wanted to say that I did not and do not in the least blame you for what you did and do. There is an old saying that business is business, and it is quite true. It is a shark's game.'

'Well, so it is —'

You see, since I have been with you — you know how many letters I have taken for you — to your clients — to your friends — I wanted to say, before I left you — you see, you have continually been saying to these .men with whom you do business — "I am no business man." You are always playing the innocent. You put on an air. You make yourself appear naïve. Please, Mr. Anderson, don't keep it up until you believe it yourself!'

She closed the door. She entered into the sacred bonds of matrimony. I thought she would probably do all right as a wife.

I have always, from the beginning, been a rather foxy man, with a foxiness which at times approached slickness. If ever by chance you get into a horse trade with me, be a little careful.

This slickness. It is the curse of the world. It is in too many of our diplomats, our statesmen, governors, politicians. Business is lousy with it. It invades the world of art, is in families, in groups of so-called friends, it is everywhere.

'How can I use this man or woman? What can I make this one do for me?'

We do it under the cloak of friendship. You do it and I do it. It is a disease. When I was a boy, I heard it on all sides.

Go it, boy. Be on the alert. Watch your chance, then push forward. Oh, onward and upward, over the shoulders of others, trample them down.

It has grown stronger, the cry, since the first World War. Could that be helped? Some psychic wound, some inflation, chilling, hardening would seem the inevitable result of having to take part in such wars.

Why, lives were thrown away like worn-out shoes. Men had to renounce too much of their self-esteem. Killing and being killed became mechanical. Is there any wonder that so much of present-day writing, of story-telling, is concerned with death? Death in the morning, in the afternoon; death at night; death of animals, of men; death in poetry, in prose?

In peacetime there is a chance that life here on these streets, new life ever pushing up from the wombs of women, will touch us, enter into us, take us out of, interest us in, restore us to, ourselves. Not always, however. Sometimes I think we Americans are the loneliest people in the world. To be sure, we hunger for the power of affection, the self-acceptance that gives life. It is the oldest and strongest hunger in the world. But hungering is not enough.

A curious sickness overcame me. Then one night I began writing. It was a little tale of something seen or felt, something remembered out of my experience of people.

The act did something for me. I kept writing little tales of people. I put them through experiences I had myself been through and suddenly there came a new revelation. It was this — that it is only by thinking hard of others that you can attain self-knowledge.

Man cannot think clearly of self, cannot see himself, except through others. The self you seek, the true self you want to face, to accept, perhaps to love, is hidden away.

It is in the man you just met in the street. It is in the eyes of a child. It is in a tired old woman, in a thief. It is everywhere in others.

There are shades of things to be caught, a little the story of lives to be put down, the eternal challenge, something by which you can breathe.

My luck has held. I have found work that engrosses me all my days and continually enlarges my horizon. Whether or not I have succeeded in permanently curing myself of the sickness I so hated in myself, I have, at least, found the road to health.

My life has been so rich and crowded that I want to tell something about it before the bell rings. It began just at the right hour and I hope it may not carry on too far. Physical life doesn't so much matter — the ability to win footraces, hit a baseball, ride a horse over jumps — but I would like to quit living just before that terrible time when the brain, the imagination, ceases from activity.

Still, whose life is this? What is your own life? I am one thing in my own consciousness, another as you see me, still another as I seem to Jane Grey or Tom Smith or John Emerson. Is there even such a thing as a life of one's own? Is it not some illusion, some limitation in ourselves that makes us feel there is? It seems to me that all lives merge.

And do I want in any case to write about this apparent life of my own? When one writes of self, one inevitably makes a hero of self. No, I want to use my own life only as a kind of springboard. What difference when I was born, what women I made love to, what friends I betrayed? What is interesting is the woman loved, the friend betrayed, the friend to whom I was loyal. My ambition to become rich, to be a big man as we in our town thought of big men when I was a boy, that is to say, a money-maker, did pass: I became interested in people — and I want to make my book, my rambling house of a book, a book of people.

But here is something I must also explain. It happens that I have met, in the course of the life I just have briefly outlined, a good many so-called 'notable' men and women, famous writers, painters, singers, actors, publishers. Whom have I not met? I have remained a restless man, ever on the move. As writer, I came into writing at a time when new paths were being made. Often nowadays my name is coupled with that of Theodore Dreiser, Sinclair Lewis, Edgar Lee Masters, Carl Sandburg, Eugene O'Neill, and others as, shall I say, a 'pioneer'? Naturally I am interested in these men met, women met, so-called notable men and women with many of whom I have formed friendships. But — this fact may disappoint you who have happened to pick up this book — these notable ones are not and have not been my central interest. Some of them may appear in the pages of my book and others may not; and if they do appear, it will be but incidentally — for, in my writing, I have always written of 'obscure' people. It is these who have given me life.

There is still another desire. I would like to write a book of the life of the mind and of the imagination. Facts elude me. I cannot remember dates. When I deal in facts, at once I begin to lie. I can't help it. I am by nature a story-teller. No one ever taught me. Like such men as Erskine Caldwell, Ring Lardner, and others I've known, I'm a natural.

Once, many years ago, I sat down to write the story of my own boyhood in a Middle-Western town. I couldn't do it.

When, for example, I wrote of my own father and mother, I depicted people my brothers and my sister could not recognize.

'Anyway,' I said to myself, 'I have made a picture of my father and mother—' They were my father and mother as I felt them.

I remember once, a good many years ago, going on a fishing trip with several men friends. Marco Morrow, later Senator Arthur Capper's right-hand man out in Topeka, Kansas, publisher of Arthur's *Topeka Capitol* and a lot of farm papers, was of the party, and Frank Dunn, then publisher of the *Chicago Post,* was along. There were half a dozen of us, all except myself newspaper men and we were staying at a fishing lodge somewhere far up in Minnesota.

The point is that the proprietor of the lodge was a man who took my fancy. He was one of the sort of men I am always making up stories about. Such stories became very real to me. All sorts of odd, absurd things happened at the table up there in the fishing lodge.

Well, our host had a certain quality. Everything he said had to me a certain delightful naïveté. I began to invent speeches for him.

And then later, one night in Chicago at a dinner table, I began to report some of the man's absurd and amusing remarks. I was going good. I had the whole table laughing at some of the remarks made by that man of the Minnesota lakes and woods when a man at the end of the table caught my eye.

It was Marco Morrow, and there was a look of astonishment in his eyes.

I was just about to launch forth on a new anecdote when he spoke.

'Ladies and gentlemen,' he said, 'we have here with us this evening the champion liar of the world. He has been telling you stories of happenings in a fishing lodge up in Minnesota. He has been using me as a stooge for some of his stories. He forgot that I was here, listening. You see I was also one of this party of which he has been speaking. Not one of all these happenings with which he has been amusing you really happened.

Marco rose in his place at the table and bowed to me.

'Go ahead, you liar,' he said. 'Don't let me stop you. Don't let the truth get in your way.' Just the same, and although Marco did rather take the wind out of my sails that evening (I had forgotten that he was one of the party and I had convinced myself that all the stories I was telling that evening were true) — just the same, I swear that, although I may have been inventing some, I had really got the quality of our host at the fishing camp. If he had not said some of the things I made him say, he should have said them.

What I am here trying to do comes to the same thing. I believe in the imagination, its importance. To me there is a certain music to all good prose writing. There is tone and color in words as in notes in music. Persons also have a certain tone, a certain color. What care I for the person's age, the color of his hair, the length of his legs? When writing of another being, I have always found it best to do so in accordance with my feeling. Besides, men do not exist in facts. They exist in dreams. My readers, therefore, those who go along with me, will have to be patient. I am an imaginative man.

Besides, I shall tell the tale as though you, my readers, were personal friends. We are walking together, let's say on a country road. The road follows a stream and the day is pleasant. We are unhurried. We stop at times to sit on rocks beside the stream. We arise and walk again and I talk.

I keep talking, love to talk. I am telling you that this thing happened to me, that that thing happened.

Do you wish I would stop talking, let you talk? Why, then, dear readers, go write your own books.

Discovery of a Father

ONE OF THE STRANGEST RELATIONSHIPS in the world is that between father and son. I know it now from having sons of my own.

A boy wants something very special from his father. You hear it said that fathers want their sons to be what they feel they cannot themselves be, but I tell you it also works the other way. I know that as a small boy I wanted my father to be a certain thing he was not. I wanted him to be a proud, silent, dignified father. When I was with other boys and he passed along the street, I wanted to feel a glow of pride: 'There he is. That is my father.'

But he wasn't such a one. He couldn't be. It seemed to me then that he was always showing off. Let's say someone in our town had got up a show. They were always doing it. The druggist would be in it, the shoe-store clerk, the horse-doctor, and a lot of women and girls. My father would manage to get the chief comedy part. It was, let's say, a Civil War play and he was a comic Irish soldier. He had to do the most absurd things. They thought he was funny, but I didn't.

I thought he was terrible. I didn't see how Mother could stand it. She even laughed with the others. Maybe I would have laughed if it hadn't been my father.

Or there was a parade, the Fourth of July or Decoration Day. He'd be in that, too, right at the front of it, as Grand Marshal or something, on a white horse hired from a livery stable.

He couldn't ride for shucks. He fell off the horse and everyone hooted with laughter, but he didn't care. He even seemed to like it. I remember once when he had done something ridiculous, and right out on Main Street, too. I was with some other boys and they were laughing and shouting at him and he was shouting back and having as good a time as they were. I ran down an alley back of some stores and there in the Presbyterian Church sheds I had a good long cry.

Or I would be in bed at night and Father would come home a little lit up and bring some men with him. He was a man who was never alone. Before he went broke, running a harness shop, there were always a lot of men loafing in the shop. He went broke, of course, because he gave too much credit. He couldn't refuse it and I thought he was a fool. I had got to hating him.

There'd be men I didn't think would want to be fooling around with him. There might even be the superintendent of our schools and a quiet man who ran the hardware store. Once I remember there was a white-haired man who was a cashier of the bank. It was a wonder to me they'd want to be seen with such a windbag. That's what I thought he was. I know now what it was that attracted them. It was because life in our town, as in all small towns, was at times pretty dull and he livened it up. He made them laugh. He could tell stories. He'd even get them to singing.

If they didn't come to our house, they'd go off, say, at night, to where there was a grassy place by a creek. They'd cook food there and drink beer and sit about listening to his stories.

He was always telling stories about himself. He'd say this or that wonderful thing had happened to him. It might be something that made him look like a fool. He didn't care.

If an Irishman came to our house, right away Father would say he was Irish. He'd tell what county in Ireland he was born in. He'd tell things that happened there when he was a boy. He'd make it seem so real that, if I hadn't known he was born in southern Ohio, I'd have believed him myself.

If it was a Scotchman the same thing happened. He'd get a burr into his speech. Or he was a German or a Swede. He'd be anything the other man was. I think they all knew he was lying, but they seemed to like him just the same. As a boy that was what I couldn't understand.

And there was Mother. How could she stand it? I wanted to ask, but never did. She was not the kind you asked such questions.

I'd be upstairs in my bed, in my room above the porch, and Father would be telling some of his tales. A lot of Father's stories were about the Civil War. To hear him tell it he'd been in about every battle. He'd known Grant, Sherman, Sheridan, and I don't know how many others. He'd been particularly intimate with General Grant so that when Grant went East, to take charge of all the armies, he took Father along.

'I was an orderly at headquarters and Sam Grant said to me, "Irve," he said, "I'm going to take you along with me."'

It seems he and Grant used to slip off sometimes and have a quiet drink together. That's what my father said. He'd tell about the day Lee surrendered, and how, when the great moment came, they couldn't find Grant.

'You know,' my father said, 'about General Grant's book, his memoirs. You've read of how he said he had a headache and how, when he got word that Lee was ready to call it quits, he was suddenly and miraculously cured.

'Huh,' said Father. 'He was in the woods with me.

'I was in there with my back against a tree. I was pretty well corned. I had got hold of a bottle of pretty good stuff.

'They were looking for Grant. He had got off his horse and come into the woods. He found me. He was covered with mud.

'I had the bottle in my hand. What'd I care? The war was over. I knew we had them licked.'

My father said that he was the one who told Grant about Lee. An orderly riding by had told him, because the orderly knew how thick he was with Grant. Grant was embarrassed.

'But, Irve, look at me. I'm all covered with mud,' he said to Father.

And then, my father said, he and Grant decided to have a drink together. They took a couple of shots and then, because he didn't want Grant to show up potted before the immaculate Lee, he smashed the bottle against the tree.

'Sam Grant's dead now and I wouldn't want it to get out on him,' my father said.

That's just one of the kind of things he'd tell. Of course the men knew he was lying, but they seemed to like it just the same.

When we got broke, down and out, do you think he ever brought anything home? Not he. If there wasn't anything to eat in the house, he'd go off visiting around at farmhouses. They all wanted him. Sometimes he'd stay away for weeks, Mother working to keep us fed, and then home he'd come bringing, let's say, a ham. He'd got it from some farmer friend. He'd slap it on the table in the kitchen. 'You bet I'm going to see that my kids have something to eat,' he'd say, and Mother would just stand smiling at him. She'd never say a word about all the weeks and months he'd been away, not leaving us a cent for food. Once I heard her speaking to a woman in our street. Maybe the woman had dared to sympathize with her. 'Oh,' she said, 'it's all right. He isn't ever dull like most of the men in this street. Life is never dull when my man is about.'

But often I was filled with bitterness, and sometimes I wished he wasn't my father. I'd even invent another man as my father. To protect my mother I'd make up stories of a secret marriage that for some strange reason never got known. As though some man, say, the president of a railroad company or maybe a Congressman, had married my mother, thinking his wife was dead and then it turned out she wasn't.

Now they had to hush it up, but I got born just the same. I wasn't really the son of my father. Somewhere in the world there was a very dignified, quite wonderful man who was really my father. I even made myself half-believe these fancies.

And then there came a certain night. Mother was away from home. Maybe there was a church that night. Father came in. He'd been off somewhere for two or three weeks. He found me alone in the house, reading by the kitchen table.

It had been raining and he was very wet. He sat and looked at me for a long time, not saying a word. I was startled, for there was on his face the saddest look I had ever seen. He sat for a time, his clothes dripping. Then he got up.

'Come on with me,' he said.

I got up and went with him out of the house. I was filled with wonder, but I wasn't afraid. We went along a dirt road that led down into a valley, about a mile out of town, where there was a pond. We walked in silence. The man who was always talking had stopped his talking.

I didn't know what was up and had the queer feeling that I was with a stranger. I don't know whether my father intended it so. I don't think he did.

The pond was quite large. It was still raining hard and there were flashes of lightning followed by thunder. We were on a grassy bank at the pond's edge when my father spoke, and in the darkness and rain his voice sounded strange.

'Take off your clothes,' he said. Still filled with wonder, I began to undress. There was a flash of lightning and I saw that he was already naked.

Naked, we went into the pond. Taking my hand he pulled me in. It may be that I was too frightened, too full of a feeling of strangeness, to speak. Before that night my father had never seemed to pay any attention to me.

'And what is he up to now?' I kept asking myself. I did not swim very well, but he put my hand on his shoulder and struck out into the darkness.

He was a man with big shoulders, a powerful swimmer. In the darkness I could feel the movement of his muscles. We swam to the far edge of the pond and then back to where we had left our clothes. The rain continued and the wind blew. Sometimes my father swam on his back and when he did, he took my hand in his large powerful one and moved it over so that it rested always on his shoulder. Sometimes there would be a flash of lightning and I could see his face quite clearly.

It was as it was earlier, in the kitchen, a face filled with sadness. There would be the momentary glimpse of his face and then again the darkness, the wind and the rain. In me there was a feeling I had never known before.

It was a feeling of closeness. It was something strange. It was as though there were only we two in the world. It was as though I had been jerked suddenly out of myself, out of my world of the schoolboy, out of a world in which I was ashamed of my father.

He had become blood of my blood; the strong swimmer and I the boy clinging to him in the darkness. We swam in silence and in silence we dressed in our wet clothes, and went home.

There was a lamp lighted in the kitchen, and when we came in, the water dripping from us, there was my mother. She smiled at us. I remember that she called us 'boys.' 'What have you boys been up to?' she asked, but my father did not answer. As he had begun the evening's experience with me in silence, so he ended it. He turned and looked at me. Then he went, I thought, with a new and strange dignity, out of the room.

I climbed the stairs to my own room, undressed in darkness and got into bed. I couldn't sleep and did not want to sleep. For the first time I knew that I was the son of my father. He was a story-teller as I was to be. It may be that I even laughed a little softly there in the darkness. If I did, I laughed knowing that I would never again be wanting another father.

Girl by the Stove

HERE IS SOMETHING VERY CURIOUS about the way in which stories grow in the mind of a story-teller. When I was a man past forty I wrote a story that became the title story to a book of short stories.

The story I called 'Death in the Woods,' and to my mind it is one of the best, the most solid of all my stories.

I was a long time writing it. I tried, time and again, through several years and it would not come off.

Often you have to go far back into childhood to recapture some of the impressions that become part of such a story.

In the story, as I finally wrote it, there was a little old woman, the wife of a brutal husband and the mother of an equally brutal son.

I dare say that, when I was a boy, I saw many such women. They are women who are compelled, by fate, to spend their lives feeding the animal in both men and animals. They feed farm animals and dogs. They feed chickens. They feed the animal lust in men.

The little old woman of my story froze to death in the winter woods. She was very old, very small, very weary. She carried on her back a pack of dog meat, given her by a sympathetic small-town butcher. She was accompanied on her journey home through the woods by several large hungry dogs.

When she was dead, the dogs tore the pack from her back and in doing so tore the clothes from her body. She lay there frozen and naked in the winter roads. In death her slender old body had become strangely like the lovely body of a young girl——

A boy had come to me filled with excitement, when I was perhaps twelve or thirteen.

It was in the winter. There was deep snow on the ground.

704

'Do you want to see something?'

He would not tell me what he had in store for me.

'You come tonight, when it is dark.'

He was very mysterious. He was one of the boys of our neighborhood with whom I had been engaged in the young boys' search for some of the secrets of life.

Once, during the summer before, he had come to me equally filled with excitement. There was, at that time, a place in the town where a sidewalk had been built over some low swampy land. The sidewalk was on stilts. It was a plank walk set up on posts sunk into the swampy ground. We crawled under the walk. We thought that when women came along the sidewalk we might be able to see, through cracks in the walk, up under their skirts.

Small boys are often like that. We were. We stayed for hours lying on wet grass under the sidewalk. I do not remember that there was any addition made to our knowledge of life.

I went to the boy's house at night, through the deep snow, and he was waiting for me. I had crept out of our own house and he was waiting in the barn back of his father's house.

'Come on. I'll show you. You'll see something you never have seen.'

We went through several streets to where there was a house at the edge of town. It was, as I remember it, an old brick house, set in a large yard that was surrounded by a sage-apple hedge. There were many bushes and trees in the yard.

We crept into the yard and stood in the deep snow behind one of the bushes. My boy friend had not told me why we had come.

I was a good deal frightened. I was very cold. I kept questioning him, but he would tell me nothing.

'You wait. You'll see.'

We stood where we could look into a downstairs room of the house. Earlier it had been snowing, but now the snow no longer fell and the sky began to clear. The house, near the window of which we stood in the soft winter darkness, was occupied by an old man and his wife.

They had taken a young girl, a niece, of about my own age, to live with them. She had come there from another town. I knew about her because I had already become the town newsboy and delivered a morning paper to that house.

I had seen the strange young girl through a window and once she had spoken to me.

That was also during the same winter. I had come to the house with the morning Cleveland paper and she had opened the door. She spoke to me.

'Hello.'

'Why, hello.'

We were both embarrassed. She was a straight-bodied slender little thing just a little beginning to grow into young womanhood.

We had stood looking at each other.

'Come around to the kitchen door,' she said, 'I have something for you.'

She gave me some cookies her aunt, the old woman, had baked. She had wanted to be friends. She was a strange girl in the town.

I had muttered some words of thanks and had hurried away, but on other mornings, when I took the paper to that house, I had hoped to see her again.

I hadn't, but I had been dreaming of her. I had thought about her at night when I was in bed with one of my brothers. She had become increasingly beautiful to me.

I was there with that boy, at night, behind the bush, near the window. There was a room with chairs and a table. There was an old-fashioned stove of the sort called base-burners. There was an oil lamp, turned low.

I do not know how long we stood in the cold and the darkness, but at last she came. The old aunt and uncle must already have gone to bed.

She had come into the room to undress before the stove. It was that my boy friend had, by some accident, seen on the night before.

She was there in the room before the glowing stove. She undressed slowly. When she was quite nude, she began to turn her young body slowly before the stove. The stove had isinglass windows. She was slowly warming all of her body.

We stood there, quite close to the window, staring at her, and then suddenly something strange happened to us ——

Years later, many years later, a New York surgeon once took me with him to a hospital where he was doing an appendectomy on another such a young girl, having got me into the operating room by passing me off as a visiting doctor.

I had wanted, for the sake of some story I was writing, to see such an operation. Perhaps I never wrote the story.

Anyway, I was in the hospital, in the operating room, and there was a young and slender girl, quite nude, lying on the operating table.

I thought her body very beautiful. I could not bear to see the surgeon cut her body. I turned and hurried out of the room. The surgeon thought I was frightened by the thought of blood about to be shed, but it wasn't that.

I wanted to grab the surgeon's arm.

'Don't. It't too beautiful. Don't cut it.'

That was what I felt when as a young boy I stood in the snow back of the bush before that house ——

Or was it something other I felt on that winter night? I don't know. I was standing there with the other small-town boy. I was seeing something I had long thought I most wanted to see — a naked woman.

And then suddenly, for some obscure reason, I turned and struck my boy friend as hard as I could in the face with my fist.

I knocked him into the snow and then I ran. The young girl was still warming her slender young body by the glowing stove. She was turning her young body slowly around before the stove.

I struck him in the face with all my might and then I ran. I kept running and for a long time couldn't go home. I just walked about alone in the winter streets of the town. I hadn't been angry with the other boy when I hit him with my fist and ran away. It may be that I didn't like what was in his mind and in my own mind. It may be that I really wanted to hit myself as hard as I could with my own fist. How do I know? In any case, the figure of the girl by the stove has always been curiously confused in my mind with that of another beautiful young girl under the knife of a surgeon and of an old woman I once saw frozen in the winter woods, her ragged old clothes torn from her body by a pack of hungry dogs.

White Spot

I AM QUITE SURE that some of the women I had during this period never became real to me. I do not even remember the names. They exist for me as a kind of fragrance as Ruth, Prudence, Genevieve, Nelly, etc., etc. There were the very brutal-looking, very sensual women seen one night in a low dive in Chicago. I would have been with certain business men on a spree. The business men were better when drunk. The shrewdness was gone. They became sometimes terrible, sometimes rather sweet children.

For example, there was Albert, short, fat, baby-faced. He was the president of a certain manufacturing company for which I wrote advertisements. We got drunk together.

He had a wife who was rather literary and already I had published a few stories. Albert had bragged to her about me and once he took me to his house, in an Illinois town, to dine.

She would have talked only of books . . . as such women do talk. They can never by any chance be right about anything in the world of the arts. Better if they would keep still. They never do.

Albert being much pleased. 'The little wife — you see, Sherwood. In our house also we have a high-brow.' He was proud of her, wanted to be loyal. As woman, in bed with her man, she wouldn't have been much.

Albert knowing that and wanting in the flesh. He had got himself a little warm thing, bought her fur coats, sent her money. He could never go to her except when he had been drinking.

He explained to me, when we were drunk together. 'I am faithful to my wife, Sherwood.' He had his code. 'To be sure, I sleep with my Mable, but I have been faithful. I never kissed her on the lips.' His reserving that as his own rock on which to stand. I thought it as good as most rocks upon which men stand.

But I was speaking of women . . . certain women, who touched me vitally in the flesh, left something with me. It's all very strange sometimes. I have just thought of that rather big, thick-lipped woman seen in a cheap restaurant, half dive, in South State Street. There was a little burlesque show a few doors up the street.

Business men, perhaps clients of the firm for which I worked, explaining to me. The president of our company would have been deacon in some suburban church.

'Take these men out and entertain them. You do not need to make an itemized account of expenses.

'I would not want company money spent for anything evil.'

Oh, thou fraud!

I would have been blowing money. The burlesque women came down along a dirty alleyway from the stage door of the cheap show and into the restaurant, half dive. They may have got a percentage on the cost of the drinks bought for them.

And there was that big one, with the thick lips, sitting and staring at me. 'I want you' — and myself wanting her. Now! Now!

The evil smell of the terrible little place. Street-women's pimps sitting about, the business men with me. One of them made a remark. 'God, look at that one.' She had one eye gone, torn out perhaps in a fight with some other woman over some man, and there was the scar from a cut on her low forehead.

Above the cut her shining blue-black hair, very thick, very beautiful. I wanted my hands in it.

She knew. She felt as I felt, but I was ashamed. I didn't want the business men with me to know.

What?

That I was a brute. That I was also gentle, modest, that I possessed also a subtle mind.

The women would have been going and coming in at a back door of the place, as the act they did, a kind of weird, almost naked dance before yokels, was due to be repeated. I went out into the alleyway and waited, and she came.

There were no preliminaries. Now or never. There were some

boxes piled up and we got in behind them. What evil smells back in there. I got my two hands buried deep in her beautiful hair.

And afterward, her saying, when I asked her the question — Do you want money — 'A little,' she said. Her voice was soft. There were drunken men going up and down. There was the loud rasping sound from a phonograph, playing over and over some dance tune in the burlesque place.

Can a man retain something? I had no feeling of anything unclean. She laughed softly — 'Give me something, fifty cents. I don't like the foolish feeling of giving it away.'

'O.K.'

Myself hurrying back to the businessmen, not wanting them to suspect.

'You were a long time.'

'Yes.' I would have made up some quick lie.

That other one, met on a train, when the train was delayed because something went wrong with the engine. Is there a sense in which the rational man loves all women? The train stopping by a wood and that woman and I going into the wood to gather flowers.

Again. 'Now. Now.' 'You will be gone.' We may never meet again.

And then our coming back to the train. She going to sit with an older woman, perhaps her mother, taking her the flowers we had got.

It was Sally, the quiet one, who saw the white spot. It was in a room in a hotel in Chicago, one of that sort. You go in without baggage. You register . . . Mr. and Mrs. John Jones . . . Buffalo, New York. I remember a friend, who was a woman's man, telling me that he always used my name.

We were lying in there in the dark at night, in that rabbit warren of a place. For all I knew, the place was full of other such couples. We were in the half-sleep that follows, lying in black darkness, a moment ago so close, now so far apart.

Sound of trains rattling along a near-by elevated railroad. This may have been on an election night. There was the sound of men cheering and a band played.

We are human, a male and a female. How lonely we are!

It may be that we only come close in art.

No. Wait.

There is something grown evil in men's minds about contacts.

How we want, want, want! How little we dare take!

It is very silent, here in the darkness. The sounds of the city, of life going on, city life, out there in the street.

A woman cry of animal gratification from a neighboring room.

We exist in infinite dirt, in infinite cleanliness.

Waters of life wash us.

The mind and fancy reaching out.

Now, for an hour, two, three hours, the puzzling lust of the flesh is gone. The mind, the fancy, is free.

It may have been that fancy, the always busy imagination of the artist-man, she wanted.

She began to talk softly of the white spot. 'It floats in the darkness,' she said softly, and I think I did understand, almost at once, her need . . .

After the flesh the spirit. Minds, fancy, draw close now.

It was a wavering white spot, like a tiny snow-white cloud in the darkness of a close little room in a Chicago bed-house.

You not wanting what our civilization has made of us.

It is you men, males, always making the world ugly.

You have made the dirt. It is you. It is you.

Yes. I understand.

But do you see the white spot?

Yes. It floats there, under the ceiling. Now it descends and floats along the floor.

It is the thing lost. It eludes us.

It belongs to us. It is our whiteness.

A moment of real closeness, with that strange thing to the male — a woman.

I had a thought I remember. It was a game I played with my brother Earl when I was a lad and he not much more than a babe. We slept together for a time and I invented a game. With our minds we stripped the walls of a room in a little yellow house quite away. We swept the ceiling of our room and the floors away. Our bed floated in space. Perhaps I had picked up a line from some poem.

'We are between worlds. Earth is far, far beneath us. We float over
Earth.'

All this on a hot August night, but we could feel the coolness of
outer space. I explained the game to the woman in the room and we
played it, following on our floating bed the white drifting spot her
fancy had found in that space.

How strange afterward, going down into the street. It might have
been midnight, but the street was still crowded with people.

'And so we did float. We did see and follow the white spot and we
are here. You make your living writing advertisements and I have a
job in an office where they sell patent medicine.

'I am a woman of twenty-eight and unmarried. I live with my
sister who is married.'

The cheap little hotel run for such couples as we were had its office
on the second floor. There was a little desk with a hotel register.
What rows of Jones, Smiths, and, yes — Andersons. That friend of
mine might have been in that place. He might have put my real
name down there.

I would have gone down the stairs first, looked up and down the
street. 'O.K.,' the pair of us dodging out. 'You'd better take a taxi
home. Let me pay.'

'But can you? It is such a long way out. It will cost so much.'

'Yes. Here.'

Who was it invented money? There it lies, the dirty green bill in
her hand. The taxi-man looking, perhaps listening.

'But, but . . . does anything of beauty cling to me? Is it to be remembered?'

'Yes. You are very beautiful. Good night.'

A lie . . . there was no beauty. The night, the street, the city, was
the night, the street, the city.

All Will Be Free

I WAS ALWAYS a little sore at Ben Hecht that he first told the story.
When last I saw him in New York, he was at work making it into a
movie.

However, I cannot resist the temptation to tell my impression of the
man. He was so cheerful, seemingly so full of life.

We had gone, Ben and I, with some four or five others to lunch at
the German restaurant. It was a cold rainy day in the late fall, let us
say in November, and we were all in a cheerless mood.

For one thing it was during the time of prohibition and, on such a
Chicago day, in the mood we were in, we all wanted drinks. But
drinks were expensive.

Yes, they could be had in the place, at say fifty cents a drink, for
second-rate stuff.

So we sat there growling at each other. Except for myself, all the
others were newspaper men. Although at bottom Ben Hecht is one
of the kindest men I have ever known, he has always had a talent for
insult.

We had begun insulting each other, insults thrown back and forth,
each man trying to get some other fellow's dander up.

We were interrupted by the waiter.

'That man over there, that little dark man sitting in the corner,
wants to buy you all a drink.'

'Listen, man, don't attempt to torture us.'

'Is this some crude and cruel attempt at a joke?'

We were all staring at the little foreign-looking man who smiled
blandly at us.

'No, he means it. What will you have?' the waiter was asking us.

There was no one else in the place except ourselves and the man at the table in a corner at the back of the room.

'Sure. Sure. Hell, yes.'

'He wants you to have the best stuff.'

Ben half arose from his chair.

'I've a notion to go and kiss him,' he said.

The drinks were brought and we raised our glasses to the man and in a few minutes, there the waiter was again.

'He wants you to have another drink.'

It was too much. We were all so filled with gratitude that we were struggling to keep the tears from running down our cheeks.

'What a man! What a man! Bring him over here.'

Two of us arose to escort him to our table. This wasn't a fellow to miss. Why, the drinks we had been having were costing seventy-five cents each.

The man came. It is something shameful in me that I have forgotten his name.

He was so cheerful, so generous, so happy-seeming.

We began to question him and he talked. More drinks flowed. Ben later told the story in a book called *A Thousand and One Afternoons*. At this point in the story he made me begin singing a song. Ben couldn't remember the words of the song he put into his story. He invented words. He made me responsible for his misquoting of the words of the song I didn't sing. He was, I dare say, too lazy to look them up. Or he was just taking a good-natured shot at me.

'This is the song as Sherwood sang it.' He said something of that sort.

Anyway, there we were at the table in that place and a gloomy cheerless day had become bright and shining. More and more drinks kept coming.

The man we had thus found was a little dark Russian Jew. He was in a mood for talk. He told us his history.

He had been born a poor Russian Jewish boy in a ghetto. He was drafted into the Russian army. He went to serve in the Caucasus.

He spoke at length of that, describing his life in the army under the Czar, the mountain villages seen, the herds of cattle on the green hills, the rushing rivers, the beautiful village girls.

'They were Tartar maidens,' he said.

'Oh, they were so strong, so straight, so full-bosomed.' He went into a kind of ecstasy as he described the mountain maidens seen while he was a Russian soldier.

And then he was in America, had escaped from the army life and had come here. He was in New York, working there, having hard enough times.

'But, oh, the beautiful country, America. Life so free here. Here, in America, and here only, on all the earth's surface, such a poor Russian Jew as I has my chance.'

Words kept flowing from the man's lips and the liquor, at seventy-five cents the drink, also kept flowing.

'You are all newspaper men, are you not?'

Except for myself, all were. The others put me in among themselves.

'Yes, yes. We are all newspaper men.'

'I knew it. I could tell by looking at you. You all have such intelligent faces.'

'You must have been looking at me,' Ben Hecht said.

He had, he said, come to Chicago and had become a manufacturer.

'I make boxes in which other manufacturers ship their goods. It is a box factory.'

He explained that his factory was in the northwest section of the city. He had begun in a small way, but his business had grown large. There had come the necessity of building a larger factory and he had done that. The factory was almost completed.

'It is now November, but by Christmas time it will be completed. Or, let us say, by the first of the year, on New Year's Day.

'Here is the point,' he cried. He had become more and more excited. His eyes were shining.

On that very morning he had gone to have a look at his new factory.

'Oh, it is so beautiful. It is such a beautiful factory.'

He had walked about on the floor of the new factory. There was, he said, a great room, as large as a hall. He had been standing in the great room there and looking about.

And then a thought had come. It had come upon him suddenly. He had gone pale. It was, he said, as he stood in the new factory (this he explained was in the very early morning before the workmen who were building the factory had come) as though there were voices coming out of the walls and calling to him.

'It is like this,' he said. 'I cannot manufacture boxes in that factory. It is too beautiful. I can't do it. I can't. I can't.'

He explained that he had suddenly realized what America had meant to him. He had come here so poor. He was a Russian Jew, but America had opened her arms to him.

'I can go on with my old factory. What do I care? I have money enough. I am prosperous enough.'

He had decided that he would make of the new factory, when it was completed, a place of joy. That was it. It would be a place for dances and plays. Everyone could come. It would cost the people nothing. He would build a stage, would hire musicians to play music.

'It is to be free, free, like America itself, a place of joy.

'There is more joy wanted, more places of joy!'

The little man got up from the table at which we had all been sitting, listening and drinking his drinks. At that time in Chicago there was an intense struggle for control of the streets going on between the Yellow and the Checker taxicabs. Battles between them were being fought in the streets.

He was proposing that we all write of his plan in our newspapers. We were to invite the whole city to come. Everything would be free. He kept saying the word over and over.

'Everything is to be free. A place of joy. It will all be free.'

He had taken a little notebook from his pocket. He took each of our names and addresses. We were to bring our friends. All would be refined. It was to be a place of refined joy. As he wrote our names and addresses, saying that the great opening would be on the day of the beginning of the New Year and that he would send a taxicab for each of us, he asked us each a question.

'Do you prefer a Yellow or a Checker taxicab?' he asked.

He had got up to leave. It was growing dark outside in the street. It was still raining a cold drizzle of rain. At the bar he stopped and bought for us another expensive bottle of whiskey.

He bought a quart. He bought us a box of expensive cigars. He stood at the door smiling his joyous smile.

Would we all come? Would we write it all up? Would we promise him?

'Yes, yes,' we cried.

'By the gods, we'll give you a send-off.

'We'll be there.

'We'll be there.'

The man had gone and we sat stunned. The men with me were all so-called 'hard-boiled' newspaper men, but they had believed. There had been something so very convincing about the man.

'He means it.'

'Yes, he does.'

'Sure, he means it. What are you talking about?'

We separated, each going his way, all convinced. It may be that the impulse in the man was something we all secretly wanted in ourselves.

We also wanted freedom. We wanted more places of joy in our city.

It wasn't until the next morning that I found out the truth. Ben phoned me and he was excited.

'You come over here and at once,' he said.

It was true that the little man we had met in the restaurant was a box manufacturer. He had been.

He had owned a little box factory over on the northwest side of the city, but it had failed.

On the morning of the day when we had met him he had found himself on the edge of bankruptcy. He had gone to his bank and there was a little money left, perhaps a hundred dollars, and he had drawn it out.

He had come down into the city and to the German restaurant and he had found us there. He had had the afternoon with us, had built for us his new factory, that was to be his place of joy.

The place where all would be free.

He had left us and had walked alone in the cold rain-washed streets. He had come to a bridge over the Chicago River and had thrown himself in.

Ben told me that when they hauled out his body they found ten cents in his pocket.

How could I help hoping that he had found his place of joy, the place where all is free?

It is Ben's story, but it is also mine. I was there. I was a part of it. Such a story will bear telling over and over, from many angles. It should become — by someone's telling — one of the classic stories of American life.

I Build A House

A T THE TIME HORACE LIVERIGHT was the outstanding figure in the American publishing world. Having come to New York from Philadelphia he had got a job on the Stock Exchange and, by a quick succession of speculations, run a few hundred dollars into a hundred thousand dollars.

What a place — 'Horace Liveright'! Here in this publishing house was none of the dignity, the formality, of the older publishing houses, the Scribners, Harpers, Century, Macmillans, etc. The place was a sort of madhouse, and I remember that when I told Ben Huebsch that I would at last have to quit him and that I was going to Horace Liveright, he was shocked.

For Horace was in and out of the Stock Exchange. He was in the theater. When we went to see him in his publishing house often enough the whole outer office was filled with chorus girls.

Horace, it seemed, was figuring on putting on a musical comedy, and there they were. It wouldn't have surprised me when I went there to have had one of the women jump up and, with a practice swing, kick my hat off.

And there was Horace in the midst of it all. Men and women were rushing in and out, phones were ringing. Horace was talking to casting agencies in regard to players for some show he was producing; he was buying or selling stocks through some broker; authors were coming and going. It was a bedlam, a madhouse, and yet a man felt something very gratifying in it all.

Liveright had a way of trusting his authors. If at that time you went to him with a new man, and during the days of his splendor

719

I did take both Hemingway and Faulkner to Horace with their first printed books, he took your word for it.

'Do you think they are all right, men of real talent?

'All right, I'll take them on. You send them to me.'

And there was his checkbook, always on hand, often with a bottle of whiskey on the desk beside it.

It was all rather crazy, rather splendid. Horace was a gambler and if he believed in you would gamble on you. I have always thought, since the man's death, that too much emphasis has been put on the reckless splendor of the man rather than on his never-ending generosity and his real belief in men of talent. I dedicated one of my books of verse to him and I have always been glad I did. In a way, I loved the man.

As he lived he died. Certainly it was not his generosity to authors that broke him. The Stock Exchange did that, and I shall always remember the last sight I had of him.

His publishing house had failed, dragged down by his plunges on the Stock Exchange, and after an attempt to find for himself a place in Hollywood, he had returned to New York.

On the street I saw Tommy Smith, who had been his editor-in-chief. 'Horace,' he said, 'is at such and such an address. He is in bad shape. Do go and see him.'

And so I went to the address given and there he was. It was summer and some friend had given him the use of his apartment. He was there surrounded, as always, by people. It was morning, but there had evidently been a night of carousal and Horace was in black pajamas.

As for the people about him, they were of a sort you would only find in New York. They were failures in the theater, men and women who hadn't made it, but were desperately keeping up a bluff. There was much loud talk, much boasting.

Horace was sitting on a couch, and the morning sun was streaming through a window. He was very pale, very thin, and one of his long arms had almost withered away. I was told later that the withered arm was the result of a struggle with a woman. It was said that she had bitten him and that the arm had become infected.

And so I stood in that place, in that motley crowd. There were drinks going about. I had seen, a few weeks before, the picture called the *Cabinet of Doctor Caligari*, and there he was. Horace had become that.

He was, I think, a little ashamed of his surroundings. He arose and went with me into a hallway. He put his good arm about my shoulder. 'Well, what the hell, Sherwood! I'm sunk,' he said.

He said that and then braced. His shoulders straightened a little. I said something about his having lost control of his publishing house. As he knew, and I knew, the house had been sold by the receivers at a low price. Its glory was quite gone. It had been something no other publishing house in America had ever been. It had put me on my feet.

'Why, I am not out of the publishing house,' Horace said proudly. 'It is to be reorganized on a big scale,' he said.

He said he did not think that with all the other interests he had, in the theater, in Hollywood, on the Stock Exchange, he would be able to take any very active part in the new and bigger Liveright.

'I'll just be chairman of the board,' he said; and then, with a bitter little laugh and knowing that I knew what I knew, he turned and walked away.

As for myself, I took the elevator down and out of that apartment building and walked in the street below with tears half-blinding my eyes.

A new, strange life again had begun for me.

I had been in New Orleans through a summer and winter. I had very little money. Having lived through one New Orleans summer, with its oppressive heat, I wanted, if possible, to avoid another.

I began to write letters to men I knew.

'Tell me, if you can, of some place to which I can go, where it is cool and where it doesn't cost much to live.'

The letters brought me several suggestions, among others one from Julian Harris. Julian was at that time running his newspaper at Columbus, Georgia. He had made a fine and courageous fight against the Ku Klux Klan, and I was full of admiration for him. In his letter he spoke of a Mrs. Greear, at Trout Dale, Virginia, and I have the impression that he said that Trout Dale was a place to which his father, Joel Chandler Harris, had often gone fishing. I wrote to Mrs. Greear, and received an answer. I could, she said, come to live in her family for a dollar a day.

'That will be for a room,' I thought. I found, in fact, that it meant a room, my meals, my washing and mending. It meant living in a delightful family.

So I was here, where I am now, in the southwest Virginia hill country. I had come by train to the town of Marion, where I later ran two newspapers, one Democratic and the other Republican, and from there had gone on to Trout Dale by a lumber railroad.

The train, pulled by an engine geared to climb steep hills with the drive wheels apparently flying at a furious rate, sparks flying out often setting afire the neighboring woods, really crawled along at ten miles an hour.

It was a strange, a new sort of country to me. On all sides were the magnificent hills, in the Greear family a troop of boys. They all bore Biblical names — John, Joshua, David, Philip, Solomon. There was a corn field beyond a hillside apple orchard in a little hollow in the hills, and in the corn field a small one-room cabin that had not been occupied for years.

The cabin stood in the tall corn. It had no windows. For years the dust had blown in through the openings where the windows had been and through the open door. It was a foot thick on the floor.

The boys came with shovels and brooms. They cleared it out. They built in a rude table at which I could sit. They brought a chair from the house.

It was a long summer without rain in the hills, and the daily train from down in the rich Holston Valley, down in the place of paved roads and prosperous farms, sent sparks into the dry woods. The engine of the train, built for hauling long trains of cars loaded with heavy logs, went slowly. It crawled painfully up wooded Trout Dale mountain-sides, throwing off a stream of sparks. The little lumber town of Trout Dale was in decay. Now all the best of the timber had been cut out.

This town in the hills had tried valiantly to go on being a town; the merchants, men who had saved money working in the lumber camp, tried to establish an industry. There had been a little bank and my host, John Greear, had been the cashier.

So all of the money of the community had been put into the building of a factory and it had failed, impoverishing the little mountain village. From the Greear house I could see the remnants of the factory. All of it but a tall brick chimney had been torn away and beside

the chimney lay a huge old iron boiler brown now with rust. The
chimney that had furnished the power for the factory seemed to leer
at you as you went past it on the dirt road that led over the mountains
to the prosperous land beyond.

I was in the corn field at work. I wrote a book there, a book of
childhood I called *Tar*.

I was alone there, often all morning at my table. It was cool up
there in the hills, or at least it seemed cool after New Orleans, and
the sunlight came in to me through the tall corn.

The corn had begun to wither in the long drought. When there
was a breeze blowing, there was a sharp rustling sound. My feet, as
I sat writing, were on the warm earth of the little floorless cabin. The
corn seemed talking to me.

'What an ideal place for an American writer!' I thought. I grew
lyrical.

'The corn, the corn, how significant in all American life!' I thought.
I thought of all the great corn fields of the Middle West, of how when
I was a small boy I had often crept into them at the edge of my own
Ohio town.

I used to crawl in there and lie under the corn. It was warm and
close in there. On the ground, under the tall corn, pumpkins grew.
There was the singing of the insects. Little insects flew about my head
or crawled along the warm ground. Then also the corn fields had
talked to me. Like Henry Wallace, whom I was to know later, I became, for the time, a kind of corn-field mystic.

I even tried what I had often thought of doing. When I had written
a chapter of my book, I went outside my cabin and read it aloud to
the corn. It was all a little ridiculous, but I thought, 'No one knows.

And the corn did seem to talk back to me.

'Sure, you are all right. Go ahead,' it seemed to say.

I had rented an old horse and buggy and in the afternoon drove by
many dirt roads over the mountains.

The old horse went slowly. I had a book with me and, putting the
reins on the dashboard, let the old beast take his own way. I might
well have had with me a volume of George Borrow, *Lavengro* or the
Romany Rye. They were books I loved and always carried in my
bags.

I kept meeting mountain men and women who turned to stare at me. The mountaineers are like the gypsies described by Borrow. They look directly at you with a strange, fixed, somewhat disconcerting stare. For a long time after you begin to know him, they say little. They are watching you.

'What sort of fellow is this?'

Sometimes, as I rode thus, often in forest roads, some mountain man appeared suddenly out of a path that led away into the deep bushes. There was an old bearded man sitting on a log with a rifle on his knees. It was not until I had lived in the mountains for several years that Dave, one of the Greear boys, told me of how I was all that summer under suspicion.

'They were watching you, quite sure you were a revenuer,' he said. He explained how people came to the Greear house asking. All of this was during the time of prohibition and the business of making moonshine was flourishing.

The mountain man was poor. He lived far from the railroad. His little patch of corn, often but three or four acres, would not support his family.

The mountain families were prolific. One of my neighbors, Will Pruitt, who became a friend after I built my own house in the hills, had nineteen children by one wife. He was still vigorous, still strong. He went out on horse-trading expeditions. The farm I later bought had on it a little frame tenant house, and after I had built my own house the American sculptress, Lucile Swan, once came to live in the tenant house.

She was young and beautiful. She bought and rode a great black horse, and once Will stopped in the road.

'That woman,' he said. 'It's a good thing my old woman hasn't died yet. I'd never let that woman get out of the country.'

But that came later. I was there in that corn field writing. Some of the mountain men had gone to the Greears to inquire.

'Why, he's a writer. He's writing a book.'

It seemed like nonsense to them. One of the mountain men later told me about it.

'You didn't look like that to us,' he said.

He told me of how they had sent men through the corn, creeping toward my cabin. It may be that they heard me, spouting there in the corn field. It may have saved me. They perhaps thought I was crazy.

'Well, it's a good thing you didn't get out of that old buggy and walk about much in the woods. We'd have plunked you,' the man said to me. 'We thought dead sure you were a revenuer, but we couldn't be sure. There were two or three men drew a bead on you, but didn't shoot. You came out mighty lucky,' he said.

In my wanderings with my old horse that summer, I went often along a particular road out of the lumber town. It was a little winding road that followed the windings of a brook. It kept crossing and recrossing the brook by fords. I got into a little valley between the hills.

It was a sweet little valley in which there was one small farm, owned, I was told, by a widow woman. She had lost her man. He had gone off to the West Virginia mountains, to the coal mines, and had been killed there. There were two small brooks passing through the valley, and beside one of the streams, crossed by a log bridge, was a mountain cabin in which the widow lived with her children.

She was a sturdy woman and was farming her own farm and doing the work of a man.

Once I stopped at the house, and the widow being absent I spoke to the children. They had come down to the bridge to stare at me.

'Does your mother want to sell this farm?' I asked.

It was a senseless question. I had no money with which to buy a farm. I was indulging in a dream.

'If I had some money I'd buy this farm. I'd live here in these hills.' The hunger may have come down into me from my father, who, I think, had been a North Carolina hill boy.

'If I could just buy this farm, I could live, comfortably enough, in that little cabin, over there.'

My dreams ran far ahead. Sometime I might write a book that would really sell. All of that country was full of beautiful building stone. I might some day build such a stone house as I had seen in England or France.

The children, frightened by my inquiry, ran away to hide, but presently one of them, a young girl, came timidly back. She stood across the creek from me and shouted a shrill voice.

'Yes, mother wants to sell. She wants to move to West Virginia,' she screamed, and ran away. It seemed a curious desire to me.

Fall came and I still lingered in the hills that were now covered by color. An old desire to be a painter came back to me, but I did not surrender to it. I had finished my book and had written and sent off several short stories.

And then luck came my way. Two of the short stories sold and I had some money, and one day, when I was again driving down through my little valley, a book in my hand, the old horse meandering along, the hills surrounding the valley covered with flowing color as though beautiful Oriental carpets had been laid over them, I met a woman in the road.

Was it a woman or was it some kind of a monster? I reined in the horse and sat staring. The thing was coming down the hill toward me. It was a woman with a great brass kettle on her head, a kettle for making apple butter. I hailed the woman; she came out from under the kettle.

She was the coal miner's widow who owned the little farm in the valley below.

'Do you still want to sell your farm?'

'Yes, I want to move to West Virginia.'

Again that strange desire. I bought the farm there in the road.

A number of things had happened. Chief of all was the fact that Horace Liveright had made a go of *Dark Laughter*. It was the only novel of mine that ever sold in a big way, became what is called a best-seller. The sales climbed up and up. I went on a visit to New York and saw my own face staring at me from the advertising pages of newspapers, on the walls of busses and subways.

I saw men and women sitting in busses and subways with my book in their hands. They were stenographers taking it with them to the office.

'Have you read *Dark Laughter*?'

It was all very strange. It was as exciting as a young girl about to go to her first dance. I wanted to go speak to the men and women holding my book in their hands. I was in the subway, and got up and clinging to a strap stood over one such woman. She was at page 181 of my book. That would be where I told of the orgies at the

Quat'z Arts Ball in Paris in the year after the ending of the first World War. I remembered the American newspaper woman who had as an adventure gone to the ball and was telling of it.

She had told much that I hadn't dared put in the book. I had put in enough. I stood, in the New York subway, looking down at the woman whose eyes were fixed on the pages of my book. She was reading rapidly.

Why, she was such a respectable-looking woman. She was well dressed.

'She will be the wife of a lawyer, or a doctor, or perhaps a merchant,' I thought. She would live somewhere in a respectable suburb. She went to church on Sunday, belonged to a woman's book club.

I was reconstructing the life of the woman reading my book. A few years before, I had written a sort of fantasy of the flesh in a book I had called *Many Marriages*, and there had been a storm of criticism.

That the adventures told in the book could have happened to a respectable-seeming American had seemed terrible to American readers.

'That was my mistake,' I told myself as I stood over the respectable woman reading my book in the subway. In the book she was reading the adventures in sex were taking place in Paris and that made it all right. That, I thought, had had much to do with the success of the later book.

I returned to my Virginia farm in the mountains. Already, during the winter, the cabin by Ripshin Creek had been torn down and a log cabin to work in had been built on a near-by hilltop. It was to be a place in which I could work while the building of a new house went on.

For I had formed rather grand plans. Money was, for the first time, rolling in. I was what is called in the South, 'nigger rich.' I had determined to have a house of stone to stand near where Ripshin joined Laurel Creek. There was a fine old apple orchard at that spot, and my house, when built, would be protected from storms by the surrounding hills.

There was plenty of stone everywhere about, but, in all the mountain country, there were no workmen who had ever built a stone house.

However, they were all ready to try. I had got an old man named Ball to be my builder and he was full of confidence. Bill Spratling, who was then teaching architecture at Tulane University, in New Orleans, drew some plans for me. However, we could not use the plans much, as neither the builder, Ball, nor myself could understand the blue-prints.

'But never mind,' Ball said. 'We'll get along.'

Ball was a huge old man of near seventy who had been a builder of sawmills, and it was said also that, as a younger man, he had been a famous moonshiner. I had been told that he was somewhat dangerous when crossed, but he was always gentle with me.

He went about boasting of his new position. He engaged to have lumber sawed. He employed neighboring hill farmers. He set men to hauling huge stone. He stood before the store at Trout Dale boasting.

'I'm something now,' he declared. 'I've got into a new position in life. I'm secretary to that millionaire who has moved in here.'

But I was no millionaire. I had got a few thousand as royalty on my book *Dark Laughter,* and there was the hundred dollars that came every Monday from Horace Liveright.

I was intensely bothered by that. There I was. I was presumed to be a writer. 'But a writer should be writing,' I told myself.

And now Ball had engaged many of the neighboring hill farmers to work for me. I had built a small frame house in the valley below the hill on which my log cabin stood. It had been thrown up hastily. I thought, 'When my stone house is built, I'll use it as a garage.'

I slept and ate down there, but in the morning I arose and climbed faithfully up to my cabin on the hill. I sat at my desk by an open window and before me, stretching away, were the tops of other hills.

The hills running away into the distance were a soft blue. They were covered by forests and the trees were just coming into leaf. Here and there, on distant hillsides, were small cleared fields and men plowing. A mountain road climbed a distant hill and a man on horseback went slowly up the road.

It was all too grand. I sat in the cabin with my pen in hand and there were the blank sheets on the desk before me, and down below, on Ripshin Creek, the materials for my house were being brought in.

Men were at work down there and there was I up there on that hill, my pen poised in my hand, no words coming to me.

I sprang up and went outside my cabin to look out.

'Why, I cannot write. It is too exciting down there. This is the great time in a man's life. We are all, at heart, builders. It is the dream of every man, at some time in his life, to build his own house.

'And so my house is to be built and I am to stay up here, writing words on paper. How silly!'

But there was that hundred-dollar check. It came every Monday morning.

Horace had said, 'I will send it to you every week for five years. I'll take what you write.

'I'll not bother you,' he said.

Yet each week the arrival of the check was a reminder that I was not, and perhaps could not be, a writer while my house was building.

'But I am under this obligation to Horace.' I went again into my hilltop cabin. What really happened was that I never did write a word in that cabin. It may be that the view from the hilltop was too magnificent. It made everything I wrote seem too trivial. I had in the end, after my house was built, to move the cabin from the hill, tuck it away among the trees by the creek.

But I was still up there, and down below the work on my house was under way. I had to give it up. I took a train to New York.

'Please, Horace, quit it.'

'Quit what?' he asked.

'Quit sending me that money.'

I tried to explain how it affected me.

'But,' he said, 'I have made enough on the one book — I am in the clear. Why should you worry?'

I had a hard time convincing him. He even became suspicious.

'Are you not satisfied with me as your publisher? Is that it?'

It seemed, as he said, impossible to him that a writer should refuse money.

'All right, I'll quit it, but I think you are a little crazy.'

And so I was released. It is true that, when my house was half-finished, I had to go lecturing. It was bad enough, but it was better than having the checks come every Monday to remind me that I was a writer, not a builder.

And this suggests something to my mind. Do you, the reader, belong to some literary circle in your town or city? Do you attend lectures by novelists and poets? Would you like to know something of the financial standing of these men and women? If so, you do not need to go to Dun and Bradstreet. If they are lecturing, it is a hundred to one they are broke.

We were hauling stones in from the creek for the walls of my house. We were taking stone from neighboring hillsides. Mountain men from all the surrounding hills and hollows were working for me. We sawed lumber, cut shingles, dug and laid stone walls. We built a dry kiln to dry our green lumber. Mr. Ball climbed like a squirrel over the rafters of the house. My brother Karl came and made a painting of the half-completed structure and a drawing of Ball.

Ball had his own way of life. He built heavily the stone walls eighteen inches thick, all the lumber seasoned oak.

'I'm going to build you a house that will stand here until Gabriel blows that trumpet,' he said.

The small hill farmers proved to be wonderfully efficient workmen. When there was work to do on their own farms, wood to cut for their wives, corn to be cut and cultivated, or even perhaps a run of moon to be made for the West Virginia trade, they did not come.

Well, it was all right. While the money made from the sale of *Dark Laughter* held out, I did not mind. Perhaps once a month old man Ball came to me. He had been, I had noticed for several days, growing a bit irritable. I thought of shootings and knifings among the hill men. There was his son Ezra working on the job. He had killed one man.

'I'm afraid,' said the old man, 'that I will have to lay the men off for a few days. I'm not feeling so well.'

A slow grin spread over his old face.

'All right,' I said.

I knew what was coming. Marion Ball would hire a man who owned an old open-faced Ford to drive him about over the hills. He would load the car with a few gallons of local white moon, would sit sprawled on the back seat. He would drive from farmhouse to farmhouse stopping to invite men to drink with him. He would make his driver stop while he slept for an hour beside some hillside road. It was his great bragging time.

'I'm going to build that millionaire down there the finest house ever built in this country. They said I couldn't do it, that I was just a sawmill builder. Why, that fellow down there, that writer, he trusts me like a brother.'

Ball's vacation lasted for perhaps three or four days and then he would reappear. He looked as fresh as a young boy.

'It rests me up to go on a bender now and then,' he explained.

Old Man Ball had his own notion of me. I was more or less a child who had to be taken care of. There was a fireplace, upstairs in the house, for which a stone arch had to be cut. All of the mountain men, I had found out, were natural craftsmen. They loved stone-laying. They had pride in the job they were doing.

An old man came down out of the mountain. He was driving a mule and sat in a broken-down wagon. Later I learned that his wife was dead and that his children had all moved out of the country. They had, perhaps, as so many sons of mountain men did, gone off to the West Virginia coal mines. The old man lived alone in a mountain cabin somewhere back in the hills.

He stopped before my house and came to where Ball and I were standing in the yard. He was nearly bent double with disease. In truth the old man was slowly dying of cancer of the stomach.

'Do you need any stonecutters here?' he asked. He might have been Tom Wolfe's father in *Look Homeward, Angel*. This man was also a gigantic old fellow.

'And are you a stonecutter?'

'Why, I have been a stonecutter for twenty-five years,' he declared.

I looked at Old Man Ball. I had never heard of any stonecutters in the hills.

'Do you know this man?' I asked Ball. 'Is he a stonecutter?'

Ball looked over my head at the sky.

'Why, I'll tell you, man and boy, I have lived in this country for fifty years and some of the best men I've ever known in this country have been liars,' he said.

Ball laughed, and the strange old man laughed with him.

'Well, I've heard of this building going on down here,' he said. 'You know, Marion, I ain't got long to live. I got cancer, but I want a hand in building this house.'

So he got a hand. Ball took him upstairs to where the fireplace was building.

'We want an arch over that fireplace.

'You cut the stones for the arch. If they are all right, if they fit and look all right, I'll give you five dollars. Otherwise you don't get a cent.'

Ball went about his affairs and I went up to where the old man was puttering about. He had got some pieces of string and was taking measurements. He kept tying knots in the string. He muttered.

'I'll show him, damn him, I'll show him,' he kept declaring.

He put the pieces of string in his pocket, went painfully down the temporary stairway we had rigged up, and getting into his broken-down wagon, went away.

'So that,' I thought, 'is the last of him. He will be dead soon now.'

Very soon, after three or four weeks, he did die, and we built a coffin for him. We built several rude coffins for hill men and women while my house was building. We took a day off and all went up to the old man's cabin to bury him.

And then, after several more weeks, it was time to lay up the arch over the fireplace, and Old Man Ball came to me. We drove up to that other old man's empty cabin. Ball had had a hunch.

'We might as well go up there and see,' he said. He had known well the old man who had died.

'You can't tell, that old fool may have cut them stone.'

So we drove up a mountain road to the empty cabin, and there the stones were. They were in a little shed back of the cabin, and when we brought them down, they made a perfect little arch for my fireplace. The old mountain man, with the cancer eating away at him, had sat up there, slowly and painfully cutting the stones. He had managed to get a chisel and a hammer. He must have worked slowly, no doubt having to rest for long periods. He had wanted a hand in building my house. He had wanted to show Old Man Ball. He had done a fine job.

It must have seemed a very magnificent house to all the neighborhood. Their own houses were, for the most part, small unpainted shacks, often of one, two, or three rooms.

The civilization about me was not a money civilization. There was little money coming in. Moon liquor was about the only cash crop. When a man needed a new pair of shoes for his wife, a new pair of overalls, he sold a calf. Many of the people would have nothing to do with liquor-making. Often they were Primitive Baptists, and devoutly religious. For the most part I found them trustworthy, good workmen and honest. If they were suspicious of strangers, slow to establish friendships, they were also, when once they had accepted you, very loyal.

One of the mountain men explained it all to me.

'We wait until we are sure we can fellowship with a man,' he said.

The Primitive Baptists (sometimes called Hardshell Baptists) were also foot-washers. They had several big meetings during the summer, meetings called the Big June, Big July, etc. They were really great folk-gatherings, often several hundred people coming out of the hills and hollows, to gather about some church.

Whole families came, the young girls in their best dresses, the men shaved and bathed. They gathered in the road before the church and in near-by fields. All had brought food and everyone was invited to eat. Among the young men the moon bottle was passed back and forth.

It was a folk-movement in which all joined. People came in wagons and on horseback. They came in Ford cars and afoot. It was a great day for courting, girl meeting boy. If there was some drunkenness, it did not amount to much.

The Primitive Baptists had no paid preachers. Their preachers, like the members of the congregation, were farmers. Abe Lincoln once said that he liked a preacher who preached like a man fighting bees. He should have been there.

There was another folk-meeting that was very curious. There were no Negroes in our section. For years before I came there to build my house, there had been a tradition that no Negro was to come to live in that neighborhood. It was all right for a Negro to come for a few hours, but he was warned.

'Get out before dark. Do not let the sun go down on you in this neighborhood.'

I was told that the prejudice against the Negro had sprung up because of labor trouble. When lumbering in that district was at its height, there had been a strike and Negroes had been brought in to break it.

The mountain men had run them off with guns. It had set up a tradition.

And then, besides, my neighbors had before the Civil War never been slaveholders. Like the men of eastern Tennessee they had been Union men. Perhaps they felt that the Negro was in some way to blame for all the trouble and hardship brought on by the war. Some of the older men had been forced into a war they didn't understand. Government had long been to them a thing far off.

They got no benefit from it. Roads were poor and there were always Government men interfering. They sent in men to stop their liquor-making. They wanted to collect taxes.

'For what?'

What had Government ever done for them?

There was this feeling about the Negro, but there was a summer Sunday every year when it was set aside.

It was a Nigger Meeting Sunday. On that day the Negroes from all the low valley country to the north and south came to a neighboring high mountain-top. They held services there. They preached and sang all day long.

And the Negro congregations came. They were on the mountain-top with the white mountain men, women, and children. All sang together. All together walked up and down in the road. On that day, Negroes and whites fellowshiped together.

Life in the hills was changing. In a few years after I came into the hills to live, a paved road was built over our hills. I passed through Trout Dale. Big cars began running over the mountains. A garage was built, and there were two or three bright shining filling stations. The people of the hills had long been snuff-dippers, but the younger generation stopped dipping. They went down into the valley town to the movies. A few radios were bought. In the road I saw a woman of twenty-five. She had been reading some woman's magazine, had bought a cheap model of a dress of the latest New York style. Her lips, her cheeks, and even her fingernails were painted, but she still had a snuff-stick protruding from a corner of her mouth. It was a new world came into the hills and I was a part of it.

There was an old woman lived on a side road near my house. She had a little farm, her man was dead, and she with her young daughter worked the farm. She was something rare to me, and often I went to visit her, to sit with her in the evening on the porch of her little un-painted mountain cabin. She was one who proved something to me.

In the South I had been hearing much talk of aristocracy. I had not heard it among the mountain people, but, when I went down into the more prosperous valley town where later I ran the local newspaper, I heard much of it. It seemed to me to be always connected with the former ownership of slaves, with the ownership of rich valley land and money in the bank. To tell the truth, I had grown a little weary of the talk of Southern aristocracy and had been asking myself a question.

'But what is an aristocrat?'

I thought I had found one in the hills. It was my little old woman neighbor. She had pride. She seemed to feel no one below her, no one above her. She was very poor. She worked hard. Her little thin bent old body was all hardened by toil. When I had first come into her neighborhood, she had come to see me, and what poise she had had.

She had heard I was a writer of books.

'Mr. Anderson,' she said, 'I guess we are glad enough to have you come in here and build your house. You do not seem to us an uppity man, but I thought I had better come and warn you. They tell me you are a writer of books, but, Mr. Anderson, we cannot buy any books. We are too poor and, besides, Mr. Anderson, there are a lot of us who cannot read and write.'

It was a summer day, and my neighbor, the little old woman, was going to the mill.

She was going to have corn ground for flour and went along the road past my new house half-bent double with the load on her thin old shoulders.

I called her in.

'You are tired,' I said. 'Come and sit with me for a spell.'

Now my house was half-completed. Workers were scrambling up walls of stone.

We sat on a bench and I made a gesture with my hand.

'Tell me what you think of it,' I said. 'Do you not think it is going to be a beautiful house?'

'Yes,' she said. Her old eyes were looking steadily at me, and again she said she did not think I was an uppity man.

'I guess we are glad enough to have you come in here and build your house,' she said. She mentioned the fact that I was giving men work. They earned cash money working for me.

'But there is something else,' she said. 'We were all poor together in this neighborhood before you came.'

So I had set up a new standard of life, had changed things, perhaps I was profoundly disturbing a way of life that had had its own values. I could not answer the old woman. I sat looking at the ground by my own feet. What she had said had sent a queer wave of shame down through my body.

There was another arch of stone to be built in my house. It was a puzzle to us. However, we laid it out in the yard in the apple orchard behind the uncompleted house and built a wooden frame for it.

As I have said, we had no tools and there were no stonecutters, so my neighbors began bringing stones and trying to fit them into the arch. A man at work on the house would keep his eyes open as he came over the hills from his own cabin. If he saw a stone he thought might fit into the arch, he hoisted it to his shoulder and brought it along. We gradually got the arch quite complete, lying there on the ground in the orchard, and then the question arose as to which one of the men was to lay it up.

There was a good deal of controversy. Nearly all the men wanted the job, but, after a good deal of discussion, it was given to a man named Cornett.

He did a good job, and we all laid off work to watch him. The arch went up perfectly, and when it was quite completed, I went away to lunch.

Something happened. Why, I dare say the man Cornett was proud of his accomplishment. He had got hold of a chisel, may have gone off to the valley town to buy it. He carved his name in large crude letters across the face of the keystone of the arch. He did it while I and all the others were at lunch, and when I returned I was furious.

I began swearing in a loud voice. I shouted. Here was something, I thought, that we had all had a hand in doing and this man had slapped his name on it. The keystone had been specially selected. It had a beautiful face. It was ruined.

I kept on ranting and raving and all the other workmen gathered about. There were shy grins on many faces.

As for Cornett, he said nothing. He went out of the room into the yard, and when I came out there he stood with his coat on and his lunch-pail in his hand.

'I want to talk with you. Come on down the road with me,' he said.

'He is going to give me a beating,' I thought. We walked in silence along the road until we came to a bridge. I had begun to be ashamed of some of the things I had said to him. When he spoke, he spoke quietly enough.

'I'll have to quit you,' he said. 'I can't work on your house any more.'

He explained that it was because all of the others would have the laugh on him.

'All right, I made a mistake. Next Sunday, when none of the others are here, I'll come back and cut my name off the stone. But I'll tell you what you should have done — if you felt you had to bawl me out, you shouldn't have done it before the others. You should have taken me aside. Then I could have stayed on here.'

The man Cornett stood on the bridge looking at me. After all, he had done a fine job in laying up the arch.

'Let's see, you write books, don't you?' he asked. I said I did.

'Well, when you have written a book you sign it, you put your name on it, don't you?' he asked.

He had me there. I had nothing to say, and with a slow grin on his face he walked away.

We had got near to the end of our job. The walls were up and the roof was on my house, but there was the question of getting it plastered.

And then a man came, from some distant town, who was a professional plasterer.

He was quite frank.

'I'll tell you,' he said. 'I am a good man at my job, but I get drunk, and when I get drunk I stay that way.

'You'd better keep liquor away from me,' he said; and so I called the men together.

It was agreed that no one would give him a drink.

'We'll wait until the job is done, and then we'll give the fellow a real sendoff.'

So the plastering was started and presently all was done except one room. I went away to town.

It was late afternoon when I came back, and there was a scene I'll not forget. Ball later explained that they had all thought they could get a start on the celebration while they were doing the last room, but the moon liquor they had secretly brought for the occasion must have been very potent.

The craftsman instinct in all the men had taken control of them. There was a scaffold in the room and one by one they had all climbed up onto it. As they did this, they had kept taking drinks of the moon and the plaster was already, when I arrived, a foot deep on the floor. It was in their clothes, in their hair, in their eyes, but they did not mind.

'Now you let me try it, Frank.'

One by one they kept climbing to the scaffold.

Several of the men had fallen from the scaffold, and when I got there two of them were lying in the soft mess on the floor. They were shouting and singing. They were boasting of their skill.

'Come on, Anderson. You try your hand at it,' they shouted when they saw me standing at the door of the room.

And so I went away. There was nothing else to do. I left them at their game and, on the next day, nothing being said, they all came back to clean up the mess they had made.

My house was my house. It is true that I had to go on a lecture tour to pay for having it finished and, when it was finished, I had to close it for two years, being unable to support living in it. But there it was.

It was a place for my books. It was a place to come and to bring my friends. It was, I thought, a beautiful house, and in building it I had got into a new relationship with my neighbors. They were John and Will and Pete and Frank to me, and I was Sherwood to them. I was no longer a man apart, a writer, a something strange to them. I was just a man, like themselves. I had a farm. I planted corn and kept cows. They had found out that I was far from the millionaire they had at first taken me to be, and I had found my land.

XIII. TOWNS, HO!

The American Small Town

The American Small Town

I have just returned from another of my periods of wandering over America visiting many states, talking to farmers out on the wide plains of Texas and little Southern cotton-patch farmers, going to many cities, going in and out of many, many towns. Now here I am back in my own town and happy.

Familiar walks to be taken, roads to be driven over in the car, familiar faces to be seen on the street! Places to be visited, certain country roads that lead up into the hills, spots by the river bank . . .

The shapes of the hills about our town, the little bunches of trees on certain hills . . . I am a confirmed small-towner, and you know how all we small-towners feel about our town, our pride in it, our belief that it is the best town on earth, our hopes for its future. With me it's a case of love. You can see the beauty of many women and yet love only one. Perhaps I am in love with my own town of Marion and my Virginia country because I have been here for a long time now. I realize the same thing might have happened to me in Kansas, in Georgia, or Connecticut. Love of a town and a countryside, like love of a woman, may be a matter of proximity. Whatever the reason, my town and countryside seem especially beautiful to me.

Perhaps only a passionate traveler like myself can realize how lucky he is to be able to call a small town his home. My work is constantly calling me away from Marion, but I always hunger to get back. There is in the life of the small town a possibility of intimacy, a chance to know others — an intimacy oftentimes frightening, but which can be healing. Day after day, under all sorts of circumstances, in sickness and health, in good fortune and bad, we small-towners are close to one another and know each other in ways the city man can never experi-

ence. A man goes away and comes back. Certain people have died. Babies have been born. Children of yesterday have suddenly become young men and women. Life has been going on. Still nothing has really changed. On the streets, day after day, mostly the same faces. There is this narrow but fascinating panorama. In a way it is too intimate. Life can never be intimate enough.

I

There is a long letter on my desk from a young man. Something I have written and that has been published has upset him. He is one of the young men you meet everywhere now. He has a burning desire to remake life, the whole social scheme. He is a little fretful and angry at me because I like the Oak Hills, the smaller scenes, because I have doubts about the ends to be achieved by trying to be a big thinker, a mover of masses of men.

He scolds at me. I had somewhere said something about the necessity nowadays of staying put. In saying that, I had in mind staying closer home in our thoughts and feelings. The big world outside now is so filled with confusion. It seemed to me that our only hope, in the present muddle, was to try thinking small.

It must be that the young man who has written the letter to me feels that he has something great to give to the world. In his letter he speaks of the rapidity with which men now move from place to place. I had, in what I had written, spoken about the advisability of a man's wanting to live fully, at the beginning, in a small way; trying, for example, to get a little better understanding of the people in his own house, in the street on which his house stands; trying to get closer to the people of his own town.

It had seemed to me, as I wrote, that a man like Lincoln must have begun like that. With what strange sadness he left the then small town of Springfield, Illinois, to become President. There was a little speech made to the people of the town at the railroad station when he left, and it is one of the most moving things in literature. As you read, you feel Lincoln was a man who grew like a tree, beginning small, getting keen understanding of the little life about him, and emerging into the large.

The young man who has written to me says that he is going off to New York City. He feels that he must get among other intellectuals, bigger people than he finds in his home town, people who have bigger thoughts, vaster dreams. He declares that the day of the individual has passed, that now we must think of people only in the mass. A man must learn to love and work for the masses.

The proletariat, the middle class, the capitalist class! A man is no longer just a man going along, trying a little to cultivate his own senses, trying to see more, hear more. That day has passed now. The young man feels that Oak Hill is not big enough for the big life he says he feels in himself. It may be that I am being unfair to him. It seems to me that a man like Lincoln would still have been Lincoln had he never left Springfield, Illinois; that he grew naturally, as a tree grows, out of the soil of Springfield, Illinois, out of the people about him whom he knew so intimately.

It seems to me that he grew out of a house, a street, a shabby little country lawyer's office; out of his touch with the common men he met in the little country courtrooms; and that all this made him the man he became.

Such a man was not thinking, I am sure, of masses of men, the middle class, the proletariat, etc., but of other individuals about him everywhere. You will remember how angry he made some of the Civil War generals. There were country boys who went to sleep on picket duty, or grew afraid and ran away before a battle. The generals declared such boys must be shot, but Lincoln wouldn't agree. He kept pardoning them. They kept declaring he was bringing ruin to the big things, the army, the State; but he did not ruin the army or the State. In the end he saved the State.

He kept seeing the country boy as some country boy he had known. His mind and his heart functioned that way.

It may be that there is a bigness every man should seek, but the world is full now of false bigness, men speaking at meetings, trying to move masses of other men, getting a big feeling in that way; there's a trickiness in that approach to others — through applause, feeling a false power and importance.

The Oak Hills are too small for such men. Their own houses are too small. They must have a great field, millions of men as listeners to their voices.

The young man who wrote is half-angry with me because I said to him, 'Why not Oak Hill? What's the matter with Oak Hill?'

He can't wait for the slow growth of understanding of others in such a small place. That is what he says.

He says that he is going to New York and that in the great city he will learn to give himself to others.

He declares he can't do it in Oak Hill, that he isn't understood there. He feels cramped.

But as I read his letter, I kept asking myself over and over the same question:

'What's the matter with Oak Hill?'

I kept remembering that when Lincoln left Springfield, he asked his partner in a country law office to leave his name on the sign hanging out of the office window. He dreamed of coming back and taking up his old life in a small circle.

It must have been his ability to move and feel and live within the small scene that made him so effective in the larger place and that has left him such a vivid figure in our minds.

All of the big world outside was just more and more Springfield to him.

What's the matter with Oak Hill?

Why not Oak Hill?

II

The small town has always been the backbone of the living thing we call America. There is the New England town with its elms and town meetings, in its atmosphere something a little static, even a little pinched. From these tight little towns, with houses set close to the ground, and small stony fields enclosed within stone walls, there came the Adamses, the Emersons, the Thoreaus, indeed the intellectual life of practically all America, the tone that spread out over America. Something there — perhaps the hard stony soil — made life go up into the head, into the brain, made men look at something behind and beneath life, the transcendental, rather more than at life itself, and created a reticent puritanic attitude that for a long while affected the tone in thousands of towns scattered over the Middle West, till out of the place of deeper, richer soil the courage of another, closer approach came into us . . .

Perhaps it is that the small town lies halfway between the cities whence we get the ideas and the soil whence we draw the strength. Perhaps it is that the small-towner remains closer than does the city man to the source of the food he eats, to the ground on which it grows. The hunger for the soil is rooted deeply in man. As George Ade once remarked, 'Our city skyscrapers are filled with men dreaming of some day owning a farm and going into the chicken-raising business.' The small-towner can satisfy this hunger. He may own a farm, perhaps have moved into town from one. A surprising number of small-town men do own farms, merchants, doctors, lawyers. In a few minutes' run, they are out of town. It is a rare small-towner who nowadays doesn't own some kind of a car. Where do you suppose all the second-hand cars go? Even in his town the small-town man knows the farmer . . .

Out of the small towns in any case have come most of our governors of states and great numbers of our poets, thinkers, soldiers, and statesmen: besides Abraham Lincoln, R. W. Emerson, Thomas Edison, Mark Twain, Robert Fulton, John Quincy Adams, Robert E. Lee, Stonewall Jackson, William Tecumseh Sherman, U. S. Grant, Susan B. Anthony, Grover Cleveland, Walter Rede. Many names could readily be added to the list.

There has been a new pattern being made in the American towns. In the towns man in his groping, blundering way has been making a new race compounded of all the races of the Old World. The American mixture of many bloods grows constantly into a definite new race.

Do you remember when you, now for so long a city man, your hair graying, were a small-town boy, and what the railroad meant to you? Did you dream of some day being a railroad engineer?

With the coming of that railroad there was a new influx of strange people. England no longer was sending her emigrants here. They went out to England's own colonies. The great Irish immigration began, the Germans came in hundreds of thousands, the Danes, the Swedes, the Norsemen, the Finns came.

It was the great period of building, of town-making, the men of
northern Europe pushing up into Wisconsin, Minnesota, the great
Northwest, to become lumbermen there, new farmers and town workmen, makers of more towns.

Then the Italians, Greeks, men of all southeastern Europe. Mexi-
cans came up into the Southwest, the Asiatics into the Pacific Coast
country. The sons and daughters of all these learning to speak English, helping us in the making of a new language, the American language.

All over America, in the towns, we speak the English language,
but the stream of English blood in us grows thinner and thinner. It
has been growing thinner ever since the Revolutionary War.

The new race can be seen, studied, understood best in the towns. In
the cities, the new people as they came in tended to group themselves.
There was a German section, an Italian, a Chinese, a section filled
with men from southeastern Europe.

In the small town this couldn't happen. The men who went out
along the railroads settled in the towns, became a part of the life of
the whole town. The new America was made there. It is still being
made there.

You can count them by the thousands, now, the small American
towns. Long since, the telephone, automobiles, and the new roads
came in. Even in the great stretches of desert beyond the Rockies,
where the towns, often dead enough, old mining towns, lie a hundred
miles apart and old men loaf about clinging to a forlorn hope that the
great days of Virginia City, Tonapah, and Goldfield will come again;
even in the desert, you will now find paved roads with cars spinning
along at sixty, seventy, eighty miles an hour. Everywhere there is a
checking-up, a groping in new worlds of thought and feeling, with
government and world crises no longer something far away. A radio
is in almost every man's house. The President is speaking. Walter
Winchell is speaking. A Hill-Billy band is playing or a famous conductor. The market-place comes into the sitting room of small frame
houses in the towns with its toothpaste and hair-restorers along with
the war in Europe, Africa, and Asia, trade with South America, the
Nazis, the Soviets, and democracy. The Yanks have beaten the White

Sox. The old quiet sleepiness at evenings in the towns is quite gone. Most of all, the changes are due to the coming of the factories.

Factories are still going out more and more from the cities into the towns. They do it often enough in the hope that for a few years more they may avoid the inevitable struggle with organized labor. Country boys group together and pay each his share of the expense of a second-hand car to haul, often six or eight of them, to town for the day's work in some factory. The factories have long since gone into the Southern towns. Go by car from Atlanta, Georgia, to Charlotte, North Carolina, along the big paved highway and for more than a hundred miles you will never be out of sight of a factory chimney. Millions of new bobbins are spinning the cotton of the South in Southern towns. At night the gleaming thousands of windows of factories are writing a new strangeness and a new kind of beauty across the skies of Southern nights. There is the moon, the stars, and these new millions of small new squares of light in the darkness. We still think of the South as a place of great mansions with white pillars at the front and singing Negroes in the cotton fields surrounding it. But now there are these mills in thousands of Southern towns. Often they are built outside the limits of the old towns. Mill villages are built by factory-owners. All over the South the great change has come. In Alabama, the steel center, there are towns in the hollows of the hills like those of Pennsylvania, West Virginia, Ohio, Illinois. A new South has long since come into existence.

For a long time little new blood had come into the South because of slavery. The towns were less important in the lives of the people there. Some of the smaller Southern towns have remained quite miserable shabby little places. There is a cotton gin. Often the main streets of the town are unpaved, and life in such towns, where often of a Saturday night there are three Negroes to one white person on the streets, remains pretty heavy and dull for whites. The Negroes do better. No matter how hard their lives, they can laugh. They make a joyful, dancing, singing thing of their religion. Sometimes, because of the dullness of their lives in these isolated little places, the whites break forth into a kind of madness. A Negro is lynched; something asserted against the ugly dullness of life, because of man's need of asserting himself.

But fewer and fewer such ingrown places remain. There is the industrial South, and the upper South, all the western and southwestern section of Old Virginia, Kentucky, Tennessee, and the southeastern part of Missouri. The towns in this section have become market towns for a tobacco-growing country. In the northern sections of these states, and often in wide stretches of the so-called Piedmont, there are rich farming lands, the farmers, like the men of the Middle West, often working their own lands; and the towns among them are prosperous. And in Texas, that empire thought of as a part of the South, but really neither Northern nor Southern, the desolate little towns of the Old South are not to be found. Texas towns are often bright, shining places. You get a feeling of well-being. Texas oil is flowing out of the ground. There are vast fields worked by machinery, often great stretches of barren hill country — sagebrush and cactus — and at the same time great stretches of rich black farmed land. Fields of black-waxy soil running away to the far horizon, the farm buildings in the distance mere dots on the horizon.

But now the inflow of new blood is stopping. So, too, is the old recklessness. There was so much richness on the continent that man could waste the forests, the mines, waste the richness of the soil. Now even the towns feel the problem of a corporate life more persistently than heretofore. They are no longer naïve but awake. Still, blundering and groping, the process of renovation and amalgamation goes on in them; babies being born; lads with their lassies in cars parked under trees; hopes and dreams; the life in the towns still more leisurely; the problem of living with others a little closer, more persistently present. The real test of democracy may come in the towns.

III

Our cities are made up of former small-towners.

It has long been a legend that every American small-town boy dreams of some day going away to live in the city. He is supposed to look wistfully at the racing trains passing often without stopping through his little town. Now the new streamline trains go whirling through the towns at eighty, ninety, a hundred miles an hour. There is the soft purr of a mail plane far overhead. He hungers to see the wonders in the world, to be an important figure out there.

New things, new dreams in the heads of the boys of the towns.

However, all boys do not leave their home towns. The boy whose father owns a grocery clerks in his father's store and later becomes a grocer. Or he goes away to college and comes back, sets up in his town as a doctor or lawyer. All his life he goes up and down along the same small-town streets, past the same houses, meets the same men and women. The grown people he sees daily he knew when he wore his first pair of long pants, when he began going to the town school. Like the others, when he was a boy he fell in love with a little girl who lived on his street.

He was afraid to speak to her. He trembled when he passed her on the street. When she was about, he began to show off, wrestled with other little boys in the school yard. He became furiously jealous of another and bolder boy who could walk right up to the girls, speak to them, who could give some girl a bite of his apple.

The town boy grows up, suddenly becomes a young man, begins going about with a small-town girl, takes her to church and to dances and to the moving pictures. He takes her for a ride in the evening in his father's car and presently they are married. They have children.

Friendships are formed. There were two young men, who had known each other since boyhood, seen walking about together evening after evening. They talked. It may be that, after the beginning of such a friendship, between two small-town young men, one of them later went away to some city. His name was mentioned in his small-town paper.

'Ed Horner has gone to Chicago' (or it may be New York or Cleveland or Boston or St. Louis). 'He is about to accept a lucrative position in the city.'

If we take the local editor's word for it, all the small-town boys get lucrative positions.

Such a young man may spend the greater part of his life in the city. All his life he will remember the first day or night of his arrival in the city, the strange fear of the vast crowds of people pressing in on him. A kind of terror came. There were too many people. How could he ever find friends, comrades, make a place for himself in the vast herd?

He does not forget his small-town friend. He will, all his life, remember vividly every house along the streets on which his father's house stood. It may be that, as a city man, he will never again form another friendship that will mean to him quite what his remembered small-town friendship meant.

It was with that friend of his youth that he discussed all of his early problems and dreams. To him he confessed his first love, with him smoked his first cigarette, took his first drink of beer. How vividly he remembers the night when he and his friend went together to a near-by larger town! There was something they both wanted intensely or thought they wanted. They went together to a certain notorious house, stood trembling and ashamed before the house, and then came away. They hadn't the courage to enter.

'Gee, Harry, I haven't got the nerve, have you?'

'No, Jim, I guess I've lost my nerve.'

There remains for the city man, raised in an American small town, the memory of the sharing of the experiences, the dreams, the disappointments of youth. He remembers the time he and his friend went with the town ball team to play a team in a neighboring town. Together as boys they discussed the mysteries of life, of death, of love, of religion.

'Do you believe in God? What do you think, Harry?'

'Well, I don't know, John. When a fellow looks up at the sky at night —'

The city man remembers vividly his small-town school-teacher, the place where he with the other town boys built a dam in the creek to make a swimming hole. If he comes from a Southern small town, he remembers a Negro boy with whom he went hunting coons or 'possum at night. The Northern boy remembers the hills on which he went bob-sledding, the ponds on which he learned to skate. There was always another boy who could outskate him, who could cut figure eights and other fancy strokes. When he tried it, he kept falling.

Some times the city man, remembering an old hunger, returns to the town of his youth. He walks about the streets.

The town seems strangely changed to him. It is a constant shock to him that the people of his town have also grown older.

There is a gray-haired man he remembers as a slight youth who played shortstop on the baseball team. Perhaps the main street of his town has been paved since he was a boy. The whole town seems to have shrunk in size. He remembers the long journey when, as a child, he first set off to school. Now it seems but a step from the house where he spent his childhood to the school building.

The city man returning thus to his home town has always a feeling of sadness. He resents the changes in the town, the fact that people of the town have grown older as he has, that strangers have come in.

During all his life in the city, the small town of his boyhood has remained home to him. Every house in the town, the faces of people seen on the street in his boyhood, have all remained sharply in his mind. How clearly he remembers the hill above the waterworks pond, where he, with a troop of other boys, went along a path beside a wheat field to the town swimming hole! He remembers the way the wind played in the wheat. If he is a Southern boy, he remembers the fall days when he gathered persimmons, the fires under the kettles where sorghum molasses was being made at night, Negro women skimming the yellow green froth off the boiling juice.

Or the night when he with a boyhood friend walked home together from a dance or from a spelling bee at a country schoolhouse, the dusty dirt road along which they walked, the wind in the tall fall corn, the rustling sound when the wind played among the broad dry corn leaves, rubbing them together and making a sound like ghosts running whispering through the corn.

He remembers the town's haunted house, the night when he and several other town boys played 'follow-your-leader' and a daring boy led them into the town graveyard.

He is shocked, half-wishing he hadn't returned. 'It would have been better to let my dream, my memory, alone,' he thinks.

But there is a realization in him also that the city in which he has been living for years is made up of men who have come from small towns, who remember vividly the intimacy of life in the towns, who have remained, during all the years of their life as city men, at heart small-towners. Also that city is made up of an infinite number of small towns.

There is something reached for, wanted also by the city-born fellow — to be known and recognized by the clerk in the neighboring drug store, the near-by A. & P., or the news-dealer at the corner. The city man wants also to be known and recognized by the waiters in the restaurant where he goes for his noonday lunch.

It is the old hunger for intimacy.

IV

Actually the man under forty now living in the American small town is living a life that would have seemed as strange as some fictional life on the planet Mars to his father when he was a young man. There was a time, remembered by many older living men, when the American small town had perhaps one telephone, when the receipt of a telegram frightened the citizen to whom it was addressed. Telegrams were sent only in case of death or desperate illness.

The change in the mere physical aspect of life in the towns has gone on at an accelerated pace. The time of the coming of the bicycle that was followed by the automobile and the coming of hard-surfaced roads, pavements laid down in small towns and sewer systems installed. The paved roads crept out in all directions, found their way into isolated coal-mining towns, into the hill country that in the East and Middle West separates the North from the South, reached out across the Great Plains, the mountains and the deserts, to the Far West. When the first of the hard-surfaced roads were built, road engineers placed the grades and curves for a car speed of only twenty-five or thirty miles an hour.

The Model Ts poured out of the great Ford factories. They were in every town, on every country road. The men and boys of the towns became Ford-conscious as in our day they have become air-conscious. The old landmarks of the towns, the blacksmith shops, the livery stable, the carriage-builders' shops, went rapidly out of business, the livery stable being replaced by the garage and the gas filling station. The old isolated life of the towns came to an end. The boy or man of the small town, for whose father it had been a great adventure to go for a day to a neighboring town ten miles away, could now cover hundreds of miles in a few hours.

The great mail-order houses came into existence and grew into gigantic institutions, posing a new problem for the town merchants. A hill girl, in a little mountain town of Kentucky, East Tennessee, or West Virginia, began to use lipstick, to wear low-priced editions of the latest fashionable city clothes. Occasionally a traveler in the hills met on the mountain roads a hill girl, coming into a mountain town, all dolled up thus, but with a snuff-stick in the corner of her mouth.

The chain stores came to the towns. They were owned outside the

towns and in many cases the manager of the store was from the outside. The managers were shifted frequently from town to town. The
chain store did little or no banking in the town, the day's receipts being sent away to a central office in a distant town.

In many towns the same chain-system store, hundreds of thousands,
even millions of small-town men driving the same automobile. The
old-fashioned, individualistic daily newspaper disappeared. Newspaper
editors like Horace Greeley, James Gordon Bennett, and the later
Henry Watterson, men who had individual replicas all over America,
vanished. The dailies coming into the towns, the dailies in the towns,
became more and more alike, all served by the same news service. The
same newspaper columnists wrote for many newspapers that circulated
through the towns. The small-towner reads a city newspaper, listens
to a radio.

Even before the coming of the automobile and the modern development of industry, there were sore spots, factory workers sitting in the
sun by the factory gate at the noon hour and grumbling about the
boss, an occasional badly organized strike. There was the story of the
Knights of Labor and the Homestead strike in steel, some of the
small-town young men, of neighboring Middle Western States, having
joined the local militia, marching off to help put down the strike and
coming back to their towns later to tell the story.

In some of the Western mining and lumber towns the I.W.W.
fought grimly. They went among the wheat harvesters in the West
and the Northwest. In the Pennsylvania, West Virginia, Kentucky,
Ohio, and Illinois mining towns, the struggle went on year after year,
but in the greater number of American small towns the labor struggle
was a thing outside the life of the towns, something to be read about
in city newspapers. The small towns were marketing centers, shipping points, each with its farm-trade territory.

Then the New England textile industry began to move into the
South. There were many reasons for the movement. It brought the
industry closer to its source of raw materials.

And there was the vast unused mass of labor, the so-called 'poor
whites.' Theirs was an old and often a desperate story. They were
the leftovers of a civilization founded on Negro slavery, the 'peculiar'
institution of the Old South, that, as Abraham Lincoln pointed out,
had degraded the idea of labor among the whites. There were these

poor whites, often called 'trash,' even by the slaves, white men who hadn't managed to rise in their world, own land and slaves, nevertheless making up the great majority of the men in the ranks during the long bitter American Civil War.

Reconstruction had done little or nothing for these people, and for generations they had been trying to scratch out a living, as tenant farmers, often on worn-out soil. Although they were a miserably poor people and were often illiterate, some of them bore names once counted among the big Southern landowning, slaveowning families.

The poor white families moved eagerly into the mill towns. The mill itself and the company-owned mill town were built outside the corporate limits of an older town. The workers, men and women, and for a long time even the children of eight, ten, or twelve, who went to work in the mills, had never heard of labor unions. Vast numbers of them were illiterate.

In the mining towns in many states, labor had long been more conscious. Miners work in small groups in rooms far down underground. Their lives depend upon each other. A kind of brotherhood springs up. The struggle between the miners and the mine-owners had gone on year after year, for generations. Often it flared up into open battles, the miners with their guns, and mill guards employed by the mine company, shooting it out. It was guerrilla warfare, sometimes carried on for long months at a time, miners with their rifles lying out on the wooded hills above the mines to pick off the mine guards. Often the state militia was brought in. A Pennsylvania mine-owner declared that God had intended certain men to own and profit by the mines. A few great leaders of labor came up out of the ranks of the miners. In certain counties in rich coal-mining sections of West Virginia, Kentucky, and Illinois, when a stranger came into one of the little mining towns, he was warned:

'While you are in this town and if you want to keep a whole skin, better keep your mouth shut about unions. We don't stand for no union talk here.'

There came the crash of '29, followed by the coming of the New Deal. Labor all over America came into a new consciousness.

There was a sudden shifting, a quick change of front. Industry, in the big industrial centers, was suddenly faced with a new labor problem. For the first time in the history of organized labor in America, Government began to stand back of labor in its right to organize.

The towns were eager to get new industries. In many towns, in many states, bonuses were offered. The towns raised the money to build factories, they furnished free water, free electricity. Often the industries were offered freedom from town taxes.

The labor struggle became and has been a part of the life of many small towns. Labor organizers came in. In a North Carolina town, where the speed-up had been introduced into a small mill and an efficiency man hired to time the movements of the workers, there was a sudden outbreak. The workers in the little mill suddenly revolted. Men and women, made nervous and half-hysterical by the presence of the man with the stop-watch timing all their movements, suddenly picked up stools and sticks. Women with scissors in their hands and men with their arms full of mill bobbins pursued a frightened efficiency man through the mill yard and through the main street of the town.

In another town the workers, being all deeply religious people, prices of food and clothing having gone up, feeling terribly the need of higher wages, went and knelt before the mill gate to pray.

The little stocking factories, factories making men's shirts and womens' garments, came to such a town, stayed as long as they could keep wages down, and then, as the workers became conscious and began to organize, they departed. . . .

When the first World War came, the younger men rushed to enlist. The small-town boys remembered the romantic stories that had come out of the Civil War, the war that has become to Americans what the Trojan Wars were to the old Greeks. They returned from a new kind of mechanized war, out of which no great heroic individuals could possibly come. It was something new, strange, infinitely horrible. Only the fliers, far up in the air above the battles, could become individual heroes.

Then came the boom days, during and following the war, the famous crash of '29, well-to-do farmers in the farming country for which the town had been the trade center, excited by the high prices of the boom years, going into debt for land at high prices and then going suddenly broke, small-towners going into the stock market, many of the so-called middle class of the towns jerked down to a new and lower level of living. Prohibition brought drinking into the homes of the towns as in the cities, the small-town barber shop, where formerly only men went, a place of the *Police Gazette* and shady stories, became a beauty parlor.

At the edge of every town there was a cabaret, a drinking place, and dance hall patronized by town and country, some of them innocent enough places, others pretty tough.

Into the towns, however, as into the cities there has come new frankness concerning all the aspects of life. The mysteries of sex are more openly faced and discussed. In the new generation of youth, growing up in the towns, there is a new boldness, accompanied often by a new fineness, less of an old hypocrisy. There is scarcely any aspect of the sexual life that has not loosened up. What had always gone on secretly, under the rose, is now approached more frankly and boldly. Often the frank way of facing life and its problems shocks the older people of the towns.

The people dance more. The old bans on card-playing and dancing, as evils inevitably leading to ruin, have passed, many of the older people of the towns making a sincere effort to better understand the problems of youth in our times of rapid change, to catch up with youth. As in all changes, there is a loss and a gain. Some of the intensity has gone, but so, too, has some of the terror that was part of that intensity, the superposition of moral standards, often almost viciously, the bullying of the young by the old, the old puritanic fear of play, of any expression of joy in life.

For all the loss of intensity, the greater possibility of movement, the inflow of more and more news from the outside world, the small-town life remains firm. There is a growing disinclination in the small-town man to leave the towns for the life of the cities. For a long while it went on, the flux of young life out of the towns to the cities, but with the coming of the long depression and the absence of chances for employment in the big industrial cities, there began a movement back to the towns. And modern machine-driven life has brought the land and the people of the land closer to the towns. The farmer is nearer to the towns, the thousands of farm-boys over the country who went away to some industrial center, but who have now returned to the land. Young men and women from the farms go almost nightly into the towns.

V

Something which definitely has changed in the towns is the life of the woman. Who has not heard the story of the American pioneer woman, how she went with her man into the wilderness, worked beside him, often fought beside him, bore her children without skilled medical help, worked with and for him in the newly cleared fields?

It was a hard and lonely life, and only the more hardy of the women survived. Look over old records and you will find that a surprisingly large number of early American men survived three or four wives.

There is a touch of the old life still in great stretches of the country. In little Southern towns and in towns in the mountain country that separates the North from the South, among the hill men and the so-called poor whites of the Southern coastal plains, the women, white and black, still go out of the little towns with their men to work in the fields. They make the gardens in the yards back of the little town houses, in the small communities they feed the pigs and chickens, milk the cow.

See the Southern hill man or the poor white of the South going out of one of the little towns into the fields in the early morning. There is a little procession, the woman and the children following in single file at the heels of the man. Among the Southern cotton tenant farmers, when land is let for the season, it is let, not on the basis of how much land a man can work, but on the basis of the family. The woman of such a man does not walk shoulder to shoulder with him. She trots at his heels. If the wife has a babe in arms, she takes it with her to the fields. It lies on the grass in a fence corner while all day she chops cotton or hoes corn beside her man.

In the American small town of the past there was always a cellar under every house. The fall was the great canning and storing time. Often pits were dug in the yard back of the little frame house, for burying apples, cabbages, and turnips. It was a little trench lined with straw, the apples and turnips and heads of cabbage buried in the straw and then covered with earth. Many women made their own soap. They canned, often, hundreds of cans of fruit and vegetables, sliced apples and hung them in the sun to dry. They made the clothes for their children.

In bins in the cellar under her house were piles of potatoes, pump-kins, and squash. If the woman was the wife of one of the more well-to-do men of the town, she had a sewing woman come in to live for a time with the family. The woman made clothes for the wife and the children. She made shirts for the man of the house. In an earlier day the shoemaker also came to make the shoes for the family.

And then, as it happens in America, suddenly, within a generation, everything changed. The great canneries came into existence. Why go to all the labor of canning fruit and vegetables when, often at less cost, canned food to carry the family through the winter can be had at the store? Clothes for the children, suits for the boys and dresses for the girls, could be bought at the store for less money than it cost to buy the cloth and have in a sewing woman. The clothes fitted bet-ter. It became increasingly necessary for the small-town woman or the young girl, as for her sisters in the cities, to be in the fashion.

The fashion magazines came to the small-town women as to city women. With the increased opportunity for movement brought on by the coming of the automobile, it was easier for the more prosperous small-town woman to go to the large stores in near-by cities. She did her shopping there. What had been a great adventure, something looked forward to for years and talked of for years later, a visit to some large American city became just an afternoon jaunt.

And then came the new freedom.

There was talk in the towns, as in the cities, of the rise of women. Women got the vote. More and more they pushed out of the home and began to work in factories and stores. They went into the pro-fessions and became lawyers, doctors, and even judges.

The American man had lost his grip on the American woman. His wife and daughter read Freud. They read the novels of Theodore Dreiser, Sinclair Lewis, and William Faulkner. They read Ernest Hemingway's stories. Even by the time the first world war came, they were in full flight.

. And then came prohibition, bringing drinking into the American home. It happened in the small American town as it did in the American city. There had been the town saloon with its little back room reached through an alleyway. It was the small-town man's club, the place to which he went to escape women, to be alone with other men. It was like the barber shop, a place to lie and brag and play a game of seven-up with other men.

Sometimes, earlier, a woman, accompanied by some loose-living man, slipped into the little room at the back of the saloon. Everyone in town knew about her. It was even said that she smoked cigarettes.

For that matter, even among men, the smoking of cigarettes, Sweet Caporals, was the inevitable mark of the sissy. A real man smoked cigars or a pipe.

There was a man in town who clerked in the town hotel and who smoked the things. He was called Fuzzy.

'The damn sissy, with his coffin nails.'

The lid had, however, suddenly blown off. Women were affected by the movies. They kept getting ideas into their heads. They were out to be men's equals. They got jobs, began to wear bloomers. A young high-school girl, of one of the best families in town, went with a young man to a dance and was seen taking a drink out of a bottle. Women got elected to Congress. There was even one in the United States Senate. They were on juries. They made political speeches. They read books that spoke frankly of things a man of an earlier generation wouldn't have dared whispered in the presence of a 'decent' woman. It was all very puzzling to the American man of the towns, as it was to him of the American cities. Something had got out of his hand. More and more the women of the towns, as of the cities, were pressing into the lead in fields that had formerly been exclusively men's fields. They took the lead in the intellectual and cultural life of the towns. If there was a town library established, they did it; if an orchestra was brought from the city to give a concert in the town hall or the auditorium in the high school, it was a woman who got it up; if a lecture were on the boards, some nationally known figure in the intellectual or political world coming to town to speak, the women were back of the program.

It was the women of the towns who organized clubs to beautify the towns. If there was a town park to be built, their hand was in it.

A more prosperous citizen of an American town had sent his daughter off to the state university. Secretly he thought it rather a foolish idea, but his wife insisted. And then the daughter came home for the summer vacation. She seemed a very sweet, innocent one. It was in the evening, after the evening meal and the family had gone to sit on the front porch, darkness coming, birds chirping sleepily in near-by trees. They were just sitting there, and then the daughter, taking a cigarette case out of her purse, lit a cigarette.

'Have one, Dad?' she asked.

It was just plain nonsense, worse than that. It was terrible, a knocking over of all the old standards of life.

And she did it so casually. There was a tense moment on the porch, the man's wife sitting there.

See the American small-town man. He wants to explode.

'If it was a son, I'd give him a damn good hiding,' he thinks.

But what's the trouble. A man can't give a hiding to a grown-up daughter sitting there so self-assured, smoking her cigarette.

The American man is out on a limb. He looks at his wife.

'Louise — for God's sake ——' he wants to say.

He doesn't get a chance to say it, and now his daughter is offering one of the things to her mother. Great God! she is taking it.

'Do you know, I believe I will,' she says, smiling.

So there it is — the wife, too. What is the American man to do or say?

Better go downtown, talk it over with some man friend.

'Women sure aren't what they were, but what can a man do? Let them have it. They are in the saddle. Let them ride.'

It is the story of innumerable American men, who haven't kept up with the American woman's pace, in the American small town as in the American city.

VI

Yet while there is something of an individuality to every town despite the duplication of each other from California to Maine, from Key West to Seattle, they are alike in spring.

Mr. and Mrs. Grey have spent most of the winter in a strange new kind of town somewhere in the South, a town made up of streets of trailers. Electric light wires have been strung up in its streets. Many men and women from towns of many states are living temporarily in this strange new kind of town.

In the spring the trailer town breaks up. It dissolves, ceases to be.

One by one and then in little cavalcades, the houses on wheels disappear along roads. They go away into New England towns, into the Middle West, into the far cold Northwest.

Spring has come.

In the Northern town throughout the winter months last year's rubbish lies piled in back yards of houses. There are ugly ash-piles in alleyways. During the winter the snows have come and have hidden the winter ugliness. There has been a new white world. A winter rain has turned to ice and ice clings to the limbs and branches of trees and the sun came out and scattered millions of diamonds of light over the towns.

In the smaller Southern towns mud is deep in the streets. Negroes go along the streets of bleak little Southern towns wearing shoes given them by the whites. The shoes are run down at the heels. They do not fit the feet of the Negroes, but these wear them just the same.

In New England, in the cold Northwest, men still have chains on their cars. There is an outbreak of automobile accidents. Crowds of men on relief gather about country courthouses to get the monthly pittance that keeps them alive.

Suddenly a new feeling sweeps over the town. It runs through the veins of the people. Spring — promise of spring. Robins appear and hop about on lawns before the houses. After the long winter of the North, the rain and mud of the South, the 'Northers' that sweep through Texas, Alabama, Mississippi, and Louisiana, something new comes into the air men breathe.

In the South, planting starts early. All through the Southern States men are 'burning the woods.' It is a habit they won't stop. Young trees are being killed by the fires creeping through the piney woods. It is a part of the old wasteful American way, an old notion that fire creeping through the trees makes for more young grass for the cattle. State and Government men go about telling the farmers not to do it, but it goes on year after year. On early spring evenings a haze of smoke floats over the little Southern towns. Old cotton stalks are broken down and burned. The sun goes down blood-red in the haze over Southern towns, over the red sand clay roads. Now in the turpentine forests the trees are being gashed. The white blood of pine trees falls drop by drop into little metal buckets. Fires are built in turpentine stills.

In the fields Negroes and white tenant farmers are at the spring plowing. There is the ever-amazing patient courage of man's relations to earth, felt in the towns.

Men are going through the turpentine forests gathering the sap. Negro voices lift in song under the canopy of pine trees. In New England other men are gathering the sweet sap of the sugar maples. The plowing begins far down in Texas. The plows creep northward day by day, week by week, men going out of the towns into the fields.

It is coming! Spring is coming!

The cotton crop may have been poor last year, prices down, men in the towns and on the neighboring farms filled with despair. Up in the Far Northwest, east of the river in the Dakotas, the winds out of the dry farming country have burned and buried last year's corn crop. All fall and winter the people of the towns were eating dust.

See the tenant farmer of the South, with his one mule, half broken-down wagon piled with a few sticks of furniture, driving through the streets of a little Southern town. It is the annual migration. A broken stove, a tired-looking woman with a babe at the breast, other thin ragged children clinging to the wagon. A tenant farmer is going to try a new place. Man always going back to the earth, earth smells invading the towns. Heads a little held up again.

'This year we may make it.'

In the upper South tobacco seed beds, spread with white cheesecloth, appear at the edge of the woods at the town's edge. More farmers come into the towns for seeds, for new tools, for fertilizer. There is a rush of new business in the hardware store.

March, April, May. Gardening begins back of the little American frame houses in towns all over America. The town council announces a clean-up day. 'Get the old ash-piles out of the alleyways, out of the back yards. Plant flowers, study the new seed catalogues. Clean up. Spring has come.'

In New England towns the elms will presently put forth their leaves. In towns of the Middle West, in residence streets in towns in Ohio, Indiana, Illinois, Iowa, the maples bloom. They send their winged seeds whirling through the air. There is a carpet of winged seeds on the sidewalk. The women have organized a garden club. Out on the prairie you get the long vistas. You look from your house in town across the wide prairies, trains passing in the far distance, wide expanse of sky.

Spring is the time when the country comes most into the towns, is most felt in the towns. The winds bring the message from the fields into the towns.

Ed Prouse is now going up and down Main Street with a paper for people to sign. 'Put your name down for a dollar, if you are a prosperous man for two or three dollars. We want a baseball team this year. We've got to buy uniforms, bats and balls. If you are a merchant and pay for a uniform, a player will wear the name of your store printed in big letters on his uniform.'

Plant hollyhocks along the alleyways. Trim the grapevines.

'Hell, my wife is cleaning house again. A man can't find a clean shirt, can't even find his razor.'

'When the leaves on the maple trees are as big as squirrels' ears, it is time to plant corn.'

Windows of houses all over town thrown open now, bedding out on clotheslines, the new-model cars coming in, mule markets in Kentucky, Tennessee, and Missouri.

'If I can raise the price, I am going to trade in the old car this year.'

A new aliveness in the main streets of the towns, a bit more color in the windows of stores, spring terms of court in county-seat towns, a stir, an awakening, feel of earth invading the towns, smell of earth, new hope, warm spring rains, the vivid new green of grass on lawns before the houses, the children looking forward to the end of the school year, to swimming in the town's pond or in the creek, to barefoot days.

Spring is a never-ceasing wonder in the towns, the drab days gone, a new beginning. Nowadays the almost universal owning of cars takes men more and more out of the towns into the country. Town kids can't wait for the summer days to come. There are plenty of Tom Sawyers and Huckleberry Finns left in American towns. On the first sunny days there will be the daring ones who sneak off to the creek, pond, or river, plunge in, come out shivering.

'Better get your hair dry before you go home. Ma will raise cane if she finds out you've been in.'

The great thing is the annual awakening, the apple, cherry, and peach trees coming into bloom. In the towns men become for the time half farmer, earth men. There is fear of a late frost to nip the bloom, talk of that going on in the streets, in the stores, when men gather in the town post-offices for the morning mail. In the drug stores and the groceries the seed packages stand up in racks. They add a touch of color to the stores. The women gather about. Their minds are on their flower and vegetable gardens.

Hal Grimes, the house painter, is carrying on a little business on the side. In his back yard he has built row after row of boxes with glass covers, hot-boxes for plants. He puts an ad in the town paper.

'Fine tomato and cabbage plants for sale.'

Men and women are driving out to Hal's place in their cars. This is the busy time of the year for Hal, plenty of paper-hanging and painting to do, but his wife is on the job. She has put on slacks and gloves to protect her hands. She is serving out the plants.

'They say Hal makes nearly two hundred dollars out of his plant business every spring.'

Like all the other house painters and paper-hangers, Hal has his hands full. The women nag at him.

'Hal's got a mighty fine wife. It's too bad he drinks. If he could let it alone, he would be the best house painter and sign writer in town.'

You see the great drift of cars, like swallows flying north in the spring.

Tall tales being told.

'How much did it cost you to live down there?'

'I wish I could get out of here in the winter. I can't, I've got my store, I've got my law practice, I can't take my kids out of school.'

Life in the towns spreading out in a new way, the streams of cars always flowing through the towns, endless rivers of cars, American restlessness.

The spring brings the traveler back to the home nest. He also wants to plant gardens, set out trees, arrange flowers.

'A man can't let his place run down.'

Now the young blades of the town are all wanting new spring suits, the girls new spring dresses. There is a restlessness that gets into the blood. Now you see young couples on spring evenings walking slowly along streets with hands clasped together. June will be a great time for marriages.

'I want we should live together, have a house of our own, like a man and woman should.'

The young ones drive about in the family cars, sit together beside the country road, on quiet streets under the trees on moonlit spring nights, the young corn just thrusting through the earth in near-by fields — in the South in near-by fields the young cotton; problems of the young, in the towns as in the cities — how to get started, get going, set up new families, keep the old town life going.

'Sometimes I think I'll have to join the army, get out of here.'

'Gee, I'd hate that, Jim. I'd miss you so much.'

In every town there is the slipshod, lazy man who won't clean up his place in the spring. He is slovenly and has a slovenly wife. His back yard is full of old broken boxes and tin cans. He won't clean it up. He is an individualist.

'Hell, I've got the spring fever. Whether I clean up my yard or not is my own business.'

And then there is the town tough. All through the year he gets drunk and into fights. He spends half his time in the town jail. He won't work. He lives with his mother who has a small pension. She is the widow of a soldier. All summer, fall, and winter, he loafs about, bullies his mother for a little money so he can get drunk and into trouble, but in the spring something happens to him.

He gets shaved, gets a haircut. He works in the garden. He declares he is going to begin a new life. 'I'm going to cut it out,' he says. Every spring he reforms and his reform is a new surprise and wonder to his neighbors. He keeps it up for a week, two weeks, a month, and then it ends. His year's work is done. Older people check the seasons by him.

'I see Bill Kline has got a shave. I saw him spading his mother's garden. Spring is here again.'

It is the time of new hope in the towns, the ever-recurring miracle, changing the face of the towns. East, West, North, and South, the song of new life up out of the soil, in the towns men coming out of their walled-in winter life, strolling in the town streets, neighbor calling to neighbor.

'Spring is here.'

New gladness in the voices of young and old.

Another spring.

'Spring is here.'

VII

And whether it is spring or fall, summer or winter . . .

Listen! bells are ringing, whistles blowing. Small boys rush with joyous shouts along the streets. Older people are running out of their houses. Voices call along the streets.

'Fire! Fire!'

'Where is it? Where is it?'

In the cities, as in the towns, the fire trucks go clanging through the streets, but in the cities they disappear into the traffic. You stand looking for a moment and then go on about your own affairs. The city is too vast for the meaning of the fire alarm to come close to you. There may be a few privileged ones, like Mayor La Guardia of New York City, 'The Little Flower,' who can rush off to a fire in a special police car, but for the man in the street the fire truck gives but a passing thrill.

In the American small town it is another matter. Every house, garage, store building, in the town is familiar. We small-towners know the owners, we know who lives in every house in our town. When the fire bell clangs, the sound runs down through our bodies. There is a quick, sharp spasm of fear.

'Can it be my own house?'

What a relief!

'It is Ed Wyatt's house, not mine.'

Most American towns now have their own big red fire trucks, just like the cities, but there are towns, the little places, that still have the old kind. Some of them must still be hauled through the streets by hand. In the little crossroad places, men still form bucket brigades, men and boys standing in line, water passed from hand to hand from some near-by well or a small stream. There aren't many such towns left. When a real fire breaks out, the fire company comes from a near-by larger town. Only the tiny places — what George Ade called 'the kind of a town that divides two farms' — is without a fire truck.

But in practically all the towns the firemen are volunteers. There is Ernest who works in Hankley's drug store. Ernest is a small, active, alert man, now growing a little bald. He wears glasses. He is a great joiner, belongs to the Odd Fellows, the K. of P., the Masons. He was in the first World War and belongs to the Legion. On ordinary days, he just goes along, a very polite, smiling little man, not a specially important figure in the town's life, but when the fire bell or the fire whistle blows, all is changed.

'Clang, clang!'

'Clang, clang!'

The fire bell or the fire whistle is not at all like a church bell or the factory whistle. It is insistent, demanding. When the sound comes, Ernest is transformed.

He is in his drug store selling Mrs. Gray some packages of flower seeds or some bicarbonate of soda.

'I just can't get to sleep at night,' Mrs. Gray is saying. Someone has told her that the bicarbonate of soda will be of help.

Ernest thinks it will. He bows and smiles.

'It alkalizes the blood, cuts down the acid' — Ernest is up on drugs all right. He is a licensed pharmacist, went to a college in Cincinnati or in New Orleans.

'Clang, clang, clang!'

Better look out, Mrs. Gray. Ernest is as likely as not to leap right over the counter. He may knock you down. Now you do not exist for him. He passes you like a strong wind blowing. He fairly tears the front door of the drug store off its hinges. This is his hour.

Jim Watson, who is a deputy sheriff, is standing on the front steps of the courthouse across the street. He sees Ernest leap into the street. Jim is one of the town wags.

'Go to it, Ernest! Hurrah for our hero!' he shouts.

Ernest pays no attention to him. He is too absorbed, too intent on his duty. The place where they keep the big red fire truck is just around the near-by corner in a garage at the rear of the town hall. The wits of the town like to have some fun with the volunteer firemen, but the wit is not too keenly edged. They know the 'boys' are ready to turn out night or day, winter or summer; that they'll take chances, risk their lives, if necessary, to save some neighbor's property; that they are fellows with real public spirit, taking chances and getting no pay for their efforts; that they'll go out on bitter winter days and come home covered with ice; that they will take care not only of town fires but of fires on farms, often many miles out of town.

Ernest always gets to where they keep the fire truck first. He swings open the doors, grabs his fireman's helmet, his big rubber fireman's coat. He dances impatiently up and down beside the fire truck.

And now the others appear. Fred Cowley, who runs the town print shop, is the driver of the truck. His shop is also but a few doors from the town hall. Fred is a bit phlegmatic. You can't get him excited. He knows he'll be there in time, be up in the driver's seat, the engine going, ready before the others arrive for the run.

'Fred is a good one, too. The town is proud of him. He never loses his head. He can sure put the big fire truck around corners. He misses parked cars along the main street by inches.'

'I'll say he's good.'

The whole town agrees about Fred.

And there is Joe, and Sylvester, and Harry, and Fred, and Ted, and Frank, and Will, grocery clerks, drygoods clerks, young store-owners. Some of them swing aboard the truck as it heads down the main street. You see them holding on grimly while at the same time they struggle into their rubber coats and helmets. Young Mart Curry, son of the editor of the local weekly, who goes about town getting items for the paper, always waits until the fire truck is going at full speed before he gets aboard. You tremble seeing him do it. You think he's going to break his neck, but he doesn't.

And now everyone is going to the fire. People pile into cars and follow the fire truck while others follow afoot. Boys go shouting and tearing along the streets.

It's a thing in human nature. It can't be helped. It is in us all, this love of destruction. As soon as we are quite sure that it isn't our house, we can't help having a feeling of joy.

It doesn't mean we are not sorry for Ed Wyatt.

'Gee, they say he hasn't any insurance. It's tough, I'll say.'

But just the same, if it is a real blaze, a frame house, smoke and fire leaping out of windows, volunteers carrying what they can get at of Ed's household goods out into the street, Mrs. Wyatt, with two small children clinging to her skirts, running up and down in the little strip of lawn before the house and wringing her hands in agony, Ed himself keeping pretty calm, showing the town that, in an emergency, he can keep his head — just the same, it is exciting.

The small boys of the town keep getting in the firemen's way. Advice is shouted by the bystanders —— It is mean and low down. It shows the mean side of our nature, but we just can't help enjoying it.

'It's rotten that we are made that way, isn't it, Hal?'

'Yes, but I guess we just are.'

When you stop to think of it, after the big excitement is over, you remember how Ed Wyatt has worked hard and saved his money to own a house of his own for his wife and kids. Sympathy for Ed comes when you remember that.

This is Ernest's hour. He is the fire chief. Look at him now. He is magnificent.

He seems to have grown taller. Hear him giving his orders.

'Stand back there, you!' The man addressed is the town banker, the superintendent of the Presbyterian Sunday School, the biggest merchant in town. It doesn't matter to Ernest.

'Harry, you and Frank get the axes. Get up there on the roof. Cut a hole up there.'

'No, not there, over to the left. That's the place.'

Now Ernest is walking up and down giving his orders. He is like a general on a battlefield. What a man! Now you would never know him for the little smiling, bowing drug-store clerk of ordinary days. There is a new quality to his voice, something stern and commanding.

And Ernest knows his business. Ever since he was a boy, he has been making a study of fires. It is a life passion. He knows when to turn on the water, when to shut it off, when and where to cut and chop, when to use the chemical tanks.

Ernest has courage, too. He'll go in anywhere to take a look, to see what is needed. There are murmurs of admiration running through the crowd. 'I'll bet you what — if Ernest lived in a big city, he'd be the fire chief there, too.'

Sometimes, when the fire bells go clanging, it turns out to be just someone's chimney burning out, or a second-hand Ford caught afire, but too often it is a real blaze, a home-destroyer, all of some small-towner's household goods gone up in smoke, a part of the tragedy of everyday life in an American town. Word running through the streets of the town, a feeling of relief running from man to man, woman to woman.

'Ah, it was just a false alarm.'

Or, after a real fire, when the excitement is over, when the realization of what it has meant to Ed Wyatt begins to run through the people of the town, a real display of neighborliness.

There is always some neighbor to take the Wyatts in. Everyone is wanting to do what they can for Ed. People up and down Main Street and in the houses in the evening will be talking it over. Ed isn't the kind who will take money from his neighbors. He is a man proud of the fact that he can stand on his own feet. He will move into a smaller house, pick up a few sticks of furniture, start over again. Now the house that Ed worked so hard to pay for is just a mass of black broken rafters. The momentary exultation that came when the fire bell rang and when you found out it wasn't your house, the sight of the fire that releases the impulse in you that enjoys destruction of another man's property, is all gone now. It has been pushed back by the neighborly feeling that makes life in the towns what it is.

VIII

Hot summer days have come, with summer rains in the Far South, along the Gulf Coast and in the Ohio and Missouri River valleys. The hot days and the warm, sticky nights come now to the towns in the river valleys. In little Louisiana river towns and in towns along the Gulf Coast there is the loud, sustained song of insect life. A man is lying asleep in his house in a Louisiana town. Frogs croak loudly in the near-by bayous. He gets out of bed, takes the sheets off his bed, soaks them in the bathtub or under the water tap in the kitchen, and puts them back of the bed. He hopes to get to sleep while the water is evaporating, cooling the air in the room.

In the cotton country, young Negro men and women are now out in the streets at night. In the Negro section of Southern towns you hear the soft voices and the laughter of Negroes. Old Negro men and women sit on the porches of the little unpainted houses in the long afternoons and in the summer nights. At night Negro children play under the street lights.

In the Southern cotton-mill towns men and women are going in and out of the mill gate and along the hot streets of the near-by company-owned mill town. Although it may be on level ground, the mill village is always spoken of as 'The Hill.'

Our country is a land of violent changes in climate. Hot winds come up from the southwest to blow over Iowa, Nebraska, and Kansas. The hot winds cross the great river into the states of the Middle West. In the fields near the towns there is a curious rustling of the long blades of the growing corn.

Now you will hear corn talk in all the corn shipping towns of the Middle West. The hot winds do not hurt the corn. Men call to each other on the streets of the towns.

'This is corn-growing weather all right.'

It is time now for the small-town people to be out-of-doors. In most of the countries of an old European world, the summer life of the people in the towns is led in gardens back of the houses, but here, in North America, we live during the hot months at the front of the house. We live on the front porch.

When the American small-town man has daughters of courting age, the front porch of his house is delivered over to them for the summer evening. It is on the front porch daughters receive their young men callers, the mother sitting with them for a time and then disappearing. The girls have to have their chance.

The people of the towns sit in groups on their front porches. In the warm darkness, on summer evenings, there is a movement from house to house, visits made back and forth, low-voiced talk going on. But a few years ago the stores on Main Street were open until ten or eleven at night, but nowadays, with the exception of the drug store and the town restaurants, the stores are closed at six. Main Street becomes a place of strollers, of sitters in parked cars, of groups gathered for talk.

In the street older men stand about or sit on store ledges. Story-telling and political discussions go on. Ocassionally an argument develops and a fight starts. The married man of the small town is seldom at home on summer evenings. When he doesn't take the family to the movies, he gets up from the evening meal and reaches for his hat.

'I guess I'll step downtown for a while.'

'A man has to get it off his chest. There are matters you can't talk about with your woman.'

Or the mother of a family, when her children do not demand it, is out in the family car. She picks up a woman friend. They park the car on Main Street and sit and watch the life of the street. The youngsters who are not sitting on darkened porches, hand-holding, doing their courting, drift up and down the main street into the drug store and the town movie house.

In the break-up that came to America in '29, many well-to-do-men in American towns got caught. Like the city men they had gone stock-market wild. In towns all over America there were merchants, professional men, bankers, many of whom had saved carefully for years, who went into the market. They suddenly became dreamers, dreaming of getting suddenly, miraculously rich. They went down in the crash, and the sons and daughters they had planned to send to college were out looking for jobs. They help to swell the army of the jobless.

After the big break in '29, when the CCC camps began to be scattered over the country, absorbing some of the young men out of work, there were many state parks built over the country. Nowadays, when almost every American family has managed to hang on to some kind of a car, what is a matter of fifty, sixty, or even a hundred miles if you can raise the price of the gas? The car is the last thing the American family, gone broke, will part with. Some of them will sell their beds first and sleep on the floor. Car-ownership means freedom to move about, it means standing in the town life. To the young men of the towns it means you get a girl to go out with you or you don't.

The CCC boys dammed creeks, set out trees, built park benches. Boys from New York's East Side and from the big industrial towns, out of work, joined up. They went out as workers into the camps scattered over America, they made roads, made play-places for the people. City boys from industrial towns and from grim Pennsylvania mining towns got acquainted with mountains, rivers, and forests. They made friends among the small-towners in towns all over America. Older people, the more well-to-do, growled.

'Who's going to pay for all this?'

'You'll see. Now taxes will shoot up.'

'It's all foolishness, it's crazy.'

Always now, through the long summer days and through summer evenings, the rivers of cars flow through the towns. At night the headlights of the cars make a moving stream of light. If there is a big highway passing through the town, the streets are lined with tourist houses, and tourist camps have been built at the town's edge. On summer nights, as you lie on your bed in your house in the American town, you hear the heavy rumble of goods trucks. If there is a steep grade through your town, the heavily loaded trucks, in low gear, shake the walls of your house. The man, who once owned the town hardware store or who is a cashier in the town bank and went broke in '29, still owns a big brick house. There is a sign in the street before his house. 'Tourist House,' the sign says.

The girls who work in cotton mills and live in cotton-mill towns and can't afford to own cars hire a truck, crowd into it, and off they go picnicking to the woods or swimming in some lake on Saturday afternoons. Summer is the time for the circus to come to town. Even American towns of less than five thousand have golf courses and tennis courts. On Sunday afternoon the small-town man gets his car out. His wife and children pile in and they join the great parade — America on the move. The summer days won't last too long.

It is the time of mosquitoes, of summer rains, of hot, still week-days on Main Street, no coal bills, green vegetables from the gardens, roasting-ear time. Who has the first sweet corn, whose tomatoes ripen first, what girls will get married this summer? Life in the town during the long summer days and weeks relaxes. In the Dakotas and down through Kansas, Nebraska, northern Texas, and in the Far West, it is wheat-harvesting time. It is hay-cutting, wheat-harvesting time in the small farms about New England and Middle-Western towns.

Hot, dusty days, long days, summer rains — the summer days are the best of all the year's days for the American small-towner.

IX

The eccentric is a permanent figure in American life. He is in the cities as in the small town, but in the small town you know him. Curious enough characters out of life, no doubt, pass you by the thousands in the city streets, but they come and go swiftly. You do not meet them day after day in the same streets, the same stores. You do not talk with them, know intimately their idiosyncrasies.

In every American small town there is the lonely man who seldom leaves his own house. Usually he is a bachelor. He has let a high hedge grow about the yard, almost hiding his house from the street. There are always whispered stories floating about the town concerning his life in the house. It is said that as a young man he was rejected by a beautiful woman. We Americans are born romanticists. Often there are more darkly menacing tales. In his youth it is said that he committeed some mysterious crime. It may be that he came suddenly into town from another place. Year after year his house remains unpainted. The yard before the house is overgrown with weeds. The front porch is rotting away. Occasionally he is seen emerging from his house at night. He hurries furtively along streets. He continually talks to himself.

Sid Smith is the practical joker of the town. He loves to send the town's half-wit on fool errands. He sends him to the hardware store for a left-handed monkey-wrench, to the print shop to see the type lice. He is the fellow who hands out loaded cigars that blow up in your face. When he has been successful with one of his victims, he runs up and down Main Street telling the story, boasting of his cleverness.

The man who loves an argument is downtown on Main Street every afternoon and evening. When he sees a group of men talking together, he joins them. He goes from group to group, listening to talk, and when a statement is made, he immediately challenges it.

He grows angry, he shouts, he waves his arms about. His wife is always scolding him.

'Why are you always making enemies? Why do you do it?'

He doesn't know why. He keeps making up his mind that he will be calm and quiet, talk quietly to others. He can't do it. On the next day he is at it again. He would really like to be a quiet, sensible fellow, leading a quiet, sensible life.

In every town there is the woman who is always having operations. She goes from one doctor to another. Almost everything has been cut out of her. She has grown pale and walks with difficulty, but she is a proud woman. She thinks of herself as a figure in the community. There isn't another woman in town who has been through what she has, she keeps declaring. She is one who enjoys her own suffering.

And there is always that other woman, a born nurse. She is a fat, jolly soul. When someone is sick, she comes to help. She is always

Aunt Molly, or Kate, or Sarah — is everyone's aunt. She spreads cheer, has the touch.

And the school-teacher who never marries, although she was such a fine-looking younger woman. She goes on, year after year, teaching new crops of children. She has won the respect of the town, but remains, all her life, an oddly lonely-seeming figure.

Henry Horner is the town butt. He is a man of forty-five, and his wife is dead. He lives with his wife's sister in a house out at the edge of town.

Henry once had a little money and went into business. He became a chicken fancier and concocted a chick food to put on the market. He went from town to town trying to sell it, but did not succeed. He spent all his money in the venture.

Now Henry dresses shabbily and has let his hair grow long. He carries a heavy cane, and as he goes through the streets of the town boys crow at him. They imitate the cackle of hens that have been at the business of laying eggs and the clarion cry of the rooster. Henry grows violently angry. He waves his cane about, he swears, he pursues the boys furiously, but never catches them. As he passes through Main Street, some man, standing in a group of men by the post-office, also crows. Henry approaches the group. His hands are trembling. He stands before them demanding justice.

'What man of you did that?'

All the men of the group shake their heads. They look at Henry with blank faces. The town has discovered his weakness. There is a cruel streak in men. They cannot let poor Henry live his life in peace.

A young girl of the town has gone wrong early in life. Some man or boy has got her and has gone about telling the story. Other men and boys begin the pursuit. She is always lying about with men and boys, in fields near the town or in the town graveyard. Hers is a story as old as the Bible. In the town graveyard there is a crude and brutal expression of the meeting of life and death.

Thaddeus is the town's philosopher. He is respected by all the town. The word is out that he is well-read. It is even said that he knows Latin and Greek. Every evening he sits at home reading a book. His wife is a scold, but he pays no attention to her. The men of the town speak of him with admiration and envy.

'Gee, I wish I had his education.'

Thaddeus is a quiet, serene man who is deeply religious, although he never goes to church. He has worked out his own notion of God. He is a merchant, who also owns a farm near town, and is fond of young boys. He is very gentle with them. He has no children of his own, but on summer afternoons he is always taking some boy with him to his farm. Once he caught a clerk stealing money in his store. He did not discharge the clerk.

'If the money is worth more to you than your peace of mind, keep it,' he said.

He is a mystic. 'God,' he says to the boy who has ridden with him to the farm, 'is in the growing corn. He is in the trees over there in that wood, in the grass in that meadow, in the flowering weeds along the road.' The boy does not understand, but feels happy in the presence of the quiet, smiling man.

There is the town bully. He is forever boasting of fights he has won. He goes swaggering about with a half-burned cigar in the corner of his mouth. He declares he has never lost a fight.

'I'll knock your block off! I'll bust your jaw!' he is always shouting to someone. It is the traditions of the towns that he always in the end meets his match. Some smaller man, infuriated by his insults, lights into him and beats him up. It always happens, and when it does it fills the town with joy.

A mysterious woman comes to town. She appears suddenly and rents a house in a quiet residence street. She is one who keeps to herself, makes no acquaintances. When she appears in the streets, she is always well-dressed. All sorts of whispered stories about her run through the town. Young boys hear the stories and walk far out of their way going to and from school to pass her house.

The shades are always drawn, and the town is convinced that she is a wicked, sinful woman. There is a story that she has some connection with a mysterious band of robbers.

Or it is said that she is a kept woman; that she is being kept by a rich man of some distant city. A man of the town who lives on her street declares that often, after midnight, a big expensive-looking car parks before her house and a man enters. To the young boys of the town she becomes a symbol of something strange and enticing, out of some mysterious world of sin. It is said that in her house there are luxurious carpets and expensive furniture, that she wears jewels that have cost thousands of dollars. The woman stays for a time in the house and then disappears as mysteriously as she came. She also remains in the town's imagination a figure of romance.

Arthur is a thin, wiry little man who is always gay. No matter how gloomy the day, he is full of good cheer. He knows everyone, cries gaily to others as he hurries through the streets. He goes with a half-dancing step.

'Hello! Hello!'

'How are you feeling, Art?'

'Fine! Fine!'

Arthur is as full of life as a squirrel. He hops and dances. Something inside him is always singing and dancing. He is gay, alive, small, an always cheerful streak of sunlight on the town's streets.

There is the man who goes with the same woman year after year. He goes to see her every Sunday evening, takes her to church, drives about with her on week-day evenings, in his car. He is always at her house on one or two evenings during the week, sits with her on the porch of her house. He began going with her when he and she were both in high school. That was nineteen or twenty years ago. He has never paid any attention to any other woman nor has she ever been with any other man. When she began going with him, she was quite pretty, but now she begins to look a little worn. Her mother had died and she is keeping house for her father. The people of the town see the couple going about together year after year. They are a little amused. The word is out that they are engaged. Nothing happens. He just continues to go with her year after year.

There is always the town's stingy man. People say that he gives Abraham Lincoln a headache the way he squeezes a penny. All American towns have a flare for nicknames. He is called Penny Smith, or Penny Jones.

He has a little store at the end of Main Street where he sells knick-knacks. It is called a Variety Store.

'Do you know what — I was in Penny Smith's store. He had dropped a penny on the floor. Several customers came in, but he paid no attention to them. They grew tired of waiting and went out. He was down on his hands and knees behind the counter looking for the penny he had dropped. I could have walked off with everything in the store and he wouldn't have known it. He was too absorbed in finding that penny.'

There is a young man who was once called the bright boy of the town. In school he took all of the prizes. His father sent him to college. He was the top man in his classes.

He came home and set up as a lawyer or doctor in the town and presently married. He married a daughter of one of the more well-to-do men of the town. He went along, a steady, successful, quiet man, until he was forty.

And then suddenly he went to pieces. Until he was forty, he had never been known to take a drink.

Then he began. He took bottles of whiskey up into his office, was seen on many afternoons reeling through the streets. No one knows what happened to him. He was one kind of man one day and almost on the next day he became something else.

Now he is the town drunkard, and his wife has a frightened look on her face. No one knows what made him do it. It is not explainable, something that fills the town with awe.

Carl is the small-town man who has the gift. He may have been the son of one of the more well-to-do citizens of the town or he may have been a poor man's son. It doesn't matter. Carl was one destined from birth to get on in the world. If he had been a big city man or had lived in one of the industrial cities, he might have become a captain of industry, a millionaire. In his own town he does well enough.

He is a born trader. He began as a boy. He will trade anything. 'He would trade his wife or daughter if he made a profit in the trade,' men say of him. In every trade he makes he comes out ahead.

Often he has no particular business, goes to no office. He walks about, making trades, he lends money, trades in real estate. Dollars stick to his fingers. Every year, in hard times and good times, he keeps getting ahead. He is one who has the gift, who never overlooks a chance. To the people of the town, he seems a good-natured, quiet fellow, but he is not very inclined to make friends. The town secretly admires him.

And then there is the man who throws it away. He keeps inheriting money from dying relatives, but he cannot keep it. He had ten thousand dollars from an aunt who died in Kansas. Every time he makes an investment, something goes wrong with it. He buys a house and forgets to take out insurance and on the next day it burns. He has several well-to-do relatives and keeps inheriting money, but always it slips away from him.

There is a Carrie Nation in almost every American town. She takes it upon her shoulders to look after the town morals. She is always accusing others of some mysterious sin. During the time of prohibition, she became a powerful figure. She was always telephoning to the sheriff, accusing some man of making or selling liquor. A young man is walking along the street smoking a cigarette and she stops before him. She stamps her foot, scolds at him.

'Take that cigarette out of your mouth, you filthy thing!' she cries.

She is against the use of tobacco in all forms, against the drinking of any kind of intoxicants, against boys playing baseball or swimming on Sunday, against card-playing. She hates all kinds of expressions of gaiety or joy, is down on dancing. She declares dancing leads young girls straight to ruin. She goes to see the girls' mothers, haunts the town editor. The whole weight of the town's moral life is on her shoulders.

The 'characters' of the towns give the towns their color. In the small towns every man's idiosyncrasies are known. They cannot escape you. Life in the towns can be at times terrible or it can be infinitely amusing and absorbing.

Without quite knowing it, you may yourself be one of the 'characters' of your town. If your neighbors are sometimes odd, it may be that they also think of you as odd. The life in the town is the test of man's ability to adjust himself. It tells the story of his skill in living with others.

X

Fall in the towns is the checking-up time, the harvesting of the year's efforts of the American man to survive, getting a little forward in life. To the poor it brings dread of the long, cold days of the North, the rain and mud of the South. Now in the gardens back of the houses in the towns the potato and tomato vines are withered and blackened. Men and women walk with a new soberness along the streets. In many hearts there is a creeping fear.

'How are we ever going to get through the winter, keep warm, feed and clothe the children?' a small-town wife says to her husband.

In Southern towns now the trucks and wagons piled high with the newly picked cotton stand waiting their turn at the small-town cotton gins. Along the roads leading into town, weeds, bushes, and trees are decorated with clinging bunches of cotton. Soon the rows of baled cotton will be standing in the vacant lot about the gin or on the freight-station platform. They will go off to the Southern mill towns or to the compresses in near-by cities to be squeezed small for shipment abroad. Great trucks, piled high with bales, are running along Southern highways and through Southern towns. Formerly the cotton went by wagon to the nearest river steamboat landing, river towns having a boom time, songs of the Negro stevedores floating up from river boats.

It is settlement time in the Southern towns; the tenant farmers of the South, white, black, and brown, come in to check up on the year's work. There is the eternal hope of a little money coming in. The landowners have stood good for the tenants at the town stores, fertilizer bought in the spring, a tenant farmer allowed a little credit for fat-back and meal during the year. It is Tobacco Road come to town.

Men, women, and children of the Southern towns, white and black, go out into the fields for the fall cotton-picking, children wanting shoes, the men new overalls, the women new dresses. The cotton crop and the price it brings is a vital story to them.

The coming-South of the cotton mills brought hordes of the poor tenant farmers into the towns. Often the mill seems the town's one hope. Stock in some of the mills was sold by the preachers in the churches. It was done with prayer in which the town joined, hoped-for employment, a little actual money coming in, often a chance for some sort of education for the children in the mill-town schools.

In the upper South in the fall the tobacco markets are opened in the towns, in the sugar belts down Louisiana way it is the time of cane-cutting. The big cane mills are pressing out the juice from the cane. You see the children of the towns, white and black, each sucking away at a joint of cane.

The tobacco markets enliven the streets of the town in the tobacco country — in Virginia, North Carolina, Kentucky, and Tennessee.

The tobacco-buyers, shrewd, fast-working men, have come to town. They are living in the town hotel. They seem like supermen to the tobacco-growers. They are to make the price for the year's tobacco crop. In the evening they go together to the movies or sit together in a hotel room playing cards. It is hard to convince the tobacco-growers and town people that they do not get together on prices. When prices are down, you hear people along the street growling at them as they go back and forth to the big warehouses.

'Hey, you, how much tobacco you going to steal today?'

There are huge trucks, loaded with the tobacco in 'hands' coming into town. Little broken-down trucks climb painfully the steep grade into town in the hill country. Automobiles have tobacco piled high in the back seat.

It is a nervous waiting time. Here again, when the towns of the upper South have not become factory towns, the whole year's chances for prosperity hang on the price the crop brings, on the condition of the crop. Everything counts in making the price — the color, the texture of the leaf. In the light-yellow tobacco country of North Carolina and in Tidewater, Virginia, the tobacco is kiln-dried, but in the burley country of southwestern Virginia, Kentucky, and Tennessee, it is cured in big tobacco barns or sun-cured on poles in the field.

A hailstorm on the growing tobacco can ruin it. Not too many growers know the secret of grading. They mix the bad with the good, the rain-splashed leaves at the base of the plant, called 'ground lugs,' with the broad clean leaves out of the center of the plant's middle, and the whole crop goes off at a low price.

In the big tobacco warehouses of the towns there is the sustained, queerly Oriental chant of the auctioneers. Farmers wait about for their turn to get their tobacco on the sales floor. They stand by the loaded trucks, lined up in the town streets. They wait on the warehouse floor, anxiously watching as the prices go up and down. Where there is a big market, farmers sleep on their loads in the town streets.

Town pin-hookers are on the job, the pea and thimble man has come to town, the seller of patent medicine, pitch men of all sorts. The pin-hooker is a town man who has made a keen study of tobacco. He goes onto the sales floor to buy badly graded lots, regrades the tobacco. Often a skillful pin-hooker will make more in a week than a tobacco-grower makes for his year's work.

The growers stand about in the streets of the town. Wives and children stand waiting. There is a curious intensity in faces. Merchants of the town also wait anxiously. Will it be a good or a bad year?

The buyers for the big tobacco and cigarette companies are going up and down pulling 'hands' out of the great baskets, making their bids. They become temporarily half gods, deciding the fate of growers and town men alike.

What the cotton crop means to the towns of the lower South and tobacco to the upper South, the potato crop means to the communities in the northern New England States, to Colorado and Idaho, the apple crop to North Pacific Coast towns and to the Valleys of Virginia.

In the Middle West it is corn-cutting time, and at the edge of some of the towns, corn-husking contests are held. Champion corn-huskers come to town to win prizes. Trucks loaded with yellow corn run swiftly through the streets of Middle Western towns, some of the yellow ears falling in the streets. There are yellow ears fallen from trucks along the sides of roads leading into town. In some of the states the corn shocks stand like armies on parade. In other states they break the ears out of the stalks and turn the cattle into the fields. On still nights in little towns you hear the crash of cattle among the dry standing corn in near-by fields. When the corn is shocked, you see the piles of gold against the brown earth.

Although the coming of the factories has changed life tremendously in many small American towns, the greater number of them are still tied to the soil. Hay prices, cattle prices, cabbage, wheat, corn, oats, potato prices, abundance or failure of crop, prices the crops bring, tell the story of hard or good times in the towns.

The fall is the time for the town boys to go nut-gathering in the woods, the hunters to clean their guns and go into the fields with their bird and rabbit dogs.

Apples to be picked and cider made, the women of the little frame houses of the towns doing their fall canning.

Only a generation or two ago in all the smaller American towns, a hog was kept in a pen in the back yard, but now the town man, instead of killing his own hog, goes out into the country and buys a pole hog. There is lard and sausage-making, hams and slabs of bacon are hung up to be cured. For the most part the old-fashioned family cellar, with its bins of apples and potatoes, its long rows of fruits in glass jars on shelves, is disappearing. There is more dependence on the canned goods bought in stores, put up by the big canneries. The town man is a little less close to the life of the farms, but with the coming of tight times there is, in many small towns, a going-back to the old ways.

In the houses of the town when fall comes, the radios bring the result of the baseball world series and the big football games. High-school boys are being put through football practice on the playground back of the town high-school building. Where is your American small town, in the coal-mining country, the North, South, East, or West, without its high-school football team? If a town boy shows up well, has speed and power, he may be able to make football carry him through some big state college or university. It happens.

In the coal-mining towns the mines have speeded up production. In the late summer and fall the roar of coal down the tipple goes on all day long, a black dust settling over the towns, winds carrying it over near-by fields, dimming the fall colors in trees. It is in your hair, your nose, your eyes, your clothes. An increasingly big amount of coal is carried away from the mine towns in trucks, over hundreds of miles of paved highways, to towns outside the mining section. The fall is the time for strikes, for a tightening-up of the labor front, quite as much as the time of the termination of the Jacksonville agreement. As in the Southern cotton mill towns, the houses in which the miners live are owned by the companies that operate the mines.

The fall is election time in the towns. The politicians are about, often going from house to house, shaking hands with the men, caressing babies, making promises.

Can a man make the old overcoat last through another year; can he get new shoes for the kids; will the town factory run full-handed this year; what about the price of coal; can the wife make the old cookstove stand up through another winter?

'I tell you what, Jake, I wish I was one of the lucky ones. I wish I could put the family in the old car, go off South to Florida or West to California. I wonder if we will ever have real prosperity back again, plenty of jobs, plenty of work for a man to do?'

'Say, have you put anti-freeze in your car yet?'

'Gee, but the summer seemed short. Seems like a wind just blew it away.'

XI

John McNutt has been caught stealing chickens. He is an old offender. John lives out at the edge of town in the little shack down behind the gully that is the town dump. He owns an old half-ton truck and has several kids. He has been in jail many times, and this time has been caught red-handed. Three of his kids, half-wild little creatures, were with him when they raked him in.

This worries John. He is afraid the little boys will also be put in jail or sent to a reform school. He pleads with the trial judge.

'Sure, I'm guilty, but my boys aren't.' He declares that the boys did not know what he was up to, and they are let off. John is sentenced to three months' work on the roads, and the crowd of small-towners gathered to hear the trial move out of the little courtroom.

The sheriff, two deputies, the trial judge, and the town editor remain. They have a talk with John and he tells them how he worked it.

'I send the kids out,' he explained. 'I have them carry fish poles on their shoulders, or, in the fall, bags for gathering nuts, and in the winter a pair of skates. I have spotted some farmer who has a lot of chickens I can get at. I send the kids to hang about his place. If he has a dog, they try to coax him to follow. They throw him bones and pieces of meat. Then, when we go back there at night, maybe they can keep the dog quiet.

'I station the kids where they can watch and give the alarm. I'm an expert at this business, a good workman. I can lift a hen off the roost without her making a sound. The kids and I carry them away to where we have the truck hidden in a near-by woods. By the next morning I have the chickens sold in some town a hundred miles away.'

John is pleased with himself. He grins at his listeners.

'Well, you caught me this time all right. One of my kids I had hid along that road when you came up on me went to sleep. You fellows have to admit that I have been a good workman on my job all right.'

The trial judge, the deputies, and the newspaper man are grinning at John.

'Well, I guess I'll get plenty of exercise breaking them stones on the road,' he says as they lead him away.

Since the players rarely come now to the small towns, the court becomes the theater of the towns. What amusing, often tragic stories come out into the light! In many of our states there are elected justices of the peace who try all the minor cases. The justice may be a farmer or any ordinary citizen of the town. He is a man who buys and sells cattle and hogs, or a small-town real-estate dealer. The petty thieves are brought before him. Sometimes two or three justices sit in on a case.

Or there is a quarrel over a horse trade.

Down below the freight station, in the poorer district of the town, there is a little Holy Roller church. The Rollers make so much noise that Jim Watson, who lives down that way, cannot sleep at night. Jim formerly ran a little meat market on the main street of the town. He is a man with a violent temper. Some years ago he had a quarrel with his wife and it upset him so that he destroyed his own meat market. He took his meat cleaver and cleaned the place up, smashed all the windows, chopped up the door of his icebox, threw his stock of meat out into the street.

A crowd gathered and cheered him and, as he went forward with his work of destruction, Jim kept shouting that he wasn't going to run any meat market to earn money to support any such woman as his wife.

Later Jim and his wife made it up, but Jim had no money to restock his store. He is always very humble and apologetic after one of his outbreaks. The Holy Rollers kept him awake, and he went and began to hurl rocks through the windows of the church. He is bound over to the next term of the circuit court. It is a serious matter, this disturbing people in the act of worshiping their God, and it doesn't make any difference how noisy they are about it. The justice tells Jim that. He gives Jim a thorough going-over, and Jim's wife, a small, patient-looking woman who is seated in the courtroom, puts her hands to her face and begins to sob.

'Jim, I told you not to do it. I begged you not to do it,' she keeps saying.

In a good many states our justices work on the fee system. If the man brought into court is cleared, they get no fee, and it is pretty hard to escape a fine, with 'costs,' in such a court.

The cow of a well-to-do farmer has got over into Ed Wyatt's corn field and he hales the farmer into court. Ed is a renter. You can't get a cent out of him, but he is always lawing someone. The farmer offered Ed five dollars for the damage done to his little corn patch, but Ed wouldn't take it. He wanted twenty-five, wanted to gouge the man. His claim is absurd, but Ed is a notorious trouble-maker. There are two justices sitting on the case. They decide to send two or three citizens out to look at Ed's corn patch and estimate the damage. Presently they return.

'Three dollars would be a generous settlement,' they say.

The justices put the cost of the trial on the farmer and he protests.

'But I offered him five dollars. He brought this case into court, I didn't. I'll gladly pay the three dollars' damages, but I don't see why I should be stuck for the costs.'

The two justices take the farmer aside.

'The trouble is that we can't get a cent out of Ed,' they explain. 'We've got to have three dollars apiece for our fee.'

One of the justices gets an idea.

'I'll tell you what we'll do,' he says. 'We'll award Ed three dollars' damages and one of us will keep that. Then we'll divide the cost, sticking you and Ed three dollars apiece. You pay another three dollars, and that will make up the six dollars. You've already offered Ed five. This way you pay one dollar more and Ed doesn't get a cent.'

The farmer is a little puzzled. He scratched his head. Then he gets the idea and grins.

'O.K.,' he says. 'Anyway, it's a chance to put one over on Ed.'

In a small town in the hill country of eastern Tennessee a small-town lawyer was coming out of the 'chambers' of a circuit court judge. This was during the time of prohibition and he had been making a plea to the judge.

Some months before, a stranger had come to town and, after a short stay and after conferences with several prominent town men, had rented a house in the hills, some miles out of town, on a lonely hill road. He had been arrested and brought into court by the sheriff.

The sheriff had found a still in his house and he had been caught making what all the boys said was a mighty good grade of apple, peach, and blackberry brandy. A neighbor woman had informed on him, and the sheriff had been put on the spot. He had to go and get him. The judge had fined him three hundred dollars and had given him a suspended jail sentence, and the lawyer had been pleading with the judge to cut it down.

'Judge, it is too steep a fine for a first offense,' the lawyer had pled.

He had kept at the judge for two hours, but the judge had been stern.

'No. He'll have to pay every cent of it or go to jail.'

A second lawyer, meeting the first one on the courthouse steps, spoke to him on the matter.

'I don't understand the judge,' he said. 'He isn't usually so hard on a first offender. He was sure hard-boiled in this case.'

'I'll say he was,' said the lawyer who had made the plea, 'and do you know what — the judge had got to put up a third of that three hundred himself.'

There is a crowd of country people gathered about the courthouse and loafing on the courthouse lawn. It is a county-seat town and the circuit court is in session. For several days the court has been busy with so-called 'civil cases,' cases concerned with suits for damages, the location of the line between two farms, the responsibility for an automobile accident. A team of mules, loose in the road, has wandered onto a railroad. But now it is time for the criminal court cases to come up. Many witnesses have been summoned. They are town people and country people gathered in, often a little frightened and nervous. It may be that there is even a murder case to be tried, and there is a waiting tenseness in the people.

The sheriff appears and stands at the top of the courthouse steps.

'Hear yees! Hear yees!' he calls. His voice goes booming along the little town's street.

And now court has opened. The jury has been sworn in, after much wrangling between lawyers. As every lawyer knows, the selection of the jury is all-important, and the small-town lawyer knows every man in his county, knows his prejudices, what lodge or lodges he belongs to, what church he attends. He has made a hard fight to get on the jury a few men he thinks may be inclined to be friendly to his side of the case.

The lawyers are sitting by a long table before the jury. When there are two lawyers on a side, they keep whispering to each other. Witnesses are taken aside for whispered consultations. During the conduct of the case some of the lawyers shout while others speak in low tones. The general opinion is that it is better for the lawyer to do a good deal of shouting. It gives an impression of sincerity, of earnestness, of conviction.

There is a case concerned with a man who has wronged a young girl. She has had a child, and the man, who is unmarried, has brought in witnesses to declare that the girl has been the common property of several other men. Her lawyer, as he sums up his case, goes for the young man. He does what Abe Lincoln used to call 'Skinning the witness.'

'What kind of a man is it who will get up here in this public place, in this open court, before all these people, and swear away the honor of an innocent young girl, seduced by a soft-speaking villain, a man who has made her many promises, has whispered silken lies into her innocent young ears?'

The lawyer takes a handkerchief from his pocket and wipes his eyes.

'Have you men on this jury any young daughters of your own?' he asks.

'I have,' he declares. He speaks of two innocent, guiltless young girls in his own house. He shudders. He convicts the man, and later the man gets out of it by marrying the girl. He is even a little flattered by the declaration that he, an awkward country boy, is capable of whispering silken words into a girl's ear.

'Oh, well,' he says, 'I guess I'd better marry her, but gee, I made no promises at all.'

'I wish I could be dead sure it is going to be my kid,' he says.

There is a kind of crude justice to it all, although often witnesses are rather brutally bullied. Many of them, in testifying, keep wandering away from the point.

'Answer yes or no, yes or no!' the lawyers keep shouting at them.

Efforts are always being made to confuse the witnesses, to catch them making contradictory statements. When several witnesses have agreed before they come to court as to just the story they are to tell, the common mistake is often made of all telling the story too much alike. They agree too minutely in all the details.

'I was coming along the road. It was just ten minutes after nine. I struck a match and looked at my watch.'

Other witnesses appear with equally plausible stories as to just how they happened to know the exact time. There is an outbreak of match-lighting on a dark country road, all of them suddenly becoming intent on the time. When the witnesses are striving to tell the truth, they are uncertain and hesitant. Their stories never exactly agree.

The lawyers jump up and sit down. They hold whispered consultations, make objections to testimony or to the way an opposing lawyer handles a witness. Many of the small-town judges are keen-witted men with well-developed streaks of humor.

There is a man on trial who has no money to hire a lawyer and the judge appoints two of the town's younger lawyers to defend him.

'I appoint two of you so that each of you will have someone to whisper to,' he says.

The people gather into the little small-town courtroom. Here is drama straight out of life. Some of the witnesses, country men and women, are so frightened that when they come to the witness stand they speak with difficulty. The judge speaks kindly to them.

'Now don't be afraid. Tell the truth and no one is going to hurt you. I'll look out for you. Face the jury and speak plainly.'

There has been a fight between two farm families. The father of a young woman of one family commanded her to have nothing to do with a son of the other.

But the young man has come at night and has parked his car in the road and the young woman has run out to him. One of her brothers saw her go and called his father, and the men of her family armed themselves with clubs, stones, and pitchforks.

They ran down along a dirt road to the house in which lives the young man's family. He had taken his sweetheart to his own home. They were preparing to go off to town and get married.

A fight started. Stones were thrown and clubs used. The young girl's 'menfolks' managed to get her away and half-drag her along the road to her father's house, and the sweetheart has brought the matter into court.

There are frightened, confused witnesses. When the young woman is brought to the witness stand, she sobs. The father of her sweetheart has long been the enemy of her father. Years before they had a fight over a horse trade. It is a down-to-earth drama, played out in the small-town courtroom, witnesses telling lies, witnesses trying to tell the truth. It is living drama of the everyday lives of everyday Americans, played out in the courtroom in an American small town.

XII

In the towns, winter, for all the radios and the movies, is the waiting time. It is the time between for the American small-towner. In spite of the spread of factories to the towns, North and South, the American small town remains close to the life of the land. The land sleeps and waits and the towns wait.

In the Far Northern States of New England and up through the Northwest, the bitter cold days come early, the spring with its new beginning is far away. Weatherwise old men have been up and down the Main Streets making predictions. They say that all of the animals have put on a thick coat of fur. It will be a long, hard winter. In Southern towns, on Saturday afternoons, countrymen, Negroes and whites, come into the towns bringing loads of firewood. They come in one-mule wagons or in worn-out trucks, to stand about the town square, patiently waiting for buyers. In some of the towns public markets have been built. The country women bring in their canned goods, potatoes, and cabbage. They sit in their little booths wrapped in heavy overcoats. Now the road men of the North get out the snow-moving machinery. The big highways that run through the towns must be kept clear. The cars must move. America must keep rolling.

In the early winter in the towns, all over America, Christmas decorations go up along Main Street, the store windows take on a new gaiety, wreaths of evergreen are hung on the doorknobs of houses, the local weekly is full of Christmas advertisements. You go up to the high school to watch the high-school football team in a game with the boys of some near-by town, stand about shivering, only, alas, too often, to see your home-town boys get a licking. You get the flu.

You get through Thanksgiving, eat your share of turkey, if you can afford one. You get all of your relatives in, have a big feast, get into an argument with your brother-in-law. He is a Republican and you are a Democrat. The argument gets hot, becomes a quarrel, and your wife tries to patch it up, to make peace. Very likely, when your brother-in-law has gone angrily away, you get down-the-river from your wife.

You have to go on living with people day after day, week after week. You can't just ignore your brother-in-law, forget him as you might in a city. Tomorrow you will meet him on the street. You will be meeting him in the stores and in the post-office. Better make it up, start over again.

'I'm sorry, Jim, if I was a little rough on you.'

'Oh, that's all right, Fred. Sometimes I'm a little hot-headed my-self.'

It is the old problem of living with men, finding a common ground on which you can stand with your fellows, this intensified in the towns.

Now is the time to go skating. The boys have taken up the new sport of skiing. If there is a hill near town, it is time to get out the bob-sleds.

'Jake, do you remember the old days when Al Wright kept the livery stable? Do you remember how he used to keep a couple of pretty good trotters? He got them out when the sleighing was good. He and Doc Payne, who owned that big ambling pacer, and Judge Crawford with his little sorrel, would be having it lickety-split up and down Main Street.'

'Yes, and the farmers with their bob-sleds coming into town, the boys flipping on, stealing a ride; parties we used to go on out to some farmer's house or to a barn dance.'

'I'll tell you what, Ike, I don't know sometimes whether all these modern inventions we've got are a good thing or not.'

There used to be show troupes come into the towns in the winters, the actors walking on the streets in the afternoons. The movies killed them off. Almost every winter a burlesque show came. Only the men went to that. It was called a 'leg show.' Going was a nice wicked thing to do.

The Christmas tree has been brought in from the woods and set up in the parlor. Some of the more well-to-do have set up trees in the front yards. They are covered with small many-colored electric lights. In Southern towns they shoot off firecrackers. Tourists come back to the Northern towns in the spring and tell about it. 'They make a Fourth of July out of Christmas down there,' they say. The Five-and-

Tens have done a booming business. The churches hold special Christmas services. Some of them have Christmas trees, and kids who have been regular attendants at Sunday School through the year get their reward.

Over most of America the real winter comes after Christsmas. It may be that the town's women's club gets up a lecture course. They canvass the town selling tickets. This is where we get our culture. You've got to buy a season ticket and go to show you're cultured. It is the women who keep up the cultural tone for us. College boys come with their glee clubs and sing in the town hall, the courthouse, or in one of the churches. Miss Grayson, who is unmarried but wrote a book on how to live a happy married life, comes and lectures to us; a magician comes and does his tricks.

Some of our more cultured women, our local literati, have formed a book club. The druggist's wife who went to Smith College reviews the latest best-seller. The high-school boys have a basketball team; there is always the radio and the movies, and in the back of Cal Hurd's shoe repair shop there is a checker game going on.

Upstairs over the bank in Fred Travey's law office on dismal winter afternoons, you can get into a poker game if you are looking for sport. Better look out. Fred and Theodore Shovely, the coal and lumber dealer, will clean you out.

In every American town, as in our cities, there is a section beyond the railroad tracks where the poor live. We in the towns also have our slums. In the summer and fall the men who live down there manage to pick up a day's work now and then, but in the winter there is nothing doing. There are a half-dozen children in the family, and the mother tries to keep things going by doing the washing for our well-to-do families. You will see her on bitter cold days hanging out a wash. Her hands are blue with cold. In the houses the children huddle about the one stove in the kitchen, wood and coal to be bought, shoes for the children. It is a long winter for that family. The woman who is hanging out the washed clothes is a proud one. She'll work her arms off, she says, rather than go on relief. The long depression, unemployment, has killed the spirit of more than one such woman. They have had to throw in the sponge, give it up. They couldn't make it.

In the winter the small-town doctors, East and West, North and

South, are up and out day and night, through mud and snow. There are babies to be delivered, people down with the flu. Since the depression and the end of prohibition, the small-town lawyer finds the pickings thinner. There are too many people hard up. They can't afford to take their quarrels into court. The small-town doctors have a hard time collecting their bills.

There is the weekly meeting of the Kiwanis and the Rotary Clubs. Some of the so-called 'service clubs' meet for dinner in the evening at the town hotel. It lets the women out for that evening, no evening meal to prepare. It gives the men a chance to make speeches, tell the others what is the matter with the town.

'We ought to get more factories,' the speakers keep saying.

On lodge nights the women pick up a 'snack' and go off to the movies. In many towns, no matter how small, there is a women's card club. Only the more well-to-do are invited into that.

There is a dance on Saturday night, country girls coming into town with their beaus. If there is a factory in the town, the factory hands go. There are revivals being held in the churches. In the very small town the church becomes the center of social life. The church women will be giving suppers to raise money to help pay the preacher. In the South a little unpainted wooden Negro church fills the winter lives of the town Negroes. There are cries and shouts, a swaying of brown bodies, a rhythmic beating of feet on cold wooden floors, something released, the pent-up emotions of a race.

Winter is, in a curious way, the test time for the people of the towns, the test of men and women's ability to live together. There is that brother-in-law with whom you had a quarrel. You and he made it up. You have quarrels with other men, even sometimes with the wife. You have to forget it, start over again.

XIII

The small-town jails have long since been the black holes of the towns. Usually the hoosegow is small, a few barred cages for unruly prisoners, women prisoners all thrown together in one room. In some of the smaller towns, both North and South, the jails are thoroughly filthy little holes, with the toilets, when there are any, in the same little barred rooms in which prisoners must eat and sleep, men, boys, and even women staying in these airless rooms often for thirty, sixty, or ninety days.

In many states the prisoners in the town jails are fed on the contract system, the jailer taking the contract at so much per head per day, his profit to be made by trimming as closely as possible both the quality and the quantity of the food.

In the South there are jails moving about the counties on wheels, cages on trucks that move about over the roads of the county, the prisoners working on the roads, the moving jails following the workers about the county. Driving in the Southern back country, you come upon one of these gruesome cages at night, the prisoners packed in trucks like chickens being taken in their crates from country towns to city markets.

Or you travel into little Southern towns and see on the streets bands of prisoners in their striped prison uniforms, at work with heavy iron balls and chains fastened to their ankles.

There are stories of cruelty and brutality. They have got into our literature. In some of our states prison labor has been let out on contract, to work in mines, in lumber camps, or on plantations.

Some years ago the prohibition laws filled the jails of the towns. Drinking having become an adventure young boys and even high-school girls sometimes got drunk and drove cars recklessly through the streets of the towns. Cars were wrecked, and young men and sometimes young women were often put into little airless rooms with hardened and diseased prostitutes.

In the great stretch of hill country, running across America from the capital at Washington through Missouri, in all the southern Appalachian Range, the Blue Ridge Mountains, the Cumberlands, the Ozarks, lived a race of men who had for generations been makers of illicit liquor. They were poor men living on poor mountain land, and often the little farms in the valleys in the hills were off any passable road. The little hillside corn fields yielded but a few bushels an acre.

It could be made into a money crop. The mountain man went into the deep laurel near some small mountain stream and set up his still. It was difficult to find. He fermented his corn in boxes set in the ground and well concealed, made his beer, and then, in a home-made still, distilled his 'moon.'

It was thus he could bring to market the crop of corn, raised in the little hillside fields, in a compact, easily concealed form.

Prohibition brought a great boon to the business. The mountain men, being a genius at the business, learned quicker and quicker ways of turning out moon. Sugar whiskey could be turned out in one night's run. After a Government investigation in one hill county, it was discovered that five thousand pounds of sugar had been shipped into the county in one year for every man, woman, and child in the county.

The liquor-maker in the hills became a romance. Before prohibition, Federal men went into the hills to find the stills, but their work was dangerous. Often whole communities were involved and it was difficult to get information, and when a Federal man appeared, the alarm ran far ahead of him over the hills.

Prohibition came bringing its boom to the business. The county officers, the sheriff and his deputies, who, before prohibition, had left the finding of 'the blockaders' to Federal agents, were put on the tracks of the local county moon-makers. What had been a Federal offense became also a state and county matter.

And all across the country, in hill towns of southwestern Virginia, West Virginia, Kentucky, North Carolina, northern Georgia, and Alabama, Tennessee, and Missouri, the mountain men were raked in, and the lawyers in the little hill towns began doing a booming business.

The jails were crowded, for the most part with young mountain men, lean, straight-bodied young fellows who could see no crime in the making of liquor.

Liquor-making had been a tradition for generations in their families.

'I raised the corn, didn't I? It was my corn. What business is it of the Government what I do with it?'

'I tell you it was my corn raised on my land.'

'What has the Government ever done for me?'

For a hundred years the mountain men, usually of English and Scotch-Irish stock, had lived aside from the main drift of what we call American progress. But few railroads had penetrated into the great stretch of hill country, the swift-running mountain streams were not navigable, and there had been little road-building. Even a wagon could not penetrate into some of the remote valleys, called 'hollers' by the mountain men. A state like Virginia, embracing before the Civil War all of what is now West Virginia, had produced, in Tidewater Virginia, the Washingtons, Jeffersons, Monroes, and Madisons, but the hill men had produced the pioneers, the adventurers, the Sam Houstons, the Daniel Boones, the Andrew Jacksons, and Andrew Johnsons. Abraham Lincoln's mother and father had come out of the hill country.

The hill men were honest, lean-bodied fellows inclined to be clannish, suspicious of strangers, and extremely loyal to friends. They have been both romanticized and despised. Mark Twain wrote of them with contempt, while men like John Fox, Jr., make them into romantic heroes.

They are men made by their environment and by the physical circumstances of their lives. They are sometimes illiterate, but rarely lacking in shrewdness.

The county sheriff has come to a little mountain cabin at night with his deputies — this in the time of prohibition. He has got a tip that there is a still being run on the hillside farm. He knocks on the door of the cabin and is admitted.

But the hill man has been warned. A barefooted boy has run over a mountain path to warn him. The sheriff and his men have stopped at a garage in a neighboring hill town and the warning is out over the hills.

So there is the hill man in his one-room cabin in the presence of the 'law.' His wife is lying in the bed in the room and the hill man tells the officers that she is just about to have a baby.

'I got to get to town to see a doctor,' he keeps saying.

There is a quantity of moon, some three or four gallons, in halfgallon glass jars, in the cabin, but he has put them into the bed with his wife. She looks strangely bloated. While the officers are in the cabin, she keeps groaning pitifully.

The officers leave the cabin and search through the neighboring hills and find the still. Some enemy of the mountain man has tipped them off, but while they are searching, the man has concealed all the liquor except three or four jars. These he puts in to a grain bag he calls a 'poke,' and on top of the liquor also puts in the poke several live chickens, and when the officers return with the still, he asks for a ride to town.

'I got to sell these chickens and get me some money to get a doctor out here for my old woman,' he explains.

So the mountain man gets a ride to town, gets the officers to carry his liquor to town, delivers it to a customer, collects the money, and hangs about until the officers have gone to bed. He has served time in the little town jail and knows how to break in.

He does break in and recovers his still, carries it over the hills on his shoulder to conceal it in a new place.

But all the mountain men are not so clever or so lucky. The jails in the mountain towns during prohibition were crowded with them. They were almost always young men and used to hard living. Such stories as the one told here of the mountain man who got the officers to deliver his liquor and then recovered his still filled them with delight. They took the miserable cramped weeks in the dirty little jail in their stride. To them going to jail for making moon was no disgrace. Some one of them always took his guitar with him. From the jails they made the little mountain hill towns ring with their mountain songs.

'And why should I feel any disgrace? I didn't steal nothing. It was my corn. It was my liquor I made from my own corn they caught on me.'

In most American small towns there is little of the bullying of the prisoners, such as often goes on in our cities, the so-called 'third degree.' The prisoners are usually known to the local sheriff and his deputies.

'Well, Ed, we've got you again.'

Ed is a petty thief. He is a good mechanic and could make a living going straight. He is a laughing, good-natured fellow.

He says: 'I just can't seem to get over it. I don't want to be a thief, but I'm always thinking up some scheme. Then I want to try it out to see if it will work, if I can put it over on you fellows.'

There have always been certain men in our towns who, when they drink, want to fight and who cannot keep out of jail. There are other fighters and petty thieves. There are men who are hauled in because they will not work and support their families. The coming of the long depression also has tended to increase the petty theivery in many communities. Often men, unable to find work, go forth at night to rob farmers' meat storage houses or their chicken coops. The coming of the automobile has made the work of the local sheriff and the town marshal more difficult. A robbery is committed in a town at night and, before daylight the next morning, the thief with his plunder is two or three hundred miles away, often in another state.

There has been also an increase in the drifting population all over America. The drifters come into the little towns and go to the town jailer. They are permitted to sleep on the floor of the jail at night. Sometimes a good-hearted jailer gives them a breakfast before they are again on their way. Often whole families on the drift, hitch-hiking when they can pick up a ride. There is a man from Kansas with a tired, sick-looking wife and two children. He tells the jailer that his wife has a brother on a farm in northern New York. If he can get there, his wife's brother says he can give him work.

A man from northern New York has a brother on a farm in Kansas. He is trying to get out there.

'My brother says, anyway, he guesses he can take care of us until I can get on my feet again.'

The drifters come to the little town jails. It is cold or it is raining, and they have nowhere else to go. Anyway, it may be dry and warm in the jail. The drifter's only guilt is that he has no money. The little town jail is a temporary haven for him.

But with the change in the life of the towns there has also come an improvement in the jails now built to replace the old little dark holes. And a stop has been put to the more objectionable cruelty in some of the road camps. In most states the men condemned to road work no longer wear the ball and chain. There have been laws passed putting a stop to the contracting-out of small-town prisoners to mining and lumber companies, and in most states the men working thus on the roads no longer wear the prison stripes.

And life in the hills has also changed. The coming of the TVA has changed it tremendously over a vast stretch of the long-neglected hill country. Paved roads more and more penetrate into the hills. Modern life has moved in on the hills, men and the jails in the little hill towns are no longer crowded.

XIV

Most of the news in the best of the small-town weeklies isn't, in the big-city newspaper sense, news at all. If there is a revolution in Spain, give it a paragraph. If Mr. Morley's little girl gets bitten by a dog and there is danger of rabies, it's worth a column or two. Why not? The whole town is anxious. Nowadays almost every small-towner has a radio. He gets the world news and the national news in the same split second as the city man, hears the same wise-cracks, his woman wears the same kind of clothes, hears the same canned music.

The small-town newspaper, a weekly, is intensely local. The editor must take the world of his town and the neighboring farm country as the center of his universe.

There is column after column of 'personals.' The idea is to try to catch the color, the smell, the feel, of the everyday life of everyday people.

'Mrs. Wilbur of the young married set gave a bridge luncheon on Wednesday.'

'Ed Hall's daughter, Julia, has gone to New York, where she has taken a "lucrative position." '

Julia has an aunt in the city. The aunt is married to a man who works in a gasoline filling station and Julia is really working as a waitress in a small city restaurant, but Ed is a regular subscriber to the paper and he has taken out a year's subscription for Julia. You've got to give Julia a break in the news.

It is late fall and the farmers, in the country about town, are killing hogs. It is the time of sausage-making, lard-making. Very likely the editor will get several good messes of spareribs brought in by his subscribers. In January, Taylor's department store is going to have a big 'white sale.' Mrs. Kregs slipped on the ice in front of the post-office and hurt her hip. It is August and the country is needing rain. The towns' water supply is running a little low. One of the town council has been to see the editor. He wants the editor to ask the town people to go a little easy with their lawn sprinkling.

E. P. Brewer of Oklahoma City, Oklahoma, who hasn't been seen on the street of the town since he was a young fellow, twenty-five years ago, has been home on a visit. He has been up and down Main Street shaking hands with old friends. E. P. is now a big oil man in the West. With Mrs. Brewer he is on his way to New York. He says it is wonderful the way our town has grown and improved, declares it is the best-looking town he has seen on his trip. He is the cousin of our Miss Lizzie Brewer who has taught in our high school for so many years and who is one of our most esteemed citizens.

The truth is that Lizzie lost out. When she was just out of high school, she had a chance to marry Frank Reed, who was at that time cashier of the First National Bank. Frank's wife had died several years before and he had a great crush on Lizzie. She turned him down because she thought she was going to get Harold Graves, son of John Graves, who was at that time superintendent of schools.

Harold was about the smartest boy who ever went to the town schools. He went away to an Eastern city and became a big corporation attorney. He married a rich girl in the city.

When he had first left our town, Harold used to write letters to Lizzie almost every day, but after a time he stopped writing. She kept thinking that he would come back for her, but he never came. When Harold was a young fellow in the town, he and Lizzie used to walk about in the streets on summer evenings. They went to dances together. She was called the best-looking girl in town then. They kissed, made vows to each other.

Now Harold is a big man in the big Eastern city and Lizzie is still in the town. After twenty years of teaching school, she looks faded and tired. Her cousin, E. P. Brewer, came to town in a big car and took Lizzie with him to the city. He paid all her expenses.

The town editor knows Lizzie's story. It is just another of the thousands of little everyday stories of lives in his town. Lizzie's father once owned a grocery store on Main Street, but he went broke and then died, and for fifteen years before she died, Lizzie supported her mother. She was a querulous old woman, always scolding and complaining.

There are plenty of such stories in every American town. The editor knows them, but they do not get published. If he is a good editor, he is a man who runs the little weekly on the theory that his town is the very center of the universe. He knows he can't compete with the big dailies and with the daily radio digests of news. The best of the small-town editors are always on the alert for the town news, the little everyday happenings in the lives of everyday people. Like the country doctor and the lawyers there is much he knows that he doesn't print. He doesn't intend to get down too deeply under the people's skins.

'What's the use?' he asks himself. 'If there is a scandal in the town, some married woman getting mixed up with another woman's man, something of that sort, everyone knows it.' The editor doesn't aim to rob people of their self-respect. He knows what to print. He knows that life goes hard enough at best with most of his subscribers.

Get their names in the paper is the way to do it, tell as many as possible of the daily happenings in many people's lives. When a citizen of the town dies, he gets a good send-off in the paper. On a hook back of the one linotype there are always a number of obituaries, waiting to be dropped into the paper. There is always a literarily inclined woman in the town who makes a specialty of writing them.

The obituaries tell what church the departed belonged to, it names his relatives. There are usually a few verses touching upon his probable standing 'On the Other Shore.'

Your Will Smith went from town out to the coal-mining country. He was making good out there, saving money. He had got married and had a fine young wife, owned his own home.

'And no sooner did he get all of these fine prospects than ten tons of slate fell on him,' the obituary says.

There was a time in the towns, after the eighteen-eighties, when the great surge out of the small towns to the cities was at its height, when the American small-town weeklies began to go downhill. The earlier weeklies were often mere political organs, but among the earlier country editors, all over the country, were many sharp, shrewd men. The country weekly produced some of the great writers, the humorists and the wits of their time. There were fighting gun-toting editors, violent men filling their little sheets with violent tirades, editors controlled by state politicians, others, because of their wit and humor, becoming national figures.

It was a time when the state and national politicians, going from town to town, on speech-making tours, could present a new face to every community, a time when few people in the towns took daily newspapers, when there were few telephones.

In another day the small-town editor, with his little four-, six-, or eight-page paper was the voice of the big outside world coming in. Being a country editor was the first step to political preferment. Country editors became Congressmen or United States Senators. The editor got railroad passes, could travel up and down his state, go to political conventions. Being a small-town editor pretty much meant also being a politician.

And then a change came as changes do come quickly in American life.

The kind of young man, with perhaps a yen for writing, who formerly would have begun his training in the local newspaper office, went off to a near-by city to get a job on a city daily. City firms began to put out what is called 'patent insides.' For a small sum the editor could get each week whole pages for his paper shipped to him by express, no type to be set, whole pages for his paper all ready to lock into his flat-bed press.

It was pretty vague stuff, most of it, having little to do with the town life. There was a discussion of some national problems, so put that no one reading it could decide whether the writer was for or against the proposition he was discussing, notes on gardening, on women's wear, recipes for cooking. In many towns two-thirds of the local weekly was taken up with matter touching but vaguely the daily lives of the people of the community.

The linotype invaded the country print shop. The journeyman printer, wandering from town to town, always a colorful figure, began to disappear. Men who were mere small-town job printers, with little or no interest in journalism, were running more and more the country papers, much of the wit and humor of the old-time country editor quite gone, the Heywood Brouns, the Frank Adamses, the Cappers, the O. O. McIntyres and Peglers, who in another age might have stayed in the towns and become editors of small-town weeklies, became city newspaper columnists, writing for syndicates. More and more country weeklies were owned in chains like the grocery stores, the drug stores, and the Five-and-Tens. Often two-thirds of the space in the town weekly was taken up by material manufactured in Chicago or New York.

Now another change has come. The small-town weekly is becoming alive again. There are more and more keen young men coming every year into the field. After the great depression struck America in '29, city streets were filled with good newspaper men out of jobs. The schools of journalism were turning out more young newspaper men. There was a new realization that being a small-town editor, with all of its occasional scraping of the pot to get the paper out, the necessity of keeping on the heels of the local merchants for advertising enough to keep going, could mean, after all, a pretty good living.

There is no deadline for the journalist on the small-town weekly. If his paper issues on Wednesday and the fishing is good, or it is bird-hunting time in the fall, the paper can come out on Thursday. The journalist in the small-town field doesn't get rich, but, if he has at all a flare for it, he can get by, live rather decently. He occupies a position of respect and responsibility in the community. He can stay pretty close to American life as it is lived by the commonalty of Americans down near the grass roots.

XV

The church bells are ringing in the towns — Methodist bells, Catholic, Baptist, Presbyterian, Disciples, Lutheran, Episcopal, Congregational bells. Now the cars are parked thick in all the streets before the churches. Men and women are coming afoot, fathers and mothers, followed by their troops of children. The little girls not minding all the fuss, the hair-combing, the scrubbing, the dressing-up. It is an instinct.

It begins early in the female. They like it.

See the little boys with their clean, shining faces, their carefully combed hair. There goes one who seems to like it. 'He is a sissy. That's what he is.'

In the towns the Methodists and Baptists lead the procession in the number of churches. North and South, at the time of the last official count, there were some fifty-three thousand white and Negro Baptist churches. The Methodists ran them a close race. The Baptists lead all the others in the number of Negro churches.

Then there are the Roman Catholics with nearly twenty thousand churches, the Presbyterians with about twelve thousand, the Disciples and the Protestant Episcopalians with some seven or eight thousand each, the Church of Christ with six thousand, the Congregational with five thousand, and the Lutherans, counting both the Missouri Synod, the United and the Norwegian Lutheran, with some eleven thousand.

And there are some fifty-five thousand other Protestant churches, the Quakers in many sections strong, the Adventists and the Dunkards, the Christian Scientists, the United Brethren, the Unitarians, the Plymouth Brethren, the Mennonites, not to mention the Great I-Ams, the Zionists, the Two Seeds in the Spirit Baptists, the Christadelphians, the Duck River Baptists, the Shakers, the Holiness churches, the Church of Daniel's Band, the Moravians, and the Defenseless Moravians. The great number and variety of sects, all worshiping the same God, is but another expression of American individualism. It is something come down to us out of pioneer days, men and women of many nationalities pouring in, often coming to us to escape religious persecution.

Jim Watson doesn't belong to any church, but his wife does, so Jim contributes to the Baptist church in his town. The Baptist preacher meets Jim on the street.

'Jim, now you tell me, why don't you come to church with your wife?'

Jim says he does.

'I come once a year,' he says, and grins.

'Now you look here, Preacher,' says Jim, 'I chip in fifty dollars a year, don't I? I come to church once a year. That's fifty dollars a sermon. You haven't got another single member in your church who puts up more than that for just one sermon.'

Jim stays at home on Sunday mornings. He reads the Sunday newspaper. It is nice and quiet at home with the wife and kids all gone off to church and Sunday School. Now and then he discusses religion with his special man friend.

'Sure, I believe in God,' Jim says. 'I just think it doesn't make any difference whether a man goes to church or not. I don't think God keeps books on churchgoers, do you, Ed?'

The old Puritanical tightness of the Sabbath has softened a good deal in the American small town. As everyone knows, it never did clamp down hard on the Catholics.

Formerly, in smaller American towns, there were no Sunday afternoon ball games; on summer Sundays no one but the pronounced sinners ever went swimming; there were no shows, no movies. But nowadays, in many American towns, the movies are open on Sunday afternoons; there are ball games with teams from neighboring towns; half the town people are out in cars on summer Sunday afternrons; in

the churches there is less insistence on hell fires; somewhat fewer re-
vival meetings are held.

The church does, however, exert a tremendous influence on life in
the American small town. Many a Catholic priest or a Protestant
preacher is first friend to the members of his church when trouble
comes.

He is the one who comes into the family circle when things go bad.
He performs the marriage ceremony for the son or daughter. You can
talk things over with him. He is taken into the family circle and into
the confidence of the family when there is sickness or death. He is
there with his hand in that of the husband when a man's wife is on
her deathbed, when a son has gone bad, when a daughter has been
careless and has got herself into a fix. Often he is able to patch up a
break threatened between man and wife, hold a breaking family together.

The church you belong to in the American small town fixes the
group you belong to. It fixes your social standing in the town life.

It is the church that takes in the newcomers to the town, his fellow
church members seeing that the newcomer meets people, is made to
feel a part of the town's life. It is a part of the setup of small-town life
that enables the young man to meet the girl who will later become his
wife.

The church is the center of innumerable activities reaching into
many phases of American small-town life. It is and remains the chan-
nel through which the average American keeps a kind of touch with
the mystery, with the strange fact of birth and death, the mystery of
stars, of winds, of the renewal of life in nature in the spring.

XVI

Many American men over forty love to tell the story of how bravely
they stood a beating in school when they were kids and of what little
devils they were. It was the thing to do, to put it over on the teacher.
There was that early American story of school days, *The Hoosier
Schoolmaster,* by Edward Eggleston, one of the first of the American
best-sellers. It was a tale of an upstanding young man come into an
early backwoods settlement in Indiana, his war with the local bullies

among the big boys, of horse-thievery and rascality, the young school-teacher plunged into the thick of it.

The war between the small-town school-teacher and the children in the school went on for a long time. To the average small-town child school days were unpleasant and necessary interludes to childhood. There you were, in the schoolroom, on a spring day, and the windows of the room were open. What went on in the room was a dull recital of certain facts. It was impressed upon you that five and five made ten. A certain farmer got into a foolishly complex deal over some apples he had for sale. You had yourself often hung about the cider mill in your town when the farmers were bringing in wagonloads of apples and their business transactions with the cider-mill man had never got so foolishly complex. You did a thing called parsing sentences, and what an unjust, terrible thing to do to a seemingly innocent sentence! You outlined the boundaries of states. It seemed that the State of Arkansas was bounded on the north by Missouri.

Or was it Kansas?

The school was a kind of prison. How you hated it! What was the good of all this parsing sentences to one who was going to be a railroad engineer, a driver of race-horses, or to one who, as soon as he got a little older, was going to cut out West and be a cowboy or go off to sea and be a sailor?

There was a man who lived in your town and who was a railroad engineer on the Big Four. You had heard him talk. He was your father's friend, and he didn't bother about grammar. You thought that the teacher would have a tough time parsing some of his sentences. You'd be willing to bet anything he didn't know what British general was defeated at the Battle of New Orleans or who won the Battle of Lake Erie. Put it up to him to bound the State of Idaho and he'd be stuck. The Big Four didn't go out there.

The idea of education and its value has always been a passion to the American. The American man is grimly determined that his sons and daughters shall be educated. He wants them to have some chance that did not seem to come his way. The passion is in the poor as well as the rich.

It is in Mrs. Kreiger, whose husband got drunk and was killed by a train. Mrs. Kreiger didn't get much chance when she was a young girl. She had to quit school and go to work in the kitchen of a store-keeper in the town.

Then she got married and her husband wasn't much good and she kept having children.

But Mrs. Kreiger is determined that her children shall have their chance. She dreams of them becoming doctors or lawyers or school-teachers. She will work herself cheerfully into the grave in order that the children rise a little in the world. Sending them to school means that to her.

And gradually, more and more, the school grows closer to the life in the towns. There is a constant increase in the number of American children of the small towns who go out of the grades into the high school. The school building in many towns is nowadays used, more and more, by the whole community. It becomes the town forum, where the problems of the town are discussed. It may be because of the long depression, throwing many of the town's better-educated, better-prepared, men and women out of other professions, but nowadays no one can make a study of our American small-town schools without being struck and impressed by the improvement in the quality of the teaching.

In almost every one of our states the school has become the center of the effort to bring education closer to everyday life. There is in many schools more and more intensive study of the individual student, less depends on fixed and rigid tests. In a growing number of schools the problems of citizenship are taken up and studied, the children taught the meaning of such problems as the conservation of soil, the girls taught cooking and dressmaking, the meaning of the courts and of elections brought home to the children, a continual effort to train the hands as well as the head. National questions, such as the tariff, are taken up and discussed. Often the child of the town schools is taken to the local factory to see goods made, camera clubs are sometimes organized to teach the use of the eye, and children are encouraged to make drawings. Local activities of the town are studied, the way the town council works, what becomes of the money collected for the taxes, the setup of the water and sewer systems. All this tends to bring the school closer and closer to the actuality of living in the towns.

XVII

It is Saturday night, fiesta night.

In the factory towns the workers have been paid for the week of labor. In most American towns they now have Saturday afternoon off, and all afternoon and through the evening the stores of the town have been crowded. Nowadays the towns, like the cities, have their parking problems. Cars are parked solidly along the length of Main Street and in all the residence streets that lead into Main Street.

The country lads, with their red, sunburned faces, have put on their best Sunday-go-to-meeting clothes. A good many of them these days are movie-touched. In towns all over the East, the Middle West, and the South imitation cowboys, with ten-gallon hats and belts studded with brass, are to be seen on the streets, and some of these drug-store cowboys are farm lads.

The girls are out. They hunt in couples, and they also have been to the movies. On Friday afternoon or on Saturday morning, they have been to the beauty parlor. Now the small-town barber shop is no longer a place of off-color stories and the *Police Gazette*. In the barber shop the women of the town, like the men, are waiting to be dolled-up. Country girls and town girls have done their fingernails, rouged and lip-sticked their faces. That tall, striking brunette you see going along Main Street has for a companion, on her evening hunt, a little fat blond. All evening the two of them will march up and down, being looked at by the boys, hearing the comments of the young town and country blades.

A dance is going on in a hall on the second floor of a building on the lower end of Main Street and they go there. It may be a square dance. Over the sound of chattering voices, the hum of motors, the laughter of the streets, you hear the voice of the 'caller-off.'

> Swing the lady to your right,
> Grand right and left;
> If the lady you find shy,
> Grab her tight and swing her high.

This is the big night in the towns. Step high there, boy! Girl, look your best! Blue Monday is coming soon. It is grim times now in many of the towns. There are wars over the world, threats of war in the air. Jobs are scarce.

'Let's forget it for tonight. Let's go down to Joe's and have a beer.'

There is little Susan stepping along. She is young, but already she looks faded. She has fixed herself up the best she can. Susan has been reckless. You will find her in every town, the little local 'push over.' The word is out among the town and country boys that she can be had.

Susan isn't very pretty. She is a little lame. Her dad got drunk one night, when she was just a kid, and threw her down a flight of stairs. He was mighty sorry later when he got sobered up. He used to go about town talking about it. You, even, after a time, began to feel sorry for him. He couldn't forget what he had done to Susan.

'They say that Tom Howe, that young fellow who works in Long's drygoods store, started her. He made her all sorts of promises and then he didn't keep them.'

'I wouldn't do that to any girl, would you?'

'I'll tell you what, when a poor girl gets her name up for being easy, she's sunk. A lot of men won't let her alone. See her going along, limping along, trying to act proud.'

There may be a roller-skating rink in the town and a good many of the town and country boys go there. Or they take a ride in a car out along some country road. Kisses are exchanged, shy approaches made to a partnership in living. Nowadays the big question for the girls can be simply put.

'Has he got a good steady job?' Jobs are hard to get. The question is of importance to the girl. She has to keep it in mind.

The family men are out with their wives and children. On this night the movie-house is crowded, but the streets are more crowded. No one knows just why it is so, but in every American town the greater part of the crowd stays on one side of the main street. On Saturday night the families of the more prosperous citizens, the merchants', the doctors', the lawyers' wives and daughters, stay at home. They even speak a little contemptuously of the riff-raff crowding the town streets, but their sons are out.

Young Tom Howe, who started Susan the wrong way, has a rich aunt. 'They say he'll inherit a lot of money some day.'

'I guess you can't blame Tom if he doesn't want to marry Susan, but he should have left her alone.'

In the Southern town there is a side street of stores patronized only by the Negroes. Young Negro lads and lassies are parading on the streets. High, shrill laughter floats on the evening air out of the street. There is a store down there where they sell cheap phonograph records. They've got a phonograph going on the street outside the store.

> 'Goen' down to the river
> And set on a log,
> For I'ze too good of a woman
> To be treated like a dog.'

In the Southern towns the mill girls are also out. The well-to-do speak of them as 'lint-heads.' It is the old evil things, contempt by the soft-handed for the hard-handed. The mill girls are likely to fade fast, but there are many beauties among them. They are proud, keep with their own crowd, go with their own 'bunch.' A good many of them have come to the towns from Southern tenant farms. They come from poor-white families, but just the same some of them bear names of some of the so-called aristocratic families of the Old South. There is a curious tightness about young mouths. The mill girls know what hard living means. They have been taught young. They also have been to the beauty parlor. Nowadays cheap copies of all the latest and most fashionable models in women's dresses are quickly rushed out to the small towns. The new model that the New York millionaire's wife wears to the theater on Monday night will be worn by a mill girl on a Saturday night in a Georgia town.

It is a colorful changing scene, the American town on a Saturday fiesta night. In the stores clerks fly busily about, the Five-and-Ten is crowded. Before the stores town and farm men and their women discuss the need of rain, the price of eggs, wheat, corn, or cotton, the new pest that has come into the crops. Children wander away from parents and get lost. The local politician, who is up for the state legislature, goes up and down shaking hands. He doesn't forget names. He knows them all. He goes to all the funerals, the public auction sales, to folk-gatherings of all sorts. He doesn't miss the Saturday nights.

On a near-by corner a group of men put their heads together. Thad Jones is telling Bob Smith, Frank Croncheit, and Sylvester Bottomley a new one he has just heard. The men keep turning their heads to be sure their women don't hear.

The stories Thad tells are not parlor stories. The men break into loud guffaws, slap each other on the back.

'That Thad, he is a regular devil.'

'I'll tell you what, he's a card.'

The young unmarried girls walking up and down, up and down, the girls in couples, the young blades in groups. Being in a group gives the lads courage to call to the girls. This is all-important to the small-town girl. You get a man for yourself or you miss. You get a good steady one with a job, not too wild, not always chasing after other girls, or you get a bad one. 'That kind will make you all sorts of promises. He'll tell you he is crazy about you, and then, if you are fool enough to listen to him, you are in trouble.'

The girls whisper together, young beauties and plain ones, fat ones and thin ones. Excitement is in the air. The young lads laugh loudly. They push each other about, showing off. It is the big night of the week. It begins in the afternoon and lasts, on summer nights, until midnight, the restless motion, laughter, reunion of friends, meetings out of which marriages grow. Night of fiesta for what Abe Lincoln called the common folks.

On the main street there is a young boy wearing his first pair of long pants, a shy girl walking out with her first beau, the working-man who has got drunk and has blown in his week's wages that should have been spent for food for his family. He feels guilty. When he gets home and his wife begins to scold, he will roar at her, fright-ening the children. The children will huddle together upstairs in a room of a workingman's house. In their fright they cling together. Their dad has suddenly become something strange and terrible to them.

But most of the family men start home soberly enough at ten. They have taken the kids to the movies. Now they have to get them to bed. They have done the shopping earlier, and on the way home have stopped at the grocer's to get their packages. They trail off along resi-dence streets, little groups, families, hard-working, sturdy people, am-bitious for their kids. The Saturday night is over for them. Now for a Sunday of rest and then another week of toil.

XIV. LAST STORIES

The Corn-Planting

THE FARMERS who come to our town to trade are a part of the town life. Saturday is the big day. Often the children come to the high school in town.

It is so with Hatch Hutchenson. Although his farm, some three miles from town, is small, it is known to be one of the best-kept and best-worked places in all our section. Hatch is a little gnarled old figure of a man. His place is on the Scratch Gravel Road and there are plenty of poorly kept places out that way.

Hatch's place stands out. The little frame house is always kept painted, the trees in his orchard are whitened with lime halfway up the trunks, and the barn and sheds are in repair, and his fields are always clean-looking.

Hatch is nearly seventy. He got a rather late start in life. His father, who owned the same farm, was a Civil War man and came home badly wounded, so that, although he lived a long time after the war, he couldn't work much. Hatch was the only son and stayed at home, working the place until his father died. Then, when he was nearing fifty, he married a school-teacher of forty, and they had a son. The school-teacher was a small one like Hatch. After they married, they both stuck close to the land. They seemed to fit into their farm life as certain people fit into the clothes they wear. I have noticed something about people who make a go of marriage. They grow more and more alike. They even grow to look alike.

Their one son, Will Hutchenson, was a small but remarkably strong boy. He came to our high school in town and pitched on our town baseball team. He was a fellow always cheerful, bright and alert, and a great favorite with all of us.

For one thing, he began as a young boy to make amusing little drawings. It was a talent. He made drawings of fish and pigs and cows and they looked like people you knew. I never did know before that people could look so much like cows and horses and pigs and fish.

When he had finished in the town high school, Will went to Chicago, where his mother had a cousin living, and he became a student in the Art Institute out there. Another young fellow from our town was also in Chicago. He really went two years before Will did. His name is Hal Weyman, and he was a student at the University of Chicago. After he graduated, he came home and got a job as principal of our high school.

Hall and Will Hutchenson hadn't been close friends before, Hal being several years older than Will, but in Chicago they got together, went together to see plays, and, as Hal later told me, they had a good many long talks.

I got it from Hal that, in Chicago, as at home here, when he was a young boy, Will was immediately popular. He was good-looking, so the girls in the art school liked him, and he had a straightforwardness that made him popular with all the young fellows.

Hal told me that Will was out to some party nearly every night, and right away he began to sell some of his amusing little drawings and to make money. The drawings were used in advertisements, and he was well paid.

He even began to send some money home. You see, after Hal came back here, he used to go quite often out to the Hutchenson place to see Will's father and mother. He would walk or drive out there in the afternoon or on summer evenings and sit with them. The talk was always of Will.

Hal said it was touching how much the father and mother depended on their one son, how much they talked about him and dreamed of his future. They had never been people who went about much with the town folks or even with their neighbors. They were of the sort who work all the time, from early morning till late in the evenings, and on moonlight nights, Hal said, and after the little old wife had got the supper, they often went out into the fields and worked again.

You see, by this time old Hatch was nearing seventy and his wife would have been ten years younger. Hal said that whenever he went out to the farm they quit work and came to sit with him. They might be in one of the fields, working together, but when they saw him in the road, they came running. They had got a letter from Will. He wrote every week.

The little old mother would come running following the father. 'We got another letter, Mr. Weyman,' Hatch would cry, and then his wife, quite breathless, would say the same thing, 'Mr. Weyman, we got a letter.'

The letter would be brought out at once and read aloud. Hal said the letters were always delicious. Will larded them with little sketches. There were humorous drawings of people he had seen or been with, rivers of automobiles on Michigan Avenue in Chicago, a policeman at a street crossing, young stenographers hurrying into office buildings. Neither of the old people had ever been to the city and they were curious and eager. They wanted the drawings explained, and Hal said they were like two children wanting to know every little detail Hal could remember about their son's life in the big city. He was always at them to come there on a visit and they would spend hours talking of that.

'Of course,' Hatch said, 'we couldn't go.'

'How could we?' he said. He had been on that one little farm since he was a boy. When he was a young fellow, his father was an invalid and so Hatch had to run things. A farm, if you run it right, is very exacting. You have to fight weeds all the time. There are the farm animals to take care of. 'Who would milk our cows?' Hatch said. The idea of anyone but him or his wife touching one of the Hutchenson cows seemed to hurt him. While he was alive, he didn't want anyone else plowing one of his fields, tending his corn, looking after things about the barn. He felt that way about his farm. It was a thing you couldn't explain, Hal said. He seemed to understand the two old people.

It was a spring night, past midnight, when Hal came to my house and told me the news. In our town we have a night telegraph operator at the railroad station and Hal got a wire. It was really addressed to Hatch Hutchenson, but the operator brought it to Hal. Will Hutchenson was dead, had been killed. It turned out later that he was at a party with some other young fellows and there might have been some drinking. Anyway, the car was wrecked, and Will Hutchenson was killed. The operator wanted Hal to go out and take the message to Hatch and his wife, and Hal wanted me to go along.

I offered to take my car, but Hal said no. 'Let's walk out,' he said. He wanted to put off the moment, I could see that. So we did walk. It was early spring, and I remember every moment of the silent walk we took, the little leaves just coming on the trees, the little streams we crossed, how the moonlight made the water seem alive. We loitered and loitered, not talking, hating to go on.

Then we got out there, and Hal went to the front door of the farmhouse while I stayed in the road. I heard a dog bark, away off somewhere. I heard a child crying in some distant house. I think that Hal, after he got to the front door of the house, must have stood there for ten minutes, hating to knock.

Then he did knock, and the sound his fist made on the door seemed terrible. It seemed like guns going off. Old Hatch came to the door, and I heard Hal tell him. I know what happened. Hal had been trying, all the way out from town, to think up words to tell the old couple in some gentle way, but when it came to the scratch, he couldn't. He blurted everything right out, right into old Hatch's face.

That was all. Old Hatch didn't say a word. The door was opened, he stood there in the moonlight, wearing a funny long white nightgown, Hal told him, and the door went shut again with a bang, and Hal was left standing there.

He stood for a time, and then came back out into the road to me. 'Well,' he said, and 'Well,' I said. We stood in the road looking and listening. There wasn't a sound from the house.

And then — it might have been ten minutes or it might have been a half-hour — we stood silently, listening and watching, not knowing what to do — we couldn't go away —— 'I guess they are trying to get so they can believe it,' Hal whispered to me. I got his notion all right. The two old people must have thought of their son Will always only in terms of life, never of death.

We stood watching and listening, and then, suddenly, after a long time, Hal touched me on the arm. 'Look,' he whispered. There were two white-clad figures going from the house to the barn. It turned out, you see, that old Hatch had been plowing that day. He had finished plowing and harrowing a field near the barn.

The two figures went into the barn and presently came out. They went into the field, and Hal and I crept across the farmyard to the barn and got to where we could see what was going on without being seen.

It was an incredible thing. The old man had got a hand corn-planter out of the barn and his wife had got a bag of seed corn, and there, in the moonlight, that night, after they got that news, they were planting corn.

It was a thing to curl your hair — it was so ghostly. They were both in their nightgowns. They would do a row across the field, coming quite close to us as we stood in the shadow of the barn, and then, at the end of each row, they would kneel side by side by the fence and stay silent for a time. The whole thing went on in silence. It was the first time in my life I ever understood something, and I am far from sure now that I can put down what I understood and felt that night — I mean something about the connection between certain people and the earth — a kind of silent cry, down into the earth, of these two old people, putting corn down into the earth. It was as though they were putting death down into the ground that life might grow again — something like that.

They must have been asking something of the earth, too. But what's the use? What they were up to in connection with the life in their field and the lost life in their son is something you can't very well make clear in words. All I know is that Hal and I stood the sight as long as we could, and then we crept away and went back to town, but Hatch Hutchenson and his wife must have got what they were after that night, because Hal told me that when he went out in the morning to see them and to make the arrangements for bringing their dead son home, they were both curiously quiet and Hal thought in command of themselves. Hal said he thought they had got something. 'They have their farm and they have still got Will's letters to read,' Hal said.

A Walk in the Moonlight

T HE DOCTOR told the story. He got very quiet, very serious, in speaking of it. I knew him well, knew his wife, his sons and his daughter. He said that I must know, of course, that in his practice he came into intimate contact with a good many women. We had been speaking of the relations of men and women. He had been living through an experience that must come to a great many men.

In the first place, I should say, in speaking of the doctor, that he is a rather large, very strong, and very handsome man. He had always lived in the country where I knew him. He was a doctor, and his father had been a doctor in that country before him. I spent only one summer there, but we became great friends. I went with him in his car to visit his patients, living here and there over a wide countryside — valleys, hills, and plains. We were both fond of fishing, and there were good trout streams in that country.

And then, besides, there was something else we had in common. The doctor was a great reader, and, as with all true book-lovers, there were certain books, certain tales, he read over and over.

'Do you know,' he said, laughing, 'I one time thought seriously of trying to become a writer. I knew that Chekhov, the Russian, was a doctor; but I couldn't make it; found that when I took pen in hand I became dumb and self-conscious.' He looked at me, smiling. He had steady gray eyes and a big head on which grew thick, curly hair, now turning a little gray.

'You see, we doctors find out a good many things.' That, I of course knew. What writer does not envy these country doctors the opportunity they have to enter houses, hear stories, stand with people in times of trouble? Oh, the stories buried away in lonely farmhouses, in the houses of town people, of the rich, the well-to-do, the poor; tales of love, of sacrifice and of envy, hatred, too. There is, however, this consolation: the problem is never to find and know a little the people whose stories are interesting. There are too many stories. The great difficulty is to tell the stories.

'When I got my pen in hand, I become dumb.' How foolish! After I had left, the country doctor used to write me long letters. He still does sometimes, but not often enough. The letters are wonderful, little stories of the doctors' moods on certain days as he drives about in the country, descriptions of days, of fall days and spring days . . . How full of true feeling the man is — what a deep and true culture he has . . . Little tales of people, his patients. He has forgotten he is writing. The letters are like his talk.

But I must say something of the doctor's wife and of his daughter. The daughter was a cripple, a victim of infantile paralysis, moving about with great difficulty. She would have been, but for this misfortune, very beautiful. She died some four years after the summer when her father and I were so much together. And there was the wife. Her name was, I remember, Martha.

I did not know well either the wife or the daughter. Sometimes there are such friendships formed between men. 'Now you look here . . . I have a certain life, inside my own house. I have, let me say, a certain loyalty to that life, but it is not the whole of my life. It isn't that I don't want to share that intimate life with you, but — I am sure you will understand — we have chanced upon each other . . . You are in one field of work, and I another.'

There is a life that goes on between men, too — something almost like love can be born and grow steadily . . . what an absurd word that — love! — it does not at all describe what I mean.

Common experience, feelings a man sometimes has, his own kind of male flights of fancy, as it were — we men, you see . . . I wonder if it is peculiarly true of Americans . . . I often think so. We men here, I often think, depend too much upon women. It is due to our intense hunger, half shy, for each other.

I wonder if two men, in the whole history of man, were ever much together that they did not begin to speak presently of their experiences with women. I dare say that the same thing goes on between women and women. Not that the doctor ever spoke much of his wife. She was rather small and dark, a woman very beautiful in her own way — the way, I should say, of a good deal of suffering.

In the first place, the doctor, that man, so very male, virile, naturally quick and even affectionate in all his relation with people, and particularly with women, was a man needing more than one outlet for his feelings. He needed dozens. If he had let himself go in that direction, he could have had his office always full of women patients, of the neurotic sort. There are that sort, plenty of them, on farms and in country towns as well as in the cities. He could not stand them. 'I won't have it. I will not be that sort of doctor.' They were the only sort of people he ever treated rudely. 'Now you get out of here, and don't come back. There is nothing wrong with you that I can cure.'

I knew, from little tales he told, of what a struggle it had been. Some of the women were very persistent, were determined not to be put off. It happened that his practice was in a hill country to which in the summer a good many city people came. There would be wives without husbands, the husbands coming from a distant city for the week-end or for a short vacation in the hot months . . . Women with money, with husbands who had money. There was one such woman with a husband who was an insurance man in a city some two hundred miles away. I think he was president of the company, a small rather mouselike man, but with eyes that were like the eyes of a ferret, sharp, quick-moving little eyes, missing nothing. The woman, his wife, had money, plenty of it from him, and she had inherited money.

She wanted the doctor to come to the city. 'You could be a great success. You could get rich.' When he would not see her in his office, she wrote him letters and every day sent flowers for his office, to the office of a country doctor. 'I don't mind selling her out to you,' he said. 'There are women and women.' There were roses ordered for him from the city. They came in big boxes, and he used to throw them out of his office window and into an alleyway. 'The whole town, including my wife, knew of it. You can't conceal anything of this sort in a small town. At any rate, my wife has a head. She knew well enough I was not to be caught by one of that sort.'

He showed me a letter she had written him. It may sound fantastic, but she actually offered, in the letter, to place at his disposal a hundred thousand dollars. She said she did not feel disloyal to her husband in making the offer. It was her own money. She said she was sure he had in him the making of a great doctor. Her husband need know nothing at all of the transaction. She did not ask him to give himself to her, to be her lover. There was but one string to the offer, intended to give him the great opportunity, to move, let us say, to the city, set up offices in a fashionable quarter, become a doctor to rich women. He was to take her as a patient, see her daily.

'The hell!' he said. 'I am in no way a student and never have been. By much practice I have become a fairly good country doctor. It is what I am.'

'There is but one other thing I ask. If you are not to be my lover, you must promise that you will not become the lover of some other woman.' He was, I gathered, to keep himself, as she said, 'pure.'

The doctor had very little money. His daughter was the only living child of his marriage. Two sons had been born, but they had both died in the outbreak of infantile paralysis that had crippled the daughter.

The daughter, then a young woman of seventeen, had to spend most of her life in a wheeled chair. It was possible that, with plenty of money to send her off to some famous physician, perhaps to Europe —the woman in her letter suggested something of the sort—she might be cured.

'Oho!' The doctor was one of the men who throw money about, cannot save it, cannot accumulate. He was very careless about sending bills. His wife had undertaken that job, but there were many calls he did not report to her. He forgot them, often purposely.

'My husband need know nothing of all this.'

'Is that so? What, that little ferret-eyed man? Why, he has never missed a money bet in his life.'

The doctor took the letter to his wife, who read it and smiled. I have already said that his wife was in her own way beautiful. Her beauty was certainly not very obvious. She had been through too much, had been too badly hurt in the loss of her sons. She had grown thin and, in repose, there was a seeming hardness about her mouth and about her eyes, which were of a curious greenish-gray. The great beauty of the doctor's wife only came to life when she smiled. There was then a curious, a quite wonderful transformation. 'By this woman, hard or soft, hurt or unhurt, I will stand until I die . . .

'It is not always, however, so easy,' said the doctor. He spoke of something. We had gone for an afternoon fishing and were sitting and resting on a flat rock under a small tree by a mountain brook.

We had brought some beer packed in ice in a hamper. 'It is not a story you may care to use.' I have already said that the doctor is a great reader. 'Nowadays, it seems that there is not much interest in human relations. Human relations are out of style. You must write now of the capitalists and of the proletariat. You must give things an economic slant. Hurrah for economics! Ecomonics forever!'

I have spoken of his wife's smile. The doctor seldom smiled. He laughed heartily, with a great roar of laughter that could frighten the trout for a mile along a stream. His big body and his big head shook. He enjoyed his own laughter.

'And so it shall be an old-fashioned story of love, eh, what?'

Another woman had come to him. It had all happened some two or three years before the summer when I knew him and when I spent so much time in his company. There was a well-to-do family, he said, that came into that country for the summer, and they had an only child, a daughter, crippled as was his own daughter. They were not, he said, extremely rich, but they had money enough, or at first he thought they had. He said that the father, the head of that family, was some sort of manufacturer.

'I never saw him but twice, and then we did not have much talk, although I think we liked each other. He let me know that he was very busy and I saw that he was a little worried. It was because things at his factory were not going so well.

'There was the man's wife and daughter and a servant, and they had brought for the daughter a nurse. She was a very strong woman, a Pole. They engaged me to come on my regular rounds to their house. They had taken a house in the country, some three miles out of town. There were certain instructions from their city doctor. There was the wish to have within call a doctor, to be at hand in case of an emergency.

'And so I went there.'

I have already spoken of sitting with the doctor at the end of an afternoon's fishing. Certain men and also women a man meets leave a deep impression. Moments and hours with such people as the doctor are always afterward remembered. There is something — shall I call it inner laughter — to speak in the terms of fighters, 'They can take it.' They have something — it may be knowledge, or better yet maturity — surely a rare enough quality, that last, that maturity. You get the feeling from all sorts of people.

There is a little farmer who has worked for years. For no fault of his own — as everyone knows. Nature can be very whimsical and cruel — long droughts coming, corn withering, hail in the young crops, or sudden pests of insects coming suddenly, destroying all. And so everything goes. You imagine such a one struggling on into late middle life, trying to get money to educate his children, to give them a chance he did not have; a man not afraid of work, an upstanding, straight-going man.

And so all is gone. Let us think of him thus, say on a fall day. His little place, fields he has learned to love, as all real workers love the materials in which they work, to be sold over his head. You imagine him, the sun shining. He takes a walk alone over the fields.

His old wife, who has also worked as he has, with rough hands and care-worn face — she is in the house, has been trying to brace him up. 'Never mind, John. We'll make it yet.' The children with solemn faces. The wife would really like to go alone into a room and cry. 'We'll make it yet, eh?'

'The hell we will! Not us.'

He says nothing of the sort. He walks across his fields, goes into a wood. He stands for a while there, perhaps at the edge of the wood, looking over the fields.

And then the laughter, down inside him — laughter not bitter. 'It has happened to others. I am not alone in this. All over the world men are getting it in the neck as I am now — men are being forced into wars in which they do not believe . . . There is a Jew, an upright man, cultured, a man of fine feeling, suddenly insulted in a hotel or in the street — the bitter necessity of standing and taking it . . . A Negro scholar spat upon by some ignorant white.

'Well, men, here we are. Life is like this.

'But I do not go back on life. I have learned to laugh, not loudly, boisterously, bitterly, because it happens that I, by some strange chance, have been picked upon by Fate. I laugh quietly.

'Why?

'Why, because I laugh.'

There must be thousands of men and women — they may be the finest flowers of humanity — who will understand. It is the secret of

America's veneration for Abraham Lincoln. He was that sort of man.

'And so,' the doctor said, 'I went to that house. There was the woman, the mother of the crippled girl, a very gentle-looking woman, in some odd way like my wife.

'There was the crippled girl herself, destined perhaps to spend her life in bed, or going laboriously about in a wheeled chair. Would it not be wonderful to have some of these cocksure people explain the mystery of such things in the world? There is a job for your thinker, eh, what?

'And then there was the woman, the Polish woman.'

The doctor, with a queer smile, began to speak of something that often happens suddenly to men and women. He was a man at that time forty-seven years old, and the Polish woman — he never told me her name — might have been thirty. I have already said that the doctor was physically very strong, have tried to give the suggestion of a fine animal. There are men like that who are sometimes subject to very direct and powerful calls from women. The calls descend on them as storms descend on peaceful fields. It happened to him with the Polish woman the moment he saw her, and as it turned out, it also happened to her.

He said that she was in the room with the crippled girl when he went in. She was sitting in a chair near the bed. She arose and they faced each other. It all happened, I gather, at once.

'I am the doctor.'

'Yes,' she said. There was something slightly foreign in her pronunciation of even the one simple English word, a slight shade of something he thought colored the word, made it extraordinarily nice.

For a moment he just stood, looking at her as she did at him. She was a rather large woman, strong in the shoulders, big-breasted, in every way, he said, physically full and rich. She had, he said, something very full and strong about her head. He spoke particularly of the upper part of her face, the way the eyes were set in the head, the broad white forehead, the shape of the head. 'It is odd,' he said, 'now that she is gone, that I do not remember the lower part of her face.' He began to speak of woman's beauty. 'All this nonsense you writers write concerning beauty in women,' he said. 'You know yourself that the extraordinary beauty of my own wife is not in the color of her eyes, the shape of her mouth ... This rosebud-mouth business, Cupid's bow, eyes of blue, or, damn it, man, of red or pink or lavender for that matter!' I remember thinking, as the man talked, that he might have made a fine sculptor. He was emphasizing form, what he felt in the Polish woman as great beauty of line. 'In my wife beauty comes at rare intervals, but then how glorious it is! It comes, as I think you may have noted, with her rare and significant smile.'

He was standing in that room, with the little crippled girl and the Polish woman.

'For a time, I do not know how long, I couldn't move, could not take my eyes from her . . .

'My God, how crazy it now seems!' the doctor said.

'There she was. Voices I had never heard before were calling in me, and, as I later found out, in her also. The strangeness of it. "Why, there you are. At last, at last, there you are."

'You have to keep it all in mind,' said the doctor, 'my love of my wife, our suffering together over the loss of our two sons, our one child, one daughter, a cripple as you know.

'And there I was, you see, suddenly stricken like that — by love, ha! What does any sensible man know of this love?

'I did not know that woman, had never seen her until that moment, did not know her name. As it was with me, so it turned out it was with her. In some way I knew that. Afterward she told me, and I believed her, that as the Bible puts it, she had never known man.

'I stood there, you understand, looking at her and she at me.' He spoke of all this happening, as he presently realized when with an effort he got himself in hand, in the presence of the little crippled girl in the bed. 'It seemed to me that the woman was something I had all of my life been wanting with a kind of terrible force, you understand, with my entire being.'

The doctor's mind went off at a tangent. The reader is not to think that he told me all this in a high, excited voice. Quite the contrary. His voice was very low and quiet, and I remember the scene before us as we sat on the flat rock above the mountain stream — we had driven a hundred miles to get to that stream: the soft hills in the distance beyond the stream, which just there went dashing down over the rocks, the deepening light over distant hills and distant forests. Later we got some very nice trout out of a pool below the rapids above which we sat.

It may have been the stream that sent him off into a side tale of a fishing trip, taken alone, on a moonlight night, in a very wild mountain stream, on the night after he had buried his second son; the strangeness of that night, himself wading in a rushing stream, feeling his way sometimes in half darkness, touches of moonlight on occasional pools, the casts made into such pools, often dark forests coming down to the stream's edge, the cast, and now and then the strike, himself standing in the swift running water.

Himself fighting, all that night, not to be overcome by the loss of the second and last of his sons, the utter strangeness of what seemed to him that night a perfectly primitive world. 'As though,' he said, 'I had stepped off into a world never before known to man, untouched by any man.'

And then the strike, perhaps of a fine big trout — the sudden sharp feeling of life out there at the end of a slender cord, running between it and him — the fight for life out there, and at the other end of the cord, in him.

The fight to save himself from despair.

Was it the same thing between him and the Polish woman? He said he did manage at last to free himself from the immediate thing.

He had a terrible week, a time of intense jealousy. 'Would you believe it, it did not seem possible to me that any man could resist that woman,' he said. He suspected the child's father. 'That man, that manufacturer — he is her lover. It cannot be otherwise.' The doctor laughed. 'As for my wife, she was, for the time, utterly out of my life. I do not mean to say I did not respect her. What a word, eh, that respect! I told myself that I loved her. For the rest of the week I was in a muddle, could not remember what patients needed my services. I kept missing calls; and of course my wife, who, as I have told you, attends to all the details of my life, was disturbed.

'And, at that, she may well have been deeply aware. I do not think that people ever successfully lie to each other.'

It was during that week he saw and talked briefly to the manufacturer from the city, the father of the crippled child, going there to that house, he said, hoping again to see the woman. He did not see her; and as for the man — 'I had been having such silly suspicions. I wonder yet whether or not, at the time, I knew how silly they were.

'The manufacturer was a man in terrible trouble. Afterward I learned that at just that time his affairs were going to pieces. He stood to lose all he had gained by a lifetime of work. He was thinking of his wife and of his crippled daughter. He might have to begin life again, perhaps as a workman, with a workman's pay. His daughter would, perhaps, all her life be needing the care of physicians.'

I gathered that the city man had tried to take the country doctor into his confidence. They had gone into the yard of the country house and had stood together, the doctor's heart beating heavily. 'I am near her. She is there in the house. If I were a real man, I would go to her at once, tell her how I feel. In some way I know that this terrible hunger in me is in her also.' The man, the manufacturer, was trying to tell him.

'Yes, yes, of course, it is all right.'

There were certain words said. The man in trouble was trying to explain.

'Doctor, I shall be very grateful if you can feel that you can come here, that we can depend upon you. I am a stranger to you. It may be you will get no pay for your trouble.'

'Aha! What, in God's name, could keep me away?'

He did not say the words. 'It is all right. I understand. It is all right.'

The doctor waited a few days; then he went again. He said he was asleep in his own house, or rather was lying in his bed. Of a sudden, he arose. To leave the house, he had to pass through his wife's room. 'It is,' he said, 'a great mistake for a man and wife to give up sleeping together. There is something in the perfectly natural and healthy fact of being nightly so close physically to the other. It should not be given up.' The doctor and his wife had, however, I gathered, given it up. He went through her room, and she was awake.

'It is you, Harry?' she asked.

Yes, it was he.

'And you are going out? I have not heard any call. I have been wide awake.'

It was a white moonlight night, just such a night as the one when he went in his desperation over the loss of his second son to wade in the mountain stream.

It was a moonlight night, and the moonlight was streaming into his wife's room and fell upon her face. It was one of the times when she was, for some perverse reason, most beautiful to him.

'And I had got out of bed to go to that woman, had thought out a plan.'

He would go to that house, would arouse and speak to the mistress of the house. 'There has been an accident. I need a nurse for the night. There is no one available.'

He would get the Polish woman into his car.

'I was sure — I don't know why — that she felt as I did. As I had been lying so profoundly disturbed in my bed, so she in her bed had been lying.'

She was almost a stranger to him. 'She wants me. I know she does.'

He had got into his wife's room. 'Well, you see, when at night I had to go out to answer a call, it was my custom to go to my wife, to kiss her before I left. It was a simple enough thing. I could not do it.

'I knew that the Polish woman was waiting for me. I will take her into my car. We will turn into a wood, and there, in the moonlight ...

'A man cannot help what he is. After this one time, it may be that things will get clear.'

He was hurrying thus through his wife's room.

'No, my dear, I have had no call.'

'A feeling has come to me,' he said. 'It is that girl, the crippled one, crippled as is Katie, our daughter. I have told you of her. It is, my dear, as though a voice has been calling me.

('And what a lie, what a terrible lie!)

'All right. I accepted that. There was a voice calling to me. It was the voice of that strange woman, the woman I scarcely knew, who had never spoken but the one word to me.'

The doctor was hurrying through his wife's room. There was a stairway that led directly down out of the room. His crippled daughter slept in another room on the same floor; and a servant, a colored woman who had been in the household for years, slept in the daughter's room on a cot. The doctor had got through his wife's room and was on the stairs when his wife spoke to him.

'But Harry!' she said. 'You have forgotten something. You have not kissed me.'

'Why, of course,' he said. His feet were on the stairs, but he came back up into her room. She was lying there, wide awake. 'I am going to that woman. I do not know what will happen. I must, I must.

'It may all end in some sort of scandal, I do not know, but I cannot help doing what I am about to do. There are times when a man is in the grip of forces stronger than himself.

'What is this thing about women, about men? Why does all of this thing, this force, so powerful, so little understood, why with the male does it all become suddenly directed upon one woman and not upon another?

'There is this force, so powerful. I have suddenly, at forty-seven, a man established in life, fallen into its grip. I am powerless.

'There is this woman, my wife, in bed here, in this room. The moonlight is falling upon her upturned face. How beautiful she is! I do not want her, do not want to kiss her. She is looking up expectantly at me.' The doctor was by his wife's bed. He leaned over her.

'I am going to this woman. I am going. I am going.'

He was leaning over his wife, about to kiss her, but suddenly he turned away. His wife's name is Martha.

'Martha,' he said, 'I cannot explain. This is a strange night for me. I will, perhaps, explain it all later.

'Wait. Wait.'

He was hurrying away from her down the stairs. He got into his car. He went to that house. He got the woman, the Polish woman. 'When I explained to her, she was quite willing.' He thought afterward that she had been on the whole rather fine, telling him quite plainly that as he had felt when he saw her, so she also had felt.

She was definite enough. 'I am not a weak woman. Although I am thirty, I am still a virgin. However, I am in no way virginal.'

She had been, the doctor said, half a mystic, saying that she had always known that the man who would answer some powerful call in her would some day come. 'He has come. It is you.'

They went to walk. She told him that since she had first seen him, she had made some inquiries. She had found out about the loss of his two sons, about his crippled daughter, about his wife.

All this, the doctor explained, as, having left his car by the roadside, they walked in country roads. It was a very beautiful night, and they had got into a road lined with trees. There were splashes of moonlight falling down through the leaves in the road before them as they walked, not, as it turned out, ever touching each other. Sometimes they stopped and stood silent for a long time. He said that, several times, he put out his hand to touch her, but each time he drew it back.

'Why?'

It was the doctor himself who asked the question. He tried to explain. 'There she was. She was mine to possess.' He said that he thought she was to him the most beautiful woman he had ever known or ever would know.

'But that is not true,' he said. 'It is both true and untrue.

'It may be that if I had touched her, even with my finger-ends, there would have been quite a different story to tell. She was beautiful, with her own beauty, so appealing, so very appealing to me; but there was also, at home — lying as I knew, awake in her bed — my wife.'

He said that in the end, after he had been with the Polish woman for perhaps an hour, she understood. He thought she must have been extremely intelligent. They had stopped in the road and she turned to him; and again, as in the room with the cripple, there was a long silence. 'You are not going to make love to me,' she said. 'I have never wanted love until I saw you. I am a woman of thirty, and it may be that now I never shall have love.'

The doctor said he did not answer. I 'couldn't,' he explained. What was to be said? He thought that it was the great moment of his life. He used the word I have also used in speaking of him. 'I think, a little, I have been, since that moment, a mature man.'

The doctor had stopped talking, but I could not resist questioning him.

'And you ended by not touching her?' I asked.

'Yes. I took her back to her place, and when I next went there to see the crippled girl, she was gone and another woman had taken her place.'

There was another time of silence. After all, I thought, 'This man has, from his own impulse, told me this tale. I have not asked for it.

'There is a question I think now that I may dare ask,' I ventured. 'Your wife?'

There was that laugh that I so liked. It is my theory that it can come only from the men and women who have got their maturity.

'I returned to her. I gave her the kiss I had denied earlier that night.'

I was, of course, not satisfied.

'But——' I said.

Again the laugh.

'If I had not wanted to tell you, I should not have begun this tale,' he said. We got up from the flat stone on which we had been sitting and prepared for the great moment of trout fishing, as every trout fisherman knows the quivering time, so short a time between the last of the day and the beginning of the night. The doctor preceded me down across a flat sloping rock to the pool, where we each got two fine trout. 'I was in love with my wife as I had never really been with the Polish woman, and in the same way. Not the troubles we had shared, all we had gone through together, not scruples of conscience —I was in love with my wife in a way that I never had been until after that walk in the moonlight with another woman.'

The doctor stopped talking, but did not look at me. He was selecting a fly.

'When I returned to her that night and when I kissed her, she, for a moment, held my face in her hands. She said something. "We have been through it again, haven't we?" she said. She took her hands away and turned her face from me. "I have been thinking for the last week or two that we had lost each other," she said. "I do not know why," she added, and then she laughed. It was the nicest laugh I ever heard from her lips. It seemed to come from so far down inside. I guess all men and women who have got something know that it might be easily lost,' the doctor said, as he finished his tale. He had hooked a trout, and was absorbed in playing his fish.

THE SHERWOOD ANDERSON READER

His Chest of Drawers

W E WORKED in the same advertising office for several years, both copy men, our desks beside each other, and from time to time he confided in me, telling me many little secrets of his life. He was a small, very slender, and delicately built man, who couldn't have weighed over a hundred and twenty pounds, and he had very small hands and feet, a little black mustache, a mass of blue-black hair, and a narrow chest. That was one of his difficulties and he frequently spoke of it.

'Look at me,' he said. 'How can I ever get on in business? How can I ever rise?'

Saying this, he arose and walked over to my desk. He slapped himself on the chest.

'I want space and spread there,' he said. 'The world is full of stuffed shirts, and what chance have I? I have no place to wear a shirt front.'

Although he was a man of Spanish descent, with much of the sensitivity and the pride of the Spaniard, my friend's name was Bill. When I first knew him, he had been married for several years and he was the father of four children, all girls. He spoke of this occasionally. 'It's a little tough,' he said. He was a devout Catholic and once confided to me it had been his ambition to be a priest. 'I wanted to be a Jesuit priest,' he said, 'but I got married.'

'Not,' he added, 'that I would have you think I have anything against my wife.' He thought that we men should honor women.

'You look at me now. I know well enough that I am insignificant-looking. A woman marries such a man as myself. She bestows her favors upon him. He would be an ungrateful man if he complained, but, you take the life of a priest now, he cannot marry, you see. He can be small or he can be large. He is respected by his people.'

With Bill it was as it was with all of us who were writers of advertising copy. There were other men, also employed by the advertising agency which employed us, who were called 'solicitors.' Nowadays I believe they are called 'contact men.' These men, having to bring in clients, keep them satisfied; convince them that we who wrote their copy were men of talent, quite extraordinary men; had, of course, to put up a front. They were provided with private offices, often expensively furnished; they arrived and departed, seemingly at will, did not have to ring time clocks, went off for long afternoons of golf with some client; while we copy men, herded together as we were in one room, away at the back, a room that looked out upon a lofty building, through the windows of which we could see rows of women sewing busily away, making men's pants, felt all the time that we were the ones who kept the whole institution going. We kept speaking of it to each other.

'We furnish the brains, don't we? If we don't, who does?'

'Surely it isn't these other guys, these stuffed shirts, out there in front,' we said.

In our agency, as in all such institutions, there was an occasional flurry. One or another of us in the copy department had prepared for some advertiser a series of advertisements that were taken by one of the salesmen to the client. He dismissed them with a wave of his hand.

'They are no good,' he said, and when this happened, we copy men burned with inner anger.

'I guess the guy's got indigestion,' we said. As for our own work, or the work of others in our department, we never spoke ill of that. The man, the client, simply didn't know good work when he saw it.

Or it was the fault of the salesman, the contact man. It was his business to sell our work. If he couldn't do that, what good was he? Why was he provided with a private office, why permitted to lead a life of leisure, while we, poor slaves that we were, had to do all the work?

We used to get ourselves all heated up over these things, and occasionally, when we thought that it had got too thick, one or another of us went off on a binge. It was a thing to be expected and for the most part it was overlooked; but once, when it had happened to Bill, at a time when a client whose work he had long been doing had suddenly appeared in the city and it was felt that he was badly needed, I was sent to look for him, and if possible to straighten him out. It was understood that the client could be stalled overnight.

'You find him and sober him up. You get him in here,' they said to me.

And so I went to find Bill, and knowing something of his habits, I did find him. He was in a certain saloon, run by a brother Spaniard, and when I found him he was leaning against a bar, a group of men for whom he was buying drinks gathered around, and he was delivering a talk on the position of small men in a civilization that, as he said, judged everything by size.

I had got Bill out of the place and we were in a Turkish bath and he was in a solemn mood.

'You think you know the reason why I got drunk, but you don't,' he said. He began to explain. He said that this time his getting drunk had nothing to do with affairs at the office.

'There is a greater tragedy in my life,' he said. We were in the hot room in the bath and as the sweat ran in streams from our bodies he explained that, while his size — his inability, as he had often said, to wear a big shirt front — had, as I well knew, been a handicap to his business; I had perhaps not known that the same handicap had operated against him in his home.

'It's true,' he said, shaking his head solemnly. 'You see, my house is overrun with females.' He explained that, being unable because of his handicaps to make a big salary, he was compelled to live in a small house in a certain suburb.

'You know,' he said, 'that I have a wife and four daughters.' His daughters were rapidly growing up. 'I have given up having a son,' he said, and went into a long explanation of how, his house being small and the closet space therefore somewhat limited, he had been compelled — he had thought it the only decent thing to do — to cut down on his wardrobe.

'What's the use of buying clothes to put on a little runt like me?' he asked, and added that, as his daughters were growing up, he had needed all the money he could spare to buy clothes for them.

'I guess they've got to get husbands. I've got to give them a break.'

He explained that in following out this policy, he had gradually given up using any closet space in his house, and that for two or three years he had confined himself, in this matter of space in which to put his clothes, to a certain chest of drawers, and as he talked on, becoming all the time more earnest, I came to understand that the chest of drawers had become a kind of symbol to him.

It had come to the point where the chest of drawers had begun to mean everything in the world to him. He was sure I couldn't understand and said that no man, not put in the position he was in, living as he did in a house with five females . . . all of whom he declared he profoundly respected . . . could ever understand.

It had gone on so in his house for several years, but some several weeks before, his eldest daughter had become engaged. She had been getting a wardrobe together and one day, when he came home, he had found the top drawer to his chest of drawers gone.

He had stood for that. 'I guess the girl has to have clothes,' he said. He hadn't even complained.

And then, two days before, his wife's mother had come on a visit and he had lost the second drawer in his chest.

'It was a hard dose to swallow, but I swallowed it,' he said.

His wife, who he kept declaring was a good woman — ('I don't want you to think I am criticizing her,' he said)— had been, he presumed, doing the best she could. She had taken his things — his shirts, underwear, except what he needed from day to day — and had put them in a box. 'She put it under the bed,' he said, and added that, on the evening when he had gone home and had found the second drawer to the chest gone, he hadn't said a word.

'I didn't say a word, but when we were at dinner that evening and I was trying to take a boiled potato out of a dish, to put it on my wife's mother's plate, I was so wrought up and my hand trembled so that, when I had it nicely balanced on a fork and was just going to put it on her plate, it fell off into a bowl of gravy.'

He had gone home and to his chest of drawers, to the last drawer of new dresses.

It made his wife sore because she thought he had been drinking when he hadn't at all.

And then it had come to the evening before. A sister of his wife had come. He thought the women had become excited because his eldest daughter had become engaged. They were gathering in — 'I guess to look at the guy,' he said.

He had gone home and to his chest of drawers, to the last drawer of his chest of drawers, and it was gone.

'But no,' he said; 'I want to be fair. It wasn't all gone.'

His wife had left him half of the last drawer. He thought his wife had done the best she could; she should, he thought, have married a salesman, not a little runt of a copy man, such as he was.

'I think we ought to treat our women with respect,' he said.

'After all,' he said, 'they do bestow their favors upon us.

'I just looked at the drawer a moment and then I came away. I took a train back to town, I got drunk. Why not?' he asked.

He thought that sometimes, when a man was drunk, he could get temporarily the illusion that he cut some figure in life.

Not Sixteen

SHE KEPT INSISTING ON IT. She whispered it in the barn at night, after the day in the corn field. Her father was milking a cow. John could hear the milk strike against the side of the pail. When the sound stopped, they had to dodge into an empty horse stall.

He was pressing her body against a board wall. She was limp, relaxed in his arms. Was he in love? He didn't know. He thought he was.

There had been moments during the weeks he was there on her father's farm, working there . . . he was helping with the fall corncutting . . . when he had wanted her to marry him. He spoke of it.

'Shall we get married?' he asked.

'No,' she said. 'I am not sixteen.'

'Well,' he said.

'No, and not that either,' she said. 'Not yet,' she said. 'I am not sixteen.'

He thought about it at night in bed.

'It would be too stupid to get married now,' he thought. He had no money and he didn't want to go on, perhaps all of his life, being a farmhand.

She had a baffling attitude about it all. They had spoken of it, John pressing the question.

'Let's,' he said.

'There won't nobody know,' he said.

'Let's! Just once! Let's!' he pleaded.

He talked and talked, exaggerated his suffering, his pain, his sleeplessness. He threatened to go away.

'Please don't,' she said. 'You stay here. It won't be long. I'll be sixteen in a year.'

She kept insisting. She was slender, with bright red spots on her pale cheeks. Her mouth was inviting, her eyes were inviting.

She was curiously frank, had not been shocked by John's words, when he began to plead with her. She knew what he meant.

She came down into the field to work with John and her father.

John had got the job on the farm. It was in the fall, after the spring when he came home from the first World War.

'I'll work,' he had thought. 'I'll take any job I can get, for say another year. I'll save my money.' He had brought some money home from the war — had hidden it away. It wasn't much.

The war, the traveling about, the seeing strange places, mountains, the sea, the being in a foreign land — all of these things had made him restless. He didn't know what he wanted.

'I want her, but I don't want to settle down, not yet.'

He had come home to his Michigan town with other soldiers and there had been parades. There had been a banquet in the town hall. He and the other soldiers had been called heroes again. He thought it was the bunk. He had been lucky, hadn't been in any battles. He was only nineteen and that girl, Lillian, on the farm, was only fifteen. When he came home from the war and was called a hero, he spoke to other men who had been soldiers.

'All this talk. It's bushwa,' he said.

'They are handing us the lousy bunk,' he said.

There was no work to be had. When he had gone off to war, he had chucked a job. That was in Detroit in an automobile plant. He didn't want to go back. He had been on the line in the plant.

The job had got his goat. He said so. 'This here bunk,' he said. 'I didn't go to be no hero. The job had got me. I didn't sleep good at night.

'All right,' he said. 'I'll go take a look.' He thought he would go on the bum for a time. There was an old man in the Michigan town who had a deformed hip. The Michigan town was near the larger town, Kalamazoo, where grand circuit trotting meetings are held and the old man had been a race-horse driver. Now he owned a garage, but he still kept two or three good ones. He had been thrown from a sulky during a race and his hip had been broken. It had never been properly mended. He walked in a curious way, swinging his body from side to side.

He stopped John in a street. Before the war and before John went away to Detroit, he had worked for the man, whose name was Yardley. It was when John was sixteen. He had been a swipe. He had got the race-horse bug.

'If you want to work for me again, you can,' the man said.

He said that he already had two men in his barn.

'I don't need another one, not now, not till the races begin, but if you want to come, you can.

'I can't pay you anything. You can take care of "What Chance," ' he said.

'What Chance' was a trotter. He was a bay gelding, a three-year-old. He was fast.

'You take care of him this winter and jog him on the roads. It won't be much work. I can't pay you anything, but you can come up and live at my house. You can sleep there, get your meals there.'

The man Yardley said he was making John the offer because he admired the boys who had the guts to go out and fight for their country. They walked over to the barn, the man Yardley swaying along behind John. He was chewing tobacco. He kept spitting. They went into the box-stall to the horse.

It had been a temptation to John. He went to caress the horse. He ran his hand along his back and down his legs. 'He's a good one,' he thought.

He thought of the drifting from town to town. In time he might become a driver. It was an old dream come back. Yardley would be doing the half-mile tracks. With a good one like 'What Chance' they might clean up.

John had a little money. He'd be on the inside. He could lay some bets.

He thought of nights in strange towns with the other swipes. There'd be drinking, there'd be some whoring done. He stood looking at the horse.

'Naw,' he thought, 'I got to cut that out.'

'These race-horsemen,' he thought, 'where do they ever get?'

'I'll see. I'll let you know,' he said to Yardley. He took a walk.

'I can't,' he told himself. He had brought a little money home from the war. When he had been a kid around the tracks, he had learned to juggle dice. He had got into crap games in the camp, in France, on the boats, going and coming.

He wanted to go with Yardley, but he felt guilty. There was his sister. John's mother was dead and his sister was running the house.

His father was out of work and John's sister, three years older than John, was wanting to get John's two younger brothers through school.

'I ought to tell her about the money, give it to her,' he thought.

'I can't,' he thought.

It seemed to him that if he gave up the money he had won at craps, he would be sunk.

'If I could go to school now, just for two or three years,' he thought.

He could maybe get into business, become a prosperous man. John had a picture in mind, of himself, a man risen in the world, money in pocket, good clothes to wear.

'If I can pull it off I can do ten times as much for the kids,' he thought.

It seemed to him that everything depended upon his getting an education. 'If I don't do it now I'm gone.' If he did not get an education he would remain as he was — sunk, a worker, a man going through life with his feet in the mud.

There was a ladder up which you climbed. Education was the thing that did it.

'O.K.,' John had said to himself. 'But I'll give up going to school this year. I'll give up what I want to be, a horseman.' John had been through grade school. He had an idea that presently he would take the money put secretly away, and would go somewhere, perhaps to a business college.

There was a young man he knew who was going to dental college. John thought he might do that. There was another who was away from home at a school where you learned to fix watches.

'That might be better,' he thought.

You begin by repairing watches. You save your money. Then presently you own a store where jewelry is sold. You sell rings and watches. You dress well. Very likely you marry — say now, a rich girl.

It might be that her father would be the one that would set you up in your own business. When you had such a business of your own, you could, if you chose, own some horses of your own.

So you get a clerk to take care of your store. You go away to the races. You drive your own horses.

John had got on a freight train at night and had begun beating his way from town to town, looking for work. He thought he would earn some money and send it home. Pretty soon what little money he had in his pockets was gone, and he had to take what he could get. He had got down into Ohio, was in a town in Ohio. He had hired out to the farmer. He was cutting corn. It was a new kind of work for John. He thought it was a pretty hard job, but he could stand it all right.

Her name was Lillian, and her father and mother were old. They seemed old to John. The man, her father, was a renter. Once he had owned a farm of his own, but, he told John, he had had hard luck and had lost it.

His wife was a small woman, with bright eyes, like Lillian's, John thought.

The mother had a curiously bent back. 'They must have been married a long time,' he thought. He was always doing things like that, wondering about people, thinking of them. 'I wonder if, when you get old and live with your wife, you have any fun,' he thought. There had been four children, three of them grown now and all married except Lillian. The others were gone. Lillian told John about it all when she came down into the field where he was cutting corn.

She got him at once. 'Oh, Lord, she's got me,' he thought. She was small, but she could cut corn like a man. She was shy, and at the same time bold. She looked weak, but she was strong. The work was new to John and she kept showing him how. There was a certain swing you got. You learned to ease yourself.

You have to cut the tall-corn and carry it to the shock. You hold it in one arm and swing the knife with the other. There is a way you handle your body, easing it to the load. When you know how, it's twice as easy. She showed John how.

They talked and talked. When her father was with them, working with them, they worked in silence, he continually looking at her and she at him, but when her father had gone, to the barn or the house, they talked. It was something new to John. He talked and talked. He looked at her. 'I wonder whether she will,' he thought.

'She doesn't seem so young,' he thought. Right away he knew she liked to be with him.

They talked at night. There were moonlight nights.

'Come. Let's go and work awhile,' she said. It wasn't in the agreement that John was to work at night, but he went. He was glad to go.

Her father, the farmer, did not come at night. He said he was tired. He said he was getting too old. She told John of a sister who was married and lived with her husband, a railroad brakeman in another town. The sister had been fifteen years old before Lillian was born. 'She got married when she was fifteen, but I am not going to,' she said. John wanted to ask whether it was a shotgun marriage. He didn't.

'How do you reckon I came to come so late?' she asked. She asked John that and laughed.

'I'd 'a' thought they'd got so old they couldn't,' she said.

She kept saying bold things to John.

When they were working together thus, in the evening, in the corn field, in the moonlight, they kept talking. She didn't seem young to John. 'It may be because she came so late,' he thought. He thought she had a figure, nice, like a woman's. She seemed curiously old for her years.

They were at work in a big field and there was the part of the field where the corn was already cut. They could look across the open place. There were the shocks of corn they had cut, standing out there. There were yellow pumpkins on the ground. Beyond the open place where the corn shocks stood there was a wood. There was a strange feeling, John had, as though he were alone with her in a place where no man had ever been before. 'Like maybe in the Garden of Eden,' he thought. Out there in the field with her, like that, at night, quite far from the farmhouse, there were always strange sounds and sometimes there was a wind. The leaves were turning on the trees in the wood. They were falling. The wind made them race across the open place. They seemed like little living things, running along. 'I wonder why they let her come,' he thought. He thought maybe they wanted to get her married. 'Then maybe I'd have to stay here and work for them, for nothing, like with Yardley,' he thought. She had told him about her sister. 'I'll bet that's the way she got that brakeman,' he thought.

He talked to her of the leaves, running along the ground. 'Look,' he said. The shocked corn standing in the open place made him think of his life in the army. They could look off across the open place, where the corn was cut, to other fields on other farms. It was a flat country. They could see other corn already cut and in its shocks in other fields.

John kept talking to her. He never talked so before. He spoke of the shocks standing in the moonlight. They were like armies of soldiers standing, he said. He grew bolder as he talked. He couldn't touch her, until he began to talk and then he could.

They didn't cut much corn that night. He went to her and put an arm about her shoulders. He was quite tall and she was short. Standing thus, he could say things about the dry leaves running along the ground and the little sounds they made. He could pretend there was another world, besides the one they lived in, a world of little living things, men and women like themselves, but small, he said. 'No bigger than that,' he said. He put his thumb at the first joint of a finger. He began inventing. He told her that the little people lived, in the daytime, in the wood, that they hid there.

'Now see, they've come out to play,' he said.

'They are men and women like us,' he said, 'but they don't get married.' Two dry leaves went skipping along. 'Look,' he said. They stood in silence.

They quit working and went to stand by the fence. He had an arm about her. He made her put her head down on his shoulder. It could just reach. Their corn knives fell on the ground.

He talked and talked. He told her about his life in the army, about things he'd seen.

Then he told her about a girl he'd been with once. 'It was when I was younger than you are,' he said. He said it was a little town girl. 'It was when I was at the races. A man older than me, who worked with our outfit, got me a girl.' He said that she with another one had come at night to a fairground where they were. The man had given one of the girls to John to go with him into an empty horse-stall.

He told of it and how he felt, how he couldn't speak to the girl, how excited he was. 'It was my first,' he said. A quiver ran through her body and he held her close.

He went on talking, holding her, not feeling at all as he had with the girl in the horse-stall.

'I was afraid of her, but I'm not of you,' he said.

'Was it nice?' she asked, and he said it was.

She was like that. She seemed to come right up to him, with her mind, with all of herself, not afraid or ashamed.

'I'm going to when I'm sixteen,' she said.

'I won't wait any longer,' she said.

It had begun between them and it went on. It was in the moonlight, when they were in the corn field at night. It was in the barn. It was upstairs, in the house, at night. He went up to her. He went up in his bare feet. Her father snored and her mother snored. He waited until he heard it, and then he went up to her.

She had a room up there.

Her father and mother were asleep downstairs. She said it would be all right for him to come. He had been given a room downstairs. 'You come up. I want you to,' she said.

It seemed to John that he was near to being insane. He was very strong. Now the work didn't tire him at all.

'I'll ask her to marry me,' he thought.

Then he thought, 'No. I won't,' but he did, and she laughed. No. We won't do that,' she said. He was glad, because her people were poor. They were too much like his own people, he thought. He kept thinking that, if they got married, he couldn't ever go to school and rise in the world.

He did not speak to her of that. When he wasn't with her, alone with her, he got half frantic, but when he was with her, in the barn — while her father was milking — holding her tight, or in the field, or when he went up to her at night, he got strangely quiet.

She had fixed a blanket on the floor by her bed. She said he could lie there for a time. 'There's no harm in that,' she said. She said that if there was, she didn't care. She would be lying on the edge of her bed. The bed was low. She leaned down. She had hard little hands.

'You talk,' she said, and sometimes he did.

'Like out there, with the leaves running like that,' she said.

He would lie thus and whisper to her and sometimes she would lean down and they'd kiss. He wanted to pull her down, make her come to him, struggle with her until she surrendered, but for some obscure reason he didn't.

He talked and talked. He had never talked so before. When he was talking, he could not tell what, of all he told her, was real and what invented.

Sometimes he'd beg her, growing a little frantic, but she could quiet him.

'I can't. I'm not sixteen,' she said.

She said it would be almost a year before she could. She laughed softly.

'You can stay and wait or you can go away and come back,' she said.

'If you go away and you're not here on time . . .' she laughed.

She had a laugh that made him grow quiet. There was something in her, he thought, like a wall. 'There's no use pounding against a wall,' he thought. At times, on some nights when he had crept up there and had talked for a long time, he grew suddenly sad. Tears came to his eyes.

'Please, please,' he said.

'Be quiet,' she said.

'When I am sixteen,' she said.

She kept saying it. It was like a song in his head. He had to give it up. He stood it as long as he could, and then he ran away. He had come down from her room. It was on one of the moonlight nights and cold. He'd been lying up there on the blanket by her bed.

'When I'm sixteen.

'When I'm sixteen.'

He was a young man and a year seemed infinitely long. If he could have been with her all the time, day and night, near her, he thought he could have stood it.

He came down to his own room at night and suddenly knew.

'It's because I'm not like her,' he thought.

'She can wait and I can't.'

He dressed and slipped silently out of the house. He walked a moonlit road.

There was something in her as strong as iron, but it wasn't in him.

Her father owed him some money he never got, but he didn't care. When he had got into the road, he was suddenly proud. 'I have controlled myself,' he thought. He began to walk proudly along.

'After all, she is not sixteen,' he thought.

Tim and General Grant

I FEEL A LITTLE GUILTY about repeating Tim's story. He was so insistent on my not telling. As he pointed out, General Grant had got to be President, he had made his famous trip around the world, met as Tim said, a lot of kings and other big-bugs in countries all over the world. Tim thought you shouldn't tell things on such a man. General Grant was Tim's hero. He had the feeling that he understood Grant, that General Grant was, at bottom, a fellow a good deal like himself, a man who had known failure, who had worked at common labor. A book agent had been around and had sold Tim Grant's *Memoirs*. He had bought and read other books about his hero. Tim was born and raised in Pennsylvania and had served, during the Civil War, in the Army of the Potomac. Like so many of the men of his day who had served through the Civil War, Tim constantly relived those stirring years. He said that a lot of the other men in his Pennsylvania regiment were always bragging up General McClellan, but that Grant was his man. He kept contrasting him with General Lee.

'Lee, huh!' he exclaimed. 'Sure, he was all right. Why not? Didn't he have every advantage?

'A fellow like that. I bet, when he was a kid, he was always dressed up. I bet he went to Sunday School every Sunday, never sneaked off to play baseball or go swimming, didn't swear none.

'Say, he never had to work in a tannery, did he? He never farmed none. You'd never see him on a load of hides, hauling them down from that Illinois town to St. Louis, nothing like that.

'I guess he got born of rich folks, had a silver spoon in his mouth. Sure, he was all right, but what of it? I'd 'a' liked to see him have to buck all the handicaps General Grant had to go against.'

It was during the summer when I was fifteen, or perhaps sixteen, that I knew Tim. I had got a job as waterman with a threshing crew that was working in the country north of my home town. We were in the country south of Sandusky, Ohio, working the farms back from the bay.

There weren't any tractors owned on farms then. Our threshing engine that pulled our outfit over the dirt road from farm to farm was a huge thing, always threatening to go through bridges, and it was part of my job to keep it supplied with coal, hauled from Sandusky.

Then there was the problem of keeping water for steam on hand. It was a dry summer up in that part of Ohio, and often I had to drive miles to find a well or I had to go to the bay. I stood on top of the big box-like tank and pumped away until my arms ached, and once I got into serious trouble. I had driven down to the bay shore. 'Why pump?' I thought. I drove into the bay, figuring the tank would fill itself, but it floated offshore, dragging the team into a deep hole where the bed of the bay shelved off, so that I had to dive to cut the team loose. With the help of some neighboring farmers, I finally got all clear, but I still remember the heels of the horses swishing past my head as I dived to get them loose. I didn't tell the boss about that adventure. I told no one but Tim.

Tim Bosworth was a man of fifty. He had stiff, upstanding black hair, always during that summer filled with dust from the separator, and a little Hitlerish mustache. He had the clearest blue eyes I had ever seen, was a fast worker, seemingly tireless, and was a sincere drinker. There was always a bottle in a little handbag he carried on our pilgrimages, and at night, when we had got to some farm, had set the outfit for an early morning start, and he and I had retired to some hayloft to sleep, he got the bottle out. As the others of our crew were all of one family and as they owned the outfit, they usually got what beds were offered while Tim and I slept together in the haylofts.

'I need a drink so I can sleep,' said Tim. 'Then,' he added, 'I need one in the morning to get me going. I have had trouble,' he declared. 'I'll not speak of it, boy, but I have had terrible trouble in my day.'

Someone had told me that Tim had once been a man of substance. He had owned a farm and had been married, I was told, to a woman much younger than himself, and she had betrayed him. She had run away with another man, one who had been Tim's best friend, and Tim, who had always been a drinker, had gone on a long debauch. He had thrown money about until his farm was gone and he was reduced to such casual labor as he could get.

We were in a hayloft at night and Tim had the bottle in his hand. He had begun again speaking of General Grant.

He was a great man, a very great man,' he said. He apologized for not offering me a drink. 'You are a bit too young yet, my boy. Later,' he added, 'if you have such trouble as I have had, I advise you to take it up.' There were some words said about a broken heart and about his hatred of women, but, as he said the words, he kept putting the bottle to his lips and his words were lost in the soft sounds of the liquor flowing down his throat.

Tim had got the notion that my name was Sherman — that I was named for General Sherman, another of his heroes — and I had not corrected the impression.

'It is an honored name,' he said. 'It is the name of a man, second only to General Grant in my esteem.'

Again he began to contrast General Grant with General Lee. He spoke at length of General Grant's background. He had been a farmer as Tim had and, like Tim, had lost his farm. Month after month and year after year Grant, he said, had fallen lower and lower in the social scale. He had been an officer in the army, had gone to West Point, and then bad days had come to him as they had come to Tim.

Tim kept taking drinks from the bottle held in his hand. He told again a story of himself and General Grant that he kept telling me over and over, in many haylofts, during that summer.

It was, he said, during the last few weeks of the Civil War. He had been in the Army of the Potomac since the War had begun, had been at Fredericksburg, at Chancellorsville, and at Antietam. He had been at Gettysburg and in the Wilderness Campaign.

'But it was getting right up to the end,' he said. Lee had got out of Richmond and, with what remained of his army, was hurrying west and south and Grant was after him.

'We had him cornered,' Tim said. 'You see, boy, Sheridan had got in ahead of him.' Tim said that he had himself been on the march, day and night, for several days and that then luck had come to him. With two others he had wandered away from his regiment and the three men had captured a house.

He said it was quite a big house and that there was no one at home but two women. He thought the men of the house were very likely in Lee's army.

'We didn't want to harm the women, of course,' Tim said. 'We just thought we'd look around.'

They had looked around and in the cellar of the house had found six bottles of what Tim declared was mighty good whiskey.

'I took my two and then I left the others,' he said. He thought the others might be faster drinkers than he was and would be wanting more than their share. He said he didn't think General Grant would be needing him much; that he didn't see much sense to wearing himself all out chasing General Lee, when they already had him cornered.

'And, besides, I was mighty thirsty,' he said.

He had got into a wood and was sitting under a tree. He said he emptied one of the bottles, slept for a time, and then tackled the other.

'I didn't know then that General Lee had already sent word to General Grant that he was ready to call it quits. I only heard about that later.

'So there was General Lee, ready to call it quits and they couldn't find General Grant,' he said. He said he guessed that Grant was riding around and looking things over.

However, they did find him, riding with his staff along a country road and he was hurrying to go to where Lee was waiting for him. With his staff he came riding along a road through the woods where Tim was sitting with the second of his two bottles in his hand and his back against a tree. General Grant got off his horse and came alone, right into the wood where Tim was.

Tim explained how it happened.

'Well, you see, boy, how it was with him,' he said. 'There he was. He wasn't a fellow to dress up much. He had been riding around in the mud. He had on an old suit, maybe just a private's uniform, and an old worn-out hat.

'You see he knew that General Lee would be all dressed up.

'Suppose, now,' Tim said, 'you had to go into a bank, or into a church, or to call on some nice girl, and you looked like that. You know how you'd feel.

'Especially on an historic occasion like that,' Tim said.

Tim thought that General Grant had come into the wood to maybe fix his hair and to get some of the mud off his clothes. He came right up to where Tim sat with the bottle in his hand.

'I was pretty lit-up or, of course, I wouldn't have had the nerve to say to him what I did. He was standing right in front of me and looking down at me.

'"Hello General Grant," I said to him.

'"We sure got General Lee cornered at last, haven't we, Sam," I said. I guess I was lit-up all right to have the nerve to call him Sam like that.

'"Come on, General, have a drink with me. Let's celebrate the event a little," I said to him.'

Tim declared that General Grant had just stood, looking silently down at him, and that then he reached down and took the bottle out of Tim's hand. Grant, he said, held the bottle in his hand for a time. There was, Tim declared, a thirsty look in his eyes. Then, smashing the bottle against the trunk of the tree, he turned and walked away.

'Now, wasn't there a man for you!' Tim said. 'Why, boy, you know he wanted a drink.

'How would you feel yourself?' Tim asked, sitting upright in the hayloft with the bottle clutched in his hand. 'Why, you just look at it,' he added, 'his having to go up there where Lee was, dressed up like that, him covered with mud and knowing General Lee would be all fixed up fancy, like he always was. Sure he wanted a drink, but he knew well enough he couldn't take it and then go up there, to that house, where General Lee was waiting to surrender to him, and maybe smell up the whole room in that house, where the surrender took place, with the whiskey on his breath like that.'

Tim declared that what had happened between him and General Grant that day in the woods had proven to him that Grant was a really great man.

'But just the same, I wouldn't want you to go telling what happened between me and General Grant that day,' Tim added. He said he would not like any of Grants folks to hear that he'd gone around talking about him.

'Of course, you understand, he didn't take the drink, but I figured then and I figure yet that he wanted that drink a lot more than he wanted to go, looking like he did, to meet General Lee.

'But I wouldn't want any of General Grant's kin to hear I'd said it.' He told me the story at least a dozen times during that summer and each time demanded a solemn promise that I wouldn't ever tell it on Grant.

4286

12